ADVANCES IN GENETICS

VOLUME 29

Contributors to This Volume

Victor G. Corces
N. C. Mishra
Vincenzo Pirrotta
Dennis A. Powers
Patricia A. Smith
John L. Woolford, Jr.

ADVANCES IN GENETICS

Edited by

JOHN G. SCANDALIOS

Department of Genetics
North Carolina State University
Raleigh, North Carolina

THEODORE R. F. WRIGHT

Department of Biology
University of Virginia
Charlottesville, Virginia

VOLUME 29

ACADEMIC PRESS, INC.

Harcourt Brace Jovanovich, Publishers

San Diego   New York   Boston
London   Sydney   Tokyo   Toronto

Academic Press, Inc.
San Diego, California 92101

United Kingdom Edition published by
ACADEMIC PRESS LIMITED
24-28 Oval Road, London NW1 7DX

Library of Congress Catalog Card Number: 47-30313

ISBN   0-12-017629-7   (alk. paper)

PRINTED IN THE UNITED STATES OF AMERICA
91 92 93 94   9 8 7 6 5 4 3 2 1

CONTENTS

Genetics and Molecular Biology of *Neurospora crassa*

N. C. MISHRA

The Structure and Biogenesis of Yeast Ribosomes

JOHN L. WOOLFORD, JR.

260384

Evolutionary Genetics of Fish

DENNIS A. POWERS

Drosophila Transposable Elements: Mechanisms of Mutagenesis and Interactions with the Host Genome

PATRICIA A. SMITH AND VICTOR G. CORCES

The Genetics and Molecular Biology of *zeste* in *Drosophila melanogaster*

VINCENZO PIRROTTA

CONTRIBUTORS TO VOLUME 29

Numbers in parentheses indicate the pages on which the authors' contributions begin.

VICTOR G. CORCES (229), *Department of Biology, The Johns Hopkins University, Baltimore, Maryland 21218*

N. C. MISHRA (1), *Department of Biological Sciences, University of South Carolina, Columbia, South Carolina 29208*

VINCENZO PIRROTTA (301), *Department of Cell Biology, Baylor College of Medicine, Houston, Texas 77030*

DENNIS A. POWERS (119), *Hopkins Marine Station, Department of Biological Sciences, Stanford University, Pacific Grove, California 93950*

PATRICIA A. SMITH (229), *Department of Biology, The Johns Hopkins University, Baltimore, Maryland 21218*

JOHN L. WOOLFORD, JR. (63), *Department of Biological Sciences, Carnegie Mellon University, Pittsburgh, Pennsylvania 15213*

PREFACE

Advances in Genetics was the first serial publication devoted solely to the burgeoning field of genetics. The serial was founded in 1946 by Dr. Milislav Demerec, then director of the Genetics Department at the Carnegie Institution of Washington in Cold Spring Harbor, New York. The stated purpose for the series was "that critical summaries of outstanding genetic problems, written by prominent geneticists in such form that they will be useful as reference material for geneticists and also as a source of information to nongeneticists, may appear in a single publication." Over the years, the goals set forth initially have been more than fulfilled, and a lasting tradition of excellence has been established.

In more recent years, our field has experienced some revolutionary developments emanating from the enormous technological advances that have occurred. Recombinant DNA and related molecular technologies now make possible the intricate manipulation of genetic information, in virtually every cell type and organism, that could not even have been imagined at the time when *Advances in Genetics* was initiated. These developments have led to an unparalleled information explosion.

Because of the diversity of genetics as a science, *Advances in Genetics* has adhered to the policy of publishing a series of outstanding but largely unrelated articles in each volume, and this policy will be maintained. However, the editors on occasion will depart from this format and review a central topic in a special "topical" or "thematic" volume, as this is essential in view of the extremely rapid developments in genetics. Four such volumes (Volumes 22, 24, 27, and 28) have been published to date and have been well received by the scientific community; others are in preparation.

Our purpose is not merely to inform but also to stimulate the reader—whether a beginning or an advanced scholar—to explore, question, and, whenever possible, test various hypotheses advanced herein. We intend that each volume covers some material of lasting value, in view of the very rapid developments in this field.

JOHN G. SCANDALIOS
THEODORE R. F. WRIGHT

GENETICS AND MOLECULAR BIOLOGY OF
*Neurospora crassa**

N. C. Mishra

Department of Biological Sciences, The University of South Carolina,
Columbia, South Carolina 29208

* This article is dedicated to the memory of the late Professor E. L. Tatum on the fiftieth anniversary of the formulation of the one gene–one enzyme hypothesis.

1

I. Introduction

The purpose of this review is to highlight the recent advances made in genetics and molecular biology as a result of studies carried out in *Neurospora crassa*, a filamentous fungus. At least three reviews describing the current data on transformation in fungi have appeared in recent years (Mishra, 1985; Rambosek and Leach, 1987; Fincham, 1989). Therefore, no attempt is made here to review at any length this area of *Neurospora* molecular biology. Many of the areas that are reviewed here reflect the author's personal bias and familiarity with the subject.

Neurospora is an ideal organism for studies in genetics and molecular biology. It is a haploid eukaryote with a relatively small genome size. Its seven chromosomes contain roughly 47 million nucleotide pairs (Horowitz and McLeod, 1960; Orbach *et al.*, 1988; Duran and Gray, 1989); of these, over 93% are unique sequences (Perkins and Barry, 1977; Krumlauf and Marzluf, 1979). The relative complexity of the *Neurospora* genome is presented in Table 1. *Neurospora* possesses a spectrum of nuclear, mitochondrial, and plasmid genetic systems that are amenable to analyses by methods of molecular biology. It has typical eukaryotic chromosomes containing nucleosomes, centromeres, and telomeres; in addition, the *Neurospora* chromosome V contains a nucleolar organizing region (NOR). Most genes contain exons and introns and their transcripts are usually spliced and processed to give the different kinds of RNAs that are translatable or participate in different steps of translation.

Neurospora is also capable of heterokaryon formation, a trait that renders the determination of the dominance and recessiveness of alleles easy. Production of four pairs of meiotic products (ascospores) makes tetrad analyses convenient even when all eight spores cannot always be

TABLE 1

Comparison of Genome Size and Complexity in Different Genetically Characterized Organisms

Organism	Haploid DNA content		Number of chromosomes	Unique sequence	Repeat sequence	Ref.
	Megabase[a]	Picogram[b]				
Escherichia coli	4.2	0.0046	1	99.7	0–3	Lewin (1990)
Saccharomyces cerevisiae	20	0.022	17	93	7	Lewin (1990)
Neurospora crassa	47	0.055	7	93	7	Orbach et al. (1988)
Aspergillus nidulans	31	0.034	8	97	3	Brody and Carbon (1989)
Caenorhabditis elegans	100	0.11	7	—	—	Lewin (1990)
Drosophila melanogaster	165	0.18	4	—	—	Lewin (1990)
Mus musculus	3000	3.3	20	—	—	Lewin (1990)
Homo sapiens	3300	3.6	23	70	30	Lewin (1990)

[a] 1 megabase = 1×10^6 nucleotide pairs.
[b] This is based on the estimate that 1 pg of DNA contains 9.1×10^8 bp.

scored and analyzed. Furthermore, the production of eight ascospores within a single ascus makes it feasible to determine the nature of a change that may involve a single polynucleotide chain in the DNA helix of a chromsome. Sexual and vegetative stages in the life cycle of the organism provide opportunities to study different aspects of the genetics and molecular biology of differentiation and development. Moreover, all kinds of standard microbiological practices of growth and manipulation can be used for the study of this organism (Davis and de Serres, 1970). *Neurospora* is amenable to methods of gene transfer via transformation by either unfractionated DNA or by cloned genes (Mishra, 1985). *Neurospora* chromosomes can be analyzed by the method of pulsed-field gel electrophoresis (Orbach *et al.*, 1988). Introduction of biologically active artificial chromosomes into this organism offers several opportunities for genetic manipulation of *Neurospora*. In addition to over 700 mutant strains (Perkins *et al.*, 1982), a large worldwide collection of wild-type strains of *Neurospora* obtained from different geographical locations and a library of *Neurospora* strains with different chromosomal rearrangements (Perkins *et al.*, 1976; Perkins and Barry, 1977; Perkins and Turner, 1988) are available for use in genetic and molecular biology experiments. A wide range of technical methodologies for the preparation of DNA and RNA and their detection by Southern, Northern, and dot blot and colony hybridizations and methods for *in vitro* mutagenesis and different kinds of vectors for cloning are very well established (Vollmer and Yanofsky, 1986; Schroeder, 1988; Stahl and Lambowitz, 1983; Akins and Lambowitz, 1985).

It is pertinent to mention that a number of concepts in genetics and contemporary biology have emerged from the study of *Neurospora*. Among these, the most important concept is the one gene–one enzyme hypothesis of Beadle and Tatum (1941), which gave birth to the science of biochemical and molecular genetics (Horowitz, 1987). Results of studies in *Neurospora* soon led to the elucidation of the sequence of biochemical steps in metabolic pathways (Srb and Horowitz, 1944). The other examples include the phenomenon of gene conversion (Mitchell, 1955; Case and Giles, 1958) and the hybrid DNA theory of genetic recombination as its mechanism (Whitehouse, 1963; Holiday, 1964), and the genetic control of recombination (Catcheside, 1966, 1977). Furthermore, the biogenesis of the mitochondrion (Luck, 1963; Reich and Luck, 1966), characterization of mitochondrial plasmids and introns, (Lambowitz *et al.*, 1985), the unusual nature of tRNA genes and their departure from the universal codon usage (Heckman *et al.*, 1978, 1980), the occurrence of site-specific recombination leading to deletion and rearrangement of the mitochondrial DNA (de Vries *et al.*, 1983; Gross *et al.*, 1984; Almasan and Mishra, 1988, 1991), and the import of proteins into mitochondria (Stuart *et al.*, 1987) were all elucidated in *Neurospora*. Above all, studies carried out in *Neurospora* led to the development of transformation systems in fungi (Mishra and Tatum, 1973; Hinnen *et al.*, 1978; Case *et al.*, 1979; Mishra, 1985). Characterizations of the *Neurospora* transformation system led to the discovery of the non-Mendelian transmission of donor DNA among transformants (Mishra and Tatum, 1973) and to an unusual mechanism repeat induced point (RIP) mutation that causes the inactivation of duplicate genes in this organism (Selker and Garrett, 1988; Selker, 1991). Recent molecular analyses of the *Neurospora* mating-type genes have challenged the classical concept of the allele (Johannsen, 1909; Rieger *et al.*, 1976) and have brought about the introduction of the term *idiomorph* in order to describe the DNA segments that occupy the same position on homologous chromosomes but have different nucleotide sequences and gene products (Metzenberg, 1990; Metzenberg and Glass, 1990; Staben and Yanofsky, 1990; Glass *et al.*, 1990).

II. Gene Transfer

A. DNA Transformation of Neurospora Mediated by Unfractionated or Cloned DNA

Gene transfer in filamentous fungi was reported by Mishra (Mishra *et al.*, 1973; Mishra and Tatum, 1973). Total unfractionated genomic DNA was used to treat an inl^- (inositol negative) strain of *Neurospora* in order to obtain inl^+ transformants. Later these transformation experiments were confirmed using both unfractionated and cloned DNA (Case *et al.*, 1979; see also Timberlake and Marshall, 1989). However, the significance of the original transformation experiments were recognized much later (Hinnen *et al.*, 1978; Case, 1983; Grant *et al.*, 1984; Mishra, 1985; Timberlake and Marshall, 1989; Rambosek and Leach, 1987; Fincham, 1989; Selker, 1990).

Furthermore, the results of tetrad and heterokaryon analyses (Mishra and Tatum, 1973) demonstrated the non-Mendelian transmission of the transformed character. This aspect of the inheritance of donor DNA has been confirmed in other laboratories (Grant *et al.*, 1984; Case, 1986; Selker and Garrett, 1988) using loci other than the inositol

(inl^+) marker used by Mishra and Tatum (1973) in their initial study. Originally Mishra and Tatum (1973) suggested that the rare transmission of the donor DNA resulted from its failure to be integrated into the resident chromosomes, leading to its loss during meiosis. However, the low transmission rate of the transformed characters has now been shown to be due to the inactivation of duplicate DNA sequences in *Neurospora* by the unusual RIP mechanism (Selker, 1991). Thus the different aspects of the *Neurospora* transformation system as originally described by Mishra and Tatum (1973) have been confirmed.

B. MOLECULAR BASIS OF MEIOTIC INSTABILITY OF INTRODUCED GENES IN NEUROSPORA TRANSFORMANTS

Mishra and Tatum (1973) observed the meiotic instability of an inl^+-transformed strain that, when crossed with an inl^- strain, yielded tetrads in which all spores were inl^-. This was described as non-Mendelian transmission of the transformed character. However, unlike the uniparental transmission of other non-Mendelian genes (such as mitochondrial genes), the nontransmission of the transformed characteristics in *Neurospora* was shown to be biparental. In addition, the results of tetrad analyses excluded the possibility of heterokaryosis as the basis for non-Mendelian transmission of the inl^+-transformed character (Mishra and Tatum, 1973). This initial observation regarding the meiotic instability of transformed genes was subsequently observed by various other workers in this field (Szabo and Schablik, 1982; Grant *et al.*, 1984; Case, 1986; Selker, 1990; Selker and Garrett, 1988).

Initially Mishra and Tatum (1973) explained the absence of inheritance of the phenotype due to the introduced gene in transformants to result from the inability of the donor DNA segment to be integrated and its subsequent loss during the meiotic process in *Neurospora*. This was the tenet of the exosome model proposed by Mishra and Tatum (1973). However, other explanations for the inactivation of the introduced alleles were also considered (N. C. Mishra and E. L. Tatum, unpublished data); for example, it was thought that the inactivation of the gene in transformants might have some similarity to the mechanisms that cause the inactivation of the X chromosome in the mammalian female cells (Lyon, 1972) or the instability of disomics in *Neurospora* (Mitchell *et al.*, 1952; Pittenger and Coyle, 1963; Threlkeld and Stoltz, 1970).

The molecular basis of the meiotic instability of introduced genes in *Neurospora* has been elucidated by Selker (Selker and Garrett, 1988;

Selker, 1990) in a series of elegant experiments using a recipient strain of *Neurospora* lacking the resident am^+ gene for glutamic dehydrogenase by a genetic deletion. The fate of the transformed (am^+) gene was examined by the method of Southern hybridization (Southern, 1975). Such analyses suggest that the inactivation of the introduced gene, when present in more than one copy, may be associated with methylation of DNA sequences and their mutations during the meiotic stage in the life cycle of *Neurospora*. This methylation was detected by the comparison of the profile of Southern hybridization of DNA from the *Neurospora* am^+-transformant strain after digestion with restriction enzymes *Sau*3A and *Mbo*I. It is known that both *Mbo*I and *Sau*3A can cleave unmethylated GATC sequences. However, the same DNA sequence after methylation of cytosine becomes resistant to cleavage by *Sau*3A. Therefore, the introduced am^+ gene undergoing methylation should show different cleavage patterns with *Sau*3A and *Mbo*I as visualized by a nick-translated probe on a Southern blot. This is what Selker and Garrett (1988) found when they analyzed the am^+-transformed strain (Fig. 1). The inactive gene in the transformant may undergo methylation of cytidine residues in its DNA leading to a CG-to-TA mutation as confirmed by nucleotide sequence analysis of the alleles from the wild-type and transformed strains (Cambareri *et al.*, 1989; Selker, 1990). Thus the molecular basis of the meiotic instability of the *Neurospora* transformants seems to involve the mechanism of RIP leading to inactivation of both alleles triggered by the repeat sequences of a gene introduced via transformation.

It is of interest to mention the comparison of meiotic stabilities of the hgr^r gene (conferring hygromycin resistance) and the ben^r gene (conferring benomyl resistance) in *Neurospora* transformants, because the hgr^r gene is alien to *Neurospora* whereas an allele of the ben^r gene occurs naturally in *Neurospora*. Consistent with our current knowledge of meiotic instability of introduced genes (Selker and Garrett, 1988), the nonresident hgr^r gene was found not to be inactivated and transmitted to meiotic progeny in accordance to Mendelian ratios whereas the resident ben^r gene was inactivated and showed a non-Mendelian transmission as observed earlier (Staben *et al.*, 1989). However, it is believed that multiple copies of rRNA and 5S RNA genes are not subjected to the action of RIP because of their peculiar localization or distribution (Selker, 1991). This view is supported by the fact that those rRNA genes that are moved by translocation to a region away from their original location in the NOR region then become subject to inactivation by RIP (Perkins *et al.*, 1986).

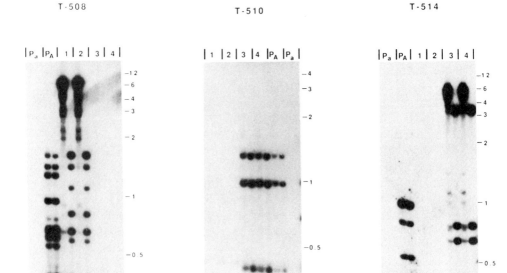

FIG. 1. Fate of transforming sequences through first cross. The three *Neurospora am*[+] transformants were crossed with strain N36 (am₁₃₂, inl, *a*). Results from a typical tetrad from each of three transformants are shown. DNA samples from the parental strains (P_A is transformant; P_a is N36) and three strains representing the meiotic products (1–4) were digested with *Sau*3A (left lane of pair) or *Mbo*I (right lane of pair), fractionated, and probed for the transforming DNA. The *Am* phenotype of each strain is indicated below the autoradiograms, and positions of selected size standards (kilobases) are shown. The *am*[+] gene copy numbers (for transformants) are 4 (T-508), 1 (T-510), and 2 (T-514). [After Selker and Garrett (1988).]

It is suggested here that the addition of 5′ azacytidine (an inhibitor of methyltransferase) into the crossing medium can reduce the level of methylation and thus prevent the inactivation of the introduced gene. Likewise, inclusion of tetrahydrodeoxyuridine (which upon phosphorylation *in vivo* acts as a potent inhibitor of dCMP deaminase) in the crossing medium might also reduce the level of mutation due to deamination of methyldeoxycytidine. Thus it is theoretically possible to rescue the introduced gene in the presence of these substances, i.e., 5′ azacytidine and tetrahydrodeoxyuridine.

C. OTHER UNUSUAL CHARACTERISTICS OF THE TRANSFORMATION SYSTEM

Theoretically, when a cloned gene is introduced into a *Neurospora* strain via transformation, the introduced gene may exist in different forms, for example, as a replacement transformant, as a linked or unlinked (ectopic) insertion, or as an autonomously replicating plasmid. Each of these modes of transformation can be distinguished by Southern analyses (Hicks *et al.*, 1979; Mishra, 1985) and all have been shown to occur during yeast transformation. However, *Neurospora* and mammalian cell transformants have been shown to contain generally only the ectopic location of the introduced gene; the replacement type of introduced gene in *Neurospora* is rare and the occurrence of the introduced gene on autonomously replicating plasmids is nonexistent in *Neurospora*.

Allelic inactivation by the RIP pathway is random for the resident and introduced alleles. However, the frequency of inactivation of the introduced gene existing as a linked insertion is much higher than when existing as an ectopic insertion (Selker *et al.*, 1987). Besides the meiotic instability of the transformants, the study of transformation in *Neurospora* resulted in several surprising findings. Usually a gene is identified as a DNA segment capable of complementing a defective phenotype in an organism upon transformation. However, it has become obvious that this is not necessarily true in *Neurospora*, as it has been shown that the van^+ gene can complement the defective phenotypes of either *nuc-1*, *nuc-2* (Mann *et al.*, 1988), or *nuc-6* mutants of *Neurospora* (M. Cooley and N. C. Mishra, unpublished data). The basis for such complementation is not yet known, but this certainly suggests that complementation by a donor DNA segment in a transformation system should not be considered as the sole criterion for identification of a gene controlling a particular function. Furthermore, we have recently shown that van^+ is unable to complement other *nuc* mutants, such as *nuc-3*, *nuc-4*, and *nuc-5* (M. Cooley and N. C. Mishra, unpublished data). It is known that *van*, *nuc-1*, *nuc-2*, *nuc-3*, *nuc-4*, *nuc-5*, and *nuc-6* are nonallelic to each other; some of them are even located on different chromosomes. In view of this fact it is amazing that van^+ can complement some of the *nuc* mutants. Further molecular genetic analyses of this system can provide certain unusual features of the intermediary metabolic pathways and their regulation in eukaryotes.

Study of transformation using van^+ and nuc^- strains of *Neurospora* has revealed certain other unusual features of the regulatory pathways

(Mann *et al.*, 1988). It has been shown that the resident *van*⁺ gene is not expressed in the *nuc-1* mutant; however, a *van*⁺ gene introduced by transformation into *nuc-1* mutants is expressed. The basis for the nonexpression of resident *van*⁺ gene in *nuc-1* mutants of *Neurospora* and that for the expression of the introduced *van*⁺ gene in *nuc-1* transformants are not known, although several possibilities have been indicated (Mann *et al.*, 1988).

D. Factors Involved in Transformation

In bacteria, the competence factor(s) that determines the physiological state of the cell for the uptake and integration of donor DNA by the recipient cell during the process of transformation are very well characterized. However, very little is known about the factors contributing to the competence of fungal cells during the process of transformation. Recently, a 110-kDa protein from *Neurospora* was described, it presumably controls the uptake of the donor DNA by spheroplasts concomitant with an increase in transformation frequency (Toth *et al.*, 1987). Mishra (1979) reported the increase in uptake of the donor DNA by the nuclease deficient (*nuc*) mutants of *Neurospora* as compared to the uptake of donor DNA the wild-type cells used as recipients. This increase in the uptake of the DNA by the *nuc* mutant was most likely due to the inability of the mutant strain to degrade the donor DNA following its uptake by the *nuc* mutant, because the latter is deficient in nuclease.

Spheroplasts or lithium chloride (Case *et al.*, 1979; Dhawale *et al.*, 1984) enhanced the transformation frequency significantly with the use of cloned donor DNA. Addition of Ca^{2+} ions has been shown to be the crucial determinant in increasing the frequency of transformation (Mendel and Higa, 1970). The exact role of calcium is not yet shown, although several possibilities have been discussed (Oishi and Irbe, 1977). Likewise, poly-ethylene glycol (PEG) has been shown to promote the process of transformation (Smith and Danner, 1981). Liposome formation is also known to positively affect the frequency of transformation (Radford *et al.*, 1981). The role of lipofectin on the process of transformation in *Neurospora* has not yet been examined.

Gene cloning in *Neurospora* has been aided by the creation of genomic (Schablik *et al.*, 1983; Akins and Lambowitz, 1985; Vollmer and Yanofsky, 1986) and cDNA libraries (Sachs *et al.*, 1986), and others have applied restriction fragment-length polymorphism (RFLP) in linkage analysis of *Neurospora* and other fungi (Metzenberg *et al.*, 1984). Yanofsky and his group (Orbach *et al.*, 1988) have utilized the ability to isolate individual chromosomes of *Neurospora* using pulsed-field gel electrophoresis to screen the genomic libraries for genes carried by particular chromosomes; this approach will certainly speed up the cloning of different *Neurospora* genes and their molecular characterization necessary to understand the organization and function of the nuclear and mitochondrial genes of this organism and their relation to other organisms.

The current frequency of transformation in *Neurospora* is quite acceptable for carrying out experiments. However, if one wants to detect the occurrence of very rare events such as the maintenance of an artificial chromosome, an increase in the current frequency of transformation would immensely help such investigations.

E. PROGRESS TOWARD A SELF-REPLICATING VECTOR IN NEUROSPORA

At present, the different vectors used in *Neurospora* transformation are unable to replicate and maintain themselves in an autonomous state. An autonomously replicating vector is required to augument the expression of cloned genes in *Neurospora*. Such situations would be desirable to study the different aspects of gene expression and the nature of several genetic elements such as promotor and upstream sequences required for the control of transcription. Also, the availability of a multicopy autonomous vector would be useful for the production of foreign proteins in *Neurospora*. This would be desirable for the study of the nature of signal peptides and glycosylation and also to determine the nature of codon preference of the different *Neurospora* translation systems.

The creation of a plasmid that can autonomously replicate, preferably in multicopy form in *Neurospora,* has been almost impossible. The addition of a putative autonomously replicating sequence (*ars*) to existing plasmids has not proved to be of much help in alleviating this problem (Radford *et al.,* 1981; Buxton and Radford, 1984).

Some of the mitochondrial plasmids that exist autonomously (Lambowitz *et al.,* 1985) might be harnessed to produce a self-replicating vector for *Neurospora* transformation systems. In this direction, we have recently used a 2.2-kb plasmid derived from mitochondrial DNA (mtDNA) of a *Neurospora* "*stopper*" mutant (Almasan and Mishra, 1990). This plasmid exists autonomously in 10–12 copies per mitochondrial DNA molecule in *Neurospora*. We have recently added the *ben*[r] gene to this plasmid. This chimeric plasmid has been shown to act as a vector during the transformation of a benomyl-sensitive strain of *Neurospora* to benomyl resistance, based on the capability of transformants to grow on media containing benomyl (M. Cooley and N. C. Mishra, unpublished data). However, the fact that this plasmid is self-replicating remains to be determined. The role of other plasmids derived from *Neurospora* mtDNA (Gross *et al.*, 1989) should also be explored in the development of such an autonomously replicating vector.

F. CONSTRUCTION OF AN ARTIFICIAL CHROMOSOME

Creation of the yeast artificial chromosome (YAC) and its successful application in molecular cloning analyses have been described (Murray and Szostak, 1983). The development of such an artificial chromosome can also help in understanding the nature of the different components of *Neurospora* centromeres and telomeres, which are perhaps typical of eukaryotes but quite different from yeast centromeres and telomeres. The possible creation of *Neurospora* artificial chromosomes (NACs) and their analyses via a *Neurospora* or yeast transformation system could provide an insight into the mechanisms responsible for the instability of disomics in *Neurospora*. It should be possible to construct a NAC by adding a *Neurospora* centromere and telomeres to an existing plasmid containing the am^+ gene and then examine its stability during mitosis and meiosis in *Neurospora* transformants obtained after the transformation of a deletion am^- mutant cell as recipient. *Neurospora* does not support the maintenance of an extra chromosome as disomics; therefore, it would be of interest to examine the effects of the different components of an artificial chromosome in controlling its stability. One can compare the effect of the presence of alien genes in the NAC in the maintenance of a disomic.

The yeast centromere identified as a 125-bp structure is very simple and is not characteristic of the eukaryotic centromeres. It has been shown that even *Schizosaccharomyces pombe* centromeres are very complex structures encompassing over 80 kbp of DNA (Clarke, 1990). In view of these facts, it would be highly desirable to clone *Neurospora* centromeres and determine their molecular structure in order to understand the interaction of these sequences with different proteins, as well as their role during cell divisions.

III. Genetic Material

Neurospora has at least three genetic systems. These include nuclear and mitochondrial chromosomes and mitochondrial DNA plasmids. The nucleus contains seven chromosomes corresponding to seven linkage groups. The mitochondrial genetic system consists of a single circular chromosome containing about 64.3 kbp. The mitochondria may also contain a number of linear or circular plasmids, which may or may not have any homology to the mitochondrial DNA (Lambowitz *et al.*, 1985).

A. CHROMOSOMES—MOLECULAR KARYOTYPE AND LINKAGE ANALYSIS

In *Neurospora* over 47×10^6 bp of DNA are distributed over seven chromosomes. Ordinarily these seven chromosomes can be identified as four groups of chromosomes separable on a gel subjected to the pulsed-field gel electrophoresis (Orbach *et al.*, 1988). Chromosomes 1 and V are the two larger chromosomes and appear together as the most slowly moving band; chromosomes IV and III appear as distinct bands of intermediate migration; chromosomes II, VI, and VII are of the same size range and appear as a single fast-moving band. Chromosomes I and V can be separated from each other by reducing the voltage and increasing the switching interval and electrophoresis time relative to the parameters normally used for the separation of the four major chromosomal groups. Likewise, the smaller chromosomes (II, VI, and VII) are distinguished by running electrophoresis for a longer time with a reduced switching interval. The individual chromosomes were identified by Southern hybridization with nick-translated cloned genes belonging to a specific linkage group (see Table 2). Thus, the numbering of chromosomes is not based on size but on correspondence to particular linkage groups (Orbach *et al.*, 1988). The assignment of a particular linkage group to chromosomes was further confirmed by identification of minichromosomes appearing in a translocation strain of *Neurospora* (Orbach *et al.*, 1988).

The use of pulsed-field gel electrophoresis has provided a direct identification of the different *Neurospora* chromosomes, their size, and their relation to the different linkage groups. Locations of a large number of genes on different chromosomes have been determined by classical genetic methods. The availability of translocation strains and easy isolation of their minichromosomes by pulsed-field gel electrophoresis can be used to screen a genomic (or cDNA) library of *Neurospora* to identify a clone harboring a particular gene of interest and to establish its linkage relationship and location to a particular chromosome (Orbach *et al.*, 1988). Furthermore, the methods for the use of restriction fragment-length polymorphisms can be applied to linkage analysis in *Neurospora* (Metzenberg *et al.*, 1984). Soon it is expected that a restriction map of the *Neurospora* chromosomes will become available. This information will be helpful in determining the nucleotide

TABLE 2
Size of *Neurospora* Chromosomes and Their Relationship to Various Linkage
Groups as Based on Molecular Analysis[a]

Chromosome or linkage group	Size (megabases)[b]	Genetic marker[c]
I	>12.6	his-3
II	5	trp-3
III	6	trp-1
IV	>7	arg-2
V[d]	10.9[d]	rDNA[d]
VI	4	tub-2
VII	4	qa-2

[a] From Orbach *et al.* (1988).

[b] The order of the size of different chromosomes (linkage groups) as based on mobility in a electrophoric field is I, V, IV, III, II, VI, and VII; of these, mobility of chromosome I is the slowest whereas that of chromosome VII is the fastest.

[c] These genes, obtained in the form of cloned DNA segments, were used after nick translation to identify an electrophoresed chromosome preparation on a Southern blot.

[d] Linkage Group V (chromosome V) contains the nucleolus organizer. Therefore, these values contain an estimate of 1.8 mb for the nucleolus organizer because it contains 200 copies of 9.2 kb of rDNA repeat units.

sequence of individual chromosomes, thus leading to the establishment of the entire sequence of the *Neurospora* genome. Knowledge of the entire sequence of the *Neurospora* genome would be highly desirable in order to understand the roles of different genes in several problems pertaining to the genetics and molecular biology of development such as meiosis, sex, heterokaryosis, conidiation, and biological clocks and their controlling mechanisms. The availability of translocation minichromosomes and the manipulation of their size by restriction digestion followed by ligation of different fragments in desired combinations may provide opportunities to assess their biological activities in transformants. Such studies may provide insights into the mechanisms of several phenomena specific to *Neurospora* (such as instability of disomics). It may also provide certain clues necessary for the construction of *Neurospora* artificial chromosomes and their biological activities and stabilities during mitosis and meiosis. Such manipulation of minichromosomes to yield equivalents of NAC can be exploited to clone different centromeres (and/or telomeres) in *Neurospora* and to determine their nature. The behavior of artificial chromosomes containing alien gene(s) or resident *Neurospora* genes can be compared upon transformation of *Neurospora* recipient strains to yield the information necessary to understand why *Neurospora* does not allow the existence of disomics during the vegetative state or the existence of an additional copy of *Neurospora* genes immediately preceding meiosis.

B. Nucleosomal Organization of Chromosomes

Neurospora was among the first organisms to be shown to possess a nucleosomal organization of its chromosome (Noll, 1976). Each nucleosome contains approximately 160 bp of DNA wrapped around an octamer of histones and about 40 bp of DNA as a linker between two adjacent nucleosomes. The nucleosomal organization of *Neurospora* chromosomes is based on the analysis of chromosomes by agarose gel electrophoresis following digestion with micrococcal and other nucleases. The amino acid analyses of the histones show the presence of H_1, H_2A, H_2B, H_3 and H_4; of these, H_3 and H_4 are highly conserved histones, whereas H_2A and H_2B are moderately conserved, and H_1 is a highly variable protein. The variability of H_1 in different cell types, such as vegetative mycelia, conidia, perithecia, and ascospores, has not been examined. The most important feature of the histone genes in *Neurospora* is the presence of introns (Woudt *et al.*, 1983). This is unusual because histone genes from a range of eukaryotic organisms have been found to lack introns. The *Neurospora* H_3 gene contains a 67-bp intron after the seventieth codon. The H_4 gene has two introns, a 69-bp intron in the third codon and a 68-bp intron in the forty-ninth codon. The H_3 and H_4 genes are linked and occur as single copy in *Neurospora*. The amino acid sequences of the H_3 and H_4 genes are conserved in *Neurospora* and yeast. However, a comparison of the nucleotide sequences of *Neurospora* and yeast genes revealed marked differences in the codon usage among these two lower eukaryotic organisms. (Woudt *et al.*, 1983).

C. Centromere, Telomere, and Replicator

In addition to a large number of genes, a eukaryotic chromosome consists of a centromere, a telomere at its ends, and several replicators. However, little is known about any of these components in *Neurospora* at the molecular level.

1. Centromere

The genetic effects of centromeres on recombination were first established in *Neurospora* (Fincham, 1951); however, a *Neurospora* centromere has yet to be cloned and analyzed at the molecular level. The centromeres from yeast have been cloned and are well characterized. Analyses of the cloned yeast centromeres show that their structure and organization are atypical of other eukaryotic centromeres (Clarke, 1990). In view of this fact, it is very important to characterize *Neurospora* centromeres at the molecular level. This may be achieved by the method of chromosome walking from a gene closely linked to a particular centromere. Such a gene can be used to screen a genomic library to identify clones harboring chromosomal segments that contain a particular centromere. For example, the *qa* gene cluster, which is close to the centromere of chromosome VII (Giles *et al.*, 1991), or the *un* gene, which is close to the centromere of chromosome I, may be used as reference points for the cloning of these centromeres via chromosome walking. Perhaps other *Neurospora* centromeres can be cloned in a similar manner. Alternatively, there is a good chance that *Neurospora* centromeres can be obtained as DNA segments resistant to digestion by restriction enzymes, because it is known that pericentric regions are resistant to restriction enzyme digestion. In order to obtain centromeres in this way, the isolated minichromosome, after digestion with different restriction enzymes, would be electrophoresed and the DNA segment resistant to further digestion with restriction endonucleases would be a candidate as possibly containing the centromeric region. This can be further confirmed by Southern hybridization probed with marker genes known to be closely linked to centromeric regions. However, this can be established only after the molecular analysis of different *Neurospora* centromeres is available. Characterization of *Neurospora* centromeres would be useful in the construction of the NAC and in the understanding of its role in cell division, as was mentioned previously regarding the construction of artificial chromosomes.

2. Telomere

Telomeres are the ends of eukaryotic chromosomes. They are required to maintain the ingegrity of the linear DNA molecules, to avoid the fusion of the ends of chromosomes, and to facilitate the replication of linear chromosomes. Telomeres from *Vaccinia virus* and from ciliate *Tetrahymena* species have been very well characterized (Chan and Tye, 1983; Blackburn and Szostak, 1984). These telomeres have been shown to contain a hairpin loop structure that is composed of a C_4A_2 repeat. The *Tetrahymena* centromere was used in the construction of yeast artificial chromosomes (Szostak and Blackburn, 1982). Thus, the study of the structure and organization of telomeres has been very useful in understanding their role in maintaining chromosomal structure and their function in facilitating replication of linear DNA molecules and in the construction of artificial chromosomes.

The *Neurospora* telomere has been isolated by Schechtman (1987, 1989, 1990) via the method of chromosome walking. This was done using clones containing the *his-6* gene, a telomere-linked marker on chromosome V of *Neurospora*. On further analysis, the telomeric region was found to contain a repeat of the hexanucleotide $(TTAGGG)_n$. This repeat sequence $[(TTAGGG)_n]$ is not found anywhere else in the *Neurospora* genome. Later, Schechtman (1989) used the oligonucleotide probe $(TTAGGG)_4$ to screen a *Neurospora* library to identify clones containing various *Neurospora* telomers; all 14 telomeres have been identified on a Southern blot. Later, seven telomeres were assigned to specific chromosomes by RFLP mapping. Thus, the telomeres IIL, IIR, IIIR, IVL, IVR, VR, and VIIL have been fully identified. The fact that the *Neurospora* telomeric nucleotide sequence (i.e., TTAGGG) is exactly the same as that found in human and other mammalian telomeres (Moyzis *et al.*, 1988) is certainly interesting. The *Neurospora* VR telomere is characterized by the presence of a transposable element-like structure (called pogo) in its vicinity; this element has an open reading frame (ORF). It is not known whether it codes for a protein, which may participate in telomere maintenance as has been shown in yeast (Greider and Blackburn, 1985).

3. Replicator

The eukaryotic chromosomes are organized into several units of replication, each containing one or more replicator or autonomously replicating sequences. The *ars* have been generally identified by their ability to increase yeast transformation frequency. The *Neurospora ars* identified in this manner, however, do not show replicator function when put back into *Neurospora* cells. This constitutes a major difficulty in isolating *Neurospora* DNA segments containing *ars*. Therefore, effort must be directed to identify DNA segments with *ars* that function in the *Neurospora* transformation system. The identification of *Neurospora ars* and their characterization are crucial to the development of an autonomously replicating vector and that of *Neurospora* artificial chromosomes.

D. ORGANIZATION OF NEUROSPORA GENES

1. Protein-Encoding Genes

Based on classical genetic analyses, it has been established that *Neurospora* genes of related functions are not clustered but appear randomly distributed throughout the genome. However, there are certain exceptions to this rule; these include the *qa* gene cluster, which comprises structural and regulatory genes (Giles *et al.*, 1991), and the *arom* gene cluster, which produces a single multifunctional polypeptide (Case and Giles, 1976).

However, nearly 100 genes of *Neurospora* have been cloned and sequenced. Based on their molecular characterization, certain general features of their structural organization have been revealed. These include the presence of a nontranslatable leader sequence (including the promoter region); variation in the intron size, frequency, and splicing; and a bias in codon preference (Gurr *et al.*, 1987). In all these features *Neurospora* markedly differs from yeast. In general, the constitutive and highly expressed genes of *Neurospora* show more codon bias than do those genes expressed at a lower level (Gurr *et al.*, 1987). *Neurospora* introns are much smaller than those in yeast; on average a *Neurospora* intron consists of 100 bp located anywhere in the gene mostly once or twice. This situation is much different from that in yeast, in which introns are usually present toward the 5' end of the nuclear genes encoding proteins (Gurr *et al.*, 1987).

2. rRNA and 5S RNA Genes

All rRNA genes are localized in the nucleolar organizer region (NOR) region of chromosome V of *Neurospora* (Perkins and Barry, 1977; Orbach *et al.*, 1988). In *Neurospora* there are about 100 copies of the 5S RNA genes, which are distributed over different chromosomes. Of the several 5S RNA genes analyzed, most occurred as single genes. A majority of them (9 of 15) demonstrated a particular nucleotide sequence designated as α. In addition to the α 5S RNA gene, four other types (designated as β, β_1, γ, and δ) have been identified. At present, it is not known whether these different kinds of 5S RNA participate in a tissue-specific manner or in preferential translation of a certain class of mRNA. The nature of the various 5S RNA genes and their evolutionary significance have been discussed (Selker *et al.*, 1981).

IV. DNA Transaction

Very little is known about the different aspects of DNA transactions at the molecular level in this organism, despite the fact that the molecular model of genetic recombination has emerged from the classical genetic studies of *Neurospora*. Also, the idea of the genetic control of DNA recombination has been based on analyses of certain mutants of *Neurospora* (Catcheside, 1966, 1977). However, the genetic analysis of DNA repair has been carried out extensively through the study of mutants sensitive to different mutagens.

A. DNA REPLICATION

Neurospora chromosomes must replicate like any other eukaryotic chromosomes, i.e., by initiation at multiple replication sites. The different DNA polymerases (α, β, and γ) have been described. The β-like DNA polymerase was first described in *Neurospora* by Elassouli and Mishra (1982); until then, this polymerase was considered to be found exclusively in animal cells (Chang, 1976). The α and β polymerases of *Neurospora* show the properties of such DNA polymerases from other cells in that they differ in their sensitivity to N-ethylmaleimide (NEM) and aphidicolin; the α DNA polymerase is sensitive to these chemicals whereas β DNA polymerase is resistant to them, as shown by *in vitro* assays. Mishra *et al.* (1990) have provided genetic evidence for the involvement of DNA polymerase in the replication of *Neurospora* chromosomes. It has been shown that the aphidicolin-resistant (aph^r) mutant of *Neurospora* possesses DNA polymerase α, which is also resistant to aphidicolin in *in vitro* assays (Mishra *et al.*, 1990). The aphidicolin-resistant and -sensitive DNA polymerase α phenotypes were found to segregate in the Mendelian ratio of 1:1 among the sexual progeny of crosses involving these alleles. Such meiotic analysis of the DNA polymerase α gene has not been possible in other organisms (Sugino and Nakayama, 1980). Some of these DNA polymerase α mutants of *Neurospora* were found to be highly sensitive to ultraviolet light, suggesting the role of DNA polymerase α in DNA repair, as has been demonstrated in other organisms (Kornberg, 1980). Other physical and chemical properties of *Neurospora* DNA polymerases have been described (Elassouli and Mishra, 1982). The yeast DNA polymerase I cDNA was found to hybridize with a *Neurospora* genomic DNA digest (Mishra *et al.*, 1990). This yeast cDNA probe has been used to screen a *Neurospora* cosmid genomic library (Vollmer and Yanofsky, 1986), and a clone harboring *Neurospora* DNA polymerase α has been identified (Mishra *et al.*, 1990). Using this cDNA probe for yeast DNA polymerase I, it has been shown that certain aphidicolin-resistant mutants of *Neurospora* (with altered and amplified DNA polymerase activity) possessed multiple copies of this gene, as detected by intense hybridization with this probe on Southern blots (Mishra *et al.*, 1990). Results of these studies provide the basis for further cloning and molecular characterization of *Neurospora* DNA polymerase. It would also be of interest to investigate the presence and characterization of *Neurospora* δ DNA polymerase.

More than 25 proteins have been identified and shown to participate in bacterial DNA replication. However, the characterization of proteins other than DNA polymerases from *Neurospora* is completely lacking. A preliminary assay of the *Neurospora* topoisomerase activity has been reported (Schroeder *et al.*, 1989).

B. DNA TRANSCRIPTION

The transcription of RNA in *Neurospora* requires the participation of RNA polymerases and a variety of initiation and other transcription factors as described for other eukaryotes. A preliminary characterization of the different RNA polymerases and transcription factors has been described (Tyler and Giles, 1984). An *in vitro Neurospora* transcription system has also been described (Kennell and Lambowitz, 1989), and this may help the characterization of the different components of transcription in *Neurospora*. All three RNA polymerases (I, II, and III) are involved in the transcription of different *Neurospora* genes. The features of typical RNA polymerase II-transcribed genes producing mRNA, and RNA polymerase I- and III-transcribed rRNA and 5S RNA genes, have been discussed previously (Gurr *et al.*, 1987; Metzenberg *et al.*, 1985a,b; Free *et al.*, 1979; Selker *et al.*, 1981).

C. DNA REPAIR

The genetics and enzymology of DNA repair have been investigated to a great extent in *Neurospora*. Evidence for the presence of excision repair, error-prone repair, and recombinational repair pathways has been elucidated by the analysis of *Neurospora* mutants lacking these pathways (Kafer, 1983; Stadler, 1983; McLeod and Stadler, 1986; Baker *et al.*, 1991) (see Table 3). Mutants sensitive to UV light, X-rays, and several mutagens have been obtained and characterized (Schroeder, 1988; Delange and Mishra, 1981; Kafer and Perlmutter, 1980) with respect to enzymes involved in DNA repair pathways. Alternatively, mutants deficient in the enzymes involved in DNA repair pathways have been created and then examined for possible DNA repair deficiency by their sensitivity to mutagens (Mishra and Forsthoefel, 1983; Mishra *et al.*, 1990). Both approaches have worked quite well in *Neurospora*. Several mutagen-sensitive mutants have been shown to be deficient in enzymes of DNA repair pathways. The nuclease and DNA polymerase mutants of *Neurospora* have been shown to be extremely sensitive to UV light and other mutagens (Mishra and Forsthoefel, 1983; Mishra *et al.*, 1990). These mutants have been very well characterized genetically and biochemically.

The discovery of the involvement of a large number of genes that

GENETICS OF *Neurospora crassa*

TABLE 3
Properties of Different Epistatic Groups of DNA Repair Mutants[a]

Group	Mutants	Important characteristics
I. Excision repair	uvs-2 (sah,sa-30) mus-8 uvs-2 mus-26 uvs-4 upr-1	Extremely UV sensitive; high UV-induced mutation rate fails to rescue a component that has been damaged by UV light; not error prone; homozygous crosses fertile; no increase in chromosomal instability; normal excision of pyrimidine dimer
II. Error-prone repair	uvs-3 (nuh-4) mus-9 mus-11 mus-14 (mus-SC10)	Sensitivity to X-rays, MMS, histidine, and hydroxyurea; meiotic defects, chromosome instability, and defective in extracellular nuclease
III. Recombination repair	uvs-6 mus-7 mus-8 mus-10 mei-3[b] mus (SC-25)[b] mus (SC-20)[b] mus-12[c]	Sensitivity to X-rays, MMS, histidine, and hydroxyurea (not sensitive to UV light); meiotic defects and chromosome instability

[a] Based on data from Baker (1983), Schroeder (1986, 1988), Newmeyer et al. (1978), Kafer (1983), Delange and Mishra (1981), Newmeyer and Galeazzi (1977), Newmeyer (1984), Srivastava and Schroeder (1989), Stadler (1983), Stadler and Moyer (1981), and Baker et al. (1991), Fraser et al. (1980).
[b] These may be allelic.
[c] Mutant mus-12 is not UV sensitive.

control the same function (such as sensitivity to ultraviolet light via a change in an enzyme of the excision repair pathway) suggests the epistatic relationship of these genes and the interaction of their gene products with the damaged DNA prior to the action of the incision and or excision steps in the excision repair pathway. This involvement of a large number of gene products in steps prior to incision and/or excision steps in the excision repair pathway is similar to what has been described for other eukaryotes, such as yeast and mammalian cell lines, including human cell lines (Friedberg, 1986).

Certain *Neurospora* mutants that are sensitive to X-rays but not to UV light or other mutagens (Delange and Mishra, 1982; Koga and Schroeder, 1987) provide the equivalent of human mutants such as those with the ataxia telangiectasia syndrome. A number of mutants with increased sensitivity to different mutagens [such as ultraviolet light, the alkylating agent methyl methane sulfonate (MMS), and X-rays] have been isolated [Schroeder, 1975; Delange and Mishra, 1981;

Kafer and Perlmutter, 1980). Fraser (1979) has shown that *uvs-3* is deficient in a nuclease. Some of the genes controlling UV sensitivity in *Neurospora* have been cloned by complementation in mutants via transformation (Oza and Kafer, 1990). Molecular analyses of these cloned genes can provide an insight into their mechanism of DNA repair and their genetic control. The most interesting observation made in this regard is the discovery that certain DNA repair-defective mutants are sensitive to histidine in the growth medium (Newmeyer *et al.*, 1978; Delange and Mishra, 1981). No biochemical basis for this has yet been determined. Delange and Mishra (1981) have also described an MMS-sensitive mutant that is temperature sensitive. They also found that the MMS sensitivity of a mutant (mms-SC-26) can be overcome with uracil even though this mutant is not a pyrimidine auxotroph (Delange and Mishra, 1981). Moreover, the pyrimidine-requiring mutants of *Neurospora* are not mutagen sensitive. However, the growth of the analogous mutants of *Ustilago maydis* (Moore, 1975) and *Saccharomyces cerevisiae* (Nakai and Matsumoto, 1967) is influenced by pyrimidines. Further analyses of this *Neurospora* mutant (mms-SC-26) should help clarify why pyrimidine-requiring mutants of *Ustilago* and yeast are sensitive to DNA-damaging agents, but those of *Neurospora* are not (Delange and Mishra, 1981). Delange and Mishra (1981) have also described two different classes of MMS-sensitive mutants, one that is sensitive to MMS present in the growth medium and another that is sensitive to MMS only when the germination of MMS-treated conidia is examined. Delange and Mishra (1981) also described MMS-sensitive mutants that require an incubation at 15°C for the expression of MMS sensitivity. Thus, a large number of *Neurospora* DNA repair-defective mutants are available whose molecular biology can provide a further insight into the mechanism of DNA repair.

D. DNA RECOMBINATION

Recombination in *Neurospora* has been extensively investigated. The mechanism of recombination involving the formation and resolution of a DNA heteroduplex structure is still the most plausible basis of recombination at the molecular level (Holliday, 1964; Whitehouse, 1963). This model is supported by results of studies in genetics, electron microscopy, and biochemistry (Orr-Weaver and Szostak, 1985; Symington and Kolodner, 1985; Catcheside, 1986; Smith, 1988). The mechanisms for the occurrence of gene conversion, its polarity, and negative interference are interrelated and explained by this model.

The genetic control of recombination was first described in *Neuro-*

spora (Catcheside, 1966). Almasan and Mishra (1988) have recently shown the involvement of a nucleotide sequence similar to the *Escherichia coli* chi element, which participates in DNA recombination in *Neurospora*. Fraser and Cohen (1983) have described an exo-endonuclease from *Neurospora* that is deficient in certain DNA repair- and recombination-defective mutants of *Neurospora* (such as *uvs-3*). This enzyme has been found to be similar to the nuclease that is deficient in the *rad52* mutants of *Saccharomyces cerevisiae* (Chow and Resnick, 1987, 1988) and to the *recBC*-encoded (ExoV) enzyme of *E. coli* (Fraser *et al.*, 1990). The facts that the *Neurospora* enzyme is homologous to *E. coli* ExoV and that ExoV has been cloned (Finch *et al.*, 1986) suggest that the molecular cloning of this important *Neurospora* enzyme is possible. Such molecular analyses alone can provide an insight into the role of this enzyme in recombination events. No equivalent of the *E. coli recA* mutant has been found in *Neurospora* except for the fact that homozygous *nuc-3* mutants have an almost negligable recombination frequency (Mishra and Forsthoefel, 1983; N. C. Mishra, unpublished data). Development of an *vitro* recombination assay using nuclear, cytoplasmic, or mitochondrial extracts of *Neurospora* can identify enzymes with specific roles in DNA recombination.

E. Enzymology of DNA Repair and Recombination

A number of enzymes (including endonucleases, exonucleases, DNA polymerase, and several other proteins, including DNA-binding proteins) are expected to be involved in genetic repair and recombination. The involvement of a large number of genes in a particular DNA repair pathway or in DNA recombination supports this view. However, only a few specific proteins are known to be involved in these processes and the biochemistry of the involvement of DNA polymerases and other proteins remains to be elucidated in *Neurospora*.

Three distinct *Neurospora* nucleases (DNase A, DNase B, and DNase C) have been identified and characterized (Fraser, 1979; Chow and Fraser, 1979; Fraser and Cohen, 1983). These nucleases were obtained after separation by chromatography on DEAE–Sepharose. DNase A was obtained as a 65-kDa Ca^{2+}-dependent endonuclease, which is active on both single- and double-stranded DNA activities but lacks RNase activity. This protein does not bind to DEAE–Sepharose and is obtained in the "wash" of the DEAE–Sepharose column. DNase B was obtained as the first peak from the DEAE–Sepharose column; it has a molecular mass of 78 kDa and is a Mg^{2+}-dependent single-stranded exonuclease acting on both DNA and RNA. DNase C was obtained as eluant from DEAE–Sepharose after DNase B. DNase C is an endo-exonuclease and occurs in masked and active forms. The masked DNase C form is activated by proteolysis into nucleases of different molecular weights with distinct nuclease activities. A large number of nucleases described from *Neurospora* are now known to be derived from the masked form of DNase C as a result of proteolysis (Fraser and Cohen, 1983; Chow, 1981). Their relationship has been established on the basis of their cross-reaction to antibody produced against a purified preparation of DNase C (Chow, 1981). DNase A and DNase B have been found as secretion proteins whereas DNase C exists exclusively as an intracellular protein found in the nucleus and mitochondria. The synthesis of DNase C can be induced by DNA-damaging agents and other stress-causing factors (Ramotar and Fraser, 1989). In *nuh-4* and *uvs-3*, a missing protease has been shown to be the cause of the deficient activity of DNase C. The role of DNA polymerase in DNA repair is inferred from the fact that certain *Neurospora* DNA polymerase mutants (isolated as resistant to aphidicolin, an inhibitor of DNA polymerase α and δ) are extremely sensitive to ultraviolet light. The precise roles of different DNA polymerases in DNA repair or recombination remain to be established (Mishra *et al.*, 1990).

F. MUTAGENESIS

An error occurring during replication or DNA repair and the failure of DNA repair to correct the error are the main causes of spontaneous mutation in any organism. In *Neurospora,* nothing is known about the role of a proofreading nuclease in the correction of the mispairing of bases during the replication of chromosomes. However, it is assumed that such mispaired bases must be removed by a proofreading nuclease existing as a part of the replication machinery. The role of DNA repair in mutagenesis is inferred from the fact that a large number of *Neurospora* mutants defective in DNA repair pathways have an increased frequency of spontaneous and induced mutations. Many of the questions regarding mutagenesis have been addressed in *Neurospora* (de Marini *et al.*, 1989). de Serres and his group have developed a two- or three-component system equivalent to the heterozygous situation of the higher eukaryotes. They have used mutations in the *ad-3* region of *Neurospora* in a heterokaryon to establish the nature of mutations caused by radiation and chemical mutagens. In this *Neurospora* heterokaryotic system containing *his-3$^+$ ad-3A ad-3B$^+$ nic* and *his-3 ad-3A$^+$ ad-3B nic$^+$*, a mutation in the *ad-3A$^+$* or *ad-3B$^+$* region can be identified as giving rise to a pink colony due to accumulation of a precursor of adenine. Among these mutants, the point mutations in the *ad-3A$^+$*

and ad-$3B^+$ regions are identified as repairable mutants capable of growth on an adenine-supplemented medium, whereas multilocus deletion mutations, including ad-$3A$ or ad-$3B$ and the region beyond them, are identified as irrepairable mutants unable to grow even in the adenine-supplemented medium. This heterokaryotic system has been very useful in answering the questions regarding the nature of mutations and their origin. It has been shown that the frequency of point mutations caused by X-rays increases directly with the dose of radiation, whereas the frequency of multilocus mutations increases as the square of the dose of radiation. Also, the point mutations are caused by lower doses of radiation whereas the multilocus mutations are caused by higher doses of radiation.

It has been further shown that the exceedingly high frequency of multilocus mutations cannot be explained on the basis of the target theory and the classical models of chromosome structure during interphase (de Serres, 1990). The target theory (Lee, 1955) assumes that the DNA of individual chromosomes is distributed randomly throughout the interphase nuclease. The data regarding the increased frequency of multilocus mutations in the ad-3 region of *Neurospora* can be explained in a model of eukaryotic interphase chromosomes in which the DNA of individual chromosomes presents a nonrandom target to X-rays. Evidence for such a model of chromosomes has been presented (Pinkel *et al.*, 1986). It is of interest to mention that these questions regarding the nature of mutations caused by X-rays first raised by Muller (1927) remained unanswered (Auerbach, 1976; Wagner and Plewa, 1985) until the development of a multicomponent heterokaryon system in *Neurospora* by de Serres (1990).

Recent studies of mutagenesis in bacteria suggest that the occurrence of mutation is rather nonrandom and that mutations favorable to bacteria occur more frequently than do neutral mutations (Cairns *et al.*, 1988; Hall, 1990). These nonrandom mutations are called Cairnsian mutations (Hall, 1990). However, there is no evidence for the occurrence of such Cairnsian mutations in eukaryotes (Hall, 1990). It seems that several auxotropic mutants of *Neurospora* that are well characterized can be utilized to answer questions regarding the occurrence and the mechanism of Cairnsian mutations in eukaryotes.

V. Mitochondria

The biogenesis of mitochondria involves the parallel development of two interacting components: the mitochondrial membrane system and the elements of oxidative phosphorylation. Of these two distinct functions, the first is controlled by nuclear genes whereas the second is

26	N. C. MISHRA

controlled by both nuclear and mitochondrial genes. That mitochondria
can exist without mitochondrial DNA establishes the independent role
of the nucleus in the biogenesis of mitochondria and the development of
oxidative phosphorylation as a later event (Attardi and Schatz, 1988).

A. MITOCHONDRIAL GENOME AND GENE ORGANIZATION

The *Neurospora* mitochondrial chromosome is circular and contains
about 64 kbp of nucleotides (see Fig. 2). A detailed restriction site map
of the *Neurospora* mtDNA has been established (Taylor and Smolich,

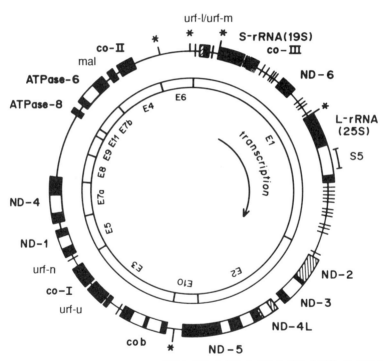

FIG. 2. Map of the *Neurospora* mtDNA: *ND-1, ND-2, ND-3, ND-4, ND-4L, ND-5,* and
ND-6, NADH dehydrogenase subunits; *cob,* cytochrome *b; col-I, co-II,* and *co-III,* cytochrome oxidase subunits; S5, ribosomal protein S5; *mal,* mitochondrial ATPase–
proteolipid-like protein; *ATPase-6* and *ATPase-8,* ATPase subunits; and *urf-l, ruf-m,
urf-n,* and *ruf-u,* unidentified reading frames. The inner circle indicates *Eco*RI fragments.
Solid and hatched boxes are open reading frames, open boxes are introns, and slashes are
tRNAs. *In vitro* transcription initiation sites are indicated by asterisks. [After Kennell
and Lambowitz (1989).]

1985). The mitochondrial chromosome contains a unique *Sal*I restriction site, five *Bst*EIII sites, 12 *Eco*RI sites, 17 *Hinc*II sites, and six *Pvu* sites (Taylor and Smolich, 1985). Over 90% of the nucleotide sequence of *Neurospora* mtDNA has been determined, and it contains 13 genes encoding different proteins, two rRNA genes, 25 tRNA genes, two genes of unknown function, and 50–100 highly conserved G/C-rich palindromic sequences, each containing two *Pst*I sites. These palindromic structures outflank most of the mitochondrial genes in *Neurospora* and were once thought to serve as signals for RNA processing (Yin *et al.*, 1981). Later analyses of a number of transcripts of different mitochondrial regions such as *cob, cox-1,* and *ND-1* have ruled out any such role of these palindromes (Breitenberger *et al.*, 1985; de Vries *et al.*, 1985). Such G/C-rich palindromes are uniquely found in *Neurospora* and are not even in the closely related fungus *Aspergillus nidulans*. The rRNA and *ND-1* genes of *Neurospora* also show size variation (Grant and Lambowitz, 1981; Küntzel and Köchel, 1981; Hawse *et al.*, 1990). In addition, the *ATPase-9* gene sequences are found both in nuclear as well as in mitochondrial DNA (Macino, 1980); of these, only the nuclear *ATPase-9* gene has been demonstrated to be transcribed and translated (Van den Boogaart *et al.*, 1982). The mitochondrial *ATPase-9* gene is denoted as *mal* (for a mitochondrial ATPase–proteolipid-like) gene. The *mal* gene has been found to exist in all *Neurospora* and *Aspergillus* species examined (de Vries *et al.*, 1983). It is believed that the nuclear (*ATPase-9*) and mitochondrial (*mal*) genes are expressed at different stages of the life cycle of the organism. Furthermore, two variants of *N. crassa* differ by a 2.1-kbp fragment that is tandemly repeated (Manella *et al.*, 1979). Several mitochondrial genes of *Neurospora* contain one or more introns. The large rRNA gene contains one intron whereas the *cob* and *ATPase-6* genes contain two introns each (Yin *et al.*, 1982; Helmer-Citterich *et al.*, 1983a,b). In addition, the genes *ND-1, ND-4L,* and *ND-5* have been shown to contain introns (Burger, 1985; Nelson and Macino, 1985). Thus the difference in size of the *Neurospora* mitochondrial genome from that of animal mitochondrial genes may be attributed to the presence of G/C-rich spacer regions, the presence of additional genes such as *mal*, as well as tandem duplications and the presence of introns in the genes. In all ascomycetes there is a clustering of tRNA genes. In *Neurospora* the tRNA gene clusters are located close to the rRNA genes. Nine tRNA genes are grouped around the *ND-6* gene and 11 tRNA genes are situated downstream between the *ND-2* and L-rRNA (25S) genes (see Fig. 2).

Most of the proteins encoded by mitochondrial genes include those involved in the electron transport and oxidative phosphorylation that is

located in the inner membrane of the mitochondrium. The different
mitochondrial genes are listed in Table 4.

B. Novel Features of Mitochondrial tRNA and Genetic Code

During the biogenesis of mitochondria, nearly all proteins are
synthesized on cytoplasmic ribosomes from nuclear mRNA and are
then imported into the mitochondria. However, a number of proteins
are synthesized within the mitochondria on mitochondrial ribosomes.
The RNA components of the mitochondrial ribosomes are coded by
genes on mitochondrial DNA. However, due to the small size of the
mitochondrial genome, it is not obvious as to how this is achieved. This
became clear when the structure of *Neurospora* tRNA was examined by
RNA sequence analysis (Heckman *et al.*, 1978, 1980). Sequence analyses revealed certain novel features of the anticodon regions indicating
that the genetic code in mitochondria may utilize a reduced number of
tRNA species. There are 25 tRNAs involved in *Neurospora* mitochondrial protein biosynthesis. This is possible due to the unusual codon-
reading ability of the mitochondrial tRNA (Heckman *et al.*, 1978, 1980;

TABLE 4

Mitochondrial Genes and Unassigned Reading Frames of *Neurospora crassa*

Gene function/genes	Gene product
Protein synthesis	
L-rRNA	Large ribosomal RNA subunit
S-rRNA	Small ribosomal RNA subunit
tRNA genes[a]	Transfer RNAs
Ribosomal protein gene[b]	S5 subunit
Respiratory chain	
co-I, co-II, co-III,	Subunits of cytochrome *c* oxidase
cob	Cytochrome *b*
ND-1 (urf-1), ND-2 (urf-2), ND-3 (urf-3),	Subunits of NADH dehydrogenase
ND-4 (urf-4), ND-4L (urf-4L), ND-5	
(urf-5), ND-6 (urf-6)	
Oxidative phosphorylation	
ATPase-6, ATPase-8, ATPase-9 (mal)	Subunits of ATPase
Unknown function	
urf-n	Codes a long polypeptide with highly repititive structure
urf-u	—

[a] There are 25 tRNA genes that appear as two or more clusters (see Fig. 2).

[b] Exists as an intron of the large rRNA gene.

Breitenberger and RajBhandary, 1985). It was found that a particular *Neurospora* mitochondrial tRNA containing an unmodified U in the first position of the anticodon could read all the codons of the four-codon family. Further studies in *Neurospora* showed that UGA, which is normally a chain-terminating codon, is read as a codon for tryptophan in mitochondria. Thus, these studies suggested a significant departure from the universal genetic coding system in mitochondria.

C. TRANSCRIPTION AND TRANSLATION

An *in vitro* transcription system for *Neurospora* mitochondrial DNA has been devised (Kennell and Lambowitz, 1989). All *Neurospora* mitochondrial genes are transcribed in the clockwise direction. The study of *Neurospora* mitochondrial transcription has proved to be quite difficult due to the failure of *in vitro* capping with guanylyltransferase. The new transcription system (Kennell and Lambowitz, 1989) acts selectively on *Neurospora* mtDNA restriction fragments to initiate RNA synthesis. The system has successfully identified the initiation sites of the promoter regions of a number of genes, including the small (19S) and large (25S) rRNAs and the cytochrome *b* (*cob*) genes. Based on the study of five mitochondrial genes using the *in vitro* transcription system, it has been possible to identify a consensus 15-nucleotide sequence [5'-ttAGARA(T/G)G(T/G)ARTRR-3'] as the initiation site for a *Neurospora* promoter element. The structure of the transcription initiation site was further confirmed by the analysis of *poky* and *slow growth* (*SG-3*) mutants, which contain a 4-bp deletion of the promoter consensus sequence at the 5' end of the small rRNA gene. The promoter regions from these mutants disrupted by the 4-bp deletion were not effective in the *in vitro* transcription system. This is consistent with the earlier findings that these mutants contained less than 5–10% of the wild-type level of the small rRNA and lacked 36–43 nucleotides on their 5' end (Akins *et al.*, 1989). A specific *Neurospora* RNA polymerase has been described (Küntzel and Schäfer, 1971; Wintersburger, 1972). This *in vitro* system can be used as an assay in the purification of *Neurospora* transcription factors.

The mitochondrial small rRNA of *Neurospora* is transcribed from at least two promoters. In the mutant *poky,* the transcription of small rRNA may be initiated at the upstream promoter and then the rRNA is processed (Kubelik *et al.*, 1990). The characterization of *Neurospora* mitochondrial RNA polymerase would be useful in understanding its origin and evolution. It has been recently proposed that mitochondrial RNA polymerases might have evolved from the RNA polymerases of certain bacteriophages of eubacteria, whereas the RNA polymerases involved in transcription of nuclear and chloroplast DNA were derived from the RNA polymerases of eubacteria (Schinkel and Tabak, 1989). In *Neurospora* several mitochondrial genes may be transcribed as a single precursor RNA unit. The precursor RNA containing the *cob, tRNA*$_{cys}$, *cox-1, tRNA*$_{arg}$, and *urf-1 (ND-1)* genes has been identified (Burger, 1985). It is believed that the tRNA sequences act as primary signals for RNA processing in *Neurospora* mitochondria (Agsteribbe and Hartog, 1987).

The mitochondrial ribosome contains a number of components; of these, the small rRNA subunit, the large rRNA subunit, and a small protein are coded by mitochondrial genes. Over 50 other proteins that are involved in mitochondrial ribosomes are coded by nuclear genes; they are synthesized by ribosomes in the cytoplasm and then imported to the mitochondria. Some of the nuclear genes encoding mitochondrial proteins have been cloned and characterized (Kraeder *et al.*, 1989). The only mitochondrial ribosomal protein, S5, is coded by an 2295-bp intron of the large rRNA gene (La Polla and Lambowitz, 1979, 1981; Breitenberger and RajBhandary, 1985).

D. MITOCHONDRIAL GENES AND MUTANTS

1. Genes Encoding Mitochondrial Proteins

Only a small number of proteins are synthesized in the mitochondria. Some of the genes for these proteins contain one or more introns; the characteristics of these genes are summarized in Tables 4 and 5. A number of these genes have been cloned and their complete nucleotide sequence has been determined.

2. Genes Coding tRNA, rRNA, and Ribosomal Protein

There are altogether 27 tRNA genes, including *tRNA*$_{meth}$ and *tRNA*$_{fmeth}$. The majority of these genes are clustered in two regions (see Fig. 3). The two mitochondrial rRNA genes code for the small (19S) and large (25S) subunits of the mitochondrial ribosome. Of the several protein components of the mitochondrial ribosome, only one (designated S5) is coded by the mitochondrial DNA. The gene for the S5 protein occurs as an intron of the gene for the large rRNA of the mitochondria (see Fig. 2 and Tables 4 and 5).

3. Mitochondrial Mutants

The first mitochondrial mutant of *Neurospora*, called *poky* (or *mi-1*), was described by Mitchell and Mitchell (1952). This mutant showed

TABLE 5
Characteristics of Mitochondrial Genes with and without Introns in *Neurospora*

Gene	Characteristic[a]
I. Genes with introns	
L-rRNA	1 (2295 bp), codes for ribosomal protein S5
ND-1[b]	1 (915 bp), contains an ORF
ND-3	1
ND-4	1
ND-4L[c]	1 (1490 bp), contains an ORF continuous in frame with upstream
ND-5[c]	2 (1408 and 1135 bp), contains an ORF 306–475 bp long continuous with upstream exon
cob	2 (1260 bp each), intron I capable of self-splicing; intron II has an ORF that may code a maturase
ATPase-6[b]	2 (93 and 1370 bp)
II. Genes without introns	
co-I	Continuous in laboratory strain 74A but split in natural wild-type strain (Collins and Lambowitz, 1983)
co-II	Synthesized as a percursor protein (Van den Boogaart *et al.*, 1982a,b,c)
co-III	Cloned and sequenced (Browning and RajBhandary, 1982)
ATPase-8, ATPase-9	Nucleotide sequence determined (Macino and Tzagaloff, 1979)

[a] The number, size, and other characteristics are given if they are known.

[b] The *ND-1* ORF may encode a protein of 304 amino acids with endonuclease activity (Hawse *et al.*, 1990); this endonuclease may promote gene conversion.

[c] Considerable homology exists in the ORF of these introns.

slow growth and lacked cytochromes aa_3 and *b*. The mutant phenotype of *poky* was inherited uniparentally from the perithecial parent in a cross with the wild-type strain. A large number of slow-growing mitochondrial mutants were later described. These mutants were classified into three major groups by Bertrand and Pettinger (1972). The characteristics of the mutants belonging to Group I, Group II, and Group III are summarized in Table 6.

Niagro and Mishra (1989, 1990) have described the characteristics of an ethidium bromide-induced "*stopper*" mutant (*ER-3*). In addition to the typical stop–start growth phenotype of the Group III mutants, it showed the phenomenon of senescence. Like other Group III mutants, *ER-3* was found to be female sterile and the maternal transmission of the mutant phenotype characters could not be established. However, unlike *abn* mutants, *ER-3* lacked a suppressive phenotype in heterokaryons with the wild-type strain. A molecular analysis of *ER-3, abn-1*,

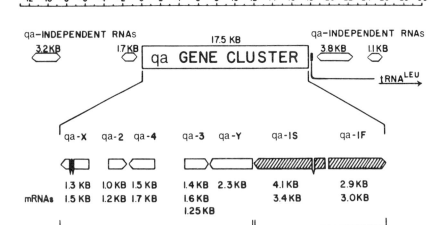

FIG. 3. Transcriptional map of the 42-kb region containing the *qa* gene cluster and adjacent regions. Seven adjacent mRNA transcripts show induction by quinic acid and define the 17.5-kb region of the *qa* gene cluster. Other mRNAs, including the immediately adjacent tRNA[leu], show no induction by quinic acid and therefore are not part of the cluster. The direction of transcription for each of the *qa* genes is indicated, as well as the size of the principal mRNA transcript (immediately below each gene), plus additional minor mRNA transcripts, detected by DNA–RNA blot hybridization. The positions of short introns in *qa-X* (two) and *qa-1S* (one) are indicated. [After Giles *et al.* (1985).]

and *abn-2* mutants showed that these mutants contained a small amount of the wild-type mitochondrial DNA molecule but that a majority of mutant mtDNA molecules existed in which a 25-kbp DNA segment containing several genes (from *ND-5* to *co-II* on the mtDNA map; see Fig. 2) had been deleted. Such deletions in a number of independently derived stopper mutants involved site-specific recombination between two small oligonucleotide segments of consensus sequence CCCCGCCCC flanked by a *pst-1* site (Almasan and Mishra, 1988, 1990, 1991). These recombination hot spots (i.e., CCCCGCCCC sequences) are clustered on the mitochondrial chromosome of *Neurospora*. It has been further shown that a *Neurospora* exo-endonuclease can cleave mitochondrial DNA near these recombinational hot spots (Fraser *et al.*, 1989, 1990). This finding suggests the involvement of the enzyme exo-endonuclease in the site-specific recombination of mitochondrial DNA.

Heteroplasmons constructed between the wild-type and certain *stopper* mutant strains of *Neurospora* usually display a mutant phenotype. This has been called the suppressiveness of the mutant mitochondrial DNA and is explained on the basis of replicative advantage of the mutant mtDNA molecules due to the smaller size such that mutant DNA molecules outnumber the wild-type molecules. However, this

TABLE 6
Different Groups of *Neurospora* Mitochondrial Mutants

Group/genes	Characteristic
Group I (*slow growth*)	Lack cytochromes aa_3 and b
poky (*mi-1*), *SG* (*slow growth*), *Stp* (*stopper*), *exn* (*extranuclear*)	Deficient in small ribosomal subunits (S5 protein) due to a 4-bp deletion in the small rRNA gene
Group II (*slow growth*)	
mi-3	Normal level of cytochromes
Group III (mutants with "stop–start" growth phenotype)	Deficient in cytochromes aa_3 and b
[a]*Stp E35*	*E35* (with a 5-kb deletion)[b] lacks *urf-2* and *urf-3;* low cytochrome oxidase activity; all subunits of cytochrome aa_3 present but not assembled
[a]*abn-1, abn-2,* and *ER-3*	*ER-3, abn-1,* and *abn-2* lack part of *ND-5, cob, urf-u, co-I, urf-n, ND-1, ND-4, ATPase-8, ATPase-9, mal,* and part of the *co-II* genes

[a] The *stopper* mutants contain a mixture of a small amount of wild-type and predominantly mutant mtDNA molecules.

[b] Group I is dominant over the wild type in the heteroplasmon.

view of the suppressiveness of mtDNA has to be modified in view of the finding of the presence of a small number of mutant DNA molecules in the revertants of *stopper* as revealed by the polymerase chain reaction (PCR) analysis (Almasan and Mishra, 1991). The results of the PCR analysis of mtDNA in the revertants of *stopper* suggest that suppressiveness is determined by the copy number of the mutant plasmid and not by the smaller size of the mutant plasmid.

E. MITOCHONDRIAL PLASMIDS AND THEIR RELATIONSHIP TO INTRONS

In recent years a number of mitochondrial plasmids have been described from *Neurospora* strains. These plasmids are defined as the DNA molecules that exist in mitochondria but do not have any homology to the mitochondrial DNA of *Neurospora* (Lambowitz *et al.*, 1985). Of these, the Mauriceville, Varkud, Labelle, Kalilo, and Maranhar plasmids have been very well characterized at the molecular level (Natvig *et al.*, 1984; Nargang *et al.*, 1984; Pande *et al.*, 1989; Akins *et al.*, 1988; Bertrand and Griffiths, 1989). Some of the characteristics of these plasmids have been presented in the Table 7. Both the Mauriceville and Varkud plasmids contain an open reading frame that codes for the enzyme reverse transcriptase (Lambowitz *et al.*, 1985; Kuiper and

Lambowitz, 1988; Kuiper *et al.*, 1990). The actual presence of this enzyme has been demonstrated in Mauriceville- and Varkud-containing strains of *Neurospora* (Kuiper *et al.*, 1990). Kalilo and Maranhar plasmids have similar genome organizations despite their dissimilar nucleotide sequences (Bertrand and Griffiths, 1989). Both plasmids are covalently linked to proteins at their 5′ ends. The Kalilo plasmid contains a terminal repeat of 1301 bp, and Maranhar contains one less than 600 bp. The ends of these linear molecules have no similarity to the telomeres of nuclear chromosomes. It is possible that the covalently linked proteins at the termini of these plasmids may help maintain the integrity of these linear molecules. Both Kalilo and Maranhar plasmids carry two long open reading frames coding for RNA polymerase and DNA polymerase. The plasmid-encoded RNA polymerase seems to be related to the bacteriophage T3/T7 RNA polymerase. The plasmid-encoded DNA polymerase is similar to the DNA polymerase of *Bacillus subtilis* phage 29, and that of the S1 mitochondrial plasmid of maize (Kumin and Kevchenko, 1987). These open reading frames are transcribed divergently from promoters terminating in the long open reading frames (Bertrand and Griffiths, 1989). The linear mitochon-

TABLE 7
Neurospora Mitochondrial DNA Plasmids[a]

Configuration	Size (kbp)	Source	Comment
Circular			
Mauriceville	3.6	*N. crassa*, Mauriceville strain	Both Mauriceville and Varkud plasmids are characterized
Varkud	3.8	*N. intermedia*, Varkud strain	by the presence of an ORF and a discrete transcript and
Labelle	4.07	*N. intermedia*, Labelle I-b strain	by the presence of a *pst-1* palindrome; the ORF codes
Fiji	5.2	*N. intermedia*, Fiji N-6-6	for the enzyme reverse transcriptase
Linear			
Kalilo	9	*N. intermedia*, Kauai strain	Both plasmids contain two ORFs coding for RNA
Maranhar	7.2	*N. crassa*,Maranhar strain	polymerase and DNA polymerase; Kalilo has a terminal repeat of 1361 bp whereas Maranhar has a terminal repeat of less than 600 bp

[a] The occurrence of certain double-stranded RNA viruses has been reported in various strains of *Neurospor* (Meyers *et al.*, 1988). All of these mitochondrial DNA plasmids are capable of integration at a specific site(s) i mtDNA and cause senescence of the mycelium.

drial plasmids of *Claviceps purpurea* also contain DNA polymerase and RNA polymerase genes similar to those of Kalilo and Maranhar plasmids (Oeser and Tudzynski, 1989).

All of these mitochondrial plasmids (i.e., Mauriceville, Varkud, Kalilo, and Maranhar) have been found to be inserted into the mitochondrial DNA of different *Neurospora* strains, leading to mycelial senescence (Lambowitz *et al.*, 1985; Bertrand and Griffiths, 1989). The insertion of these plasmids, mediated by reverse transcriptase, leads to mutation and dysfunction of mitochondrial genes (Akins *et al.*, 1986; Lambowitz, 1989). Molecular analyses of *Neurospora* mitochondrial plasmids showing certain features, such as codon usage and the presence of certain short nucleotide sequence elements (E, P, Q, R, E', and S) (Lambowitz, 1989), have suggested that these plasmids are related to Group I mtDNA introns.

F. NUCLEAR–MITOCHONDRIAL INTERACTIONS

The biogenesis of mitochondria involves a large number of proteins encoded by nuclear genes; only about 15 proteins are encoded by mitochondrial DNA. The nuclear proteins are synthesized on cytoplasmic ribosomes and are imported into the mitochondria. A large number of nuclear genes whose mutant gene products have drastic effects on the biogenesis of mitochondria are described in Table 8. Among these genes, the mutants that affect (1) cytochrome *c* hemelyase protein, which is responsible for the import of apocytochrome *c* after its conversion into holocytochrome, (2) mitochondrial ribosomal protein S24, or (3) trans-acting protein factors required for splicing of Group I mitochondrial introns have been very well characterized (Lambowitz *et al.*, 1985; Drygas *et al.*, 1989; Kuiper *et al.*, 1988a). The import of apocytochrome *c* has been studied in several other systems (Stuart *et al.*, 1987).

As mentioned earlier, a large number of proteins synthesized on cytoplasmic ribosomes are imported into different compartments of mitochondria. Import of a number of these proteins in mitochondria has been very well investigated (Nickolson and Neupert, 1989). These proteins are listed in Table 9. Most of these proteins bear a signal sequence on their N terminus. Some of them interact with receptors on the mitochondrial surface and require energy for their transport. The import of apocytochrome *c* has been characterized in *Neurospora,* both *in vivo* and *in vitro* (Ness and Weiss, 1987). The C-terminal residues of this protein appear to play a role in its transport into mitochondria. In the mutant *cyc-1,* apocytochrome *c* has a few additional amino acid residues at the C terminus. This is due to the failure of the splicing of the short intron present toward the end of the gene. This mutant

TABLE 8
Nuclear Genes Affecting Mitochondrial Biogenesis

Mutant gene	Defective enzyme/protein	Comment
cyt-2 (VIL)	Cytochrome c hemelyase	Import of apocytochrome c and its conversion to holocytochrome is impaired due to defective cytochrome c hemelyase in the mutant; the gene is isolated as 9.6-kb BamHI fragment coding for a 340-amino acid protein containing two introns (Drygas et al., 1989)
cyt-21 (IIL)	Mitochondrial ribosomal protein S24	The gene codes for a 107-amino acid protein and contains a short intron; in the mutant there is a gross deficiency of mitochondrial small ribosome subunit (Kuiper et al., 1988b)
cyt-4 (IR), cyt-18 (IR), cyt-19 (IVR) (allelic to cyt-3)	Three distinct tran-sacting factors (proteins) required for splicing of Group I introns (i.e., mitochondrial large RNA introns, cob, oli-2, and col-I) (Lambowitz et al., 1985). cyt-18 codes for a tyrosyl-tRNA synthetase that participates in the splicing of several mitochondrial gene transcripts. cyt-18 mutants defective for splicing or for amino acylation have been identified and characterized (Akins and Lambowitz, 1987)	The cyt-4 mutants are cold sensitive (i.e., mutant at 25°C but with normal phenotypes at 37°C); cyt-18 mutants are phenotypically wild type at 25°C but are mutant at 37°C, with defective splicing of several pre-mRNA. The cyt-19 mutant is defective in splicing large rRNA at 25 and 37°C. This mutation causes defective splicing of cob and oli-2 genes but to a less severe degree than cyt-18 mutation.

protein is unable to be imported into the mitochondria of *Neurospora* (Ness and Weiss, 1987). Furthermore, for proper mitochondrial import, apocytochrome c must be first converted to holocytochrome c by a covalent joining to heme by cytochrome hemelyase. A *Neurospora* mutant (cyt-21-1) deficient in cytochrome hemelyase is unable to transport apocytochrome c. The imported proteins are processed to remove the

TABLE 9

Localization of Certain Cytoplasmic Proteins in *Neurospora* Mitochondria

Location	Mass (kDa)		Import checked		Ref.
	Mature	Processor	*In vivo*	*In vitro*	
Matrix					
Citrate synthase	45	47	+	—	Harvey and Neupert (1979)
Inner membrane					
Adenine nucleotide translocator	32	32	+	+	Zimmermann and Neupert (1980)
F_1F_0 ATPase subunit IX (proteolipid, DCCD-binding protein)	8.2	14	+	+	Michel et al. (1979)
Cytochrome c_1	31	38	+	+	Teintze et al. (1982)
Intermembrane space	12	12	+	+	
Outer membrane					
Porin	31	31	+		Freitag et al. (1982)

signal sequences in mitochondria; in *Neurospora*, two such proteases have been identified and characterized at the molecular level (Howlitschek, 1988 and Schulte, 1989). In the yeast mutants defective for either of these proteases, the proper assembly of imported proteins does not occur (Yaffe *et al.*, 1985). Recently *Neurospora* chaperonins which assist proper polypeptide folding and assembly into correct multisubunit structures have been characterized (Hutchinson *et al.*, 1989). Results of these studies in conjunction with those carried out in yeast and other organisms would be instrumental in providing the complete picture of the import of nuclear-encoded proteins and genetic control during the biogenesis of mitochondria (Hay *et al.*, 1984; Douglas *et al.*, 1986; Attardi and Schatz, 1988). A further example of nuclear mitochondrial interaction is elucidated by the demonstration of the fact that a nuclear mutation *nd* encodes a function required for the maintenance of mtDNA (Seidel-Rogol *et al.*, 1989).

VI. Membrane

The bilamellar plasma membrane is generally associated with a large number of other proteins. Two distinct classes of plasma membrane ATPase have been described based on their properties. These are the F_1-F_0 ATPase and the E_1-E_2 ATPase. The F_1F_0 found in prokaryotes and in the organellar membranes of eukaryotes is composed of several proteins and is physiologically an ATP synthetase. The *Neurospora* plasma membrane ATPase is of the E_1-E_2 type. This is composed of a single protein of about 100 kDa containing 920 amino acids coded by the *pma-1* gene located on chromosome 2 of *Neurospora* (Nakamoto and Slayman, 1989). This gene has been cloned and the ATPase has been characterized with respect to its catalytic properties, its location in the bilamellar membrane, and its physiological role. It is suspected that in addition to *pma-1*, *Neurospora* may have another gene that encodes another plasma membrane ATPase (Nakamoto and Slayman, 1989).

VII. Metabolism and Gene Regulation

In *Neurospora*, the regulation of metabolism involving nitrogen, phosphorus, sulfur, amino acids, and certain carbon sources has been extensively investigated. The regulatory circuits of these metabolic pathways provide model systems for the study of coordinate gene regulation.

A. Control of Sulfur Metabolism

The regulatory system controlling sulfur metabolism is composed of tran-sacting regulatory genes and structural genes that encode enzymes involved in the uptake and assimilation of a number of sulfur compounds (Burton and Metzenberg, 1972; Metzenberg, 1979); these genes are expressed coordinately when *Neurospora* is grown under derepressing conditions of sulfur limitation. The structural genes involved in sulfur utilization encode arylsulfatase, cholinesulfatase, choline sulfate permease, methionine permease, sulfate permease I and II, and an extracellular protease; the genes encoding these proteins are unlinked. Sulfur metabolism is controlled in a positive manner by the *cys-3*$^+$ gene, which encodes a 25.9-kDa protein. This protein contains a DNA-binding domain adjacent to a leucine zipper and is homologous to the oncogene *fos* and the yeast controller gene *GCN4* (Fu *et al.*, 1989; Paietta *et al.*, 1987; McNight, 1991).

B. Control of Nitrogen Metabolism

Nitrogen metabolism is also controlled by a number of genes. The *nit-2* and *nit-4* gene products act in a positive manner whereas the *nmr* gene product may act in a negative control pathway. The *nit-3* and *nit-6* genes encode nitrate reductase and nitrite reductase, respectively. All these genes have been cloned and characterized. The *nit-2* gene is the major positive-control gene that encodes a protein of 1036 amino acids with a putative zinc finger DNA-binding domain (Fu and Marzluf, 1988a,b, 1990a,b); the *nmr* gene encodes a transcript of 1.8 kb (Fu *et al.*, 1988).

C. Control of Phosphate Metabolism

Two distinct phosphate transport systems have been known to exist in *Neurospora* (Burns and Beever, 1977); these include system I and system II. System I is constitutive, pH dependent, and has a low affinity for phosphate pathways, whereas system II is phosphate repressible, pH independent, and has a high affinity for phosphate pathways (Mann *et al.*, 1989). At least three genes (*nuc-1, nuc-2,* and *preg*) are known to control the expression of system II. These genes act in a epistatic manner resulting in a hierarchical relationship among them (Littlewood *et al.*, 1974). *Neurospora* possesses at least seven enzymes that are repressible by orthophosphates; these include acid phosphatase, alkaline phosphatase, 5'-nucleotidase, alkaline phosphatase permease, two nucleases, and ribonuclease N_1 (Hasunuma, 1977). These enzymes are coordinately derepressed in the wild-type strain of *Neurospora* but not in *nuc-1* or *nuc-2* mutants. In addition, the product of the *nuc-1*$^+$ gene is required for the expression of structural loci such as *van*$^+$ and *pho-4*$^+$ genes.

The *van*$^+$ gene encodes a permease of system II; this permease also transports vanadate, a phosphate analog and inhibitor of plasma membrane ATPase (Bowman, 1983; Bowman *et al.*, 1983). The product of the *preg* gene negates the action of *nuc-1*$^+$, whereas the *nuc-2*$^+$ gene product interferes with *preg* activity. The action of the *nuc-2* gene is inhibited by phosphate and its derivatives. The *nuc* genes are also involved in the regulation of nucleic acid utilization as a phosphate source. The role of the six *nuc* genes in this manner has been described. The *nuc* mutants have been shown to be deficient in nucleases (Forsthoefel and Mishra, 1983) and have increased sensitivity to mutagens (Mishra and Forsthoefel, 1983).

D. CONTROL OF AMINO ACID METABOLISM

The control of amino acid synthesis was first discovered in *Neurospora* when it was first observed that enzymes of different amino acid pathways became derepressed when cells were either starved for a particular amino acid or were grown in the presence of an analog of amino acids, such as the histidine analog, 3-amino-1,2,4-triazole (Carsiotis and Lacy, 1965; Carsiotis and Jones, 1974; Carsiotis *et al.*, 1974; Barthelmess, 1982, 1984). The molecular basis of this interactive control of amino acid biosynthetic pathways was elucidated first in yeast (Hope and Struhl, 1985) and then in *Neurospora* (Paluh *et al.*, 1988) as a cascade regulation mediated by the positive action of the *GCN4*-encoded protein in yeast or of the *cpc-1*-encoded protein in *Neurospora*. The *cpc-1* gene product has been characterized and found to promote the transcription of genes involved in amino acid synthesis by binding to TGACTC sequences located in the 5'-nontranscribed region of these genes. The *cpc-1* gene product is similar to the yeast *GCN4* product and has the DNA-binding domain of the oncogene *v-jun*-encoded protein (Paluh *et al.*, 1988) and other leucine zipper proteins (McNight, 1991).

The control of arginine synthesis and degradation has been investigated in somewhat greater detail among the metabolic pathways for different amino acids. The genes and proteins involved in the synthesis of arginine from glutamate in the mitochondria, of polyamines from ornithine, and of arginine degradation to urea and finally to CO_2 and ammonia in the cytosol have been characterized (Davis, 1979, 1986; Davis and Weiss, 1988). The arginine-specific carbamyl phosphate synthetase (CPS-A) is localized in mitochondria whereas the pyrimidine-specific carbamyl phosphate synthetase (CPS-P) is found in the nucleus. Thus, the regulatory mechanisms involved in control of arginine metabolism include the compartmentalization of the arginine biosynthetic enzymes in *Neurospora* (Davis and Weiss, 1988) in addition to feedback inhibition, induction, and repression.

E. CONTROL OF QUINIC ACID METABOLISM

Neurospora can utilize quinic acid as a carbon source. The enzymes involved in quinic acid utilization are encoded by a gene cluster located on chromosome VII close to the centromere and are induced by the presence of quinic acid as a carbon source in the growth medium. The organization of the quinic acid (*qa*) gene cluster (Fig. 3) reveals certain unique features of the control mechanism. The structural genes *qa-2*, *qa-4*, and *qa-3* encode proteins directly involved in the utilization of quinic acid. The *qa-Y* gene encodes a permease that facilitates the mycelial uptake of quinic acid. The function of the *Qa-X* gene is still unknown. The *qa-1S* and *qa-1F* genes are regulatory genes that control the transcription of the various genes in the *qa* gene cluster. The *qa-1S* gene encodes a repressor protein that is inactivated by quinic acid (an inducer of the quinic acid pathway). In the absence of inducer (i.e., quinic acid), the repressor inhibits the transcription of genes from the *qa* gene cluster. At least two mutant alleles (*qa-1S*$^-$ and *qa-1S*^{c}) of this gene are known. The *qa-1S*$^-$ mutant produces a superrepressor that is insensitive to inhibition by quinic acid; *qa-1S*^{c} produces an inactive repressor protein. *Neurospora* strains carrying this allele (*i.e., qa-1S*^{c}) therefore become constitutive with respect to the transcription of the *qa* gene cluster. The other regulatory gene, *qa-1F*, encodes an activator protein that exerts a positive control on the transcription of the *qa*-gene cluster by inactivating the repressor (the product of the *qa-1*^{2} gene) via a protein–protein interaction and by binding with a specific nucleotide sequence (GGGTAARYRYTTAYCC) present in the 5' end of each *qa* gene cluster.

The activator protein (i.e., the product of the *qa-1F* gene) contains 816 amino acids and has at least two domains. One of these interacts with the repressor protein and the other interacts with the DNA sequence. The activator protein binds to the C-terminal region of the repressor protein. The repressor protein contains 918 amino acids and all mutant alleles described so far contain mutations in the region containing the N-terminal 300 amino acids. Significantly, this repressor is not a DNA-binding protein and is therefore unlike classical repressors (such as the *lac* repressor of *E. coli*). Rather, it acts by binding to the activator (i.e., protein–protein interaction) instead of binding to the operator region of an operon (i.e., DNA–protein interaction). Thus the elucidation of the mechanism of repressor–activator interaction controlling the *qa* gene cluster indeed presents a novel concept in regulatory biology (Giles *et al.*, 1987).

The entire *qa* gene cluster has been sequenced and its characteristics at the molecular level as discussed above have been elucidated by Giles and co-workers (1985, 1987, 1991; Geever *et al.*, 1989).

VIII. Molecular Biology of Development

Neurospora undergoes differentiation into several cell types through the processes of conidial formation, trichogyne differentiation, perithecial development, and spore formation after meiosis. The fungus also undergoes the phenomenon of senescence and demonstrates circadian rhythms. Furthermore, the fusion of cells during the vegetative cycle leading to heterokaryon formation and during the mating process provides an array of genetically controlled cell interactions. All these situations provide unique opportunities to probe the molecular aspects of development.

A. MATING TYPES AND VEGETATIVE INCOMPATIBILITIES

Neurospora species display a spectrum of heterothallic, pseudoheterothallic, and homothallic sex patterns. In heterothallic species, the fusion of the trichogyne with the conidium (or other vegetative cell) of the opposite mating type (designated as *A* and *a*) can lead to the development of a perithicium with asci, each containing eight ascopores. The fusion of the trichogyne with a vegetative cell of opposite mating type is promoted by pheromones (Bistis, 1981, 1983). The trichogyne does not fuse with conidia of the same mating type. In pseudohomothallic species such as *Neurospora tetrasperma,* the mating-type loci *A* and *a* are located in different nuclei of the same cell type and the trichogyne developed from one cell type always interacts with the conidia developed from the cell carrying the opposite mating type. In homothallic species, however, the trichogyne fuses with the conidium of the same mating type.

The mating-type loci of heterothallic species such as *Neurospora crassa* have been cloned (Vollmer and Yanofsky, 1986) by conferring the abilities for perithecial and ascospore formation after meiosis to sterile mutant strains carrying mutations either at the *A* or *a* locus (Griffiths and Delange, 1979; Griffiths, 1982). In *N. crassa,* the *A* and *a* loci have been identified as 5.3- and 3.2-kbp DNA segments, respectively, located on chromosome I (Glass *et al.*, 1988). These two DNA segments that control the mating-type interactions in *Neurospora* are dissimilar in their nucleotide sequences and hence do not qualify as alleles as previously thought; therefore, they are now designated as *A* and *a* idiomorphs (Metzenberg and Glass, 1990). The *A* and *a* idiomorphs control mating-type interactions, which include fusion of trichogyne to conidium, secretion and response to pheremones, perithecial development, and ascospore formation after meiosis. Vegetative incompatibility (in heterokaryon formation) is also controlled by *A* and *a*.

The two idiomorphs have been cloned and extensively characterized at the molecular levels (Glass *et al.*, 1990; Staben and Yanofsky, 1990). The *A* idiomorph consists of 5301 bp of which a 928-bp region contains an ORF with an intron. Located distal to the centromere, this ORF *mt-A-1* encodes a protein of 228 amino acids similar to yeast mating-type protein *MATα1*. The minimum fragment that can effectively restore mating-type interactions in the sterile *a* strain via transformation consists of only 750 bp. The *a* idiomorph consists of 3235 bp; of this, a 1260-bp region controls the mating-type interaction. It contains an ORF (*mt-a-1*) with two introns and encodes a protein of 382 amino acids. This protein is similar to *S. pombe mat-Mc*-encoded polypeptide. The mating-type interactions and heterokaryon incompatibility are controlled by the N-terminal and C-terminal regions, respectively, of this 382-amino acid protein in *N. crassa* (Staben and Yanofsky, 1990).

The heterothallic species (*N. crassa, Neurospora sitophila, Neurospora intermedia,* and *Neurospora discreta*) contain either the *A* or *a* idiomorph DNA segment in the opposite mating types. The self-sterile cultures of pseudohomothallic *N. tetrasperma* contain either *A* or *a* idiomorphic DNA segments but never both. Molecular analysis of homothallic species shows that *Neurospora africana* and *Neurrospora dodgei* contain only the *A* idiomorph whereas *Neurospora terricola* contains both *A* and *a* idiomorphs. Results of these analyses suggest that homothallic species evolved from the heterothallic species (Metzenberg and Glass, 1989). It is believed that in homothallic species the target genes for the mating-type idiomorphs have undergone mutations in order to respond to *A* idiomorph alone (Metzenberg and Glass, 1990).

It is known that heterokaryon incompatibility of the mating-type idiomorph in *Neurospora* is suppressed by another gene designated as *tol*. It is believed that the lack of heterokaryon incompatibility of mating-type genes in *N. sitophila* (Mishra, 1971), *N. tetrasperma* (Metzenberg and Alhgren, 1973; Perkins, 1988), and *N. discreta* (Perkins and Raju, 1986) is due to the presence of a *tol* gene (Perkins, 1988). Because the *tol* gene suppresses the heterokaryon incompatibility of the mating-type locus, it is therefore possible to clone and characterize this gene. It would be of interest to investigate its interactions with the *mt-a-1*-encoded protein.

In *Neurospora,* cell-to-cell interactions are manifested in the form of the vegetative incompatibility that controls heterokaryon formation. Successful heterokaryon formation is possible only when the two fusing strains are isogeneic for the vegetative incompatibility genes designated as het^+ genes. Besides the mating-type idiomorphs, more than 10 genes control the fusion of vegetative cells leading to successful heterokaryon formation (Perkins, 1988). The vegetative incompatibility is displayed in four major cellular interactions as discussed by Perkins (1988). These include (1) the lack of stable heterokaryon formation with continued growth, (2) the microscopically visible protoplasmic killing of cells participating in fusion (this killing can also be induced after the injection of a protease-sensitive but DNase-insensitive cellular extract to incompatible cells) (Williams and Wilson, 1966), (3) the abnormal growth accompanied by pigmentation of strains carrying incompatible genes in a nucleus in the form of segmental aneuploid or disomics (Newmeyer and Taylor, 1967; Mylyk, 1976), and (4) the phenomenon of barrage formation following confrontation of incompatible strains growing toward each other on a Petri plate (Griffiths and Delange, 1979; Griffiths and Rieck, 1981; Perkins and Raju, 1986). The various aspects of the genetics of vegetative incompatibility have been recently reviewed (Perkins, 1988). However, the role of the different genes in causing these cellular interactions has yet to be elucidated at the biochemical and molecular level. A better understanding of the vegetative incompatibility is possible via the cloning and characterization of the various genes controlling the various aspects of this phenomenon.

Molecular analysis of the two mating types in *Neurospora* clearly shows that *Neurospora* differs from yeast in that it lacks mating-type alleles and that no extra copy of the mating-type idiomorph is present in either of the *Neurospora* mating types. The lack of an extra copy of the mating-type idiomorph explains the failure of mating-type conversion in *Neurospora* (Perkins, 1987).

B. Spore Killer, Segregation Distorter, and Meiosis

The phenomenon of segregation distortion and its genetic basis have been very well established in *Drosophila* and in the mouse (Hartl and Hiraizumi, 1976; Silver, 1985). A similar phenomenon has been recently observed in *Neurospora* (Perkins and Barry, 1977). In *Neurospora,* at least three genes (*sk-1, sk-2,* and *sk-3*) control the segregation distortion effect. A typical cross (Sk × Sk^s) yields four black (viable) and four white (abortive) spores in each ascus. This phenotype of the *sk* gene is called spore killer. The *sk-2* gene has been mapped to the centromere of linkage Group III (Perkins and Barry, 1977). Meiosis and ascus development in crosses involving Sk × Sk^s are normal when analyzed by light microscopy. However, no biochemical or molecular basis of the killer phenotype is yet known. It is now possible to clone the *sk* gene and probe the nature of the gene that controls the killer phenotype and the segregation distortion effects of the *sk* gene. Likewise, it is possible to clone at least some of the *mei* genes (i.e., genes *mei-1*, *mei-2*, and *mei-4*) that control different stages of meiosis in *Neurospora* and determine the nature of encoded proteins and their involvement in meiosis. Molecular cloning and characterization of these genes are feasible in *Neurospora* and will provide excellent opportunities to understand the different stages of meiosis in eukaryotes.

C. MORPHOGENESIS, CONIDIATION, CIRCADIAN RHYTHM, AND BIOLOGICAL CLOCK

The morphogenesis of *Neurospora* has been extensively studied at the biochemical level (Mishra, 1977). A computer model for generating cell shape has been recently developed (Bartnickc-Garcia *et al.*, 1990). This model aids our understanding of the different dimensions of fungal morphogenesis. The application of scanning electron microscopy to reveal the architecture of mycelia, conidia, ascospores, and other fungal structures has revealed certain aspects of morphogenesis that can now be probed at the biochemical and molecular levels (Mishra, 1975; Springer, 1989). A *Neurospora* genomic library has been screened with cDNA from conidiating cultures in order to identify the genes controlling the process of conidiation. In this manner a number of genes that are present specifically during conidiation in *Neurospora* have been identified (Berlin and Yanofsky, 1985).

Among the many events of differentiation, conidiation in *Neurospora* is expressed in a manner analogous to circadian rhythm. The latter is the manifestation of an intermolecular clock designated as the biological clock. The genetic basis of this clock has been investigated in detail in *Neurospora*. A number of genes that control the different parameters of this internal clock have been identified (Dunlap, 1990). Recently the *Neurospora* clock gene, *frequency* (*frq*), has been cloned (Loros *et al.*, 1989) and has been shown to display sequence homology with the *Drosophila* clock gene, *period* (*per*) (McClung *et al.*, 1989). Both *Neurospora frq* and *Drosophila per* genes have been found to possess a cluster of potential O-linked and N-linked glycosylation sites within and around the TG repeat in their ORFs and a perfect PEST sequence (Rogers *et al.*, 1986) characteristic of proteins with rapid turnover (Dunlap, 1990). It is obvious that further molecular analysis of the biological clock so readily feasible in *Neurospora* will elucidate the nature of the components of the clocks that are present in other biological systems.

D. AGING AND SENESCENCE

In *Neurospora,* the onset of aging and senescence can be caused by the dysfunction of mitochondria resulting from mutations in mtDNA or due to the integration of plasmids into mtDNA (Akins *et al.,* 1986; Niagro and Mishra, 1990; Bertrand and Griffiths, 1989). Thus a detailed molecular analysis of the dysfunction of mitochondria and that of the integration of plasmids can provide insights into the mechanisms underlying the process of aging and senescence (Niagro and Mishra, 1989, 1990). These analyses also provide opportunities to investigate the factors that control the maintenance (especially of the mtDNA copy number and of mitochondrial plasmids) as well as the amplification and segregation of mtDNA during the biogenesis of the organelle.

IX. Transposons

Neurospora seems to be essentially free of transposons; only two transposon sequences have been found to occur, and are designated pogo and tad. The pogo transposon (1.6 kb) is found close to the chromosome V telomeric region (Schectman, 1987) and contains a 300-bp terminal repeat. A LINE-like element, tad, has been reported to occur in a strain of *N. crassa* collected from the wild in Adiopodoume, Ivory Coast (Kinsey and Habler, 1989; Kinsey, 1990). The tad transposon is about 7 kb in length and is not related to pogo. Unlike pogo, the tad transposon does not contain any ORF-coding genes that are involved in its maintenance. Therefore, it is not known how these transposons are maintained in *Neurospora.* However, tad has been known to transpose between nuclei in a heterokaryon (Kinsey, 1990). The existence of a RIP system in *Neurospora* that eliminates any repeat DNA sequences might be the main cause of the lack of transposons in *Neurospora* (Selker, 1990).

X. Biotechnology

The fact that *Neurospora* cannot maintain a (multicopy) plasmid capable of autonomous replication is considered to be a hindrance in the development of this organism as a host for the cloning of the commercially important genes. However, cloned genes can exist in multicopies, tandemly integrated into *Neurospora* chromosomes, and these are expressed. Thus, *Neurospora* can overproduce certain proteins from such cloned genes. In this respect *Neurospora* is as effective as mammalian cells in terms of the production of foreign gene products and in their glycosylation and transport. Further, *Neurospora* is uniquely provided for studies of genome organization and regulation and this outweighs any disadvantages that this organism may have. *Neurospora* is also capable of certain biochemical reactions that may be commercially important. The fact that *Neurospora* can solubilize low-grade coal and possesses an 84-kDa protein capable of such a property *in vitro* (Odom *et al.*, 1989; Odom, 1990) may be useful in the generation of new avenues for the development of energy resources and for the bioremediation of environmental pollutants. These attributes of *Neurospora* surely provide a conceptual scheme for a biological approach to these problems.

XI. Discussion

Neurospora is unique among other genetically characterized organisms. It is obvious that further investigations of all aspects of the molecular biology of *Neurospora* as discussed above can provide new insights into the intricacies of nature.

Further investigation of the process whereby *Neurospora* fails to maintain extra genes in the form of autonomous plasmids, or in the form of integrated DNA in its chromosomes or in the disomics, may provide insights into the nature of these elements and the mechanism responsible for the maintenance of extra genes. It is known that disomics are stably maintained in *Aspergillus* but not in *Neurospora*. This provides an unusual opportunity to understand why and how chromosomes are maintained in the cell. Certain information regarding the genetic control of the maintenance of extra chromosomes can be obtained by the analysis of *Neurospora* cells transformed with *Aspergillus* chromosomes or *Aspergillus* cells transformed with *Neurospora* chromosomes. In such experiments, it is expected that certain *Neurospora* chromosomes may have a destabilizing effect on the maintenance of extra chromosomes in *Aspergillus;* alternatively, certain *Aspergillus* chromosomes may have a stabilizing effect on the maintenance of extra chromosomes in *Neurospora*. Thus the genes controlling the maintenance of chromosomes can be identified. The technology for the transformation of fungal cells with chromosome-size DNA as well as the methodology for the construction of hybrids between cells of diverse origins are available (Allshire, 1990; Albertsen *et al.*, 1990; Pachnis *et al.*, 1990). It is of interest to mention that the study of parasexual genetics of filamentous fungi such as *Neurospora* and *Aspergillus* (Pontecarvo, 1958; Pontecarvo and Kafer, 1958) led to the development of mammalian somatic cell genetics and mapping of several genes on human chromosomes (Ruddle, 1981). However, information regarding the nature of the factor controlling the retention and maintenance or loss of chromosomes in somatic cell hybrids is missing. This gap in our knowledge can be filled by the construction and analysis of interspecific somatic cell hybrids between *Neurospora* and *Aspergillus*. Such somatic cell hybrids can be readily facilitated by mixing PEG-treated spheroplasts of *Neurospora* and *Aspergillus* cells carrying appropriate complementing genetic markers. Such somatic hybrids should be further analyzed cytologically, genetically, and by analysis of chromosomes separated by pulsed-field gel electrophoresis, followed by their identification by hybridization using appropriate probes. Such analyses can reveal the role of genetic factors involved in the maintenance or loss of chromosomes. A detailed analysis of RIP as well as that of the meiotic mutants, feasible only in *Neurospora*, can provide the details of meiosis, which would be of immense value in understanding not only the mechanics of inheritance but also genetic and developmental control and ultimately the process of evolution. Existence of the phenomenon of RIP provides a better understanding of the organization of DNA sequences in *Neurospora* and the basis for the lack of selfish DNA and transposons in *Neurospora*.

Further molecular analysis of vegetative incompatibility factors can add to our knowledge of cellular interactions. In such studies, PEG-mediated fusion of spheroplasts could be utilized to construct heterokaryons between strains carrying different combinations of *het* genes. Much remains to be discovered about the different stages involved in development of a trichogyne and its hormonal control and development into the perithecium.

The fact that regulation of metabolic pathways is controlled by similar mechanisms such as repression, induction, feedback, inhibition, and compartmentalization of metabolic pathways is significant and indicates the commonality of these control mechanism in eukaryotes. The fact that the *cpc-1*-encoded protein controlling the amino acid pathways in *Neurospora* is similar to yeast *GCN4*-encoded protein further strengthens our understanding of the units of regulatory mechanism of eukaryotes. The control of the *qa* gene cluster provides a new dimension to our understanding of the regulatory mechanisms by the activator protein (*qa-1F* gene product) via its interaction with DNA sequences in front of each *qa* gene as well as its interaction with the repressor protein (*qa-1S* gene product). X-Ray crystallography studies of these proteins and their complexes will certainly enhance our understanding of the elements involved in the control of gene action. Elucidation of the interaction between *cpc-1*-encoded protein molecules and DNA segments can provide a better understanding of regulation at the molecular level. Thus the recent advances made in the genetics and molecular biology of *Neurospora* certainly indicate that our understanding of the genetic control of biochemical reactions has progressed a long way from the conceptualization of the one gene–one enzyme theory of 50 years ago. It also asserts that we have to go still further in our understanding of the secrets of nature that might be revealed by the future study of this organism.

ACKNOWLEDGMENTS

I thank a number of colleagues who readily provided reprints and preprints of their work. My special thanks go to Drs. N. H. Giles, A. M. Lambowitz, and E. U. Selker for Figs. 1–3 and to Drs. A. Almasan, Michael Dewey, C. B. Odom, and Ms. Debra Williams for several suggestions during the preparation of this manuscript. I further thank Ms. Catherine Abbott for her patience during the typing of this article. Work carried out in my laboratory was supported by a grant from the U.S. Department of Energy (DE-FG22-88PC88936).

REFERENCES

Agsteribbe, E., and Hartog, M. (1987). Processing of precursor RNAs from mitochondria of *Neurospora crassa*. *Nucleic Acids Res.* 15, 7249–7264.

Akins, R. A., and Lambowitz, A. M. (1985). A general method for cloning *Neurospora crassa* nuclear gene by complementation of mutant. *Mol. Cell. Biol.* 5, 2272–2278.

Akins, R. A., and Lambowitz, A. M. (1987). A protein required for splicing group I introns in *Neurospora* mitochondria is mitochondrial tyrosyl tRNA synthetase or a derivative thereof. *Cell* 50, 331–345.

Akins, R. A., Kelley, R. L., and Lambowitz, A. M. (1986). Mitochondrial plasmids of *Neurospora:* Integration into mitochondrial DNA and evidence for reverse transcription in mitochondria. *Cell* 47, 505–516.

Akins, R. A., Grant, D. M., Stohl, L. L., Boltorff, D. A., Nargang, F. E., and Lambowitz, A. M. (1988). Nucleotide sequence of the Varkud mitochondrial plasmid of *Neurospora* and synthesis of 2 hybrid transcripts with a 5' leader derived from mitochondrial RNA. *J. Mol. Biol.* 204, 1–25.

Akins, R. A., Kelley, R. L., and Lambowitz, A. M. (1989). Characterization of mutant mitochondrial plasmids of *Neurospora* spp. that have incorporated tRNAs by reverse transcription. *Mol. Cell. Biol.* 9, 678–691.

Albertsen, H. M., Abderrahim, H., Casm, H. M., Dausset, J., Paslier, D. L., and Cohen, D. (1990). Construction and characterization of a yeast artificial chromosome library containing seven haploid human genome equivalents. *Proc. Natl. Acad. Sci. U.S.A.* 87, 4256–4260.

Allshire, R. C. (1990). Introduction of large linear mini chromosomes into *Schizosac-*

charomyces pombe by an improved transformation procedure. *Proc. Natl. Acad. Sci. U.S.A.* **87,** 4043–4047.

Almasan, A., and Mishra, N. C. (1988). Molecular characterization of the mitochondrial DNA of a new stopper mutant ER-3 of *Neurospora crassa. Genetics* **120,** 935–945.

Almasan, A., and Mishra, N. C. (1990). Characterization of a novel plasmid-like element in *Neurospora* derived mostly from the mitochondrial DNA. *Nucleic Acid Res.* **18,** 5871–5877.

Almasan, A., and Mishra, N. C. (1991). Recombination by sequence repeats with formation of suppressive or residual mitochondrial DNA in *Neurospora. Proc. Natl. Acad. Sci. U.S.A.* **88,** 7684–7688.

Attardi, G., and Schatz, G. (1988). Biogenesis of mitochondria. *Annu. Rev. Cell Biol.* **4,** 289–333.

Auerbach, C. (1976). "Mutation Research." Chapman & Hall, London.

Baker, T. I. (1983). Inducible nucleotide excision repair in *Neurospora. Mol. Gen. Genet.* **190,** 295–299.

Baker, T. I., Cords, C. E., Howard, C. A., and Radloff, R. J. (1991). The nucleotide excision repair epistasis group in *Neurospora crassa. Mutat. Res.* (In press).

Barthelmess, I. B. (1982). Mutants affecting amino acids cross-pathway control in *Neurospora crassa. Genet. Res.* **39,** 169–185.

Barthelmess, I. B. (1984). A lethal allele at the putative regulatory locus, *cpc-1,* of cross-pathway control in *Neurospora crassa. Mol. Gen. Genet.* **194,** 318–321.

Bartnickc-Garcia, S., Hergert, F., and Gierz, G. (1990). A novel computer model for generating cell shape: application to fungal morphogenesis. *In* "Biochemistry of Cell Wall and Membranes in Fungi" (P. J. Kahn, A. P. J. Trinci, M. J. Jung, M. W. Goosey, and L. G. Copping, eds.), pp. 43–59. Springer-Verlag, Berlin.

Beadle, G. W., and Tatum, E. L. (1941). Genetic control of biochemical reactions in *Neurospora. Proc. Natl. Acad. Sci. U.S.A.* **27,** 499–506.

Berlin, V., and Yanofsky, C. (1985). Isolation and characterization of genes differentially expressed during conidation of *Neurospora* crassa. *Mol. Cell. Biol.* **5,** 849–855.

Bertrand, H., and Griffiths, A. J. F. (1989). Linear plasmids that integrate into mitochondrial DNA in *Neurospora. Genome* **31,** 155–159.

Bertrand, H., and Pettinger, T. H. (1972). Isolation and classification of extranuclear mutants of *Neurospora crassa. Genetics* **71,** 521–533.

Bistis, G. N. (1981). Chemotropic interactions between trychogynes and conidia of opposite mating-type in *Neurospora crassa. Mycologia* **73,** 959–975.

Bistis, G. N. (1983). Evidence for diffusible, mating type specific trichogyne attractants in *Neurospora crassa. Exp. Mycol.* **7,** 292–295.

Blackburn, E. H., and Szostak, J. W. (1984). The molecular structure of centromere and telomere. *Annu. Rev. Biochem.* **53,** 163–194.

Bowman, B. J. (1983). Vandate uptake in *Neurospora crassa* occurs via phosphate transport system II. *J. Bacteriol.* **153,** 286–291.

Bowman, B. J., Allen, K. E., and Slayman, C. W. (1983). Vandate-resistant mutants of *Neurospora crassa* are deficient in a high affinity phosphate transport system. *J. Bacteriol.* **153,** 292–296.

Breitenberger, C. A., and RajBhandary, U. L. (1985). Some highlights of mitochondrial research based on analysis of *Neurospora crassa* mitochondria: Use of transfer RNA sequence as signals. *Trends Biochem.* **54,** 478–483.

Breitenberger, C. A., Browning, K. S., Alzner-DeWeerd, B., and RajBhandary, U. L. (1985). RNA processing in *Neurospora crassa* mitochondria: Use of transfer RNA sequence as signals. *EMBO J.* **4,** 185–196.

Brody, H., and Carbon, J. (1989). Electrophoretic karyotype of *Aspergillus nidulans. Proc. Natl. Acad. Sci. U.S.A.* **86,** 6260–6263.

Browning, K. S., and RajBhandary, U. L. (1982). Cytochrome oxidase subunit III gene in *Neurospora* mitochondria. Location and sequence. *J. Biol. Chem.* **257,** 5253–5256.

Burger, G. (1985). Unassigned reading frames in the mitochondrial DNA of *Neurospora crassa. In* "Achievements and Perspectives of Mitochondrial Research" (E. Quagliariello, E. C. Slater, F. Palmieri, C. Saccone, and A. M. Kroon, eds.), Vol. 2, pp. 305–316. Elsevier, Amsterdam.

Burns, D. J. W., and Beever, R. E. (1977). Kinetic characterization of the two phosphate uptake systems in the fungus *Neurospora crassa. J. Bacteriol.* **132,** 511–519.

Burton, E. G., and Metzenberg, R. L. (1972). Novel mutation causing derepression of several enzymes of sulfur-metabolism in *Neurospora crassa. J. Bacteriol.* **109,** 140–151.

Buxton, F. P., and Radford, A. (1984). The transformation of mycelial spheroplasts of *Neurospora crassa* and the attempted isolation of an autonomous replicator. *Mol. Gen. Genet.* **196,** 334–337.

Cairns, J., Overbaugh, J., and Miller, S. (1988). The origin of mutants. *Nature (London)* **335,** 142–145.

Cambareri, E. B., Singer, M. J., and Selker, E. U. (1989). Repeat induced G-C to A-T mutations in *Neurospora. Science* **244,** 1571–1575.

Carsiotis, M., and Jones, R. F. (1974). Cross-pathway regulation: Tryptophan-mediated control of histidine and arginine biosynthetic enzymes in *Neurospora crassa. J. Bacteriol.* **119,** 889–892.

Carsiotis, M., and Lacy, A. M. (1965). Increased activity of tryptophan biosynthetic enzymes in histidine mutants of *Neurospora crassa. J. Bacteriol.* **89,** 1472–1477.

Carsiotis, M., Jones, R. F., and Wessling, A. C. (1974). Cross pathway regulation: histidine-mediated control of histidine, tryptophan and arginine biosynthetic enzymes in *Neurospora crassa. J. Bacteriol.* **119,** 893–898.

Case, M. E. (1983). Transformation in fungi. *In* "Genetic Engineering in Eukaryotes" (P. K. Lurguin and A. Kleinholfs, eds.), pp. 1–5. Plenum, New York.

Case, M. E. (1986). Genetical and molecular analyses of *Qa-2* transformants in *Neurospora crassa. Genetics* **113,** 569–587.

Case, M. E., and Giles, N. H. (1958). Evidence from tetrad analysis for both normal and aberrant recombination between allelic mutants in *Neurospora crassa. Proc. Natl. Acad. Sci. U.S.A.* **44,** 378–390.

Case, M. E., and Giles, N. H. (1976). Gene order in the *Qa* gene cluster of *Neurospora crassa. Mol. Gen. Genet.* **147,** 83–89.

Case, M. E., Schweizer, M., Kushner, S. R., and Giles, N. H. (1979). Efficient transformation of *Neurospora crassa* by utilizing hybrid plasmid DNA. *Proc. Natl. Acad. Sci. U.S.A.* **76,** 5259–5263.

Catcheside, D. E. A. (1986). A restriction and modification model for the initiation and control of recombination in *Neurospora. Genet. Res.* **47,** 157–165.

Catcheside, D. G. (1966). A second gene controlling allelic recombination in *Neurospora crassa. Aust. J. Biol. Sci.* **19,** 1039–1046.

Catcheside, D. G. (1977). "The Genetics of Recombination." Arnold, London.

Chan, C. S. M., and Tye, E. K. (1983). Organization of DNA sequences and replication origins at yeast telomeres. *Cell* **33,** 563–573.

Chang, L. M. S. (1976). Phylogeny of DNA-polymerase-beta. Science **191,** 1183–1185.

Chow, T. Y.-K. (1981). A single-strand DNA binding endo-nuclease of *Neurospora crassa.* Thesis, McGill Univ., 1982.

Chow, T. Y.-K., and Fraser, M. J. (1979). The major intracellular alkaline deoxyribonuclease activities expressed in wild-type and Rec-like mutants of *Neurospora crassa. Can. J. Biochem.* **57,** 889–901.

Chow, T. Y.-K., and Resnick, M. A. (1987). Purification and characterization of an endo-exonuclease from *Saccharomyces cerevisiae* that is influenced by the *RAD52* gene. *J. Biol. Chem.* **262**, 17659–17667.

Chow, T. Y.-K., and Resnick, M. A. (1988). An endo-exonuclease activity of yeast that requires a functional *RAD52* gene. *Mol. Gen. Genet.* **211**, 41–48.

Clarke, L. (1990). Centromeres of budding and fission yeasts. *Trends Genet.* **6**, 150–153.

Collins, R. A., and Lambowitz, A. M. (1983). Structural variations and optional introns in the mitochondrial DNAs of *Neurospora* strains isolated from nature. *Plasmid* **9**, 53–70.

Davis, R. H. (1979). Genetics of arginine biosynthesis in *Neurospora crassa*. *Genetics* **93**, 557–575.

Davis, R. H. (1986). Compartmental and regulatory mechanisms in the arginine pathways of *Neurospora crassa* and *Saccharomyces cerevisiae*. *Microbiol. Rev.* **50**, 280–313.

Davis, R. H., and de Serres, F. J. (1970). Genetic and microbial research techniques for *Neurospora crassa*. *Methods Enzymol.* **17A**, 79–103.

Davis, R. H., and Weiss, R. L. (1988). Novel mechanisms controlling arginine metabolism in *Neurospora*. *Trends Biochem. Sci.* **13**, 101–104.

Delange, A. M., and Mishra, N. C. (1981). The isolation of MMS- and histidine-sensitive mutants of *Neurospora crassa*. *Genetics* **97**, 247–259.

Delange, A. M., and Mishra, N. C. (1982). Characterization of mutagen sensitive mutants of *Neurospora*. *Mutat. Res.* **24**, 1–13.

de Marini, D. M., Brockman, H. E., de Serres, F. J., Evans, H. H., Stankowski, L. F., and Hsie, A. W. (1989). Specific-locus mutation induced in eukaryotes by radiation and chemicals: a perspective. *Mutat. Res.* **220**, 11–29.

de Serres, F. J. (1990). X-ray induced specific-locus mutations in the *ad-3* region of two component heterokaryons of *Neurospora crassa* VI. Induction, kinetics of gene/point mutations, multilocus deletions and multiple locus mutation. *Mutat. Res.* **231**, 109–124.

de Vries, H., de Jonge, C. J., Arnberg, A., and Peijneburg, A. A. C. M. (1983). The expression of the mitochondrial genes for subunit 1 of cytochrome *c* oxidase and for an ATPase proteolipid in *Neurospora crassa:* Nucleotide sequences and transcript analysis. *In* "Mitochondria 1983" (R. J. Schweyen, K. Wolf, and F. Kaudewitz, eds.), pp. 343–356. de Gruyter, Berlin.

de Vries, H., de Jonge, J. C., and Schrage, C. (1985). The *Neurospora* mitochondrial "stopper" mutant, [E35], lacks two protein genes indispensable for the formation of complexes I, III and IV. *In* "Achievements and Perspectives of Mitochondrial Research" (E. Quagliariello, E. C. Slater, F. Palmieri, C. Saccone, and A. M. Kroon, eds.), Vol. 2, pp. 285–292. Elsevier, Amsterdam.

Dhawale, S. S., Paietta, J. V., and Marzluf, G. (1984). A new rapid and efficient transformation procedure for *Neurospora*. *Curr. Genet.* **8**, 77–79.

Douglas, M. G., McCammon, M. T., and Vassarotti, A. (1986). Targeting proteins into mitochondria. *Microbiol. Rev.* **50**, 166–178.

Drygas, M. E., Lambowitz, A. M., and Nargang, F. E. (1989). Cloning and analysis of *Neurospora crassa* gene for cytochrome *c* hemelyase. *J. Biol. Chem.* **264**, 17897–17906.

Dunlap, J. C. (1990). Closely watched clocks: molecular analysis of circadian rhythms in *Neurospora* and *Drosophila*. *Trends Genet.* **6**, 159–165.

Duran, R., and Gray, P. M. (1989). Nuclear DNA: an adjunct to morphology in fungal taxonomy. *Mycotaxon* **36**, 205–219.

Elassouli, S. M., and Mishra, N. C. (1982). Properties of *Neurospora* DNA polymerases. *FEMS Microbiol. Lett.* **13**, 181–185.

Finch, P. W., Wilson, R. E., Brown, K., Hickson, I. D., Tomkinson, A. E., and Emmerson,

P. T. (1986). Complete nucleotide sequence of the *Escherichia coli recC* gene and of the *thyA–recC* intergenic region. *Nucleic Acids Res.* **14**, 4437–4451.

Fincham, J. R. S. (1951). A comparative study of the mating type chromosomes of two species of *Neurospora*. *J. Genet.* **50**, 221–225.

Fincham, J. R. S. (1989). Transformation in fungi. *Microbiol. Rev.* **53**, 148–170.

Forsthoefel, A. M., and Mishra, N. C. (1983). Biochemical genetics of *Neurospora* nucleases I. *Genet. Res.* **41**, 271–286.

Fraser, M. J. (1979). Alkaline deoxyribonucleases released from *Neurospora crassa* mycelia: two activities not released by mutants with mutagen sensitivities. *Nucleic Acids Res.* **6**, 231–246.

Fraser, M. J., and Cohen, H. (1983). Intracellular localization of *Neurospora* endo-exonuclease and its putative precursor. *J. Bacteriol.* **154**, 460–470.

Fraser, M. J., Chow, T. Y.-K., and Kafer, E. (1980). Nucleases and their control in wild-type and *nuh* mutants of *Neurospora*. *In* "DNA Repair and Mutagenesis in Eukaryotes" (W. M. Generoso, M. D. Shelby, and F. J. de Serres, eds.), pp. 63–74. Plenum, New York.

Fraser, M. J., Hatchet, Z., and Huang, X. (1989). The action of *Neurospora* endo-exonuclease on double strand DNAs. *J. Biol. Chem.* 13093–13101.

Fraser, M. J., Koa, H., and Chow, T.Y-K. (1990). *Neurospora* end-exonnuclease is immunologically related to the recC gene product of *Escherichia coli*. *J. Bacteriol.* **172**, 507–510.

Free, S. J., Rice, P. W., and Metzenberg, R. L. (1979). Arrangements of gene coding for ribosomal ribonucleic acids in *Neurospora crassa*. *J. Bacteriol.* **137**, 1219–1226.

Freitag, H., James, M., and Neupert, W. (1982). Biosynthesis of mitochondrial porin and insertion into outer membrane of *N. crassa*. *Eur. J. Biochem.* **126**, 197–202.

Friedberg, E. (1986). "DNA Repair." Freeman, San Francisco, California.

Fu, Y.-H., and Marluf, G. A. (1988a). Characteriation of *nit-2,* the major regulatory gene of *Neurospora crassa*. *Mol. Cell. Biol.* **7**, 1691–1696.

Fu, Y.-H., and Marzluf, G. A. (1988b). Metabolic control and autogenous regulation of *nit-3,* the nitrate reductase structural gene of *Neurospora crassa*. *J. Bacteriol.* **170**, 657–601.

Fu, Y.-H., and Marzluf, G. A. (1990a). *Nit-2,* the major positive acting nitrogen regulatory gene of *Neurospora crassa* encodes a sequence specific DNA-binding protein. *Proc. Natl. Acad. Sci. U.S.A.* **87**, 5331–5335.

Fu, Y.-H., and Marzluf, G. A. (1990b). *Nit-2,* the major nitrogen regulatory gene of *Neurospora crassa* encodes a protein with a putative zinc finger DNA binding domain. *Mol. Cell. Biol.* **10**, 1056–1065.

Fu, Y.-H., Young, J. L., and Marzluf, G. A. (1988). Molecular cloning and characterization of a negative-acting regulatory gene of *Neurospora crassa*. *Mol. Gen. Genet.* **214**, 74–79.

Fu, Y.-H., Paietta, J. V., Mannix, D. G., and Marzluff, G. A. (1989). *Cys-3,* the positive-acting sulfur regulatory gene of *Neurospora crassa* encodes a protein with a putative leucine zipper DNA binding element. *Mol. Cell. Biol.* **9**, 1120–1127.

Geever, R., Huiet, L., Baum, J., Tyler, B. M., Patel, V. B., Rutledge, B. J., Case, M. E., and Giles, N. H. (1989). DNA sequence, organization and regulation of the *Qa* gene cluster of *Neurospora crassa*. *J. Mol. Biol.* **207**, 15–34.

Giles, N. H., Case, M. E., Baum, J., Geever, R., Huiet, L., Patel, V., and Tyler, B. (1985). Gene organization and regulation in the *qa* gene cluster of *Neurospora crassa*. *Microbiol. Rev.* **49**, 338–358.

Giles, N. H., Case, M. E., Baum, J., Geever, R., and Patel, V. (1987). Mechanisms of positive and negative regulation in the *Qa* gene cluster of *Neurospora crassa*. *In* "Genetic Regulation of Development," pp. 13–32. Alan R. Liss, New York.

Giles, N. H., Geever, R. F., Asch, D. A., Avalos, J., and Case, M. E. (1991). Organization and regulation of the *Qa* (quinic acid) genes in *Neurospora crassa* and other fungi. *J. Hered.* **82**, 1–7.

Glass, N. L., Vollmer, S. J., Staben, C., Grotelueschen, J., and Metzenberg, R. L. (1988). DNAs of the two mating-type alleles of *Neurospora crassa* are highly dissimilar. *Science* **241**, 570–573.

Glass, N. L., Groteleuschen, J., and Metzenberg, R. L. (1990). The *Neurospora crassa A* mating type region. *Proc. Natl. Acad. Sci. U.S.A.* **87**, 4912–4916.

Grant, D. M., and Lambowitz, A. M. (1981). Mitochondrial ribosomal RNA genes. *In* "The Cell Nucleus" (X. H. Busch and L. Rothblum, eds.), pp. 387–408. Academic Press, New York.

Grant, D. M., Lambowitz, A. M., Rambosek, J. A., and Kinsey, J. A. (1984). Transformation of *Neurospora crassa* with recombinant plasmids containing the cloned glutamate dehydrogenase (*am*) gene: Evidence for autonomous replication of transforming plasmid. *Mol. Cell. Biol.* **4**, 2041–2051.

Greider, C. W., and Blackburn, E. H. (1985). Identification of a specific telomere terminal transferase activity in *Tetrahymena extracts. Cell* **43**, 405–413.

Griffiths, A. J. F. (1982). Null alleles of the *A* and *a* mating type alleles of *Neurospora crassa. Can. J. Genet. Cytol.* **24**, 167–176.

Griffiths, A. J. F., and Delange, A. M. (1979). Mutation of the *a* mating type in *Neurospora crassa. Genetics* **88**, 239–254.

Griffiths, A. J. F., and Rieck, A. (1981). Perithecial distribution in standard and variant strains of *Neurospora crassa. Can. J. Bot.* **59**, 2610–2617.

Gross, S. R., Hsieh, T. S., and Levine, P. H. (1984). Intramolecular recombination as a source of mitochondrial chromosome heteromorphism in *Neurospora. Cell* **38**, 233–239.

Gross, S. R., Levine, P. H., Metzger, S., and Glaser, G. (1989). Recombination and replication of plasmid like derivatives of a short section of the mitochondrial chromosome of *Neurospora crassa. Genetics* **121**, 693–701.

Gurr, S. J., Unkles, S. E., and Kinghorn, J. R. (1987). The structure and organization of nuclear genes of filamentous fungi. *In* "Gene Structure in Eukaryotic Microorganisms" (J. R. Kinghorn, ed.), pp. 93–139. IRL Press, Oxford.

Hall, B. G. (1990). Spontaneous point mutations that occur more often when advantageous than when neutral. *Genetics* **126**, 5–16.

Hartl, D. L., and Hiraizumi, Y. (1976). Segregation distortion. *In* "The Genetics and Biology of *Drosophila*" (M. Ashburner and E. Novitski, eds.), Vol. 1B, pp. 616–666. Academic Press, New York.

Harvey, M. A., and Neupert, W. (1979). Biosynthesis of mitochondrial citrate synthetase in *Neurospora crassa. FEBS Lett.* **108**, 385–389.

Hasunuma, K. (1977). Control of the production of orthophosphate repressible extracellular enzymes in *Neurospora crassa. Mol. Gen. Genet.* **151**, 5–10.

Hawlitschek, G., Schneider, H., Schmidt, B., Tropschug, M., Hartl, F. U., and Neupert, W. (1988). Mitochondrial protein import: Identification of processing peptidase and of PEP, a processing enhancing protein. *Cell* **53**, 795–806.

Hawse, A., Collins, R. A., and Nargang, E. (1990). Behavior of the [mi-3] mutation and conversion of polymorphic mtDNA markers in heterokaryons of *Neurospora crassa. Genetics* **126**, 63–72.

Hay, R., Bohini, P., and Gasser, S. (1984). How mitochondria import proteins. *Biochim. Biophys. Acta* **779**, 65–87.

Heckman, J. E., Hecker, L. I., Schwartzbach, S. D., Barnett, W. E., Baumstrak, B., and RajBhandary, U. L. (1978). Structure and function of initiator methionine tRNA from the mitochondria of *Neurospora crassa. Cell* **13**, 83–95.

Heckman, J. E., Sarnoff, J., Alzner-DeWeerd, B., Yin, S., and RajBhandary, U. L. (1980). Novel features in the genetic code and codon reading patterns in *Neurospora crassa* mitochondria based on sequences of six mitochondrial tRNAs. *Proc. Natl. Acad. Sci. U.S.A.* **77**, 3159–3163.

Helmer-Citterich, M., Morelli, G., and Macino, G. (1983a). Nucleotide sequence and intron structure of the apocytochrome *b* gene of *Neurospora crassa* mitochondria. *EMBO J.* **2**, 1235–1242.

Helmer-Citterich, M., Morelli, G., Nelson, M. A., and Macino, G. (1983b). Expression of split genes of the *Neurospora crassa* mitochondrial genome. *In* "Mitochondria 1983" (R. J. Schweyen, K. Wolf, and F. Kaudewitz, eds.), pp. 357–369. de Gruyter, Berlin.

Hicks, J. B., Hinnen, J. B., and Fink, G. R. (1979). Properties of yeast transformation. *Cold Spring Harbor Symp. Quant. Biol.* **43**, 1305–1313.

Hinnen, A., Hicks, J. B., and Fink, G. R. (1978). Transformation of yeast chimaeric colE1 plasmid carrying LEU2. *Proc. Natl. Acad. Sci. U.S.A.* **75**, 1929–1933.

Holliday, R. (1964). A mechanism for gene conversion in fungi. *Genet. Res.* **5**, 282–304.

Hope, I. A., and Struhl, K. (1985). GCN4 protein, synthesized *in vitro*, binds HIS3 regulatory sequence. *Cell* **43**, 177–188.

Horowitz, N. H. (1987). The origins of molecular genetics: one gene, one enzyme. *BioEssays* **3**, 37–39.

Horowitz, N. H., and McLeod, H. (1960). The DNA content of *Neurospora* nuclei. *Microb. Genet. Bull.* **17**, 6–7.

Hutchinson, E. G., Tichelaar, W., Hofhaus, G., Weiss, H., and Leonard, K. R. (1989). Identification and electron microscopic analysis of a chaperonin oligomer from *Neurospora crassa* mitochondria. *EMBO J.* **8**, 1485–1490.

Johannsen, W. (1909). "Elemente der Exacten Erblichkeitslehre." Fischer, Jena.

Kafer, E. (1983). Epistatic grouping of repair-deficient mutants in *Neurospora:* comparative analysis of two *UVS-3* alleles, *UVS-6* and other *mus* double mutant strains. *Genetics* **105**, 19–33.

Kafer, E., and Perlmutter, E. (1980). Isolation and genetic analysis of MMS-sensitive *mus* mutants of *Neurospora*. *Can. J. Genet. Cytol.* **22**, 535–545.

Kennell, J. C., and Lambowitz, A. M. (1989). Development of an *in vitro* transcription system for *Neurospora crassa* mitochondrial DNA and identification of transcription initiation sites. *Mol. Cell. Biol.* **9**, 3603–3613.

Kinsey, J. K. (1990). Tad, A LINE like transposable element of *Neurospora*, can transpose between nuclei in heterokaryons. *Genetics* **126**, 317–323.

Kinsey, J. A., and Habler, J. (1989). Isolation of a transposable element from *Neurospora crassa*. *Proc. Natl. Acad. Sci. U.S.A.* **86**, 1929–1933.

Koga, S. J., and Schroeder, A. L. (1987). Gamma-ray-sensitive mutants of *Neurospora crassa* with characteristics analogous to ataxia telangiectasia cell lines. *Mutat. Res. DNA Repair Rep.* **183**, 139–141.

Kornberg, A. (1980). "DNA Replication." Freeman, San Francisco, California.

Kreader, C. A., Langer, C. S., and Heckman, J. E. (1989). A mitochondrial protein from *Neurospora crassa* detected both on ribosomes and in membrane fractions. *J. Biol. Chem.* **264**, 317–327.

Krumlauf, R., and Marzluf, G. A. (1979). Characterization of sequence complexity and organization of the *Neurospora crassa* genome. *Biochemistry* **18**, 3705–3713.

Kubelik, A. R., Kennell, J. C., Akins, R. A., and Lambowitz, A. M. (1990). Identification of *Neurospora* mitochondrial promotors and analysis of synthesis of the mitochondrial small rRNA in wild-type and the stopper mutant poky. *J. Biol. Chem.* **265**, 4515–4526.

Küntzel, H., and Köchel, H. G. (1981). Evolution of rRNA and origin of mitochondria. *Nature (London)* **293**, 751–755.

Küntzel, H., and Schäfer, K. P. (1971). Mitochondrial RNA polymerase from *Neurospora crassa*. *Nature (London), New Biol.* **231**, 265–269.

Kuiper, M. T. R., and Lambowitz, A. M. (1988). A novel reverse transcriptase activity associated with mitochondrial plasmids of *Neurospora*. *Cell* **55**, 693–704.

Kuiper, M. T. R., Akins, R. A., Holtrop, M., de Vries, H., and Lambowitz, A. M. (1988a). Isolation and analysis of the *Neurospora crassa Cyt 21* gene (a nuclear gene encoding a mitochondrial ribosomal protein). *J. Biol. Chem.* **263**, 2840–2847.

Kuiper, M. T. R., Holtrop, M., Vennema, H., Lambowitz, A. M., and de Vries, H. (1988b). A 3' splice site mutation in a nuclear gene encoding a mitochondrial ribosomal protein in *Neurospora crassa*. *J. Biol. Chem.* **263**, 2848–2852.

Kuiper, M. T. R., Sabourin, J. R., and Lambowitz, A. M. (1990). Identification of the reverse transcriptase encoded by the Mauriceville and Varkud mitochondrial plasmid of *Neurospora*. *J. Biol. Chem.* **265**, 6936–6943.

Kumin, E. V., and Kevchenko, I. V. (1987). S_1 plasmid from CMS-S-maize mitochondria encodes a viral type DNA-polymerase. *Nucleic Acids Res.* **15**, 6758–6764.

Lambowitz, A. M. (1989). Infectious introns. *Cell* **56**, 323–326.

Lambowitz, A. M., Akins, R. A., Garriga, G., Henderson, M., Kubelik, A. R., and Maloney, K. A. (1985). Mitochondrial introns and mitochondrial plasmid. *In* "Achievements and Perspectives of Mitochondrial Research" (E. E. Quagliariello, E. C. Slater, F. Palmieri, C. Saccone, and A. M. Kroon, eds.), Vol. 2, pp. 237–247. Elsevier, Amsterdam.

La Polla, R. J., and Lambowitz, A. M. (1979). The binding of mitochondrial ribosomal proteins to a mitochondrial ribosomal precursor RNA containing a 2.3 kb intron. *J. Biol. Chem.* **254**, 11746–11750.

La Polla, R. J., and Lambowitz, A. M. (1981). Mitochondrial ribosome assembly in *Neurospora crassa*. Purification of the mitochondrially synthesized ribosomal protein, S-5. *J. Biol. Chem.* **256**, 7064–7067.

Lee, E. E. (1955). "Actions of Radiation on Living Cells." Cambridge Univ. Press, London.

Lewin, B. (1990). "Genes IV (1989)." Oxford Univ. Press, New York.

Littlewood, B. S., Chia, W., and Metzenberg, R. L. (1974). Genetic control of phosphate-metabolizing enzymes in *Neurospora crassa*: relationships among regulatory mutation. *Genetics* **79**, 419–434.

Loros, J. J., Denome, S. A., and Dunlap, J. C. (1989). Molecular cloning of genes under control of the circadian clock in *Neurospora*. *Science* **243**, 285–388.

Luck, D. J. L. (1963). Genesis of mitochondria in *Neurospora crassa*. *Proc. Natl. Acad. Sci. U.S.A.* **49**, 233–240.

Lyon, M. F. (1972). X-chromosome inactivation and developmental patterns in mammals. *Biol. Rev. Cambridge Philos. Soc.* **47**, 1–35.

Macino, G. (1980). Mapping of mitochondrial structural genes in *Neurospora crassa*. *J. Biol. Chem.* **255**, 10563–10565.

Macino, G., and Tzagaloff, A. (1979). Assembly of the mitochondrial membrane system—partial sequence of a mitochondrial ATPase gene in *Saccharomyces cerevisiae*. *Proc. Natl. Acad. Sci. U.S.A.* **76**, 131–135.

Manella, C. A., Goewert, R. R., and Lambowitz, A. M. (1979). Characterization of variant *Neurospora crassa* mitochondrial DNAs which contain tandem reiterations. *Cell* **18**, 1197–1207.

Mann, B., Akins, R. A., Lambowitz, A. M., and Metzenberg, R. L. (1988). The structural gene for a phosphorus-repressible phosphate permease in *Neurospora crassa* can complement a mutation in positive regulatory gene *nuc-1*. *Mol. Cell. Biol.* **8**, 1876–1879.

Mann, B. J., Bowman, B. J., Grotelueschen, J., and Metzenberg, R. L. (1989). Nucleotide sequence of *Pho-4+*, encoding a phosphate-repressible permease of *Neurospora crassa*. *Gene* **83**, 281–289.

McClung, R. C., Fox, B. A., and Dunlap, J. C. (1989). The *Neurospora* clock gene frequency shares a sequence element with the *Drosophila* clock gene period. *Nature (London)* **339**, 558–562.

Mcleod, H., and Stadler, D. (1986). Excision of pyrimidine dimers from DNA of *Neurospora*. *Mol. Gen. Genet.* **202**, 321–326.

McNight, S. L. (1991). Molecular zippers in gene regulation. *Sci. Am.* **264**, 54–63.

Mendel, M., and Higa, A. (1970). Calcium-dependent bacteriophage infection. *J. Mol. Biol.* **53**, 159–162.

Metzenberg, R. L. (1979). Implications of some genetic control mechanisms in *Neurospora*. *Microbiol. Rev.* **43**, 361–383.

Metzenberg, R. L. (1990). The role of similarity and differences in fungal mating. *Genetics* **125**, 457–462.

Metzenberg, R. L., and Alhgren, S. K. (1973). Behavior of *Neurospora tetrasperma* mating type genes introgressed into *N. crassa*. *Can. J. Genet. Cytol.* **15**, 571–576.

Metzenberg, R. L., and Glass, N. L. (1990). Mating type and mating strategies in *Bio-Essays* **12**, 53–59.

Metzenberg, R. L., and Glass, N. L. (1990). Mating type and mating strategies in *Neurospora*. *BioEssays* **12**, 53–59.

Metzenberg, R. L., Stevens, J. N., Selker, E. U., and Morzycka-Wroblewska, E. (1984). A method for finding the genetic map position of cloned DNA fragments. *Neurospora Newsl.* **31**, 35–39.

Metzenberg, R. L., Stevens, J. N., Selker, E. U., and Morzycka-Wroblewska, E. (1985a). Identification and chromosome distribution of 5SrRNA genes in *Neurospora crassa*. *Proc. Natl. Acad. Sci. U.S.A.* **82**, 2067–2073.

Metzenberg, R. L., Selker, E. U., Morzycka-Wroblewska, E., and Stevens, J. N. (1985b). Dispersed multiple copy genes for ssRNA: what keeps them honest? *In* "Molecular Genetics of Filamentous Fungi" (W. E. Timberlake, ed.), pp. 295–307. Alan R. Liss, New York.

Meyers, C. J., Griffiths, A. J. F., Kraus, S. R., and Martin, R. R. (1988). Double-stranded RNA in natural isolates of *Neurospora*. *Curr. Genet.* **13**, 495–502.

Michel, R., Wachter, E., and Sebald, W. (1979). Synthesis of a larger precursor for the proteolipid subunit of the mitochondrial ATPase complex of *Neurospora crassa* in a cell wheat germ system. *FEBS Lett.* **101**, 373–376.

Mishra, N. C. (1971). Heterokaryosis in *Neurospora sitophila*. *Genetics* **67**, 55–59.

Mishra, N. C. (1975). The surface architecture of different *Neurospora* strains as revealed by scanning electron microscopy and their relation to morphology. *J. Microsc. Biol. Cell.* **26**, 151–159.

Mishra, N. C. (1977). Biochemical genetics of *Neurospora* morphogenesis. *Adv. Genet.* **19**, 341–405.

Mishra, N. C. (1979). DNA-mediated genetic changes in *Neurospora crassa*. *J. Gen. Microbiol.* **113**, 255–259.

Mishra, N. C. (1985). Gene transfer in fungi. *Adv. Genet.* **23**, 73–177.

Mishra, N. C., and Forsthoefel, A. M. (1983). Biochemical genetics of *Neurospora* nucleases II. *Genet. Res.* **41**, 287–297.

Mishra, N. C., and Tatum, E. L. (1973). Non-Mendelian inheritance of DNA-induced inositol independence in *Neurospora*. *Proc. Natl. Acad. Sci. U.S.A.* **70**, 3875–3879.

Mishra, N. C., Szabo, G., and Tatum, E. L. (1973). Nucleic acid. Induced genetic changes in *Neurospora*. *In* "The Role of RNA in Reproduction and Development" (M. C. Niu and S. J. Segal, eds.), pp. 259–268. North-Holland Publ., Amsterdam.

Mishra, N. C., Almasan, A., and Cooley, M. (1990). Characterization of eukaryotic DNA polymerases: aphidicolin-resistant mutants of *Neurospora* with altered DNA polymerase. *In* "Isozymes: Structure, Function and Use in Biology and Medicine." (C. Markert and Z.-I. Ogita, eds.), pp. 295–313. Wiley-Liss, New York.

Mitchell, M. B. (1955). Aberrant recombination of pyridoxine mutants of *Neurospora*. *Proc. Natl. Acad. Sci. U.S.A.* **41**, 215–220.

Mitchell, M. B., and Mitchell, H. K. (1952). Observations on the behaviour of suppressors. *Proc. Natl. Acad. Sci. U.S.A.* **38**, 205–214.

Mitchell, M. B., Pettinger, T. H., and Mitchell, H. K. (1952). Pseudo wildtypes in *Neurospora crassa*. *Proc. Natl. Acad. Sci. U.S.A.* **38**, 569–580.

Moore, P. D. (1975). Radiation sensitive pyrimidine auxotroph of *Ustilago maydis*. *Mutat. Res.* **28**, 355–366.

Moyzis, R. K., Buckingham, J. M., Cram, L. S., Dami, M., Deaven, L. L., Jones, M. D., Meyne, J., Ratliff, R. L., and Wu, J. R. (1988). A highly conserved repetitive DNA sequence (TTAGGG)n at the telomeres of human chromosomes. *Proc. Natl. Acad. Sci. U.S.A.* **85**, 6622–6626.

Muller, H. J. (1927). Artificial transmutation of the gene. *Science* **66**, 84–86.

Murray, A. W., and Szostak, J. W. (1983). Construction of artificial chromosomes in yeast. *Nature (London)* **305**, 189–193.

Mylyk, O. M. (1976). Heretomorphism for heterokaryon incompatibility genes in natural populations of *Neurospora crassa*. *Genetics* **83**, 275–284.

Nakai, S., and Matsumoto, S. (1967). Two types of radiation sensitive mutants in yeast. *Mutat. Res.* **4**, 129–136.

Nakamoto, R. K., and Slayman, C. W. (1989). Molecular properties of the fungal plasmamembrane (H$^+$)-ATPase. *J. Bioenerg. Biomembr.* **21**, 621–632.

Nargang, F. E., Bell, J. B., Stohl, L. L., and Lambowitz, A. M. (1984). The DNA sequence and genetic organization of a *Neurospora* mitochondrial plasmid suggest a relationship to introns and mobile elements. *Cell* **38**, 441–453.

Natvig, D. O., May, G., and Taylor, J. W. (1984). Distribution and evolutionary significance of mitochondrial plasmids in *Neurospora* spp. *J. Bacteriol.* **159**, 288–293.

Nelson, M. A., and Macino, G. (1985). Gene organization and expression in *Neurospora crassa* mitochondria. *In* "Achievements and Perspectives of Mitochondrial Research" (E. Quagliariello, E. C. Slater, F. Palmieri, C. Saccone, and A. M. Kroon, eds.), Vol. 2, pp. 293–304. Elsevier, Amsterdam.

Ness, S. A., and Weiss, R. L. (1987). Carboxyl-terminal sequences influence the import of mitochondrial protein precursor *in vitro*. *Proc. Natl. Acad. Sci. U.S.A.* **84**, 6692–6696.

Newmeyer, D. L. (1984). *Neurospora* mutants sensitive both to mutagens and to histidine. *Curr. Genet.* **9**, 65–74.

Newmeyer, D. L., and Galeazzi, D. R. (1977). The instability of *Neurospora* duplication *Dp(IL→IR)H4250* and its genetic control. *Genetics* **85**, 461–487.

Newmeyer, D., and Taylor, C. W. (1967). A pericentric inversion in *Neurospora* with unstable duplication progency. *Genetics* **56**, 771–791.

Newmeyer, D., Schroeder, A. L., and Galeazzi, D. R. (1978). An apparent connection between histidine, recombination and repair in *Neurospora*. *Genetics* **89**, 271–279.

Niagro, F. D., and Mishra, N. C. (1989). An ethidium-bromide induced mutant of *Neurospora crassa* defective in mtDNA. *Curr. Genet.* **6**, 303–305.

Niagro, F. D., and Mishra, N. C. (1990). Biochemical genetic and ultra structural defects in a mitochondrial mutant (ER-3) of *Neurospora crassa* with senescence phenotype. *Mech. Ageing Dev.* **55**, 15–37.

Nicholson, D. W., and Neupert, W. (1989). Import of cytochrome *c* into mitochondria: Reduction of gene mediated NADH and flavin nucleotids is obligatory for its covalent linkage to apocytochrome *c*. *Proc. Natl. Acad. Sci. U.S.A.* **86**, 4340–4344.

Noll, M. (1976). Difference and similarities in chromatin structure of *Neurospora crassa* and higher eukaryotes. *Cell* **8**, 349–355.

Odom, C. B. (1990). Biosolubilization of coal by genetically characterized fungus *Neurospora crassa*. Ph.D. Thesis, Univ. of South Carolina, Columbia.

Odom, C. B., Cooley, M., and Mishra, N. C. (1989). Bioliquefaction of coal by genetically characterized fungi, 1989. *"Proc. Bioprocess. Fossil Fuel Workshop, U.S. Dep. Energy* (P. E. Bayer, ed.), pp. 288–296.

Oeser, B., and Tudzynski, P. (1989). The linear mitochondrial plasmid pC1k1 of the phytopathogenic fungus *Claviceps purpurea* may code for a DNA polymerase and an RNA polymerase. *Mol. Gen. Genet.* **217**, 132–140.

Oishi, M., and Irbe, R. M. (1977). Circular chromosomes and genetic transformation in *Escherichia coli. In* "Modern Trends in Bacterial Transformation and Transfection" (A. Portoles, R. Lopex, and M. Espinosa, eds.), pp. 121–134. North-Holland Publ., Amsterdam.

Orbach, M. J., Vollrath, D., Davis, R. W., and Yanofsky, C. (1988). An electrophoretic karyotype of *Neurospora crassa*. *Mol. Cell. Biol.* **8**, 1469–1473.

Orr-Weaver, T. L., and Szostak, J. W. (1985). Fungal recombination. *Microbiol. Rev.* **49**, 33–58.

Oza, K., and Kafer, E. (1990). Cloning of the DNA repair gene *uvsF* by transformation of *Aspergillus nidulans*. *Genetics* **125**, 341–349.

Pachnis, V., Pevny, L., Rothstein, R., and Costantini, G. (1990). Transfer of a yeast artificial chromosome carrying human DNA from *Saccharomyces cerevisiae* into mammalian cells. *Proc. Natl. Acad. Sci. U.S.A.* **87**, 5109–5113.

Paietta, J. V., Akins, R. A., Lambowitz, A. M., and Marzluf, G. A. (1987). Molecular cloning and characterization of the *cys-3* regulatory gene of *Neurospora crassa*. *Mol. Cell. Biol.* **7**, 2506–2511.

Paluh, J. L., Orbach, M. J., Legerton, T., and Yanofsky, T. (1988). The cross pathway control gene of *Neurospora crassa*, *cpc-1*, encodes a protein similar to GCN4 of yeast and the DNA binding domain of the oncogene *v-jun*-encoded protein. *Proc. Natl. Acad. Sci. U.S.A.* **85**, 3728–3732.

Pande, S., Lemire, E. G., and Nargang, F. E. (1989). The mitochondrial plasmid from *Neurospora intermedia* strains Labelle 1b contains a long open reading frame with blocks of amino acids characteristic of reverse transcriptase and related proteins. *Nucleic Acid. Res.* **17**, 2023–2042.

Perkins, D. D. (1987). Mating type switching in filamentous ascomycetes. *Genetics* **115**, 215–216.

Perkins, D. D. (1988). Main features of vegetative incompatibility in *Neurospora*. *Fungal Genet. Newsl.* **35**, 44–46.

Perkins, D. D., and Barry, E. G. (1977). Cytogenetics of *Neurospora*. *Adv. Genet.* **19**, 133–285.

Perkins, D. D., and Raju, N. B. (1986). *Neurospora discreta*, a new heterothallic species defined by its crossing behavior. *Exp. Mycol.* **10**, 323–338.

Perkins, D. D., and Turner, B. C. (1988). *Neurospora* from natural populations: Toward the population biology of a haploid eukaryote. *Exp. Mycol.* **12**, 131–190.

Perkins, D. D., Turner, B. C., and Barry, E. G. (1976). Strains of *Neurospora* collected from nature. *Evolution* **30**, 281–313.

Perkins, D. D., Radford, A., Newmeyer, D., and Bjorkman, M. (1982). Chromosomal loci of *Neurospora crassa*. *Microbiol. Rev.* **46**, 426–570.

Perkins, D. D., Metzenberg, R. L., Raju, N. B., Selker, E. U., and Barry, E. G. (1986).

Reversal of a *Neurospora* translocation by crossing over involving displaced rDNA and methylation of the rDNA segments that result from recombinaton. *Genetics* **114**, 791–817.

Pinkel, D., Straume, T., and Gray, J. W. (1986). Cytogenetic analysis using quantitative high-sensitivity fluorescence hybridization. *Proc. Natl. Acad. Sci. U.S.A.* **83**, 2934–2938.

Pittenger, T. H., and Coyle, M. B. (1963). Somatic recombination in pseudo wild-type cultures of *Neurospora crassa. Proc. Natl. Acad. Sci. U.S.A.* **49**, 445–451.

Pontecarvo, G. (1958). "Trends in Genetic Analysis." Columbia University Press, New York.

Pontecarvo, G., and Kafer, E. (1985). Genetic analysis based on mitotic recombination. *Adv. Genet.* **9**, 71–104.

Radford, A., Pope, S., Sazci, A., Fraser, M. J., and Parish, J. H. (1981). Liposome mediated genetic transformation of *Neurospora crassa. Mol. Gen. Genet.* **184**, 567–569.

Rambosek, J. A., and Leach, J. (1987). Recombinant DNA in filamentous fungi: Progress and perspectives. *CRC Rev. Biotechnol.* **6**, 357–373.

Ramotar, D., and Fraser, M. J. (1989). *Neurospora* endo-exonuclease in heat shocked mycelia: Evidence for a novel heat shocked induced function. *Biochem. Cell. Biol.* **67**, 642–652.

Reich, E., and Luck, D. J. L. (1966). Replication and inheritance of mitochondrial DNA. *Proc. Natl. Acad. Sci. U.S.A.* **55**, 1600–1608.

Rieger, R., Michaelis, A., and Green, M. M. (1976). "Glossary of Genetics and Cytogenetics," 4th Ed. Springer-Verlag, Berlin.

Rogers, S., Wells, R., and Rechsteiner, M. (1986). Amino acid sequences common to rapidly degraded proteins. The pest hypothesis. *Science* **234**, 364–368.

Ruddle, F. H. (1981). A new era in mammalian gene mapping: somatic cell genetics and recombinant DNA methodologies. *Nature (London)* **294**, 115–120.

Sachs, M. S., David, M., Werner, S., and RajBhandary, U. L. (1986). Nuclear genes for cytochrome *c* oxidase subunits of *Neurospora crassa:* isolation and characterization of cDNA clones for subunit IV, V, VI and possibly VII. *J. Biol. Chem.* **261**, 869–873.

Schablik, M., Delange, A. M., Shums, A. A., and Mishra, N. C. (1983). Construction of a genomic library of *Neurospora. FEBS Lett.* **16**, 321–325.

Schechtman, M. G. (1987). Isolation of telomere DNA from *Neurospora crassa. Mol. Cell. Biol.* **7**, 3168–3177.

Schechtman, M. G. (1989). Segregation pattern of *Neurospora* chromosome ends: mapping chromosome tips. *Fungal Genet. Newsl.* **36**, 71–73.

Schechtman, M. G. (1990). Characterization of telomere DNA from *Neurospora crassa. Gene* **89**, 159–165.

Schinkel, A. H., and Tabak, H. F. (1989). Mitochondrial RNA polymerase: Dual role in transcription and replication. *Trends Genet.* **5**, 149–154.

Schroeder, A. L. (1975). Genetic control of radiation sensitivity and DNA repair in *Neurospora. In* "Molecular Mechanisms for the Repair of DNA" (P. C. Hanawalt and R. Sellow, eds.), pp. 567–576. Plenum, New York.

Schroeder, A. L. (1986). Chromosome instability in mutagen sensitive mutants of *Neurospora. Curr. Genet.* **10**, 381–387.

Schroeder, A. L. (1988). Use of *Neurospora* to study DNA repair. *In* "DNA Repair" (E. C. Friedberg and P. C. Hanawalt, eds.), Vol. 3, pp. 77–97. Marcel Dekker, New York.

Schroeder, A. L., Lavin, M. F., and Bohnet, S. Z. (1989). Topoisomerase activity assays in *Neurospora. Fungal Genet. Newsl.* **36**, 71–73.

Schulte, U., Arretz, M., Schneider, H., Tropschung, M., Wachter, E., Neupert, W., and Weiss, H. (1989). A family of proteins involved in bioenergetics and biogenesis. *Nature (London)* **339**, 147–149.

Seidel-Rogol, B. L., King, J., and Bertrand, H. (1989). Unstable mitochondrial DNA in natural-death nuclear mutants of *Neurospora crassa. Mol. Cell. Biol.,* **9,** 4259–4264.

Selker, E. U. (1990). Premeiotic instability of repeated sequences in *Neurospora crassa. Annu. Rev. Genetics* **24,** 579–613.

Selker, E. U., and Garrett, P. W. (1988). DNA sequence duplication triggers gene inactivation in *Neurospora crassa. Proc. Natl. Acad. Sci. U.S.A.* **85,** 6870–6874.

Selker, E. U., Yanofsky, C., Driftneuir, K., Metzenberg, R. L., Alzner-DeWeerd, B., and RajBhandary, U. L. (1981). Dispersed 5sRNA genes in *N. crassa:* structure expression and evolution. *Cell* **24,** 819–828.

Selker, E. U., Cambareri, E. B., Jensen, B. C., and Haack, K. R. (1987). Rearrangement of duplicated DNA in specialized cells of *Neurospora. Cell* **51,** 741–752.

Silver, L. (1985). Mouse t haplotypes. *Annu. Rev. Genet.* **19,** 179–208.

Smith, G. R. (1988). Homologous recombination in prokaryotes. *Microbiol. Rev.* **52,** 1–28.

Smith, O. H., and Danner, B. D. (1981). Genetic transformation. *Annu. Rev. Biochem.* **50,** 41–68.

Southern, E. M. (1975). Detection of specific sequences among DNA fragments separated by gel electrophoresis. *J. Mol. Biol.* **98,** 503–517.

Springer, M. L. (1989). An effective procedure for the preparation of *Neurospora* conidiophores for scanning electron microscopy. *Fungal Genet. Newsl.* **36,** 78.

Srb, A., and Horowitz, N. H. (1944). The ornithine cycle in *Neurospora* and its genetic control. *J. Biol. Chem.* **154,** 129–139.

Srivastava, V. K., and Schroeder, A. L. (1989). Deoxyribonucleoside triphosphate pool in mutagen sensitive mutants of *Neurospora crassa. Biophys. Biochem. Res. Commun.* **162,** 583–590.

Staben, C., and Yanofsky, C. (1990). The *Neurospora crassa a* mating type region. *Proc. Natl. Acad. Sci. U.S.A.* **87,** 4917–4921.

Staben, C., Jensin, B., Springer, M., Pollack, J., Schechtman, M., Kinsey, J., and Selker, E. U. (1989). Use of a bacterial hygromycin B resistance gene as dominant selectable marker in *Neurospora crassa* transformation. *Fungal Genet. Newsl.* **36,** 79–81.

Stadler, D. (1983). Repair and mutation following UV damage in heterokaryons of *Neurospora. Mol. Gen. Genet.* **190,** 227–232.

Stadler, D., and Moyer, R. (1981). Induced repair of genetic damage in *Neurospora. Genetics* **98,** 763–774.

Stohl, L. L., and Lambowitz, A. M. (1983). A colony filter hybridization procedure for the filamentous fungus *Neurospora crassa. Anal. Biochem.* **134,** 82–85.

Stuart, R. A., Neupert, W., and Tropschug, M. (1987). Deficiency in mRNA splicing in a cytochrome *c* mutant of *Neurospora crassa:* Importance of carboxy-terminus for import of apocytochrome *c* into mitochondria. *EMBO J.* **6,** 2131–2137.

Sugino, A., and Nakayama, K. (1980). DNA polymerase mutants from a *Drosophila melanogaster* cell line. *Proc. Natl. Acad. Sci. U.S.A.* **77,** 7053–7069.

Symington, L. S., and Kolodner, R. (1985). Partial purification of an enzyme from *Saccharomyces cerevisiae* that cleaves Holliday junctions. *Proc. Natl. Acad. Sci. U.S.A.* **82,** 7247–7251.

Szabo, G., and Schablik, M. (1982). Behavior of DNA induced inositol-independent transformants of *Neurospora crassa* in sexual crosses. *Theor. Appl. Genet.* **61,** 171–175.

Szostak, J. W., and Blackburn, E. H. (1982). Cloning yeast telomeres on linear plasmid vectors. *Cell* **29,** 245–255.

Taylor, J. W., and Smolich, B. D. (1985). Molecular cloning and physical mapping of the *Neurospora crassa* 74-OR23-1A mitochondrial genome. *Curr. Genet.* **9,** 597–604.

Teintze, M., Slaughter, M., Weiss, H., and Neupert, W. (1982). Biogenesis of mitochondrial ubiquinol: cytochrome *c* reductase (cytochrome *bc* complex): Precursor proteins and their transfer into mitochondria. *J. Biol. Chem.* **257,** 10364–10371.

Threlkeld, S. F. H., and Stoltz, J. M. (1970). A genetic analysis of non-disjunction and meiotic recombination in *Neurospora crassa*. *Genet. Res.* **16,** 29–36.

Timberlake, W. E., and Marshall, M. (1989). Genetic engineering of filamentous fungi. *Science* **244,** 1313–1317.

Toth, G., Bekese, I., Schablik, M., and Szabo, G. (1987). Isolation and characterization of a DNA-uptake stimulating protein from the culture medium of *Neurospora crassa* slime strain. *Eur. J. Biochem.* **162,** 199–202.

Tyler, B. M., and Giles, N. H. (1984). Accurate transcription of homologous 5SrRNA and tRNA genes and splicing of tRNA *in vitro* by soluble extracts of *Neurospora*. *Nucleic Acids Res.* **12,** 5737–5755.

Van den Broogaart, P., Samallo, J., and Agsteribbe, E. (1982a). Similar genes for a mitochondrial ATPase subunit in the nuclear and mitochondrial genome of *Neurospora crassa*. *Nature (London)* **298,** 187–189.

Van den Broogaart, P., Samallo, J., van Dijk, S., and Agsteribbe, E. (1982b). Structural and functional analysis of the genes for subunit II of cytochrome aa_3 and for a dicyclohexylcarbodiimide-binding protein in *Neurospora crassa* mitochondrial DNA. *In* "Mitochondrial Genes" (P. Slonimski, P. Borst, and G. Attardi, eds.), pp. 375–380. Cold Spring Harbor Lab., Cold Spring Harbor, New York.

Van den Broogaart, P., Van Kijk, S., and Agsteribbe, E. (1982c). The mitochondrially made subunit 2 of *Neurospora crassa* cytochrome aa_3 is synthesized as a precursor protein. *FEBS Lett.* **147,** 97–100.

Vollmer, S. J., and Yanofsky, C. (1986). Efficient cloning of genes of *Neurospora crassa*. *Proc. Natl. Acad. Sci. U.S.A.* **83,** 4867–4873.

Wagner, E. D., and Plewa, M. J. (1985). Induction of micronuclei in maize root tip cells and a correlation with forward mutation at *yg-z* locus. *Environ. Mutagen.* **7,** 821–832.

Whitehouse, H. L. K. (1963). A theory of crossing over by means of hybrid deoxyribonucleic acid. *Nature (London)* **199,** 1034–1040.

Williams, C. A., and Wilson, J. F. (1966). Cytoplasmic incompatibility reactions in *Neurospora crassa*. *Ann. N. Y. Acad. Sci.* **129,** 853–863.

Wintersberger, E. (1972). Isolation of a distinct rifampicin-resistant RNA polymerase from mitochondria of yeast, *Neurospora* and liver. *Biochem. Biophys. Res. Commun.* **48,** 1287–1294.

Woudt, L. P., Pastnik, A., Veenstra, A. E. K., Jansen, A. E. M., Mager, W. H., and Planta, R. J. (1983). The genes coding for histones H_3 and H_4 in *Neurospora crassa* are unique and contain intervening sequences. *Nucleic Acids Res.* **11,** 5347–5360.

Yaffe, M. P., Ohta, S., and Schatz, G. (1985). A yeast mutant temperature sensitive for mitochondrial assembly is deficient in a mitochondrial protease activity that cleaves imported precursor polypeptides. *EMBO J.* **4,** 2069–2074.

Yin, S., Heckman, J., and RajBhandary, U. L. (1981). Highly conserved G. C. rich palindromic DNA sequences which flank tRNA genes in *Neurospora crassa* mitochondria. *Cell* **26,** 326–332.

Yin, S., Burke, J., Chang, D. D., Bowning, K. S., Heckman, J. E. Alzner-De-Weerd, B. Potter, M. J., and RajBhandary, U. L. (1982). *Neurospora crassa* mitochondrial tRNAs and rRNAs: structure, gene organization and DNA sequences. *In* "Mitochondrial Genes" (P. Slonimski, P. Borst, and G. Attardi, eds.), pp. 361–373. Cold Spring Harbor Laboratory. Cold Spring Harbor, New York.

Zimmermann, R., and Neupert, W. (1980). Transport of proteins into mitochondria: post translational transfer of ADP/ATP carrier into mitochondria *in vitro*. *Eur. J. Biochem.* **109,** 217–229.

THE STRUCTURE AND BIOGENESIS
OF YEAST RIBOSOMES

John L. Woolford, Jr.

Department of Biological Sciences, Carnegie Mellon University, Pittsburgh,
Pennsylvania 15213

I. Introduction

A little more than 30 years ago it was discovered that the ribosome is the organelle that catalyzes protein synthesis. A detailed but not yet complete understanding of the biosynthesis, structure, and function of the *Escherichia coli* ribosome has emerged since then, due in large part to inventive applications of bacterial genetics (review in Nomura, 1990). However, knowledge of the eukaryotic ribosome has lagged be-

63

ADVANCES IN GENETICS, Vol. 29

hind. With the advent of recombinant DNA technology, this information gap is narrowing. In this article I review recent progress in studies
of yeast ribosome biogenesis and structure, emphasizing results derived from experiments using classical and molecular genetics. The
reader is referred to Lee (1990), for a detailed review of yeast ribosome
structure that emphasizes biochemical approaches. Hinnebusch and
Liebman (1991) have recently described the rapid progress in using
classical and molecular genetics to study yeast ribosome function.

Studies of the biosynthesis of the yeast ribosome offer an opportunity
to investigate the coordinate expression of a moderately large set of
genes that respond to the growth rate of the cell. To understand ribosome biosynthesis, one must discern the mechanisms responsible for
the accumulation of ribosomal proteins in balance with each other and
with rRNAs, and how the synthesis of both is regulated in response to
the physiological needs of the cell. In this review I focus on the structure
and expression of ribosomal protein genes. The structure and transcription of yeast rDNA was recently reviewed by Warner (1989a) and
Woolford and Warner (1991).

The mechanisms of rRNA processing and ribosome assembly and the
role of nucleolar molecules in these processes are only beginning to be
explored in eukaryotes. A framework for pursuing a molecular genetic
analysis of these processes in yeast is described in this review, with
reference to more detailed knowledge of ribosome assembly in *E. coli*
and of nucleolar RNAs and proteins in metazoans.

II. Ribosomal Proteins

Ribosomal proteins are identified in yeast by two-dimensional gel
electrophoresis of proteins extracted from ribosomes or ribosomal subunits, from which loosely bound proteins have been stripped with
0.5–1.0 M KCl (Warner and Gorenstein, 1978b). The most frequently
used electrophoresis protocols employ a basic buffer plus urea in the
first dimension then an acidic buffer plus urea in the second dimension
(Kaltschmidt and Wittman, 1970), or acidic/urea followed by sodium
dodecyl sulfate (SDS) buffer (Mets and Bogorad, 1974; Gorenstein and
Warner, 1976). Up to 32 different proteins are found in the 40S subunit
and 45 proteins are found in the 60S subunit. Most of the proteins are
small (<10 to ~30 kDa), basic (pI > 8.6), and moderately abundant
(~0.2% total protein). Because of these properties, acid extraction and
gel electrophoresis of total yeast proteins resolve ribosomal proteins
from each other and from other proteins in the cell, enabling one to

easily and directly quantify synthesis and turnover of most yeast ribosomal proteins (Gorenstein and Warner, 1976).

Because the most frequently used gel systems for resolving yeast ribosomal proteins have employed different methods of protein preparation or different numbering systems, it has been difficult to make useful correlations of the data from different laboratories. However, careful side-by-side comparisons using four mutually related gel systems provided the basis for a uniform nomenclature (Bollen et al., 1981a; Michel et al., 1983) that has been adopted by most laboratories (Tables 1 and 2).

There has been a concerted effort to purify all of the ribosomal proteins from yeast (Otaka et al., 1982, 1984) and rat liver (Wool et al., 1990) and to determine their amino acid sequences. More recently, cloning and sequencing of large numbers of ribosomal protein genes from yeast and rats, as well as other eukaryotes, have proved to be efficient means to obtain sequence data. The 36 yeast ribosomal proteins for which amino acid sequences have been obtained directly or inferred from nucleotide sequences are listed in Tables 1 and 2. Likewise, sequences of 35 rat ribosomal protein sequences are known (Wool et al., 1990). Comparisons of two-dimensional gel profiles indicated that yeast ribosomal protein numbers and electrophoretic behavior are similar to those from rat liver and other eukaryotes. It is now evident from the considerable sequence homology among yeast and rat ribosomal proteins that there is likely to be a one-to-one correspondence among ribosomal proteins of eukaryotes from yeast to mammals. Examples of homologues for yeast ribosomal proteins are presented in Tables 1 and 2.

Although fewer homologies have been found among ribosomal proteins of eukaryotes and those of prokaryotes or archaebacteria, some proteins are clearly conserved across these organisms (Tables 1 and 2). Because the location and function of bacterial ribosomal proteins have been studied in such detail, identification of the bacterial homologue of a eukaryotic ribosomal protein may provide valuable hints about its location and function. For example, the yeast *CRY1* and *CRY2* genes encode rp59, which is approximately 80% identical in sequence to that of ribosomal protein S14 from humans, hamsters, *Drosophila, Chlamydomonas, Neurospora,* trypanosomes, and maize, and 37% identical to that of *E. coli* ribosomal protein S11 (Larkin et al., 1987). Mutations in *CRY1* or *CRY2* as well as in the hamster *EmtB* gene encoding S14 confer resistance to cryptopleurine or emetine, antibiotics which both block the EF-2- and GTP-dependent translocation of peptidyl-tRNA from the A site to the P site of ribosomes (Barbacid et al., 1975; Bucher and Skogerson, 1976; Madjar et al., 1983). *Escherichia coli* S11 is

TABLE 1

60S Ribosomal Subunit Proteins and Their Homologues

Protein[a]	Gene copy number and map position	Essential	Homologues[b]	Ref.[c]
L1 YL3 rp3,4	1	Yes	L5 (X, R)	1
L2 YL2 rp2	2	Yes	L1 (X, D)	2,3
L3 YL1 rp1	1 (*TCM1*, XVR)	Yes	L1 (T, A)	4–6
L4 YL5 rp6	2	n.d.	L7a (H, M)	7,8
L15 YL23	2		L11 (E)	9
L16 YL22 rp39	2 (*RPL16A*, VIIR; *RPL16B*, XVIR)	Yes	L5 (E); HL19 (H.c.); L21 (T)	10–14
L17a YL32	2	n.d.	—	11,15
L25 YL25	1	n.d.	L23 (E)	11,15,16
L29 YL24 rp44	1 (*CYH2*, VIIL)	Yes	L29 (N); L27a (M)	6,17,18
L30 YL21 rp29	2	No	—	7,19,20
L32 YL38 rp73	1	Yes	L30 (M,R)	7,21
L34 YL36	2	n.d.	L31 (R)	11,22
L37 YL37 rp47	1	n.d.	L35a (R); L32 (X)	7,23
L41[d] YL27	n.d.[e]	n.d.	L36a (H.R.)	24
L43[d] YL35	n.d.	n.d.	L37 (R)	25
L46 YL40	1(X)	No	L39 (R); L36 (Sch)	11,26,27
L47 YL41	2	n.d.	—	28
L?	2 (*UBII, UBI2*)	Yes	—	29,30
rp24	n.d.	n.d.	—	7
rp28	2 (*RP28A*[f], XVL; *RP28B*, XIVL)	Yes	L18 (R); L14 (X)	7,31,32
rp58	n.d.	n.d.	—	7
A0 A0	1	n.d.	P0 (H)	33,34
A1 A1	1	n.d.	P1 (H)	34,35
L44'	1 (IV)	n.d.	P1 (H)	34,36,37
L44 A2	1	No	P2 (H)	34,36,38,39
L45 YPA1	1 (IV)	No	P2 (H)	34,36,38

[a] Three different general nomenclatures used, where known, are L or S (Michel *et al.*, 1983), YL or YS (Otaka and Osawa, 1981), and rp (Warner and Gorenstein, 1978b).

[b] Homologues were identified in the original references describing protein or gene sequences or were from a collection of ribosomal protein sequences assembled by Tatsuo Tanaka (Department of Biochemistry, Yamagata University School of Medicine, Yamagata, 990–23, Japan). (A) *Arabidopsis thaliana,* (C) *Chlamydomonas reinhardtii,* (Ch) chicken, (D) *Drosophila melanogaster,* (E) *E. coli,* (H) *Homo sapiens,* (Ha) hamster, (H.m) *Halobacterium morismortui,* (H.c.) *Halobacterium cutirubrum,* (M) *Mus,* (N) *Neurospora crassa,* (R) *Rattus,* (Sch) *Schizosaccharomyces pombe,* (T) *Tetrahymena thermophila,* (Tr) *Trypanosome,* and (X) *Xenopus laevis.*

[c] References: (1) Tsay *et al.* (1991b); (2) Lucioli *et al.* (1988); (3) Presutti *et al.* (1988); (4) Fried and Warner (1981); (5) Schultz and Friesen (1983); (6) Fried *et al.* (1985); (7) Fried *et al.* (1981); (8) Arevalo and Warner (1990); (9) Pucciarelli *et al.* (1990); (10) Woolford *et al.* (1979); (11) Bollen *et al.* (1981b); (12) Teem *et al.* (1984); (13) Rotenberg *et al.* (1988); (14) Woolford (1991); (15) Leer *et al.* (1984); (16) El-Baradi *et al.* (1984); (17) Fried and Warner (1982); (18) Käufer *et al.* (1983); (19) Mitra and Warner (1984); (20) Baronas-Lowell and Warner (1990); (21) Dabeva and Warner (1987); (22) Schaap *et al.* (1984); (23) G. Santangelo (personal communication); (24) Itoh and Wittman-Liebold (1978); (25) Otaka *et al.* (1984); (26) Leer *et al.* (1985b); (27) Sachs and Davis (1990); (28) Suzuki *et al.* (1990); (29) Ozkaynak *et al.* (1987); (30) Finley *et al.* (1989); (31) Molenaar *et al.* (1984); (32) Donovan *et al.* (1990); (33) Mitsui and Tsurugi (1988a); (34) Newton *et al.* (1990); (35) Mitsui and Tsurugi (1988b); (36) Remacha *et al.* (1988); (37) Remacha *et al.* (1990b); (38) Remacha *et al.* (1990a); (39) Mitsui and Tsurugi (1988

TABLE 1 *Continued*

[d] The genes encoding L41 and L43 have not been cloned; the complete amino acid sequences of these proteins were determined. All other data in Tables 1 and 2 are derived from cloned genes.

[e] n.d., Not determined.

[f] The name of this gene is provisional until the rp28 protein has been identified by gel systems that use the L or S nomenclature (Michel *et al.*, 1983). Similarly, other genes encoding proteins not identified by the system of Michel *et al.* (1983) have provisional names.

TABLE 2

40S Ribosomal Subunit Proteins and Their Homologues

Protein[a]	Gene copy number and map position	Essential	Homologues[b]	Ref.[c]
S4 YS5 rp12	1 (*SUP44*, VII)	Yes	S5 (E)	1
S7 YS6 rp5	2	n.d.	S4 (R)	2,3
S10 YS10 rp9	2	Yes	S6 (H, M, R, Sch)	2,4–6
S11	n.d.[d]	n.d.	—	2
S13 YS11	2 (*SUP46*, IIR)	n.d.	S4 (E)	7
S16 YS16 rp55	2 (*RPS16A*, XVL; *RPS16B*, XIVL)	Yes	S12 (H.m.)	2,8–10
S21 rp52	1	n.d.	—	11,12
S24 YS22 rp50	2 (*RPS24A*, X; *RPS24B*, ?)	n.d.	S16 (H.m.) S20 (H.c.)	8,13
S26 YS25	n.d.	n.d.	S21 (R); S28 (Sch)	14,15
S31 YS23	2	n.d.	S25 (R)	8,16
S33 YS27	1	n.d.	—	8,17
S37 YS24	1 (*UBI3*)	No	S27a (R)	18–20
rp10	n.d.	n.d.	—	2
rp51	2	Yes	S17 (H, R, Ha, Ch)	11,21
rp59	2 (*CRY1*, IIIR; *CRY2*, ?)	Yes	S14 (H, Ha, D, N, Tr, C) S11 (E)	22–25
rp63	n.d.	n.d.	—	11

[a] Nomenclatures are the same as those in footnote to Table 1.

[b] Homologues were identified and abbreviations of species are the same as those described in footnote to Table 1.

[c] References: (1) All-Robyn *et al.* (1990); (2) Fried *et al.* (1981); (3) D. Synetos and J. R. Warner (personal communication); (4) Leer *et al.* (1982); (5) Leer *et al.* (1985c); (6) Kruse *et al.* (1985); (7) S. W. Liebman (personal communication); (8) Bollen *et al.* (1981b); (9) Molenaar *et al.* (1984); (10) Donovan *et al.* (1990); (11) Woolford *et al.* (1979); (12) J. L. Woolford (unpublished data); (13) Leer *et al.* (1985b); (14) Itoh *et al.* (1985); (15) Suzuki and Otaka (1988); (16) Nieuwint *et al.* (1985); (17) Leer *et al.* (1983); (18) Ozkaynak *et al.* (1987); (19) Finley *et al.* (1989); (20) Otaka *et al.* (1984); (21) Abovich *et al.* (1985); (22) Larkin and Woolford (1983); (23) Himmelfarb *et al.* (1984); (24) Larkin *et al.* (1987); (25) Paulovich *et al.* (1991).

[d] n.d., Not determined.

involved in EF-Tu-dependent amino acyl-tRNA binding (Kamp and Wittman-Liebold, 1980). The homologies among rp59, S14, and S11 may reflect that these ribosomal proteins from widely divergent organisms are involved in similar conserved reactions required for elongation steps of protein synthesis.

Homologies among ribosomal proteins also have been detected immunologically. A limitation of this approach is that it is sometimes tedious to purify a ribosomal protein sufficiently to use as an immunogen. However, this problem can be bypassed using molecular genetic techniques. For example, a TrpE–L16 fusion protein, readily purified from an *E. coli* strain containing a *TrpE–RPL16* fusion gene, was used to elicit antibodies against yeast rpL16 (Tsay and Woolford, 1991). Western immunoblot analysis indicated that L16 is structurally homologous to ribosomal protein HL19 from the archaebacterium *Halobacterium cutirubrum*, and rpL5 from *E. coli*, as well as a ribosomal protein from *Sulfolobus acidocaldarius*, *Methanobacterium thermoautotrophicum*, *Chlamydomonas reinhardtii*, maize, *Drosophila Melanogaster*, and mouse. The amino acid sequence of L16 is similar to those of L5 and HL19. Because both L5 and HL19 bind to 5S rRNA (Chen-Shneisser and Garrett, 1977; Smith *et al.*, 1978), it is possible that L16 is associated with 5S rRNA. However, L16 is not identical to the single ribosomal protein found tightly associated with 5S rRNA in eukaryotes (L1 in yeast and L5 in *Xenopus* and mammals) (Nazar *et al.*, 1979; Steitz *et al.*, 1988; Guddat *et al.*, 1990). Perhaps L16 is loosely associated with 5S rRNA and therefore near it in the ribosome.

To begin to localize L16 in the yeast ribosome, advantage was taken of the discovery that an L16–β-galactosidase fusion protein containing the first 170 of the 174 amino acids of L16 could functionally replace wild-type L16 in the yeast ribosome. An *RPL16A–lacZ* fusion gene expressed in yeast partially complemented the lethality of strains lacking L16. Sucrose gradient analysis of extracts of these cells indicated that the L16(170)–β-galactosidase fusion protein is present in active 60S ribosomal subunits. Ribosomes isolated from these strains were incubated with a monoclonal antibody against β-galactosidase, negatively stained with uranyl acetate, and visualized by electron microscopy. The positions of cross-linked dimers of subunits indicated that L16 is located near the central protuberance of the yeast 60S ribosomal subunit (Tsay *et al.*, 1991a), very similar to the location of L5 in the *E. coli* 50S ribosomal subunit (Nag *et al.*, 1987). These results provide the impetus for genetic and biochemical studies to localize L16 at higher resolution, map its nearest neighbors, and assay whether it is close to or binds 5S rRNA.

Two other yeast RP–β-galactosidase fusion proteins, RP51–β-gal and L3–β-gal, have been found to associate with ribosomes, although it is not yet clear whether these proteins are properly assembled into a functional 60S subunit (Gritz *et al.*, 1985; Moreland *et al.*, 1985). Thus commercially available antisera against either epitope tags or reporter groups such as β-galactosidase, used in concert with gene fusions expressed in yeast, may be of general use to localize ribosomal proteins.

Functional homologies have been identified among ribosomal proteins of yeast and other species. For example, the phosphorylated, acidic yeast ribosomal proteins A0, A1, L44, L44', and L45 are homologus to proteins in humans, rats, *Artemia salina*, *Drosophila melanogaster*, and *Schizosaccharomyces pombe* (Remacha *et al.*, 1988; Mitsui and Tsurugi, 1988a,c; Newton *et al.*, 1990). These proteins cycle on and off the ribosome in the cytoplasm and are involved in the interactions of soluble translational factors with ribosomes. The related L7/L12 and L10 proteins of *E. coli* form a stalk on the large subunit of the bacterial ribosome and are required for factor-dependent GTP hydrolysis (Traut *et al.*, 1986). The EF-2-dependent GDP binding and GTPase activities of yeast ribosomes depleted of L44, L45, L15, and S31 can be restored by addition of *E. coli* proteins L7/L12 (Sánchez-Madrid *et al.*, 1981). The *E. coli* L11 protein interacts with L7/L12 and L10 and also is involved in GTP hydrolysis. Addition of *E. coli* L11 to inactive yeast ribosomes lacking L15, a protein immunologically related to *E. coli* L11, restores activity *in vitro* (Juan-Vidales *et al.*, 1983).

Mouse ribosomal protein L27', which is 62% identical to yeast L29 encoded by *CYH2*, can substitute for L29 in yeast ribosomes. The mouse L27' cDNA complemented the lethality of a strain conditionally expressing L29 (Fleming *et al.*, 1989). The functional homology of other ribosomal proteins in yeast and other organisms might be assessed by similar means.

The sequences of the primary rRNA-binding proteins L25 from yeast and L23 from *E. coli* are only moderately similar, but each protein can bind to the other's binding site in rRNA (El-Baradi *et al.*, 1985). Likewise, yeast L15 and *E. coli* L11 both bind to the respective heterologous rRNAs at the binding site for the homologous protein (El-Baradi *et al.*, 1987).

Dominant mutations in the yeast *SUP44* and *SUP46* genes that encode ribosomal proteins S4 and S13 decrease general translational fidelity (All-Robyn *et al.*, 1990). Yeast S4 and S13 are homologous to *E. coli* ribosomal proteins S5 and S4, respectively, mutations in which cause ribosomal ambiguity (*ram*), i.e., increase translational errors (Rosset and Gorini, 1969). Other proteins similarly involved in translational fidelity in prokaryotes and yeast may be identified by omnipotent suppressor mutations, as well as antisuppressors that reduce the efficiency of omnipotent suppressors (Liebman and Cavenagh, 1980) and allosuppressors, which enhance efficiency of omnipotent suppressors (Song and Liebman, 1987).

Resistance or hypersensitivity to antibiotics is a phenotype often associated with alterations in ribosome biogenesis or function. For example, hypersensitivity to aminoglycoside antibiotics results from defects in rRNA processing or ribosome assembly. Mutations in four genes (*CYH2*, *TCM1*, *CRY1*, and *CRY2*) encoding three yeast ribosomal proteins confer resistance to antibiotics that inhibit specific steps in protein synthesis.

Mutations in a number of loci confer resistance to cycloheximide, an inhibitor of the peptidyltransferase involved in elongation (Cooper *et al.*, 1967). Mutations in *CYH2* on the left arm of chromosome VII result in an electrophoretically altered form of ribosomal protein L29 (Stocklein and Piepersberg, 1980). Cloning of *CYH2* led to the proof that it encodes L29 (Fried and Warner, 1981).

Trichodermin inhibits protein synthesis by binding to the 60S ribosomal subunit and blocking the peptidyltransferase step (Jiménez *et al.*, 1975; Vázquez, 1979). Trichodermin resistance is conferred by a mutation in a single gene, *tcm1* on the right arm of chromosome XV (Grant *et al.*, 1976). The 60S subunits from a *tcm1* strain have decreased binding of trichodermin (Schindler *et al.*, 1974); *tcm1* encodes ribosomal protein L3 (Fried and Warner, 1981; Schultz and Friesen, 1983).

Cryptopleurine binds to a high-affinity site on the 40S subunit and inhibits translocation (Barbacid *et al.*, 1975; Bucher and Skogerson, 1976; Dölz *et al.*, 1982). Mutations conferring a Cry^R phenotype map predominantly to *cry1*, 2.2 cM from *MAT* on chromosome III (Skogerson *et al.*, 1973; Grant *et al.*, 1974). Ribosomes isolated from *cry1* yeast bind cryptopleurine or emetine less well than do wild-type ribosomes (Dölz *et al.*, 1982). *CRY1* and a second unlinked homologous gene *CRY2* encode rp59, a 40S ribosomal subunit protein (Larkin and Woolford, 1983; Himmelfarb *et al.*, 1984; Paulovich *et al.*, 1991). Mutant alleles of the hamster *Emtb* gene, encoding the homologue of rp59, S14, also confer resistance to emetine and cryptopleurine (Madjar *et al.*, 1983). Analysis of *cry1*^{R} and *emt*^{R} mutations suggests that cryptopleurine and emetine may act through the highly conserved carboxy terminus of rp59/S14. Emetine resistance mutations in *Emtb* are caused by alterations of Arg 149 to Cys, and superresistance mutations are caused by alterations of Arg 149 to Cys and Arg 150 to His. Although these two consecutive Arg residues are present at similar positions in *Emtb* and *CRY1*, the *cry1*^{R}

mutation is a Leu-to-Ser change in the codon following the consecutive Arg codons (A. Paulovich and J. L. Woolford, unpublished data).

Two ribosomal proteins are synthesized as fusion proteins containing ubiquitin at their amino termini (Finley et al., 1989). The duplicate genes UBI1 and UBI2 encode a 60S ribosomal subunit protein fused at its amino terminus to ubiquitin. UBI3 encodes ribosomal protein S37 fused to ubiquitin. The ubiquitin moiety is necessary for the function of UBI3 but not UBI1 or UBI2. One copy of UBI1 precisely lacking the ubiquitin-encoding moiety fully complements the lethal phenotype of ubi1 ubi2 double mutants, but a similar version of UBI3 does not fully complement the slow-growth phenotype of a ubi3 null allele, unless at least three or four copies are present. Cells lacking UBI3 or containing only one copy of the ubiquitin-free gene are viable but deficient in 40S ribosomal subunits due to inefficient processing of the 20S rRNA precursor to 18S rRNA. Finley et al. (1989) speculated that the ubiquitin moiety of UBI3 may serve as a chaperone to facilitate assembly of S37 into ribosomes. Warner (1989b) pointed out that the ubiquitin moiety may not be directly involved in assembly, but could be necessary for efficient translation of such a small protein (76 amino acids), or for nuclear import of the protein, or could protect the protein from degradation. Presumably this fusion arrangement is significant, because it is conserved in nature—the human homologue of S37, S27a, is also synthesized with ubiquitin at its amino terminus (Redman and ubiquitin at its amino terminus (Redman and Rechsteiner, 1989).

Some ribosomal proteins are posttranslationally modified by acetylation, methylation, or phosphorylation, but the function of these modifications is not known. Eleven acetylated ribosomal proteins, including L16, S21, rp56, and rp59, were identified by their altered electrophoretic behavior in nat1 or ard1 mutants, in which amino-terminal methylation is blocked (Mullen et al., 1989). These mutants exhibit no apparent growth defect. S10 and its mammalian homologue S6 are phosphorylated at two adjacent serines under a number of conditions, mostly related to cell proliferation. However, a strain containing a mutant allele of S10 encoding alanines in the positions of the two serines, and thus unable to be phosphorylated, grows identically to wild-type cells (Johnson and Warner, 1987).

III. Ribosomal Protein Genes

Genes for 40 of the approximately 75 yeast ribosomal proteins have been cloned. Where possible, RPL or RPS is used to designate genes encoding proteins of the large and small ribosomal subunits, respectively, based on the nomenclature of Bollen *et al.* (1981a) and Michel *et al.* (1983).

Most of the genes were identified by colony or plaque hybridization using probes enriched for ribosomal protein mRNAs, followed by a hybrid-selection translation assay (Woolford *et al.*, 1979; Bollen *et al.*, 1981b). Alternatively, pools of clones were screened directly by the hybrid-selection assay (Fried *et al.*, 1981). *cyh2* and *CRY1* were isolated by chromosome walking from nearby loci that had already been cloned (Fried and Warner, 1982; Larkin and Woolford, 1983). *CRY1*, *tcm1*, *SUP44*, and *SUP46* were cloned by complementation of their phenotypes (Fried and Warner, 1981; Himmelfarb *et al.* 1984; All-Robyn *et al.*, 1990). Other ribosomal protein genes were isolated by screening λgt11 libraries with antibodies directed against the protein (Remacha *et al.*, 1988; Pucciarelli *et al.*, 1990), by using oligonucleotide probes designed from a partial amino acid sequence of the protein (Suzuki *et al.*, 1990; Tsay *et al.*, 1991b), or by hybridizing with cloned ribosomal protein genes from other organisms (Presutti *et al.*, 1988). Genes encoding the remaining 35 or so ribosomal proteins could be cloned by brute-force screening of an ordered collection of overlapping fragments of the yeast genome, using the hybrid-selection translation assay (Woolford *et al.*, 1979). Alternatively, amino acid sequence data from the collection of purified proteins might be used to design oligonucleotide probes (Otaka *et al.*, 1982, 1984). When the nucleotide sequence of the yeast genome is determined, any remaining uncloned ribosomal protein genes should be recognizable by virtue of their homology to those from other organisms.

Genes for 16 of the yeast ribosomal proteins are present once in the genome, and those for 18 are duplicated. In contrast, most of the ribosomal protein genes in other eukaryotes are present in a single copy per genome equivalent, although mammals also contain multiple pseudogenes. Examination of the phenotype of disrupted alleles of the duplicate yeast genes or quantitation of mRNAs expressed from them using gene-specific nucleic acid probes demonstrated that both copies of each duplicated pair are expressed. The relative levels of expression usually differ no more than two- or threefold. The functional significance of these duplicated genes is not clear (see, however, Section IV,D). The proteins encoded by the duplicate genes differ by no more than a few amino acids and are functionally interchangeable. A slow-growth phenotype often results from inactivation of one gene of a duplicated pair, but is suppressed by expression of extra copies of either gene. It cannot be ruled out that one allele serves a specific function under a physiological condition not yet tested. It would be difficult to demonstrate the existence of functionally distinct subclasses of ribosomes derived from ribosomal proteins contributed by one or the other of each pair of duplicate genes. Nevertheless, there is a precedent in *Plasmodium* for cell stage-specific ribosomes that contain distinct rRNAs (Gunderson *et al.*, 1987). A second interesting case is the human *RPS4* gene, which resides on each of the sex chromosomes and encodes isoforms differing at 19 of 263 amino acids (Fisher *et al.*, 1990). This raises the possibility of there being female ribosomes containing only one isoform of S4, and two types of male ribosomes containing one or the other form of S4.

Nucleotide sequences of the coding regions of duplicate ribosomal protein genes are very homologous, but the sequences begin to diverge near the ends of the coding regions. Transcribed 5' and 3' noncoding regions as well as nontranscribed flanking sequences are highly divergent, indicating that ribosomal protein gene duplication is a very old event. The only obvious conserved sequences outside of the structural genes are the 5' upstream activating sequences (UASs), although the number, positions, and orientations of the UASs differ among duplicate genes. The position, but not the sequence of introns within each member of a gene pair, is conserved. Only the highly conserved junction and branchpoint sequences of the introns are identical.

Unlike bacterial ribosomal protein genes, most yeast ribosome protein genes are unlinked. The *cry1*, *tcm1*, *cyh2*, *SUP44*, and *SUP46* genes were mapped by tetrad analysis, using antibiotic resistance or suppressor phenotypes (Tables 1 and 2). Eight other genes have been mapped, first to a particular chromosome using either the 2 μm method (Falco and Botstein, 1983) or by hybridization to blots of chromosomes resolved by orthogonal-field-alternation gel electrophoresis (OFAGE) (Carle and Olson, 1984). Higher resolution mapping data then were obtained using markers inserted into or adjacent to the genes.

Inspection of the cloned DNAs revealed three instances of tightly linked pairs of ribosomal protein genes and one case of three linked rp genes. Two copies of the pair *RP28* and *RPS16A* are arranged head-to-tail 600 nucleotides apart (Molenaar *et al.*, 1984) and are present at unlinked loci (Papciak and Pearson, 1987). *RPL30A* and *RPL32* are divergently transcribed from an intergenic region (Mitra and Warner, 1984). *RPL16A* and the mitochondrial ribosomal protein gene *MRP13* are transcribed in the same direction and separated by 325 nucleotides (Partaledis and Mason, 1988; J. Woolford, unpublished data). *CRY2*, *RPL46*, and *RPS24A* are the only example of three tightly linked eukaryotic ribosomal protein genes (Leer *et al.*, 1985a; A. Paulovich,

J. Larkin, J. Thompson, and J. Woolford, manuscript in preparation). The significance of these linkages is not clear. In every case, each gene is transcribed independently and bears no structural homology to the other. Curiously, each of the two copies of *RPL37* is divergently transcribed from one of the two genes encoding the small nucleolar RNA (snR17) that is necessary for rRNA processing (G. Santangelo and J. Tornow, personal communication).

It has long been a curiosity that the majority (76%) of yeast ribosomal protein genes contain a single intron near their 5′ ends (reviews in Woolford, 1989; Woolford and Warner, 1991). It has not yet been determined whether these introns are retained as a means of coordinating ribosomal protein gene expression. The presence of introns in most ribosomal protein genes is responsible for the apparent defect in total RNA synthesis originally attributed to the *rna2–rna11* mutants (Hartwell *et al.*, 1970). Subsequently, the *RNA* genes were shown to be necessary for nuclear pre-mRNA splicing (Rosbash *et al.*, 1981; Larkin and Woolford, 1983). The Rna⁻ phenotype results from the rapid turnover of rRNA in the absence of the many ribosomal proteins whose expression from mosaic genes is blocked in *rna* mutants.

Thirteen yeast ribosomal proteins are essential and five are not, as shown by gene disruption experiments. Conditional alleles, either *GAL1* promoter fusions or temperature-sensitive alleles, were used to prove that L1, L3, L16, L29, and rp59 are necessary for assembly of their respective ribosomal subunits (Nam and Fried, 1986; Moritz *et al.*, 1990; Tsay *et al.*, 1991b; Moritz *et al.*, 1991). It is interesting that 5 of 18 ribosomal proteins examined are not essential. In all but one case (L44), however, strains lacking these proteins grow slowly and are deficient in the assembly of their respective subunits (Finley *et al.*, 1989; Sachs and Davis, 1989, 1990; Baronas-Lowell and Warner, 1990; Remacha *et al.*, 1990a). Although mutants lacking L44 grow at wild-type rates, those also lacking the similar L45 protein are inviable (Remacha *et al.*, 1990a). The frequency of nonessential ribosomal proteins thus far observed in yeast (28%) is similar to that observed for *E. coli* (30%). In the latter case, viable mutants lacking a ribosomal protein were selected as revertants of antibiotic-dependent mutants (Dabbs, 1986). Sixteen different mutants lacking a ribosomal protein were identified. As in yeast, many of these mutants, although viable, grow slowly and are deficient in ribosome assembly. As has been the case with *E. coli* mutants (Dabbs, 1986), the viable yeast mutants lacking a ribosomal protein will be useful to determine the location and function of these proteins.

IV. Coordinate Expression of Ribosomal Protein Genes

A. TRANSCRIPTION

Ribosomal protein synthesis in *E. coli* is regulated mostly by an assembly-mediated translational feedback mechanism (reviews in Nomura *et al.*, 1984; Nomura, 1990), although there is regulation of the transcription of at least one operon (Lindahl *et al.*, 1983). In contrast, the equimolar accumulation of ribosomal proteins in yeast results primarily from regulation of transcription of ribosomal protein genes. There is no clear evidence for translational control.

Hybridization of cloned ribosomal protein genes to blots of yeast RNA revealed that the ribosomal protein mRNAs are all approximately equimolar and moderately abundant. Pulse-chase and DNA-excess filter hybridization experiments indicated that the rates of synthesis and turnover of the mRNAs encoded by *TCM1* (L3), *RPL16*, *RPL30*, and *RPL32* are identical (Kim and Warner, 1983a). This result is somewhat perplexing, because L16 and L30 are encoded by two genes and L3 and L32 are encoded by one.

Transcription of yeast ribosomal protein genes requires either of two common yeast upstream activation sequences, UAS_{RPG} or UAS_T, and a poly(dA–dT) sequence that functions as a constitutive promoter element. This was first demonstrated by deletion and linker–insertion mutations that alter the UAS_{RPG} or the poly(dA–dT) sequences of the *RPL16*, *RPL25*, *CRY1*, *CYH2*, *RPL32*, *RPL46*, and *RPS24* genes (Rotenberg and Woolford, 1986; Woudt *et al.*, 1986, 1987; Larkin *et al.*, 1987; Schwindinger and Warner, 1987; Dabeva and Warner, 1987; Kraakman *et al.*, 1989). Substitution of the *CYC1* UAS with UAS_{RPG} and poly(dA–dT) from *RPL16A* restored expression of a *CYC1–lacZ* construct to levels comparable to a *RPL16A–lacZ* gene fusion (Rotenberg and Woolford, 1986). Sequencing of most of the cloned yeast ribosomal protein genes has revealed that they contain one or two closely spaced UAS_{RPG} sequences followed by poly(dA–dT) sequences, 200 to 450 nucleotides 5' of their AUG translation initiation codon (Fig. 1). From comparison of these sequences, Planta and Raué (1988) derived a consensus UAS_{RPG} sequence, 5'-ACACCCATACATTT-3'. Single substitutions of most of the nucleotides in UAS_{RPG} had little effect on its function, consistent with the natural variation in reported UAS_{RPG} sequences (Nieuwint *et al.*, 1989). The five ribosomal protein genes *TCM1*, *RPS33*, *RPL2A*, *RPL2B*, and *SUP44* (S4) are exceptional in that they lack the UAS_{RPG} sequence and instead utilize the promoter

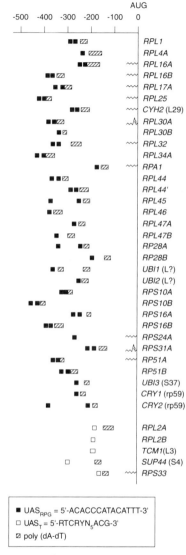

FIG. 1. Conserved promoter elements upstream of yeast ribosomal protein genes. The positions of UAS$_{RPG}$, UAS$_T$, and a thymidine-rich sequence are indicated with respect to the translation initiation codon of each gene. Approximate lengths of 5′ untranslated sequences of the mRNA are indicated by wavy lines. The symbol $\wedge$ indicates an intron in the 5′ leader.

UAS_T with the consensus sequence $5'$-$RTCRYN_5ACG$-$3'$ (Vignais *et al.*, 1987; Hamil *et al.*, 1988; Della-Seta *et al.*, 1990; All-Robyn *et al.*, 1990).

Footprinting and gel retardation analyses revealed that the protein Rap1p binds to UAS_{RPG} (Huet *et al.*, 1985; Vignais *et al.*, 1987) and that a different protein, Abf1p, binds to UAS_T (Vignais *et al.*, 1987; Hamil *et al.*, 1988; Della-Seta *et al.*, 1990). Binding of these proteins is necessary for activation of the ribosomal protein genes; mutations that prevent binding *in vitro* inactivate transcription of the genes *in vivo*.

Both Rap1p and Abf1p bind to sequences at multiple loci in the yeast genome and apparently perform several different functions. Rap1p is identical to two proteins, translational activating factor (TUF) and general regulatory factor 1 (Grf1p) (Huet *et al.*, 1985; Shore and Nasmyth, 1987; Buchman *et al.*, 1988). TUF was first identified by its binding to the UAS_{RPG} $5'$ of the *TEF1* and *TEF2* genes encoding translation elongation factor EF-1α (Huet *et al.*, 1985; Huet and Sentenac, 1987). Grf1p and Rap1p were first discovered to bind to the negative regulatory elements of the silent mating-type loci and repress their transcription (Shore and Nasmyth, 1987; Buchman *et al.*, 1988). Rap1p also binds to a repeated ($C_{1-3}A$) motif, resembling UAS_{RPG}, present in yeast telomeres (Buchman *et al.*, 1988; Longtine *et al.*, 1989; Biswas and Biswas, 1990). *rap1*^{ts} mutants contain telomeres of reduced length (Lustig *et al.*, 1990). Rap1p/TUF/Grf1p now is designated Rap1p, because the *RAP1* gene encoding this protein was cloned first (Shore and Nasmyth, 1987).

Abf1p has been variously described as a *TCM1* activation factor (TAF) (Hamil *et al.*, 1988); an S33 upstream factor (SUF) (Vignais *et al.*, 1987); GFI, an activator of nuclear-encoded mitochondrial proteins (Dorsman *et al.*, 1988, 1989); Abf1p, a protein that binds to autonomous replicating sequences (ARS) (Shore *et al.*, 1987; Buchman *et al.*, 1988; Diffley and Stillman, 1988; Kimmerly *et al.*, 1988; Sweder *et al.*, 1988); and SBF-B, a protein that activates *HMR* on binding the I site or represses *HMR* on binding the E site together with Rap1p (Shore *et al.*, 1987; Buchman *et al.*, 1988; Kimmerly *et al.*, 1988). DNA binding competition assays proved that all of these activities belong to one protein, now designated Abf1p, the product of the *ABF1* gene (Diffley and Stillman, 1988; Rhode *et al.*, 1989).

The nucleotide sequences to which Rap1p or Abf1p bind function as UASs not only for ribosomal protein genes, but also for genes involved in transcription, glycolysis, nutrient transport, and mating-type regulation (Capieaux *et al.*, 1989; Chambers *et al.*, 1989). Because these are essential genes expressed at moderately high rates that control quite different functions, it has been proposed that the abundant Rap1p and

Abf1p proteins are general transcription factors central to the control of cellular growth rate (Capieaux et $al.$, 1989).

How do Rap1p and Abf1p activate some genes and repress others? Are the telomere-binding or ARS-binding properties of these proteins related to their function(s) in transcription? Are all of these activities a result of some fundamental ability to affect chromatin structure and alter accessibility of the DNA to regulatory factors? Each of these proteins may perform its apparently different function depending on the sequence context flanking its binding site and on the spectrum of interacting proteins with which it interacts. Detailed analyses of these proteins should reveal the mechanisms by which they function and whether one or several different physical properties of each protein are involved in each function. Thus far it has been found that a large domain in the middle of Rap1p, from residues 330 to 596, is necessary for DNA binding (Henry et $al.$, 1990; D. Shore, personal communication). The amino-terminal third of Rap1p is nonessential; the carboxy-terminal third of the protein may interact with auxiliary factors to activate or repress transcription (C. Hardy, L. Sussel, and D. Shore, personal communication). Recently, it has been found that Rap1p fractionates with the yeast nuclear scaffold (Hofmann et $al.$, 1989).

Are there cis- and trans-acting elements other than UAS_{RPG}, UAS_T, Rap1p, and Abf1p necessary for the balanced constitutive transcription of ribosomal protein genes? Protein-binding sites upstream of UAS_{RPG}-driven ribosomal protein genes, other than the UAS_{RPG} sequence, have not been investigated in great detail. In most of the published experiments with ribosomal protein genes, only Rap1p-binding sites could have been detected, because the footprinting and gel retardation assays were performed with fractions enriched for Rap1p, rather than with whole cell or nuclear extracts. Santangelo and Tornow (1990) found that the $GCR1$ gene product is necessary for transcription of genes containing UAS_{RPG}, including $TEF1$, $TEF2$, and $CRY1$. Although Gcr1p has not been shown to bind to UAS_{RPG}, the following three observations suggest that it probably functions through UAS_{RPG}, at least indirectly. (1) Expression of a $K.$ $lactis$ $LAC4$ reporter dependent entirely on UAS_{RPG} is decreased ninefold in $gcr1$ mutants (Santangelo and Tornow, 1990). (2) Basal transcription of a gene containing a mutant UAS_{RPG} sequence that can no longer bind Rap1p is not affected by $gcr1$ mutations (J. Tornow and G. Santangelo, personal communication). (3) Gcr1p is distinct from Rap1p and Abf1p and is not required for their synthesis or for their activity in $vitro$ (Santangelo and Tornow, 1990). Cross-linking experiments revealed that UAS_{RPG} and

UAS$_T$ bind not only to Rap1p or Abf1p, but also to an 82-kDa protein (Hamil *et al.*, 1988). Binding of this protein required binding of Rap1p or Abf1p. The 82-kDa protein is not Gcr1p (Santangelo and Tornow, 1990). Herruer *et al.* (1989) found three protein-binding sites upstream of *RPS33* in addition to the Abf1p-binding site. One site was dependent on glucose, one was dependent on ethanol, and the third was detectable with extracts from cells grown in either carbon source. Upstream of *RPL37A* there are functional binding sites for Rap1p and also for Reb1p (G. Santangelo and J. Tornow, personal communication), an abundant protein that binds to many loci in the yeast genome, including enhancer and promoter sequences of rDNA (Morrow *et al.*, 1989, 1990; Chasman *et al.*, 1990).

B. How Is the Expression of Single-Copy and Dupicated Ribosomal Protein Genes Balanced?

Is the expression of single-copy ribosomal protein genes balanced with that of the duplicate genes? If so, how? The relative steady-state level of mRNA expressed from each member of the duplicate genes *RPL2A,B, RPL16A,B, RPS16A,B, RP51A,B*, and *CRY1/CRY2* varies from 1.5 : 1 to 8 : 1 (Abovich *et al.*, 1985; Presutti *et al.*, 1988; Rotenberg *et al.*, 1988; Donovan *et al.*, 1990; Paulovich *et al.*, 1991). It has not been tested whether differential accumulation of mRNAs from each gene results from transcriptional and/or posttranscriptional mechanisms. If this is only a result of transcription, then some complex model must be invoked to explain how the sum of activities of the promoters of duplicate genes has evolved to match each other and the activities of the promoters for each of the single-copy genes. The relative affinity of binding *in vitro* of Rap1p or Abf1p to the UASs of the *RP28* or *RPL2* gene pairs corresponds roughly to the relative activity of these promoters *in vivo* (Vignais *et al.*, 1987; Della-Seta *et al.*, 1990). However, experiments have not yet been performed in sufficient detail with enough genes to make a significant correlation between the relative expression of each member of duplicate pairs of ribosomal protein genes and the number, orientation, position, or precise sequence of the UAS for each gene. Although the measurements of Kim and Warner (1983a) indicated that the rates of transcription from two different pairs of duplicated genes were roughly equal to that for two different single-copy genes, it is not known whether this is generally the case. Now that probes can be made that discriminate between transcripts from duplicate genes, rates of transcription of each gene in a pair can be accurately measured by pulse-labeling experiments.

C. Posttranscriptional Expression of Ribosomal Protein Genes

Is the accumulation of equimolar amounts of each of the ribosomal proteins due entirely to equivalent rates of transcription of ribosomal protein mRNAs, or do posttranscriptional mechanisms operate to finely tune the process?

Results to date suggest that splicing, translation, or stability of yeast ribosomal protein mRNAs are not globally regulated; two exceptions will be discussed below. Rather, there is rapid turnover of any rRNAs or ribosomal proteins that are produced in excess of other ribosomal components as a result of imbalances in transcription.

Posttranscriptional control was assessed by measuring expression of ribosomal proteins and rRNAs in response to an increase in the dosage of individual ribosomal protein genes or upon inactivation of synthesis or processing of rRNA or ribosomal protein mRNAs. From 5 to 20 extra copies of a ribosomal protein gene were introduced into cells by transformation of high-copy 2μm-based plasmids containing a cloned ribosomal protein gene (Pearson et al., 1982; Himmelfarb et al., 1984; Abovich et al., 1985; Warner et al., 1985; El-Baradi et al., 1986; Maicas et al., 1988; Tsay et al., 1988). In some cases the amounts of ribosomal protein mRNA made or accumulated were slightly less than the copy number of the corresponding gene, suggesting that modest repression of transcription or enhancement of mRNA turnover had occurred. However, in the majority of cases, a proportionate excess of mRNA was synthesized and accumulated. All of the excess mRNAs were present in polyribosomes, associated with the same number of ribosomes as in wild-type cells, and were translated with normal efficiency. However, the excess ribosomal proteins turned over with half-lives ranging from a remarkably short 30 seconds to 24 minutes. Synthesis of excess ribosomal proteins was not detected in the initial gene dosage experiments, suggesting that there was repression of translation (Pearson et al., 1982; Himmelfarb et al., 1984; Warner et al., 1985). However, the 3- to 5-minute pulse-labeling periods employed were too long to detect the rapid turnover of these proteins. Pulses as short as 10 to 45 seconds were necessary to detect the full extent of synthesis (El-Baradi et al., 1986; Maicas et al., 1988; Tsay et al., 1988). Even using these short pulse-labeling periods, proportionate synthesis of several proteins was not detected, leaving open the possibility for their translational control or unusually rapid turnover (Warner et al., 1985; Maicas et al., 1988; Wittekind et al., 1990).

In E. coli, translation of ribosomal protein operon RNAs is repressed upon increasing the dosage and expression of genes encoding primary rRNA-binding proteins. In contrast, increasing the dosage of a ribosomal protein gene in yeast has no effect on expression of that gene or of any other ribosomal proteins or rRNAs. However, only one of the yeast genes tested, *RPL25*, is known to encode a primary rRNA-binding protein (El-Baradi *et al.*, 1986).

Limitations of these gene dosage experiments in yeast are that only a few genes have been tested, and only those genes that have been cloned could be tested. Furthermore, it is not clear whether increased gene dosage reflects the proper physiology of regulation of ribosome biosynthesis in wild-type cells. To assess the effect of an "excess" of any of the ribosomal proteins at more physiological concentrations of genes, transcripts, and proteins, one can deplete one ribosomal component and assay expression of all of the others. Wittekind *et al.* (1990) assayed ribosomal protein expression upon termination of 35S rRNA synthesis, using a strain conditional for the synthesis of an essential subunit of RNA polymerase I. When rRNA synthesis was decreased 10-fold, most ribosomal proteins were synthesized at normal rates, but were rapidly degraded. Similarly, when processing of 27S rRNA to 25S and 5.8S rRNA was blocked in an *rrp1*[ts] mutant, ribosomal protein synthesis was unperturbed (Gorenstein and Warner, 1977). Under these conditions, those proteins that are components of the 60S subunit were degraded, but proteins (and 18S rRNA) of the 40S subunit were assembled into 40S subunits and were stable. Termination of transcription of the 60S subunit protein L3, L29, or L16, or of the 40S subunit protein rp59, expressed from *GAL* promoter fusions, had no effect on synthesis of other ribosomal constituents, but those proteins and rRNAs in the same subunit as the depleted protein were turned over (Nam and Fried, 1986; Moritz *et al.*, 1990).

The experiments described above suggest that balanced synthesis of ribosomal components results, to a first approximation, from roughly equivalent rates of transcription of ribosomal genes. Any rRNA or ribosomal protein molecules made in excess presumably are degraded. Where and how are these excess ribosomal proteins degraded? Because turnover is assayed by a decrease in the amounts of each protein in their characteristic position of migration on two-dimensional gels, any modification that alters the mobility of a mature wild-type protein will result in an apparent decrease of that protein. Thus "rapid turnover" may not reflect the entire process of turnover and may simply indicate rapid modification prior to degradation. Is there a specific machinery for turnover of ribosomal proteins? Are they scavenged by a pathway that recognizes mislocalized proteins or proteins that unfold in the

absence of assembly into a stable complex? A systematic search has not
been undertaken to identify mutants that do not degrade excess unassembled ribosomal proteins. However, it has been shown that vacuolar
proteases are not involved. The half-lives of excess L16 or rp59 are
identical in wild-type cells and in *pep4-3* mutants deficient in vacuolar
proteases (Tsay *et al.*, 1988). It seems most likely that excess ribosomal
proteins do enter the nucleus and are degraded there when they are
unable to assemble into subunits. Alternatively, they may be degraded
in the cytoplasm prior to nuclear import or upon exit from the nucleus.
Does the extremely rapid turnover observed for some proteins occur
cotranslationally? An imbalance in the stoichiometry of assembling
ribosomal proteins might be recognizable in the cytoplasm and may
result in rapid cytoplasmic turnover, if the protein were a component of
a subassembly complex that formed in the cytoplasm prior to nuclear
entry. This might be analogous to histones H2A and H2B, which form a
heterodimer before nuclear entry (Weeks-Wagner and Hartwell, 1986).
Alternatively, signals indicating the state of ribosome assembly may be
transmitted from the nucleolus to the cytoplasm by molecules such as
nucleolin or B23, which are thought to shuttle between these compartments (Borer *et al.*, 1989).

D. Autogenous Regulation of Ribosomal Protein Gene Expression

Although balanced synthesis of yeast ribosomal components does not
appear to result from a complex interplay of posttranscriptional mechanisms, the expression of two ribosomal protein genes is regulated by
feedback mechanisms. The splicing of *RPL32* pre-mRNA is blocked
when extra copies of an *RPL32* genomic clone or an *RPL32* cDNA clone
are transformed into yeast (Dabeva *et al.*, 1986), or when synthesis of
35S rRNA is decreased by depleting RNA polymerase I (Wittekind *et
al.*, 1990). Sequences in the 5' splice site and the 5' end of the *RPL32*
transcript are involved in this regulation. A model was proposed
whereby L32 protein stabilizes base pairing between the 5' end of exon
1 and the 5' splice site, thereby preventing splicing by blocking association of the U1 snRNP with the 5' splice site. Point mutations in *RPL32*
that should disrupt the putative base pairing abolish the inhibition of
splicing (F. J. Eng and J. R. Warner, personal communication).

The relatively frequent occurrence of introns in yeast ribosomal
proteins, in contrast to the paucity of introns in other yeast genes,
suggests that these introns have been retained as a target for coordinate regulation of ribosomal protein genes. However, there is not evi-

dence for a global mechanism of feedback inhibition of splicing of ribosomal protein pre-mRNAs. Increasing the dosage of each of six other ribosomal protein genes did not affect splicing of their pre-mRNAs (Abovich *et al.*, 1985; Warner *et al.*, 1985; El-Baradi *et al.*, 1986; Maicas *et al.*, 1988; Tsay *et al.*, 1988; I. Bozzoni, personal communication). Although splicing of the *Xenopus laevis RPL1* gene is inhibited by excess L1 (Bozzoni *et al.*, 1984), there is no evidence that the homologous genes in yeast, *RPL2A* and *RPL2B*, are similarly regulated (I. Bozzoni, personal communication). At present the simplest approach to screen among the remaining cloned ribosomal protein genes for regulation of splicing would be to probe RNA blots for accumulation of unspliced pre-mRNA upon termination of 35S rRNA synthesis.

CRY1 mRNA normally is present in eightfold excess of *CRY2* mRNA, apparently as a result of repression of expression of *CRY2* by rp59 encoded by *CRY1* and *CRY2*. To our surprise, we found that deletion of *CRY1* had no effect on the growth rate of cells, even though rp59 is essential (Paulovich *et al.*, 1991). This paradox was explained by our subsequent observation that strains bearing a *cry1::TRP1* null allele contain near wild-type amounts of rp59, as a result of eightfold derepression of *CRY2* mRNA levels. Derepression of *CRY2* mRNA levels occurs rapidly upon inactivation of *CRY1*. When transcription of *CRY1* was terminated in a *GAL1–CRY1 cry1::TRP1 CRY2* strain by shifting from galactose to glucose medium, *CRY2* mRNA increased eightfold within 20 minutes (A. Paulovich and J. L. Woolford, unpublished data). We hypothesize that unassembled rp59 is normally present in the nucleus in modest excess of other proteins assembling into the 40S subunit. Therefore, rp59 is available to repress transcription of *CRY2* or to alter the stability of *CRY2* mRNA, resulting in low steady-state levels of *CRY2* mRNA. When *CRY1* is inactivated, the pool of unassembled nuclear rp59 shrinks and *CRY2* is derepressed.

Further experiments are necessary to determine whether the autogenous regulation of *RPL32* and *CRY2* is exceptional among yeast ribosomal protein genes, and to determine the physiological significance of regulation of these two genes. For example, we do not understand why *RPL32* and *CRY2* in particular are regulated thusly, whereas many other ribosomal protein genes that have been studied are not. Nothing yet suggests that this regulation of *RPL32* or *CRY2* affects the expression of other ribosomal protein genes. Although the feedback loop observed for *CRY1* and *CRY2* may reflect a means by which expression of duplicated genes is regulated with respect to each other, other pairs of ribosomal protein genes, including several in which one gene is expressed at much higher levels than the other, are not similarly regulated. Clearly, coupling of ribosome assembly with ribosomal gene expression could occur more readily by regulating nuclear events, such as transcription or splicing, than by regulating translation in the cytoplasm. Repression of translation is an effective global regulatory mechanism in *E. coli*, because ribosomal protein genes are arrayed in operons and translation and ribosome assembly occur in one compartment. Because this is not the case in eukaryotes, it was not surprising to find a lack of translational control of ribosomal protein expression in yeast.

V. Changes in Ribosome Biosynthesis in Response to Different Stimuli

The synthesis of yeast ribosomes increases or decreases in response to changes in environmental conditions such as a carbon source shift, heat shock, amino acid deprivation (stringent response), or nitrogen deprivation (sporulation). In most cases this has been shown to result from changes in transcription of ribosomal genes.

Upon shifting yeast from a medium containing ethanol as a carbon source to one containing glucose, the rate of growth increases threefold and the rate of synthesis of rRNA and ribosomal proteins increases sevenfold (Kief and Warner, 1981). The increase in ribosomal protein synthesis can be accounted for by higher levels of transcription, because expression of constructs containing only the 5′ nontranscribed region of *RPS16* or only the UAS$_{RPG}$ of *RPL25* is similarly increased upon a nutritional upshift (Donovan and Pearson, 1986; Herruer *et al.*, 1987). Herruer *et al.* (1989) found four protein-binding sequences upstream of *RPS33*, including an Abflp-binding site, that function differently in ethanol medium compared to glucose. Thus the carbon source-dependent transcription of ribosomal protein genes may be mediated by more than alterations in the interactions between Rap1p or Abf1p and their respective UAS binding sites.

When yeast cells are abruptly shifted from growth at 23° to growth at 36°C, a heat-shock effect is manifested by alterations in the synthesis of a large number of proteins, including ribosomal proteins (Miller *et al.*, 1982; Gorenstein and Warner, 1976). Synthesis of more than 300 proteins transiently decreases and that of at least 80 or so other proteins increases. The rates and extents of decline and recovery of synthesis vary widely among different proteins. Synthesis of most ribosomal proteins decreases fivefold within 20 minutes and returns to normal by 60 minutes after heat shock. Ribosomal protein mRNA levels are transiently decreased at least fivefold, as a result of a transient decrease in transcription and subsequent turnover of ribosomal protein mRNAs (Lindquist, 1981; Rosbash et al., 1981; Kim and Warner, 1983b; Larkin et al., 1987; Schwindinger and Warner, 1987). It is not clear which sequences upstream of ribosomal protein genes are necessary for the heat-shock effect on transcription. Deletion of either UAS$_{RPG}$ or sequences between UAS$_{RPG}$ and the transcription initiation site does not eliminate the transient decrease of ribosomal protein mRNAs (Larkin et al., 1987; Schwindinger and Warner, 1987; Herruer et al., 1988).

In response to deprivation of amino acids, rRNA synthesis and ribosomal protein mRNA levels decline five- to sixfold and two- to fourfold, respectively; the amounts of tRNA and most other mRNAs are not affected (Shulman et al., 1976; Warner and Gorenstein, 1978a). This effect is transcriptional; expression of fusions of the RPL16A, CRY1, RPL25, or RPS16A promoters to lacZ decreases upon histidine limitation, as does a construct dependent entirely on UAS$_{RPG}$. However, the ability of Rap1p to bind UAS$_{RPG}$ is not altered under these conditions (C. Moehle and A. Hinnebusch, personal communication).

The synthesis of ribosomal proteins, but not most other proteins, declines 5- to 10-fold when yeast cells are deprived of nitrogen and begin to sporulate (Pearson and Haber, 1980). Ribosomal protein mRNA levels decrease proportionately, but it has not yet been tested whether this is due to an effect on mRNA transcription or turnover (Kraig et al., 1982).

It has been possible in most cases to show that in response to altered growth conditions, yeast cells alter the rate of transcription of ribosomal genes to accommodate changing requirements for protein synthesis. However, we do not know what signals these responses. In particular, we do not understand how the synthesis of rRNAs and ribosomal protein mRNAs by different RNA polymerases is coordinately adjusted.

VI. The Nucleolus

Ribosome assembly in eukaryotes occurs primarily within a specialized region of the nucleus called the nucleolus, a prominent nonmembrane-bounded organelle first described more than 200 years ago (see Gerbi et al., 1990). The nucleolus is defined by the rRNA genes, which are cytologically observable as secondary constrictions called the nucleolar organizer region (NOR) (McClintock, 1934). The nucleolus is composed of a collection of molecules that assemble around nascent rRNA during assembly of ribosomes. Recent experiments with

Drosophila and yeast demonstrated that a single active rDNA gene is sufficient for the formation of a morphologically distinct and functional nucleolus. Cloned *Drosophila* rDNA was inserted into several different sites in the *Drosophila* genome other than the NOR. Mininucleoli containing rRNA and nucleolar antigens were associated with each site of insertion and produced functional rRNA (Karpen *et al.*, 1988). Yeast strains in which all copies of chromosomal rDNA have been deleted and which contain multiple plasmid-borne rDNAs have adjacent beadlike structures containing nucleolar antigens, arrayed like a necklace within the periphery of the nucleus (E. Morgan, personal communication).

Three compartments of the nucleolus are distinguishable cytologically: the fibrillar center (FC), the dense fibrillar component (DFC) surrounding the FC, and the granular component (GC) that occupies most of the nucleolar volume. rDNA is present in the FC, as are RNA polymerase I and topoisomerase I, both of which are required for transcription of rDNA. Transcription of rRNA occurs in the FC and perhaps the DFC, early steps of rRNA processing and ribosome assembly occur in the DFC, and later steps of rRNA processing and ribosome assembly and maturation occur in the GC (for recent reviews of the nucleolus, see Hadjiolov, 1985; Sommerville, 1986; Scheer and Benavente, 1990; Warner, 1990).

The yeast nucleolus, defined as that nuclear structure containing rDNA and pre-rRNAs, is visible in phase contrast as a silver-staining region and in electron micrographs as the more electron-dense region of the nucleus, called the "grey" or "dense" crescent (Sillevis-Smitt *et al.*, 1973). In many yeast cells, the nucleolus is a caplike structure, adjacent to the nuclear envelope, that occupies about one-third of the nuclear volume (Fig. 2). In other planes of view, the nucleolus is a disk covering the entire nucleus or a halo at the nuclear perimeter. Curiously, and as yet unexplained, the caplike nucleolus structure is most often present on the opposite side of the nucleus from the spindle pole body (Yang *et al.*, 1990; M. Deshmukh and J. L. Woolford, unpublished data). Morphologically distinct subcompartments comparable to the DFC, FC, and GC in higher cells are not well defined within yeast nucleoli.

Yeast is unusual among eukaryotes in that the 5S rRNA genes are linked to the 35S rRNA genes. There are approximately 100–200 tandem repeats of a 9.1-kb sequence containing these two genes, on the right arm of chromosome XII (Petes and Botstein, 1977; Phillipsen *et al.*, 1978). The yeast nucleolus is visible in light or electron micrographs of meiotic nuclei as a structure stained with silver or antitopoisomerase I antiserum, that covers the approximate position of the rDNA locus on

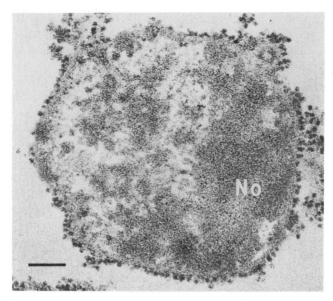

Fɪɢ. 2. Electron micrograph of a purified yeast nucleus. The nucleolus (No) is evident as a darkly staining crescent adjacent to the nuclear envelope. Bar = 0.15 μm. Photograph courtesy of Dr. John P. Aris, Laboratory of Cell Biology, Rockefeller University.

chromosome XII (Dresser and Giroux, 1988). Both the 5S rRNA and the 35S rRNA transcripts are visualized as typical "Christmas tree" structures by electron microscopy of yeast chromatin spreads (Saffer and Miller, 1986).

A. Nucleolar Proteins

What sorts of molecules might one expect to find in the nucleolus? In addition to RNA polymerase I, a number of other proteins necessary for transcription of rDNA have been identified (review in Sollner-Webb and Tower, 1986). Nucleolar ribosomal precursor particles contain, in addition to ribosomal proteins, a number of nonribosomal proteins, most of which have not yet been characterized in any detail. These might include enzymes responsible for methylation or pseudouridylation of rRNA and for the processing of rRNA precursors. The posttranslational acetylation, methylation, or phosphorylation of ribosomal proteins also may be catalyzed by nucleolar enzymes. Scaffolding proteins may exist in the nucleolus to facilitate the processing of rRNA or its packaging into ribosomes. Association of the many very basic ribosomal proteins with each other, with rRNA, or with the nascent ribosome may be facilitated by molecular chaperones. Other nucleolar molecules may be associated with preribosomal particles to signal or facilitate their export to the cytoplasm.

Approximately 100 different polypeptides are identified by two-dimensional gel electrophoresis of proteins extracted from isolated mammalian nucleoli (Orrick et al., 1973). Studies have focused on a few of these proteins that were identified using monoclonal antibodies or human autoimmune sera. The most abundant and best characterized are RNA polymerase I, topoisomerase I, fibrillarin, nucleolin (or C23), and B23 (or NO38) (reviews in Sommerville, 1986; Warner, 1990). RNA polymerase I, present in the FC, is responsible for transcription of pre-rRNA. Topoisomerase facilitates transcription of the highly active rDNA genes, presumably by relieving torsional stress (Rose et al., 1988). Fibrillarin is a 34-kDa protein present in the DFC that is associated with the U3, U8, and U13 small nucleolar RNAs and may be involved in rRNA processing (Lischwe et al., 1985; Christensen and Fuxa, 1988; Parker and Steitz, 1987; Lapeyre et al., 1990). Nucleolin is a 77- to 100-kDa protein found in the DFC and GC; it is reported to bind to rDNA spacer regions and pre-rRNA (Olson and Thompson, 1983; Olson et al., 1983; Herrera and Olson, 1986; Bugler et al., 1987). Several different motifs conserved in other nucleolar or RNA-binding proteins, including the RNA recognition motif, an acidic domain, and a Gly/Phe/dimethyl-Arg-rich domain, are present in nucleolin (Lapeyre et al., 1987; Caizergues-Ferrer et al., 1989). The protein is phosphorylated in vivo and is a substrate in vitro for the mitotic cdc2 kinase (Caizergues-Ferrer et al., 1987). It is thought that upon phosphorylation, nucleolin is proteolytically cleaved and released from rDNA, permitting rRNA synthesis. The putative association of nucleolin with processing rRNA in the DFC and with preribosomal particles in the GC suggests that it may function as a regulator to couple rRNA synthesis, processing, and assembly. Nucleolin shuttles between the nucleolus and the cytoplasm, suggesting that it may chaperone nascent ribosomes out of the nucleus or transmit regulatory signals between the nucleus and the cytoplasm (Borer et al., 1989). Thus nucleolin has many, perhaps too many, putative interesting functions. However, none of these functions has been directly proved. B23, also called NO38 or numatrin, is associated with preribosomal particles in the GC (Prestayko et al., 1974; Spector et al., 1984). B23 resembles the histone-binding protein nucleoplasmin and may function similarly by facilitating assembly of the many basic ribosomal proteins with rRNA (Schmidt-Zachmann and Franke, 1988; Schmidt-Zachmann et al., 1987; Chang et al., 1988). Like nucleolin, B23 is phosphorylated and shuttles between the nucleolus and the cytoplasm (Borer *et al.*, 1989).

Only a few nonribosomal nucleolar proteins have been identified in yeast: the RNA polymerase I 190-kDa subunit, topoisomerase, Ssb1p, and Nop1p. Topoisomerase may facilitate rDNA transcription by relieving torsional stress in chromatin that contains rDNA. Accumulation of rRNA but not mRNA or tRNA is specifically inhibited in a *top1 top2* temperature-sensitive double mutant at the nonpermissive temperature (Brill *et al.*, 1987).

Ssb1p was isolated as a single-stranded DNA-binding protein but also binds to RNA (Jong *et al.*, 1987). It contains the RNA recognition motif (RRM) found in many RNA-binding proteins and a repeating motif rich in glycine, phenylalanine, and arginine, also found in nucleolin, fibrillarin, and the hnRNP A protein involved in pre-mRNA packaging (Jong *et al.*, 1985, 1987). Ssb1p is associated with the small nucleolar RNAs snR10 and snR11, implying that it may play a role in rRNA processing (Clark *et al.*, 1990). *ssb1* null mutants are viable but grow slowly and, under certain conditions, are deficient in processing of 35S rRNA (M. Clark, personal communication). Analysis of site-directed mutants of *SSB1* should elucidate the function of the conserved RRM and Gly/Phe/Arg domains.

Nop1p is the yeast homologue of fibrillarin. Antibodies against Nop1p are cross-reactive with mammalian fibrillarin, and the inferred amino acid sequence of Nop1p is very similar to that of human, rat, Xenopus, and Physarum fibrillarins (Aris and Blobel, 1988; Hurt *et al.*, 1988; Schimmang *et al.*, 1989; Henríquez *et al.*, 1990; E. Hurt, personal communication). Like fibrillarin, Nop1p is associated with small nucleolar RNAs. Antibodies against Nop1p coprecipitate the small nucleolar RNAs snR3, snR4, snR8, snR9, snR10, snR17(U3), snR128(U14), snR189, and snR190 (Schimmang *et al.*, 1989). The association of Nop1p and fibrillarin with small nucleolar RNAs and their localization to nucleolar compartments that are sites of pre-rRNA processing or early steps of ribosome assembly suggest important roles for these proteins in ribosome biogenesis. Examination of the phenotype of a conditional null allele of *NOP1* corroborated this expectation (Tollervey *et al.*, 1991). When Nop1p is depleted in a *GAL1–NOP1* strain, processing of rRNAs is impaired. Interestingly, some unprocessed rRNAs that accumulate are not methylated. Because the amounts and nucleolar localization of most of the small nucleolar RNAs known to be associated with Nop1p are not changed, it was concluded that depletion of Nop1p primarily affects nucleolar snRNP function.

No yeast homologues of nucleolin or B23 have yet been identified, despite considerable effort using antibodies against these proteins or nucleic acid probes from other eukaryotes to screen for genes encoding these proteins.

B. SMALL NUCLEOLAR RNAs

The small nucleolar RNA U3 is found in high abundance in nucleoli of all organisms thus far examined (review in Reddy and Busch, 1988). Recently the U8 and U13 snRNAs also have been localized to the mammalian nucleolus (Tyc and Steitz, 1989). Mammalian U3 is associated with at least six proteins, including fibrillarin (Parker and Steitz, 1987). Because U3 snRNA is complementary to and can be cross-linked with various regions of pre-rRNA, it has been suggested that U3 plays a role in rRNA processing (Maser and Calvet, 1989; Stroke and Weiner, 1989). Experiments by Kass *et al.* (1990) demonstrated that U3 is necessary for the first step in rRNA processing *in vitro*. Inactivation of U3 by oligonucleotide-directed RNaseH cleavage, or immunodepletion of U3 from cell-free extracts using antifibrillarin, prevents cleavage of the external transcribed spacer of mouse rRNA *in vitro*. U8 and U13 also are associated with fibrillarin and cosediment with large complexes, suggesting that they too may be involved in ribosome biogenesis, particularly rRNA processing (Tyc and Steitz, 1989).

Nine yeast small nucleolar RNAs (snR3, snR4, snR5, snR8, snR9, snR10, snR17, snR128, and snR190) have been identified by virtue of their physical association with pre-rRNAs or nucleolar proteins, or their requirement for pre-rRNA processing (Tollervey, 1987). Surprisingly, haploid strains bearing disruptions of any one of most of these genes are viable (Reidel *et al.*, 1986; Tollervey, 1987; Parker *et al.*, 1988; Zagorski *et al.*, 1988). Only snR17, the homologue of mammalian U3, and snR128, the equivalent of the metazoan U14 or 4.5S hyb RNA, are essential for cell growth (Hughes *et al.*, 1987; Li *et al.*, 1990). Depletion of snR128 in a *GAL1–SNR128* strain conditional for synthesis of snR128 led to impaired processing of 35S rRNA to the 20S species, and a resulting deficiency of accumulation of 18S rRNA (Li *et al.*, 1990). The snR128 RNA contains four sequences (boxes A, B, C, and D) conserved among several small nucleolar RNAs in yeast and mammals (Tyc and Steitz, 1989; Jarmolowski *et al.*, 1990). Regions A and B are complementary to phylogenetically conserved sequences in 18S rRNA predicted to be single stranded. Thus base pairing between snR128 and rRNA may serve as a signal for rRNA processing. Boxes C and D in human U3 have been implicated as binding sites for fibrillarin (Parker and Steitz, 1987; Tyc and Steitz, 1989). Deletion and substitution mutations of *SNR128* corroborated the importance of these conserved sequences in yeast snR128 (Jarmolowski *et al.*, 1990). Box A and B mutants produce normal levels of snR128. The box A mutant RNAs are nonfunctional. Curiously, mutations in box B do not impair snR128 function. Box C and box D mutants have decreased levels of snR128 RNA, suggesting impaired synthesis or stability, perhaps due to altered interaction with Nop1p (fibrillarin) or other snR128 snRNP proteins.

snR17 is encoded by two genes, either of which is sufficient for viability (Hughes *et al.*, 1987). No molecular phenotype was reported for strains containing a null allele of one or the other gene, except the interesting observation that deletion of the more highly expressed *SNR17A* gene led to an increase in the amount of snR17B RNA. Examination of the phenotype of conditional lethal *snr17* mutants should reveal the function(s) of snR17 RNA in ribosome biogenesis. Deletion of the dispensable *SNR10* gene led to a cold-sensitive phenotype and a defect in processing of 35S pre-rRNA (Tollervey, 1987).

Many of the unanswered questions about nucleolar structure and about the function of nucleolar proteins and RNAs could be addressed by molecular approaches in yeast. No doubt more yeast nucleolar protein genes will be identified and will be manipulated in more detail to define their function and to identify the molecules with which they interact. Why are so many yeast small nucleolar RNAs and at least one abundant nucleolar protein (Ssb1p) important for rRNA processing, but nonetheless dispensable? Do each of these molecules serve redundant functions? What is the molecular basis for the pre-rRNA processing defects of these *snr* or *ssb1* mutants? Whether any of the potential base pairings between small nucleolar RNAs and pre-rRNAs occur and are important for ribosome biogenesis can be tested by constructing point mutations in those sequences in the snRNAs and compensatory mutations in tagged rRNAs (see below). Analysis of extragenic suppressors of snRNA mutants may identify snRNP proteins in addition to Nop1p and Ssb1p. Assembly and nucleolar localization of snRNPs, posttranscriptional modification of pre-rRNAs, assembly of preribosomal ribonucleoprotein particles, and transport of ribosomal precursors to the cytoplasm are topics about which we presently know very little, but which could and should be addressed using a combined genetic and biochemical approach in yeast.

VII. Ribosomal RNA Processing

Processing of the yeast 35S rRNA precursor to produce mature 5.8S, 18S, and 25S rRNAs occurs by a series of nucleolytic cleavage steps (Fig. 3) similar to those in other eukaryotes (Udem and Warner, 1972,

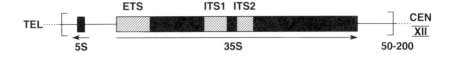

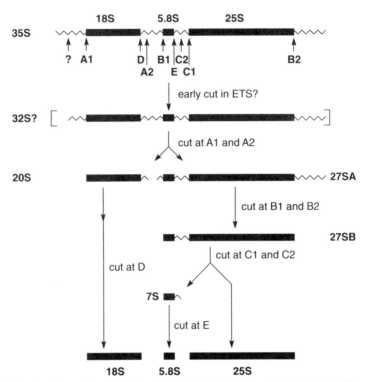

FIG. 3. The structure of one rDNA repeat unit that is transcribed into 5S rRNA and 35S rRNA is shown (top). The 35S rRNA is processed by sequential cleavages at the sites indicated by A1, A2, B1, etc. Regions corresponding to mature rRNA are shown as dark bars. Sequences that are removed from the primary transcript by processing are indicated as hatched boxes or wavy lines.

1973; Veldman *et al.*, 1981). The largest and earliest intermediate, a 32S rRNA, has not been characterized in detail, but may be produced by cleavage within the 5' external transcribed spacer of the 35S rRNA, in a step similar to the rapid first processing event reported in metazoans (Veinot-Drebot *et al.*, 1988; review in Kass *et al.*, 1990). The observation that depletion of yeast fibrillarin, a U3 snRNP protein, blocks processing of 35S rRNA is consistent with the fact that the U3 snRNP is necessary for early steps in mouse pre-rRNA processing (Kass *et al.*, 1990) In wild-type cells, 32S rRNA is rapidly processed to the relatively stable 27S and 20S rRNAs by cleavage of the 32S rRNA at the 5′ end of the 18S rRNA sequence and within the first internal transcribed spacer sequence. The 27S rRNA is processed in at least three relatively slow steps to form the 5.8S and 25S rRNAs. Processing of the 20S rRNA to the 18S rRNA occurs in the cytoplasm, during the final stages of maturation of the 40S ribosomal subunit.

VIII. Ribosome Assembly

A. A MODEL FOR BACTERIAL RIBOSOME ASSEMBLY

Most of our knowledge of the pathway of assembly of ribosomal proteins with rRNA to form mature ribosomal subunits is derived from two sorts of experiments *in vitro* with bacterial ribosomes: (1) reconstitution of functional 30S and 50S subunits from separate purified proteins and RNAs and (2) detailed biochemical and biophysical analyses of the structure and interactions among ribosomal components (review in Hill *et al.*, 1990). An *in vitro* assembly map was derived for the 30S subunit (Mizushima and Nomura, 1970; Held *et al.*, 1973). A secondary structure for 16S rRNA has been established by phylogenetic comparisons and is supported by physical and genetic analyses (Woese *et al.*, 1983; Gutell *et al.*, 1985). The positions of 21 proteins of the 30S subunit have been determined using cross-linking, immunoelectron microscopy, and neutron diffraction scattering (Capel *et al.*, 1987; Stöffler-Meilicke and Stöffler, 1990). Recent elegant experiments by Stern *et al.* (1989) monitored changes in the structure of 16S rRNA during the stepwise assembly *in vitro* of each protein with the RNA. Based on these data, the current scenario for the assembly of the bacterial 30S subunit is described below, and might serve as a framework for formulating models of eukaryotic ribosome assembly.

The process of 30S ribosomal subunit assembly in *E. coli* is a highly cooperative one that proceeds through a complex pathway of interdependent and independent protein–RNA and protein–protein interactions. Several primary binding proteins bind independently to different sites in the 16S rRNA. Subsequent association of the secondary binding proteins with the nascent 30S subunit depends on prior assembly of the primary binding proteins. Likewise, assembly of tertiary binding proteins is contingent upon assembly of the secondary proteins with the

complex as well as the presence of other tertiary proteins. Protein-
dependent conformational changes in the RNA occur, mostly during
assembly of the primary and secondary binding proteins, and are a
basis for the cooperative nature of assembly. The binding of these
proteins to the RNA occurs by recognition of the tertiary and quater-
nary structure of the RNA, rather than of specific nucleotide sequences.
There is a strong correlation between the assembly map and the structural map: many proteins linked in the assembly pathway are close to
each other in the mature ribosomal subunit. Although the subunits can
self-assemble *in vitro,* it is expected that assembly *in vivo* is stimulated
by nonribosomal factors, such as the molecular chaperones that mediate assembly of bacteriophage particles or multisubunit enzymes (Ellis,
1987; Hemmingsen *et al.,* 1988).

   In contrast, practically nothing is known about the pathway of assembly of eukaryotic ribosomes. Partially dissociated eukaryotic ribosomes have been successfully reconstituted (Cox and Greenwell, 1980;
Vioque and Palacian, 1985; Lee and Anderson, 1986), but eukaryotic
ribosomal subunits have not been reconstituted *in vitro* from entirely
separate components. Knowledge of the structure of eukaryotic ribosomes beyond that of primary sequences of RNA and proteins is quite
limited. As described for bacterial RNAs, there are accepted models for
the secondary structure of eukaryotic rRNAs, based on phylogenetic
comparisons (Lee, 1990). Limited data exist describing particular
RNA–protein or protein–protein interactions in eukaryotic ribosomes
(review in Lee, 1990).

B. YEAST RIBOSOME ASSEMBLY

   A low-resolution map of ribosome assembly in yeast was obtained by
pulse-chase experiments *in vivo* and by mapping the order with which
proteins could be dissociated from subunits *in vitro* by increasingly
stringent washes. A nuclear 90S preribosomal particle containing 35S
rRNA was detected by a 5-minute pulse labeling and could be chased to
precursors of each subunit, a nuclear 66S particle containing 27S pre-
rRNA and a predominantly cytoplasmic 43S particle containing 20S
pre-rRNA (Trapman *et al.,* 1975). The 43S particle undergoes further
maturation in the cytoplasm, including processing of the 20S rRNA to
18S rRNA (Udem and Warner, 1973). The 90S and 66S particles apparently contain a higher ratio of protein to RNA than do mature ribosomes, suggesting that subsequent steps in assembly involve not only

loss of some RNA sequences during rRNA processing but also dissociation of proteins, probably nonribosomal proteins, from the precursor
RNPs. Both nonribosomal proteins as well as ribosomal proteins are
contained in these RNPs (Warner, 1971). By following the kinetics of
labeling of individual proteins in 40S or 60S subunits in spheroplasts
incubated at 15°C, in which the period to produce mature rRNAs is
considerably longer than at 30°C, early-assembling ribosomal proteins
were distinguished from late-assembling ribosomal (Kruiswijk et al.,
1978). Early-assembling proteins include several of the so-called core
proteins that remain associated with rRNA after 0.5 M LiCl washes,
including two proteins that bind specifically to 25S rRNA, L25 and L15
(El-Baradi et al., 1984; Lee et al., 1985). As mentioned above, the
bacterial homologues of L25 and L15 are EL23 and EL11. Each of these
four proteins specifically binds to their respective heterologous as well
as homologous rRNAs, suggesting some conservation of at least early
steps in assembly of bacterial and yeast ribosomes (El-Baradi et al.,
1984, 1987). Because ribosome assembly occurs so rapidly in wild-type
yeast cells, significant amounts of assembly intermediates are not usually detectable (Warner, 1971). Future efforts to map the assembly
pathway would be facilitated by the isolation of assembly mutants that
accumulate preassembly particles in greater quantities than is observed in wild-type cells.

C. The 5S RNP: A Subassembly Particle

Studies of the biogenesis of 5S rRNA in HeLa cells and in the frog
Xenopus laevis identified a ribonucleoprotein particle containing 5S
rRNA and ribosomal protein L5, which is a precursor to ribosome
assembly. Pulse-chase studies by Steitz et al. (1988) indicated that
newly synthesized 5S rRNA is transiently associated with La protein,
an antigen detectable by a human autoimmune serum. La binds to
uridylate residues at the 3' terminus of 5S rRNA, residues that are
subsequently removed. The 5S rRNA is chased into an rpL5/5S RNP
(present in the nucleolus) that slowly assembles into ribosomes. During
Xenopus oogenesis, oocyte 5S rRNA is made long before ribosomes are
assembled. This 5S rRNA is stored in the cytoplasm of previtellogenic
Xenopus oocytes, in either a 42S RNP containing tRNA and two
proteins or a 7S RNP containing the 5S rRNA gene-specific transcription factor TFIIIA (Picard and Wegnez, 1979; Picard et al., 1980). Recently Guddat et al. (1990) have begun to define the pathway of 5S RNP

biogenesis in Xenopus. In mature Xenopus oocytes, 5S rRNA associates transiently in the nucleus with La antigen. La is then replaced with rpL5 or TFIIIA.

Yeast contains both a homologue of rpL5, i.e., L1 (Nazar *et al.*, 1979), and a TFIIIA protein (Wang and Weil, 1989), but it has not been directly determined whether TFIIIA/5S RNPs or rpL1/5S RNPs exist in yeast. Indirect evidence for a stable rpL1/5S RNP in yeast was obtained in experiments in which 60S subunit assembly *in vivo* was aborted upon depletion of L16 (Moritz *et al.*, 1990). Although most of the other RNA and protein constituents of the 60S subunit were rapidly turned over in the absence of its assembly, rpL1 and 5S rRNA were exceptional in that they were stable. As shown in Fig. 4, immunofluorescence microscopy using antiserum against rpL1/5S RNP demonstrated that the RNP accumulated at abnormally high levels in the nucleus of cells in which the 60S subunit assembly was aborted (Y.-F. Tsay, M. Deshmukh, and J. L. Woolford, unpublished data). A more direct biochemical assay of 5S RNP complexes should be undertaken to assay for free TFIIIA/5S RNPs or rpL1/5S RNPs in yeast and to determine the temporal and spatial pathway for 5S RNP biogenesis. Analysis of mutant *RPL1* genes, and of mutant 5S rDNA using one of the systems described below, may provide a complementary genetic approach to study the assembly and intracellular localization of 5S RNP.

In vitro experiments by Brow and Geiduschek (1987) suggested an interesting mechanism for coupling the synthesis of 5S rRNA with ribosomal protein synthesis or ribosome assembly. Addition of exogenous 5S rRNA inhibited transcription *in vitro* of 5S rDNA, presumably by binding to the 5S transcription factor TFIIIA. Immunodepletion of rpL1 from extracts made them more sensitive to inhibition by exogenous 5S rRNA. Thus, rpL1 may compete with TFIIIA for binding to 5S rRNA or may displace TFIIIA from a TFIIIA/5S RNP. By this means, 5S rRNA synthesis could be kept in balance with either rpL1 synthesis or assembly of the rpL1/5S RNP into the ribosome. This model predicts that as the rate of rpL1 synthesis increases, formation of rpL1/5S complexes might be favored over the assembly of TFIIIA/5S complexes, thus increasing the pool of free TFIIIA that can bind to 5S rDNA and activate its transcription. Likewise, depletion of rpL1 should lead to decreased 5S rRNA synthesis. This model assumes that TFIIIA is rate limiting for 5S rRNA synthesis *in vivo*, and that synthesis of 5S rRNA requires reassembly of a TFIIIA–promoter complex after each round of transcription. This hypothesis can now be tested with the cloning of *RPL1* and the construction of strains containing *RPL1* under the

Anti-L1 RNP   DAPI

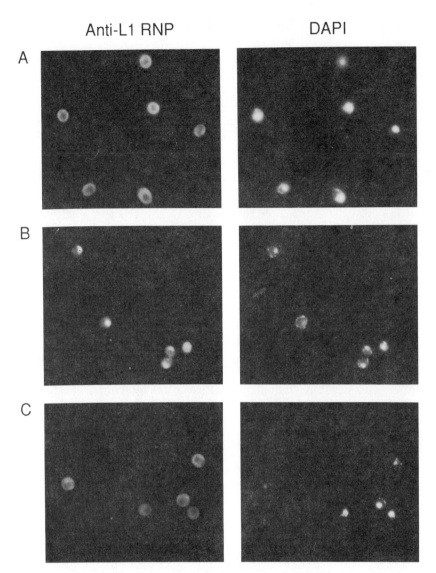

FIG. 4. A ribonucleoprotein particle containing rpL1 and 5S rRNA accumulates in the nucleus when the 60S ribosomal subunit assembly is aborted. Yeast cells were prepared for indirect immunofluorescence microscopy by fixation, then were stained with either anti-rpL1/5S RNP antiserum followed by rhodamine-conjugated goat antirabbit IgG to visualize the RNP (left), or 4,6-diamino-2-phenylinodole (DAPI) to visualize nuclei (right). (A) A *GAL1–RPL16* strain grown in galactose. Assembly of both ribosomal subunits is normal. The detectable rpL1/5S RNP is predominantly cytoplasmic. (B) A *GAL1–RPL16* strain grown in glucose for 16 hours. Assembly of 60S subunits, but not 40S subunits, is aborted. The rpL1/5S RNP signal is mostly in the nucleus (C) A *GAL1–CRY1* strain grown in glucose for 16 hours. Assembly of 40S subunits, but not 60S subunits, is aborted. The rpL1/5S RNP is mostly cytoplasmic.

control of the regulated *GAL1* promoter (M. Deshmukh and J. L. Woolford, unpublished data).

D. IMPORT OF RIBOSOMAL PROTEINS INTO THE NUCLEUS

Most ribosomal proteins rapidly assemble into nascent ribosomal subunits in the nucleolus. Consequently, an essential and early step in ribosome assembly is the transport of ribosomal proteins from their site of synthesis in the cytoplasm through the nuclear envelope and into the nucleus. Although most ribosomal proteins are small enough to enter the nucleus by free diffusion, results thus far suggest that nuclear entry of ribosomal proteins requires nuclear localization signals (NLSs) similar to those found in larger nuclear proteins. The subcellular localization of L3–β-gal, L29–β-gal, and L25–β-gal fusion proteins containing wild-type or mutant L3, L29, or L25 sequences, and analysis of the phenotypes of point mutations in *CYH2* encoding L29, led to the identification of sequences necessary for the nuclear localization of these three yeast ribosomal proteins (Moreland *et al.*, 1985; Underwood and Fried, 1990; H. A. Raué, personal communication). L29 contains two sequences, K_6TRHRG_{12} and $K_{23}HRKHPG_{29}$, which can function as NLSs (Underwood and Fried, 1990). Substitutions of some of these amino acids diminished nuclear localization of L29; most striking were the effects of altering Arg 25 to Lys or both Arg 8 and Arg 25 to Lys. Although these and other NLS sequences share limited homology, they usually contain mostly basic amino acids. Because ribosomal proteins are rich in basic residues, a putative NLS may not be unambiguously identified by inspection of ribosomal protein sequences. Further mutational analysis will be necessary to determine whether all ribosomal proteins contain a functional NLS. An alternative possibility is that nuclear entry of some ribosomal proteins may be facilitated by their association with other proteins containing an NLS. H. A. Raué and colleagues (personal communication) have shown that nuclear localization of L25 may not result from free diffusion into the nucleus and binding to a nuclear molecule; the NLS of L25 is distinct from its 25S rRNA-binding domain.

IX. Genetic Analysis of rRNA Processing or Ribosome Assembly

A. SYSTEMS TO ASSAY rDNA MUTATIONS

Specific sequences within yeast rRNA necessary for processing have been difficult to define by traditional genetic or biochemical approaches. The phenotype of mutant alleles of rRNA is obscured by the vast excess of wild-type rRNAs expressed from the many rDNA repeats in the genome. Furthermore, no cell-free system has been developed from yeast that is capable of completely processing rRNA. These problems have been partially circumvented by the development of two promising systems to assay mutations in rRNA genes *in vivo,* (1) tagging rDNA genes and (2) deleting chromosomal rDNA and replacing it with plasmid-borne copies.

Cloned rDNAs were tagged by inserting a unique oligonucleotide into expansion segments of the 18S or 25S rRNA genes. By this means it has been possible to demonstrate that not all rRNA processing steps require intact 35S pre-rRNA. Deletion of two-thirds of the 18S rRNA sequences had no effect on production of functional 25S rRNA (Musters *et al.,* 1989). In contrast, deletion of nucleotides 699–3215 within the 25S rRNA did prevent accumulation of mature 18S rRNA (H. Li and M. Fournier, personal communication). Although sequences present in mature rRNA are phylogenetically conserved, the external and internal transcribed spacers present in eukaryotic rRNAs vary considerably in length and sequence. Musters *et al.* (1990) used tagged rDNAs to show that large deletions in ETS or in ITS1 interfere with accumulation of 18S rRNA, and deletions in ITS2 prevent production of 25S rRNA. Whether these mutations directly affect rRNA processing or alter the pathway of assembly of stable ribosomal subunits remains to be determined.

Recently, a scheme has been developed, based on recessive mutations in bacterial rDNA that confer antibiotic resistance, to select for yeast cells in which all of the chromosomal rDNA genes were deleted and replaced by plasmid-borne rDNA (E. Morgan, personal communication). Yeast cells were transformed with a plasmid-containing rDNA bearing a recessive antibiotic-resistance mutation. Some of the resistant transformants that arose lacked any chromosomal rDNAs. Such strains can now be exploited to address numerous interesting issues concerning rRNA synthesis and function.

B. Mutants That Affect rRNA Processing or Ribosome Assembly

As is the case in the splicing of pre-mRNAs, the order and precise sites for processing of rRNA are dictated not only by the sequence and structure of rRNA but also by the association of proteins and small nuclear RNAs with the rRNA. Ribosomal as well as nonribosomal proteins are important for rRNA processing. When the synthesis of the majority of ribosomal proteins is prevented, 35S rRNA is transcribed but not processed and is rapidly degraded (Gorenstein and Warner,

1977). Depletion or inactivation of each of the individual ribosomal proteins L3, L16, L29, or rp59 also results in termination of processing of rRNA and turnover of other newly synthesized ribosomal proteins, but only for those molecules destined for the same ribosomal subunit as the depleted protein (Nam and Fried, 1986; Moritz *et al.*, 1990; M. Moritz, B. Pulaski, and J. Woolford, 1991). The precise steps at which rRNA processing or ribosomal subunit assembly is aborted were not evident in these experiments. Analysis of the phenotypes of tight temperature-sensitive or cold-sensitive ribosomal protein mutants may reveal whether there are specific steps in rRNA processing for which an individual ribosomal protein is required. Nevertheless, these experiments did demonstrate that association of these particular ribosomal proteins with the nascent ribosome either must occur after the formation of the 20S and 27S rRNA precursors and the separate ribosomal subunit precursor particles, or must not be necessary for steps prior to separation of the pathways of assembly of the two subunits. These experiments, as well as those using the tagged rDNA deletion mutants, also demonstrated that assembly of the 40S and 60S ribosomal subunits is not interdependent.

Biochemical identification of enzymes involved in yeast rRNA processing awaits development of a cell-free system in which to assay such activities. A second direct approach to identify molecules necessary for rRNA processing or ribosome assembly is to identify mutants defective in these processes. Because rRNA processing depends upon proper ribosome assembly, and vice versa, mutants whose primary defect is in one of these processes are also defective in the other. Therefore, searches for rRNA-processing mutants or ribosome assembly mutants are of mutual interest. Such mutants have been identified by direct screening of temperature-sensitive or cold-sensitive mutants for one of these defects or by screening for strains hypersensitive to antibiotics.

Andrew *et al.* (1976) discovered a temperature-sensitive mutant, ts351, defective in the processing of 27S rRNA to 25S and 5.8S rRNAs. At the nonpermissive temperature, the 27S precursor rRNA, and most of the newly synthesized ribosomal proteins also destined for the 60S subunit are rapidly degraded (Gorenstein and Warner, 1977). However, wild-type amounts of 18S rRNA and 40S ribosomal subunits accumulate. As is the case for many mutants with defective ribosomes, ts351 is hypersensitive to aminoglycoside antibiotics. The ts351 lesion has been designated *rrp1*, for ribosomal RNA processing. Cloning and sequencing of *RRP1* revealed that it does not encode a known ribosomal protein (Fabian and Hopper, 1987). The isolation of an extragenic suppressor of *rrp1, srd1,* may help to identify a molecule that interacts with Rrp1p or is necessary for its expression or function (Fabian *et al.,* 1990).

Gritz *et al.* (1982) described three temperature-sensitive mutants, ts205, ts212, and ts417, each of which contains identical electrophoretic variants of two proteins from the 60S subunit and two proteins from the 40S subunit. These mutants are hypersensitive to aminoglycoside antibiotics and are deficient in production of 20S and 18S rRNAs as well as 40S subunits.

Strain A224A is deficient in 40S subunits compared to 60S subunits at 36°C, as a result of slowed processing of 20S to 18S rRNA in the cytoplasm (Mitlin and Cannon, 1984). At the nonpermissive temperature, ribosomal precursor particles containing 20S rRNA accumulate in the nucleus and are transported slowly to the cytoplasm. Curiously, the phenotype of this mutant is exaggerated in a trichodermin-resistant strain, CLP8, derived from it (Carter and Cannon, 1980). CLP8 exhibits the above defects not only at 36°C but at temperatures as low as 20°C.

Recently, more wide-scale screens of temperature-sensitive strains have been conducted to search for mutants altered in rRNA processing. One such mutant accumulates RNA containing only sequences from within the 5′ portion of ITS2. A second mutant has a very pleiotropic phenotype; it accumulates greater than wild-type amounts of the 35S rRNA precursor and several abnormal transcripts, including one that extends from the 5′ end of the 35S rRNA sequence to within ITS1, and a second that extends from near the A2 site to the 3′ end of the 5.8S rRNA sequence (L. Lindahl, R. H. Archer, and J. Zengel, personal communication; K. Shuai and J. R. Warner, personal communication).

Cold-sensitive strains of bacteria or fungi have been a rich source of mutants defective in ribosome biogenesis (Guthrie *et al.,* 1969; Tai *et al.,* 1969; Nashimoto and Nomura, 1970; Bryant and Sypherd, 1974). Ursic and Davies (1974) identified one leaky cold-sensitive yeast mutant, *dip-1,* that is partially defective in production of 35S rRNA. A substantial fraction of RNA detected in short pulses was 14S RNA or smaller, rather than 35S rRNA. A cold-sensitive, streptomycin-sensitive mutant AA-89, described by Bayliss and Ingraham (1974), accumulates a 28S particle containing 18S rRNA, which cannot be chased into wild-type ribosomal subunits upon shifting back to permissive conditions. Recently, a screen of a bank of 180 cold-sensitive mutants identified 26 mutants defining at least six complementation groups; the mutants were deficient in accumulation of either 40S or 60S ribosomal subunits (Fig. 5) (T. Ripmaster and J. L. Woolford, unpublished data).

Cold-sensitive *spb1–spb7* mutants, isolated as suppressors of a lethal

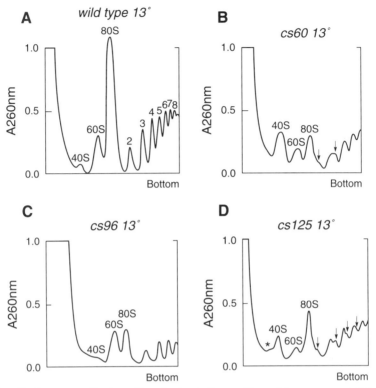

Fɪɢ. 5. Sucrose gradient profiles of extracts from cold-sensitive mutants deficient in
40S or 60S ribosomal subunits. (A) Wild type. (B) cs60 is deficient in 60S subunits.
(C) cs96 is deficient in 40S subunits. (D) cs125 is deficient in 60S subunits and accumulates a species, indicated by the asterisk, that sediments above 40S subunits and may be a
precursor particle or aberrant intermediate. The vertical arrows indicate half-mer polyribosomes, i.e., those containing an integral number of 80S ribosomes plus one extra 40S
subunit frozen at the translation initiation site, as a result of the deficiency of 60S
subunits.

null allele of the poly(A)-binding protein gene *PAB1,* are defective in
accumulation of 60S ribosomal subunits (Sachs and Davis, 1989, 1990).
SPB2 is the *RPL46* gene and it encodes ribosomal protein L46. *SPB4*
may well encode a helicase involved in 60S subunit assembly; the
sequence of *SPB4* is homologous to that of ATP-dependent RNA heli-
cases, and *spb4* mutants are defective in production of 25S rRNA (Sachs
and Davis, 1990). It is not clear whether *spb* mutants are simply deficient in 60S ribosomal subunits or else contain altered 60S ribosomal
subunits, nor is it understood how either effect might bypass the re-

quirement for poly(A)-binding protein in translation initiation. Nevertheless, other genes necessary for 60S ribosomal subunit assembly may be identified by additional selections for *spb* mutants.

None of the mutants described above has yet been characterized in sufficient detail to distinguish whether the primary defect is in rRNA processing or ribosome assembly. Unfortunately, the mutants ts205, ts212, ts417, A224A, CLP8, *dip-l,* and AA-89 have not been pursued since they were first reported years ago. Cloning of the genes defined by these processing or assembly mutants should lead to identification of the gene products and of the nature of their function in ribosome biogenesis.

X. Summary and Prospectus

Very soon the primary sequences of all of the ribosomal proteins and rRNAs of yeast and rat cells should be known, making more evident the extent of homology among ribosomal constituents of yeast and mammalian cells. A challenge in the future will be to combine effectively biochemical, biophysical, and genetic approaches to map interactions among ribosomal constitutents, and to take advantage of the conservation of eukaryotic ribosomes in planning or interpreting such experiments with different organisms. The ability to target mutations to cloned yeast rDNA or ribosomal protein genes, and to isolate conditional alleles and extragenic suppressors, provides an advantage in mapping the structure of the yeast ribosome.

Yeast ribosome biosynthesis appears to be primarily controlled at the level of transcription. The abundant proteins, Rap1p, Abf1p, and Reb1p, are necessary for the expression of these genes as well as a wide variety of other yeast genes. We have probably only begun to identify all of the cis- and trans-acting elements necessary for transcription of rDNA and ribosomal protein genes. In addition, the signals that coordinate the transcription of these genes by all three RNA polymerases have not been identified nor have signals been identified that are responsible for growth rate regulation of ribosome synthesis. There is some evidence for posttranscriptional fine tuning of ribosome synthesis, but the mechanism of turnover of excess ribosomal proteins remains unknown. Are ribosomal protein genes other than *RPL32* and *CRY2* autogenously regulated? What is the significance of these autogenous regulatory pathways and how do they function? How is the expression of single-copy and duplicated ribosomal protein genes balanced?

Our knowledge of nucleolar proteins and RNAs is mostly descriptive.

Isolation and characterization of mutant alleles of genes encoding these nucleolar molecules, and identification of extragenic suppressors, may allow us to discern the function of these molecules and to understand the basis of nucleolar structure. Successful reconstitution of eukaryotic ribosomes from totally separate *in vitro* components may remain a difficult task. However, expansion of the catalog of mutants affecting rRNA processing and ribosome assembly is likely to shed some light on this difficult problem. Improved technology with nucleic acid biochemistry should enable the development of cell-free systems for rRNA processing. By analogy to studies of mRNA processing, it should be possible to make effective use of rRNA-processing mutants or nucleolar protein or RNA mutants, in concert with a cell-free system, to define the pathway of processing in more detail and to determine the functions of trans-acting factors in this pathway. The growing interest in molecular chaperones may help determine whether such molecules facilitate ribosome assembly.

ACKNOWLEDGMENTS

The author wishes to thank numerous colleagues who contributed useful discussions and allowed citation of their unpublished data.

REFERENCES

Abovich, N., Tung, L., and Rosbash, M. (1985). Effect of *RP51* gene dosage alterations on ribosome synthesis in *Saccharomyces cerevisiae*. *Mol. Cell. Biol.* **5,** 3429–3435.

All-Robyn, J. A., Brown, N., Otaka, E., and Liebman, S. W. (1990). Sequence and functional similarity between a yeast ribosomal protein and the *E. coli* S5 *ram* protein. *Mol. Cell. Biol.* **10,** 6544–6553.

Andrew, C., Hopper, A. K., and Hall, B. D. (1976). A yeast mutant defective in the processing of 27S rRNA precursor. *Mol. Gen. Genet.* **144,** 29–35.

Arevalo, S. G., and Warner, J. R. (1990). Ribosomal protein L4 of *Saccharomyces cerevisiae:* The gene and its protein. *Nucleic Acids Res.* **18,** 1447–1449.

Aris, J. P., and Blobel, G. (1988). Identification and characterization of a yeast nucleolar protein that is similar to a rat liver nucleolar protein. *J. Cell Biol.* **107,** 17–31.

Barbacid, M., Fresno, H., and Vázquez, D. (1975). Inhibitions of polypeptide elongation of yeast polysomes. *J. Antibiot.* **28,** 453–462.

Baronas-Lowell, D. M., and Warner, J. R. (1990). Ribosomal protein L30 is dispensable in the yeast *Saccharomyces cerevisiae*. *Mol. Cell Biol.* **10,** 5235–5243.

Bayliss, F. T., and Ingraham, J. L. (1974). Mutation in *Saccharomyces cerevisiae* conferring streptomycin and cold sensitivity by affecting ribosome formation and function. *J. Bacteriol.* **118,** 319–325.

Biswas, S. B., and Biswas, E. E. (1990). ARS binding factor 1 of the yeast *Saccharomyces cerevisiae* binds to sequences in telomeric and nontelomeric autonomously replicating sequences. *Mol. Cell. Biol.* **10,** 810–815.

Bollen, G. H. P. M., Mager, W. H., and Planta, R. J. (1981a). High resolution mini-two-dimensional gel electrophoresis of yeast ribosomal proteins. A standard nomenclature for yeast ribosomal proteins. *Mol. Biol. Rep.* **8**, 37–44.

Bollen, G. H. P. M., Cohen, L. H., Mager, W. H., Klaasen, A. W., and Planta, R. J. (1981b). Isolation of cloned ribosomal protein genes from the yeast *Saccharomyces carlsbergensis. Gene* **14**, 279–287.

Borer, R. A., Lehner, C., Eppenberger, H., and Nigg, E. A. (1989). Major nucleolar proteins shuttle between nucleus and cytoplasm. *Cell* **56**, 379–390.

Bozzoni, I., Fragapane, P., Annesi, F., Pierandrei-Amaldi, P., Amaldi, F., and Beccari, E. (1984). Expression of two *Xenopus laevis* ribosomal protein genes in injected frog oocytes. A specific splicing block interferes with the L1 RNA maturation. *J. Mol. Biol.* **180**, 987–1005.

Brill, S. J., DiNardo, S., Voelkel-Meiman, K., and Sternglanz, R. (1987). Need for DNA topoisomerase activity as a swivel for DNA replication and for transcription of ribosomal RNA. *Nature (London)* **326**, 414–416.

Brow, D. A., and Geiduschek, E. P. (1987). Modulation of yeast 5S rRNA synthesis *in vitro* by ribosomal protein YL3. *J. Biol. Chem.* **262**, 13953–13958.

Bryant, R. E., and Sypherd, P. S. (1974). Genetic analysis of cold-sensitive ribosome maturation mutants of *Escherichia coli. J. Bacteriol.* **117**, 1082–1092.

Bucher, K., and Skogerson, L. (1976). Cryptopleurine—An inhibitor of translocation. *Biochemistry* **22**, 4755–4759.

Buchman, A. R., Kimmerly, W. J., Rine, J., and Kornberg, R. D. (1988). Two DNA-binding factors recognize specific sequences at silencers, upstream activating sequences, autonomously replicating sequences, and telomeres in *Saccharomyces cerevisiae. Mol. Cell Biol.* **8**, 210–225.

Bugler, B., Bourbon, H., Lapeyre, B., Wallace, M. O., Chang, J.-H., Amalric, F., and Olson, M. O. J. (1987). RNA binding fragments from nucleolin contain the ribonucleoprotein consensus sequence. *J. Biol. Chem.* **262**, 10922–10925.

Caizergues-Ferrer, M., Belenguer, P., Lapeyre, B., Amalric, F., Wallace, M. O., and Olson, M. O. J. (1987). Phosphorylation of nucleolin by a nucleolar type NII protein kinase. *Biochemistry* **26**, 7876–7883.

Caizergues-Ferrer, M., Mariottini, P., Curie, C., Lapeyre, B., Gas, N., Amalric, F., and Amaldi, F. (1989). Nucleolin from *Xenopus laevis:* cDNA cloning and expression during development. *Genes Dev.* **3**, 324–333.

Capel, M., Engelman, D., Freeborn, B., Kjeldgaard, M., Langer, J., Ramakrishnan, V., Schindler, D., Schneider, D., Schoenborn, B., Sillers, I.-Y., Yabuk, S., and Moore, P. B. (1987). A complete mapping of the proteins in the small ribosomal subunit of *Escherichia coli. Science* **238**, 1403–1406.

Capieaux, E., Vignais, M.-L., Sentenac, A., and Goffeau, A. (1989). The yeast H^+-ATPase gene is controlled by the promoter binding factor TUF. *J. Biol. Chem.* **264**, 7437–7446.

Carle, G., and Olson, M. (1984). Separation of chromosomal DNA molecules from yeast by orthogonal-field-alternation gel electrophoresis. *Nucleic Acids Res.* **12**, 5647–5664.

Carter, C. J., and Cannon, M. (1980). Maturation of ribosomal precursor RNA in *Saccharomyces cerevisiae:* a mutant with a defect in both the transport and terminal processing of the 20S species. *J. Mol. Biol.* **143**, 179–199.

Chambers, A., Tsand, J. S. H., Stanway, C., Kingsman, A., and Kingsman, S. M. (1989). Transcriptional control of the *Saccharomyces cerevisiae* PGK gene by RAP1. *Mol. Cell. Biol.* **9**, 5516–5524.

Chang, J.-H., Dumbar, T. S., and Olson, M. O. J. (1988). cDNA and deduced primary structure of rat protein B23, a nuceolar protein containing highly conserved sequences. *J. Biol. Chem.* **263,** 12824–12827.

Chasman, D. I., Lue, N. F., Buchman, A. R., LaPointe, J. W., Lorch, Y., and Kornberg, R. D. (1990). A yeast protein that influences the chromatin structure of UAS_{RPG} and functions as a powerful auxiliary gene activator. *Genes Dev.* **4,** 503–514.

Chen-Schneisser, U., and Garrett, R. A. (1977). A new method for the isolation of a 5S RNA complex with proteins L5, L18, and L25 from *E. coli* ribosomes. *FEBS Lett.* **74,** 287–294.

Christensen, M. E., and Fuxa, K. P. (1988). The nucleolar protein, B-36, contains a glycine and dimethylarginine-rich sequence conserved in several other nuclear RNA-binding proteins. *Biochem. Biophys. Res. Commun.* **155,** 1278–1283.

Clark, M. W., Yip, M. L. R., Campbell, J., and Abelson, J. (1990). SSB-1 of the yeast *Saccharomyces cerevisiae* is a nucleolar-specific, silver-binding protein that is associated with the snR10 and snR11 small nuclear RNAs. *J. Cell Biol.* **11,** 1741–1751.

Cooper, D., Banthorpe, D. D., and Wilkie, D. (1967). Modified ribosomes conferring resistance to cycloheximide in mutants of *Saccharomyces cerevisiae. J. Mol. Biol.* **26,** 347–350.

Cox, R. A., and Greenwell, P. (1980). Protein synthesis by hybrid ribosomes reconstituted from rabbit reticulocyte ribosomal core-particles and amphibian or fungal split-proteins. *Biochem. J.* **186,** 861.

Dabbs, E. R. (1986). Mutant studies on the prokaryotic ribosome. *In* "Structure, Function, and Genetics of Ribosomes" (B. Hardesty and G. Kramer, eds.), pp. 733–748. Springer-Verlag, New York.

Dabeva, M. D., and Warner, J. R. (1987). The yeast ribosomal protein L32 and its gene. *J. Biol. Chem.* **262,** 16055–16059.

Dabeva, M. D., Post-Beittenmiller, M. A., and Warner, J. R. (1986). Autogenous regulation of splicing of the transcript of a yeast ribosomal protein gene. *Proc. Natl. Acad. Sci. U.S.A.* **83,** 5854–5857.

Della-Seta, F., Ciafré, S.-A., Marck, C., Santoro, B., Presutti, C., Sentenac, A., and Bozzoni, I. (1990). The ABF1 factor is the transcriptional activator of the L2 ribosomal protein genes in Saccharomyces cerevisiae. *Mol. Cell. Biol.* **10,** 2437–2441.

Diffley, J. F. X., and Stillman, B. (1988). Purification of a yeast protein that binds to origins of DNA replication and a transcriptional silencer. *Proc. Natl. Acad. Sci. U.S.A.* **85,** 2120–2124.

Dölz, H., Vázquez, D., and Jiménez, A. (1982). Quantitation of the specific interaction of [14a-^{3}H]cryptopleurine with 80S and 40S ribosomal species from the yeast *Saccharomyces cerevisiae. Biochemistry* **21,** 3181–3187.

Donovan, D. M., and Pearson, N. J. (1986). Transcriptional regulation of ribosomal proteins during a nutritional upshift in *Saccharomyces cerevisiae. Mol. Cell. Biol.* **6,** 2429–2435.

Donovan, D. M., Remington, M. P., Stewart, D. A., Crouse, J. C., Miles, D. J., and Pearson, N. J. (1990). Functional analysis of a duplicated linked pair of ribosomal protein genes in *Saccharomyces cerevisiae. Mol. Cell. Biol.* **10,** 6097–6100.

Dorsman, J. C., Van Heeswijk, W. C., and Grivell, L. A. (1988). Identification of two factors that bind to the upstream sequences of a number of nuclear genes coding for mitochondrial proteins and to genetic elements important for cell division in yeast. *Nucleic Acids Res.* **16,** 7287–7301.

Dorsman, J. C., Doorenbosch, M. M., Maurer, C. T. C., de Winde, J. H., Mager, W. H., Planta, R. J., and Grivell, L. A. (1989). An ARS/silencer binding factor also activates two ribosomal protein genes in yeast. *Nucleic Acids Res.* **17,** 4917–4923.

Dresser, M. E., and Giroux, C. N. (1988). Meiotic chromosome behavior in spread preparations of yeast. *J. Cell Biol.* **106,** 567–573.

El-Baradi, T. T., Raué, H. A., de Regt, V. C. H., and Planta, R. J. (1984). Stepwise dissociation of yeast 60S ribosomal subunits by LiCl and identification of L25 as a primary 26S rRNA binding protein. *Eur. J. Biochem.* **144,** 393–400.

El-Baradi, T. T., Raué, H. A., de Regt, V. C. H., Verbree, E. C., and Planta, R. J. (1985). Yeast ribosomal protein L25 binds to an evolutionary conserved site on yeast 26S and *E. coli* 23S rRNA *EMBO J.* **4,** 2101–2107.

El-Baradi, T. T., van der Sande, A. F. M., Mager, W. H., Raué, H. A., and Planta, R. J. (1986). The cellular level of yeast ribosomal protein L25 is controlled principally by rapid degradation of excess protein. *Curr. Genet.* **10,**733–739.

El-Baradi, T. T., de Regt, V. C., Einerhand, S. W., Teixido, J., Planta, R. J., Ballesta, J. P. G., and Raué, H. A. (1987). Ribosomal proteins EL11 from *Escherichia coli* and L15 from *Saccharomyces cerevisiae* bind to the same site in both yeast 26S and mouse 28S rRNA. *J. Mol. Biol.* **195,** 909–917.

Ellis, R. J. (1987). Proteins as molecular chaperones. *Nature (London)* **328,** 378–379.

Fabian, G. F., and Hopper, A. K. (1987). RRP1, a *Saccharomyces cerevisiae* gene affecting rRNA processing and production of mature ribosomal subunits. *J. Bacteriol.* **169,** 1571–1578.

Fabian, G. F., Hess, S. M., and Hopper, A. K. (1990). *srd1,* a *Saccharomyces cerevisiae* suppressor of the temperature-sensitive pre-rRNA processing defect of rrp1-1. *Genetics* **124,** 497–504.

Falco, S. C., and Botstein, D. (1983). A rapid chromsome-mapping method for cloned fragments of yeast DNA. *Genetics* **105,** 857–872.

Finley, D., Bartell, B., and Varshavsky, A. (1989). The tails of ubiquitin precursors are ribosomal proteins whose fusions to ubiquitin facilities ribosome biogenesis. *Nature (London)* **338,** 394–401.

Fisher, E., Beer-Romero, P., Brown, L., Ridley, A., McNeil, J., Lawrence, J., Willard, H., Bieber, F., and Page, D. (1990). Homologous ribosomal protein genes on the human X and Y chromosomes: escape from X inactivation and possible implications for Turner syndrome. *Cell* **63,** 1205–1218.

Fleming, G., Belhumeur, P., Skup, D., and Fried, H. M. (1989). Functional substitution of mouse ribosomal protein L27' for yeast ribosomal protein L29 in yeast ribosomes. *Proc. Natl. Acad. Sci. U.S.A.* **86,** 217–221.

Fried, H. M., and Warner, J. R. (1981). Cloning of yeast gene for trichodermin resistance and ribosomal protein L3. *Proc. Natl. Acad. Sci. U.S.A.* **78,** 238–242.

Fried, H. M., and Warner, J. R. (1982). Molecular cloning and analysis of yeast gene for cycloheximide resistance and ribosomal protein L29. *Nucleic Acids Res.* **10,** 3133–3148.

Fried, H. M., Pearson, N. J., Kim, C. H., and Warner, J. R. (1981). The genes for fifteen ribosomal proteins of *Saccharomyces cerevisiae.* *J. Biol. Chem.* **265,** 10176–10183.

Fried, H. M., Nam, H. G., Loechel, S., and Teem, J. (1985). Characterization of yeast strains with conditionally expressed variants of ribosomal protein genes *tcm1* and *cyh2. Mol. Cell. Biol.* **5,** 99–108.

Gerbi, S. A., Savino, R., Stebbins-Boaz, B., Jeppesen, C., and Rivera-León, R. (1990). A role for U3 small nuclear ribonucleoprotein in the nucleolus? *In* "The Ribosome—Structure, Function, and Evolution" (W. Hill, A. Dahlberg, R. Garrett, P. Moore, D., Schlessinger, and J. R. Warner, eds.), pp. 452–469. Am. Soc. Microbiol., Washington, D.C.

108   JOHN L. WOOLFORD, Jr.

Gorenstein, C., and Warner, J. R. (1976). Coordinate regulation of the synthesis of
eukaryotic ribosomal proteins. *Proc. Natl. Acad. Sci. U.S.A.* **73**, 1547–1551.
Gorenstein, C., and Warner, J. R. (1977). Synthesis and turnover of ribosomal proteins in
the absence of 60S subunit assembly in *Saccharomyces cerevisiae. Mol. Gen. Genet.*
157, 327–332.
Grant, P., Sánchez, L., and Jiménez, A. (1974). Cryptopleurine resistance: Genetic locus
for a 40S ribosomal component in *Saccharomyces cerevisiae. J. Bacteriol.* **120**, 1308–
1314.
Grant, P., Schindler, D., and Davies, J. E. (1976). Mapping of trichodermin resistance in
Saccharomyces cerevisiae: A genetic locus for a component of the 60S ribosomal
subunit. *Genetics* **83**, 667–673.
Gritz, L., Abovich, N., Teem, J. L., and Rosbash, M. (1985). Posttranscriptional regulation
and assembly into ribosomes of a *Saccharomyces cerevisiae* ribosomal protein–β ga-
lactosidase fusion. *Mol. Cell. Biol.* **5**, 3436–3442.
Gritz, L., Mitlin, J. A., Cannon, M., Littlewood, B., Carter, C. J., and Davies, J. E. (1982).
Ribosome structure, maturation of ribosomal RNA and drug sensitivity in tem-
perature-sensitive mutants of *Saccharomyces cerevisiae. Mol. Gen. Genet.***188**, 384–
391.
Guddat, U., Bakken, A. H., and Pieler, T. (1990). Protein-mediated nuclear export of
RNA: rRNA containing small RNPs in *Xenopus* oocytes. *Cell* **60**, 619–628.
Gunderson, J. H., Sogin, M. L., Woller, G., Hollingdale, M., de la Cruz, V. F., Waters,
A. F., and McCutchan, T. F. (1987). Structurally distinct, stage-specific ribosomes
occur in *Plasmodium. Science* **238**, 933–937.
Gutell, R. R., Weiser, B., Woese, C. R., and Noller, H. F. (1985). Comparative anatomy of
16-S-like ribosomal RNA. *Prog. Nucleic Acid Res. Mol. Biol.* **32**, 155–216.
Guthrie, C., Nashimoto, H., and Nomura, M. (1969). Structure and function of *E. coli*
ribosomes VIII. Cold-sensitive mutants defective in ribosome assembly. *Proc. Natl.
Acad. Sci. U.S.A.* **63**, 384–391.
Hadjiolov, A. A. (1985). "The Nucleolus and Ribosome Biogenesis." Springer-Verlag, New
York.
Hamil, K. G., Nam, H. G., and Fried, H. M. (1988). Constitutive transcription of yeast
ribosomal protein gene *TCM1* is promoted by uncommon *cis*- and *trans*-acting ele-
ments. *Mol. Cell. Biol.* **8**, 4328–4341.
Hartwell, L., McLaughlin, C. S., and Warner, J. R. (1970). Identification of ten genes that
control ribosome formation in yeast. *Mol. Gen. Genet.* **109**, 42–56.
Held, W. A., Mizushima, S., and Nomura, M. (1973). Reconstitution of *E. coli* 30S ribo-
somal subunits from purified molecular components. *J. Biol. Chem.* **248**, 5720–5730.
Hemingsen, S. M., Woolford, C. A., van der Vies, S. M., Tilly, K., Dennis, D., Georgo-
poulos, C., Hendrix, R., and Ellis, R. J. (1988). Homologous plant and bacterial
proteins chaperone oligomeric protein assembly. *Nature (London)* **333**, 330–334.
Henriquez, R., Blobel, G., and Aris, J. P. (1990). Isolation and sequencing of *NOP1.
J. Biol. Chem.* **265**, 2209–2215.
Henry, Y. A. L., Chambers, A., Tsang, J. S. H., Kingsman, A. J., and Kingsman, S. M.
(1990). Characterization of the DNA binding domain of the yeast RAP1 protein.
Nucleic Acids Res. **18**, 2617–2623.
Herrera, A. H., and Olson, M. O. J. (1986). Association of protein C23 with rapidly labeled
nucleolar RNA. *Biochemistry* **25**, 6258–6264.
Herruer, M. H., Mager, W. H., Woudt, L. P., Nieuwint, R. T., Wassenaar, G. M.,
Groeneveld, P., and Planta, R. J. (1987). Transcriptional control of yeast ribosomal
protein synthesis during the carbon-source upshift. *Nucleic Acids Res.* **15**, 10122–
10144.

Herruer, M. H., Mager, W. H., Raué, H. A., Vreken, P., Wilms, E., and Planta, R. J. (1988). Mild temperature shock affects transcription of yeast ribosomal protein genes as well as the stability of their mRNAs. *Nucleic Acids Res.* **16**, 7917–7929.

Herruer, M. H., Mager, W. H., Doorenbosch, T. M., Wessels, P. L. M., Wassenaar, T. M., and Planta, R. J. (1989). The extended promoter of the gene encoding ribosomal protein S33 in yeast consists of multiple protein binding elements. *Nucleic Acids Res.* **17**, 7427–7439.

Hill, W. E., Dahlberg, A., Garrett, R., Moore, P. B., Schlessinger, D., and Warner, J. R. (1990). "The Ribosome—Structure, Function, and Evolution." Am. Soc. Microbiol., Washington, D.C.

Himmelfarb, H. J. Vassarotti, A., and Friesen, J. D. (1984). Molecular cloning and biosynthetic regulation of the *cry1* gene of *Saccharomyces cerevisiae*. *Mol. Gen. Genet.* **195**, 500–506.

Hinnebusch, A. G., and Liebman, S. W. (1991). Protein synthesis and translational control in *Saccharomyces cerevisiae*. *In* "The Molecular Biology of the Yeast Saccharomyces" (E. W. Jones, J. R. Pringle, and J. R. Broach, eds.). Cold Spring Harbor Lab., Cold Spring Harbor, New York. In press.

Hofmann, J. F.-X., Laroche, T., Brand, A. H., and Gasser, S. M. (1989). *RAP1* factor is necessary for DNA loop formation *in vitro* at the silent mating type locus *HML*. *Cell* **57**, 725–737.

Huet, J., and Sentenac, A. (1987). TUF, the yeast DNA-binding factor specific for UAS$_{rpg}$ upstream activating sequences: Identification of the protein and its DNA-binding domain. *Proc. Natl. Acad. Sci. U.S.A.* **84**, 3648–3652.

Huet, J., Cottrelle, P., Cool, M., Vignais, M. L., Thiele, D., Marck, C., Buhler, J. M., Sentenac, A., and Fromageot, P. (1985). A general upstream binding factor for genes of the yeast translational apparatus. *EMBO J.* **4**, 3539–3547.

Hughes, J. M. X., Konings, D. A. M., and Cesareni, G. (1987). The yeast homologue of U3 snRNA. *EMBO J.* **6**, 2145–2155.

Hurt, E. C., McDowall, A., and Schimmang, T. (1988). Nucleolar and nuclear envelope proteins of the yeast *Saccharomyces cerevisiae*. *Eur. J. Cell Biol.* **46**, 554–563.

Itoh, T., and Wittman-Liebold, B. (1978). The primary structure of protein L44 from the large subunit of yeast ribosomes. *FEBS Lett.* **96**, 399–402.

Itoh, T., Otaka, E., and Matsui, K. A. (1985). Primary structures of ribosomal protein YS25 from *Saccharomyces cerevisiae* and its counterparts from *Schizosaccharomyces pombe* and rat liver. *Biochemistry* **24**, 7418–7423.

Jarmolowski, A., Zagorski, J., Li, H. V., and Fournier, M. J. (1990). Identification of essential elements in U14 RNA of *Saccharomyces cerevisiae*. *EMBO J.* **9**, 4503–4510.

Jiménez, A., Sánchez, L., and Vázquez, D. (1975). Simultaneous ribosomal resistance to trichodermin and anisomycin in *Saccharomyces cerevisiae* mutants. *Biochim. Biophys. Acta* **383**, 427–434.

Johnson, S. P., and Warner, J. R. (1987). Phosphorylation of the *Saccharomyces cerevisiae* equivalent of ribosomal protein S6 has no detectable effect on growth. *Mol. Cell. Biol.* **7**, 1338–1345.

Jong, A. Y., Aebersold, R., and Campbell, J. L. (1985). Multiple species of single-stranded nucleic acid-binding proteins in *Saccharomyces cerevisiae*. *J. Biol. Chem.* **260**, 16367–16374.

Jong, A. Y., Clark, M. W., Gilbert, M., Oehm, A., and Campbell, J. L. (1987). *Saccharomyces cerevisiae* SSB1 protein and its relationship to nucleolar RNA-binding proteins. *Mol. Cell. Biol.* **7**, 2947–2955.

Juan-Vidales, F., Sanchez-Madrid, F., Saenz-Robles, M. T., and Ballesta, J. P. G. (1983). Purification and characterization of two ribosomal proteins of *Saccharomyces cere-*

visiae. Homologies with proteins from eukaryotic species and with bacterial protein ECL11. *Eur. J. Biochem.* **136,** 275–281.

Käufer, N. F., Fried, H. M., Schwindinger, W. F., Jasin, M., and Warner, J. R. (1983). Cycloheximide resistance in yeast: The gene and its protein. *Nucleic Acids Res.* **11,** 3123–3135.

Kaltschmidt, E., and Wittman, H. G. (1970). Ribosomal proteins. VII. Two-dimensional polyacrylamide gel electrophoresis for fingerprinting of ribosomal proteins. *Anal. Biochem.* **36,** 401–412.

Kamp, R., and Wittman-Liebold, B. (1980). Primary structure of protein S11 from *Escherichia coli* ribosomes. *FEBS Lett.* **121,** 117–122.

Karpen, G. H., Schaefer, J. E., and Laird, C. D. (1988). A *Drosophila* rRNA gene located in euchromatin is active in transcription and nucleolus formation. *Genes Dev.* **2,** 1745–1763.

Kass, S., Tyc, K., Steitz, J. A., and Sollner-Webb, B. (1990). The U3 small nucleolar ribonucleoprotein functions in the first step of preribosomal RNA processing. *Cell* **60,** 897–908.

Kief, D. R., and Warner, J. R. (1981). Coordinate control of synthesis of ribosomal ribonucleic acid and ribosomal proteins during nutritional shift-up in *Sacchraomyces cerevisiae. Mol. Cell. Biol.* **1,** 1007–1015.

Kim, C. H., and Warner, J. R. (1983a). The mRNA for ribosomal proteins in yeast. *J. Mol. Biol.* **165,** 79–89.

Kim, C. H., and Warner, J. R. (1983b). Mild temperature shock alters the transcription of a discrete class of *Saccharomyces cerevisiae* genes. *Mol. Cell. Biol.* **3,** 457–465.

Kimmerly, W., Buchman, A., Kornberg, R., and Rine, J. (1988). Roles of two DNA-binding factors in replication, segregation, and transcriptional repression mediated by a yeast silencer. *EMBO J.* **7,** 2241–2253.

Kraakman, L. S., Mager, W. H., Maurer, K. T. C., Nieuwint, R. T. M., and Planta, R. J. (1989). The divergently transcribed genes encoding yeast ribosomal proteins L46 and S24 are activated by shared RPG-boxes. *Nucleic Acids Res.* **17,** 9693–9705.

Kraig, E., Haber, J. E., and Rosbash, M. (1982). Sporulation and *rna2* lower ribosomal protein mRNA levels by different mechanisms in *Saccharomyces cerevisiae. Mol. Cell. Biol.* **2,** 1199–1204.

Kruiswijk, T., Planta, R. J., and Krop, J. M. (1978). The course of assembly of ribosomal subunits in yeast. *Biochim. Biophys. Acta* **517,** 378–389.

Kruse, C., Johnson, S. P., and Warner, J. R. (1985). Phosphorylation of the yeast equivalent of ribosomal protein S6 is not essential for growth. *Proc. Natl. Acad. Sci. U.S.A.* **82,** 7515–7519.

Lapeyre, B., Bourbon, H., and Amalric, F. (1987). Nucleolin, the major nucleolar protein of growing eukaryotic cells: An unusual protein structure revealed by the nucleotide sequence. *Proc. Natl. Acad. Sci. U.S.A.* **84,** 1472–1476.

Lapeyre, B., Mariottini, P., Mathieu, C., Ferrer, P., Amaldi, F., Amalric, F., and Cazergues-Ferrer, M. (1990). Molecular cloning of *Xenopus* fibrillarin, a conserved U3 small nucleolar ribonucleoprotein recognized by antisera from humans with autoimmune disease. *Mol. Cell. Biol.* **10,** 430–434.

Larkin, J. C., and Woolford, J. L., Jr. (1983). Molecular cloning and analysis of the *CRY1* gene: A yeast ribosomal protein gene. *Nucleic Acids Res.* **11,** 403–420.

Larkin, J. C., Thompson, J. R., and Woolford, J. L., Jr. (1987). Structure and expression of the *Saccharomyces cerevisiae CRY1* gene: A highly conserved ribosomal protein gene. *Mol. Cell. Biol.* **7,** 1764–1775.

Lee, J. C. (1990). Ribosomes from *Saccharomyces cerevisiae. In* "The Yeasts" (A. H. Rose and R. Harrison, eds.), pp. 489–539. Academic Press, New York.

Lee, J. C., and Anderson, A. (1986). Partial reassembly of yeast 60S ribosomal subunits *in vitro* following controlled disassociation under nondenaturing conditions. *Arch. Biochem. Biophys.* **245**, 248–253.

Lee, J. C., Anderson, R., Yeh, Y. C., and Horowitz, P. (1985). Extraction of proteins from *Saccharomyces cerevisiae* ribosomes under nondenaturing conditions. *Arch. Biochem. Biophys.* **237**, 292–299.

Leer, R. J., van Raamsdonk-Duin, M. M., Molenaar, C. M. T., Cohen, L. H., Mager, W. H., and Planta, R. J. (1982). The structure of the gene coding for the phosphorylated ribosomal protein S10 in yeast. *Nucleic Acids Res.* **10**, 5869–5878.

Leer, R. J., van Raamsdonk-Duin, M. M., Schoppink, P. J., Cornelissen, M. T, Cohen, L. H., Mager, W. H., and Planta, R. J. (1983). Yeast ribosomal protein S33 is encoded by an unsplit gene. *Nucleic Acids Res.* **11**, 7759–7768.

Leer, R. J., van Raamsdonk-Duin, M. M., Hagendoorn, M. J., Mager, W. H., and Planta, R. J. (1984). Structural comparison of yeast ribosomal protein genes. *Nucleic Acids Res.* **12**, 6685–6700.

Leer, R. J., van Raamsdonk-Duin, M. M., Kraakman, P., Mager, W. H., and Planta, R. J. (1985b). The genes for yeast ribosomal proteins S24 and L46 are adjacent and divergently transcribed. *Nucleic Acids Res.* **13**, 701–709.

Leer, R. J., van Raamsdonk-Duin, M. M., Mager, W. H., and Planta, R. J. (1985a). Conserved sequences upstream of yeast ribosomal protein genes. *Curr. Genet.* **9**, 273–277.

Leer, R. J., van Raamsdonk-Duin, M. M., Molenaar, C. M., Witsenboer, H. M., Mager, W. H., and Planta, R. J. (1985c). Yeast contains two functional genes coding for ribosomal protein S10. *Nucleic Acids Res.* **13**, 5027–5037.

Li, H. V., Zagorski, J., and Fournier, M. J. (1990). Depletion of U14 snRNA (snR128) disrupts production of 18S ribosomal RNA in *Saccharomyces cerevisiae. Mol. Cell. Biol.* **10**, 1145–1152.

Liebman, S. W., and Cavenagh, M. M. (1980). An antisuppressor that acts on omnipotent suppressors in yeast. *Genetics* **95**, 49–61.

Lindahl, L., Archer, R., and Zengel, J. M. (1983). Transcription of the S10 ribosomal protein operon is regulated by an attenuator in the leader. *Cell* **33**, 241–248.

Lindquist, S. (1981). Regulation of protein synthesis during heat shock. *Nature (London)* **293**, 311.

Lischwe, M. A., Ochs, R. L., Reddy, R., Cook, R. G., Yeoman, L. C., Tan, E. M., Reichlin, M., and Busch, H. (1985). Purification and partial characterization of a nucleolar scleroderma antigen (M_r = 34,000; pI, 8.5) rich in N^G,N^G-dimethylarginine. *J. Biol. Chem.* **260**, 14304–14310.

Longtime, M. S., Wilson, N. M., Petracek, M. E., and Berman, J. (1989). A yeast telomere binding activity binds to two related telomere sequence motifs and is indistinguishable from RAP1. *Curr. Genet.* **16**, 225–239.

Lucioli, A., Presutti, C., Ciafre, S., Caffarelli, E., Fragapane, P., and Bozzoni, I. (1988). Gene dosage alteration of L2 ribosomal protein genes in *Saccharomyces cerevisiae:* Effects on ribosome synthesis. *Mol. Cell. Biol.* **8**, 4792–4798.

Lustig, A. J., Kurtz, S., and Shore, D. (1990). Involvement of the silencer and UAS binding protein RAP1 in regulation of telomere length. *Science* **250**, 549–553.

Madjar, J.-J., Frahm, M., McGill, S., and Roufa, D. J. (1983). Ribosomal protein S14 is altered by two-step emetine resistance mutations in Chinese hamster cells. *Mol. Cell. Biol.* **3**, 190–197.

Maicas, E., Pluthero, F. G., and Friesen, J. D. (1988). The accumulation of three yeast ribosomal proteins under conditions of excess mRNA is determined primarily by fast protein decay. *Mol. Cell. Biol.* **8**, 169–175.

Maser, R. L., and Calvet, J. P. (1989). U3 small nuclear RNA can be psoralen-cross-linked *in vivo* to the 5' external transcribed spacer of pre-ribosomal RNA. *Proc. Natl. Acad. Sci. U.S.A.* **86**, 6523–6527.

McClintock, B. (1934). The relation of a particular chromosomal element to the development of the nucleoli in *Zea mays*. *Z. Zellforsch. Mikrosk. Anat.* **21**, 294–328.

Meeks-Wagner, D., and Hartwell, L. (1986). Normal stoichiometry of histone dimer sets is necessary for high fidelity of mitotic chromosome transmission. *Cell* **44**, 43–52.

Mets, L. J., nd Bogorad, L. (1974). Two-dimensional polyacrylamide gel electrophoresis: an improved method for ribosomal proteins. *Anal. Biochem.* **57**, 200–210.

Michel, S., Traut, R. R., and Lee, J. C. (1983). Yeast ribosomal proteins: Electrophoretic analysis in four two-dimensional gel systems—Correlation of nomenclatures. *Mol. Gen. Genet.* **191**, 251–256.

Miller, M. J., Xuong, N.-H., and Geiduschek, E. P. (1982). Quantitative analysis of the heat shock response of *Saccharomyces cerevisiae*. *J. Bacteriol.* **151**, 311–327.

Mitlin, J. A., and Cannon, N. (1984). Defective processing of ribosomal precursor RNA in *Saccharomyces cerevisiae*. *Biochem. J.* **220**, 461–467.

Mitra, G., and Warner, J. R. (1984). A yeast ribosomal protein gene whose intron is in the 5' leader. *J. Biol. Chem.* **259**, 9218–9224.

Mitsui, K., and Tsurugi, K. (1988a). cDNA and deduced amino acid sequence of 38 kDa-type acidic ribosomal protein AO from *Saccharomyces cerevisiae*. *Nucleic Acids Res.* **16**, 3573.

Mitsui, K., and Tsurugi, K. (1988b). cDNA and deduced amino acid sequence of acidic ribosomal protein A1 from *Saccharomyces cerevisiae*. *Nucleic Acids Res.* **16**,3574.

Mitsui, K., and Tsurugi, K. (1988c). cDNA and deduced amino aicd sequence of acidic ribosomal protein A2 from *Saccharomyces cerevisiae*. *Nucleic Acids Res.* **16**, 3575.

Mizushima, S., and Nomura, M. (1970). Assembly mapping of 30S ribosomal proteins from *E. coli*. *Nature (London)* **226**, 1214–1218.

Molenaar, C. M., Woudt, L. P., Jansen, A. E., Mager, W. H., Planta, R. J., Donovan, D. M., and Pearson, S. J. (1984). Structure and organization of two linked ribosomal protein genes in yeast. *Nucleic Acids Res.* **12**, 7345–7358.

Moreland, R. B., Nam, H. G., Hereford, L. M., and Fried, H. M. (1985). Identification of a nuclear localization signal of a yeast ribosomal protein. *Proc. Natl. Acad. Sci. U.S.A.* **82**, 6561–6565.

Moritz, M., Paulovich, A. G., Tsay, Y.-F., and Woolford, J. L., Jr. (1990). Depletion of yeast ribosomal proteins L16 or rp59 disrupts ribosome assembly. *J. Cell Biol.* **111**, 2261–2274.

Moritz, M., Pulaski, B., and Woolford, J. L., Jr. (1991). Submitted.

Morrow, B. E., Johnson, S. P., and Warner, J. R. (1989). Proteins that bind to the yeast rDNA enhancer. *J. Biol. Chem.* **264**, 9061–9068.

Morrow, B. E., Ju, Q., and Warner, J. R. (1990). Purification and characterization of the yeast rDNA binding protein REB1. *J. Biol. Chem.* **265**, 20778–20783.

Mullen, J. R., Kayne, P. S., Moerschell, R. P., Tsunasawa, S., Gribskov, M., Colavito-Shepanski, M., Grunstein, M., Sherman, F., and Sternglanz, R. (1989). Identification and characterization of genes and mutants for an N-terminal acetyltransferase from yeast. *EMBO J.* **8**, 2067–2075.

Musters, W., Venema, J., van der Linden, G., van Heerikhuizen, H., Klootwijk, J., and Planta, R. J. (1989). A system for the analysis of yeast ribosomal DNA mutations. *Mol. Cell. Biol.* **9**, 551–559.

Musters, W., Planta, R. J., van Heerikhuizen, H., and Raué, H. A. (1990). Functional analysis of the transcribed spacers of *Saccharomyces cerevisiae* ribosomal DNA: It takes a precursor to form a ribosome. *In* "The Ribosome—Structure, Function, and Evolution" (W. Hill, A. Dahlberg, R. Garrett, P. Moore, D. Schlessinger, and J. R. Warner, eds.), pp. 435–442. Am. Soc. Microbiol., Washington, D.C.

Nag, B., Tewari, D., Sommer, A., McKuskie, H., Glitz, D., and Traut, R. (1987). Probing ribosome function and the location of *Escherichia coli* ribosomal protein L5 with a monoclonal antibody. *J. Biol. Chem.* **262**, 9681–9687.

Nam, H. G., and Fried, H. M. (1986). Effects of progressive depletion of *TCM1* or *CYH2* mRNA on *Saccharomyces cerevisiae* ribosomal protein accumulation. *Mol. Cell. Biol.* **6**, 1535–1544.

Nashimoto, H., and Nomura, M. (1970). Structure and function of bacterial ribosomes, XI. Dependence of 50S ribosomal subunit assembly on simultaneous assembly of 30S subunits. *Proc. Natl. Acad. Sci. U.S.A.* **67**, 1440–1447.

Nazar, R. N., Yaguchi, M., Willick, G. E., Rollin, C. F., and Roy, C. (1979). The 5S RNA binding protein from yeast (*Saccharomyces cerevisiae*) ribosomes. *Eur. J. Biochem.* **102**, 573–582.

Newton, C. H., Shimmin, L. C., Yee, Y., and Dennis, P. P. (1990). A family of genes encode the multiple forms of the *Saccharomyces cerevisiae* ribosomal proteins equivalent to the *Escherichia coli* L12 protein and a single form of the L10-equivalent ribosomal protein. *J. Bacteriol.* **172**, 579–588.

Nieuwint, R. T. M., Molenaar, C. M. T., van Bommell, J. H., van Raamsdonk-Duin, M. M. C., Mager, W. H., and Planta, R. J. (1985). The gene for yeast ribosomal protein S31 contains an intron in the leader sequence. *Curr. Genet.* **10**, 1–5.

Nieuwint, R. T. M., Mager, W. H., Maurer, K. T. C., and Planta, R. J. (1989). Mutational analysis of the upstream activation site of yeast ribosomal protein genes. *Curr. Genet.* **15**, 247–251.

Nomura, M. (1990). History of ribosome research. *In* "The Ribosome—Structure, Function and Evolution" (W. E. Hill, A. Dahlberg, R. Garrett, P. B. Moore, D. Schlessinger, and J. R. Warner, eds.), pp. 3–55. Am. Soc. Microbiol., Washington, D.C.

Nomura, M., Gourse, R., and Baughman, G. (1984). Regulation of the synthesis of ribosomes and ribosomal components. *Annu. Rev. Biochem.* **53**, 75–117.

Olson, M. D. J., and Thompson, B. A. (1983). Distribution of proteins among chromatin components of nucleoli. *Biochemistry* **22**, 3187–3193.

Olson, M. O. J., Rivers, Z. M., Thompson, B. A., Kas, W.-Y., and Case, S. T. (1983). Interaction of nucleolar phosphoprotein C23 with cloned segments of rat ribosomal deoxyribonucleic acid. *Biochemistry* **22**, 3345–3351.

Orrick, L. R., Olson, M. O. J., and Busch, H. (1973). Comparison of nucleolar proteins of normal rat liver and Novikoff hepatoma ascites cells by two-dimensional polyacrylamide gel electrophoresis. *Proc. Natl. Acad. Sci. U.S.A.* **70**, 1316–1320.

Otaka, E., and Osawa, S. (1981). Yeast ribosomal proteins. V. Correlation of several nomenclatures and proposal of a standard nomenclature. *Mol. Gen. Genet.* **181**, 176–182.

Otaka, E., Higo, K., and Osawa, S. (1982). Isolation of seventeen proteins and amino-terminal amino acid sequences of eight proteins from cytoplasmic ribosomes of yeast. *Biochemistry* **21**, 4545–4550.

Otaka, E., Higo, K., and Itoh, T. (1984). Yeast ribosomal proteins. VIII. Isolation of two proteins and sequence characterization of twenty-four proteins from cytoplasmic ribosomes. *Mol. Gen. Genet.* **195**, 544–546.

Ozkaynak, E., Finley, D., Solomon, M. J., and Varshavsky, A. (1987). The yeast ubiquitin genes: A family of natural gene fusions. *EMBO J.* **6**, 1429–1439.

Papciak, S. N., and Pearson, N. J. (1987). Genetic mapping of two pairs of linked ribosomal protein genes in *Saccharomyces cerevisiae*. *Curr. Genet.* **11**, 445–450.

Parker, K. A., and Steitz, J. A. (1987). Structural analyses of the human U3 ribonucleoprotein particle reveal a conserved sequence available for base pairing with pre-rRNA. *Mol. Cell. Biol.* **7**, 2899–2913.

Parker, R., Simmons, T., Shuster, E. O., Silciano, P. C., and Guthrie, C. (1988). Genetic analysis of small nuclear RNAs in *Saccharomyces cerevisiae:* Viable sextuple mutant. *Mol. Cell. Biol.* **8**, 3150–3159.

Partaledis, J. A., and Mason, T. L. (1988). Structure and regulation of a nuclear gene of *Saccharomyces cerevisiae* that specifics MRP13, a protein of the small subunit of the mitochondrial ribosome. *Mol. Cell. Biol.* **8**, 3647–3660.

Paulovich, A., Larkin, J., Thompson, J., and Woolford, J. L., Jr. (1991). Submitted.

Pearson, N. J., and Haber, J. E. (1980). Changes in regulation of ribosomal protein synthesis during vegetative growth and sporulation of *Saccharomyces cerevisiae*. *J. Bacteriol.* **143**, 1411–1419.

Pearson, N. J., Fried, H. M., and Warner, J. R. (1982). Yeast use translational control to compensate for extra copies of a ribosomal protein gene. *Cell* **29**, 347–355.

Petes, T. D., and Botstein, D. (1977). Simple Mendelian inheritance of the reiterated ribosomal DNA of yeast. *Proc. Natl. Acad. Sci. U.S.A.* **74**, 5091–5095.

Phillipsen, P., Thomas, M., Kramer, R. A., and Davis, R. W. (1978). Unique arrangement of coding sequences for 5S, 5.8S, 18S, and 25S ribosomal RNA in *Saccharomyces cerevisiae* as determined by R-loop and hybridization analysis. *J. Mol. Biol.* **123**, 387–404.

Picard, B., and Wegnez, M. (1979). Isolation of a 7S particle from *Xenopus laevis* oocytes: a 5S RNA-protein complex. *Proc. Natl. Acad. Sci. U.S.A.* **76**, 241–245.

Picard, B., le Maire, M., Wegnez, M., and Denis, H. (1980). Biochemical research on oogenesis. *Eur. J. Biochem.* **109**, 359–368.

Planta, R. J., and Raué, H. A. (1988). Control of ribosome biogenesis in yeast. *Trends Genet.* **4**, 64–68.

Prestayko, A. W., Klomp, G. R., Schmoll, A. I., and Busch, H. (1974). Comparison of proteins of ribosomal subunits and nucleolar preribosomal particles from Novikoff hepatoma ascites cells by two-dimensional polyacrylamide gel electrophoresis. *Biochemistry* **13**, 1945–1951.

Presutti, C., Lucioli, A. and Bozzoni, I. (1988). Ribosomal protein L2 in *Saccharomyces cerevisiae* is homologous to ribosomal protein L1 in *Xenopus laevis*. *J. Biol. Chem.* **263**, 6188–6192.

Pucciarelli, M. G., Remacha, M., Vilella, M., and Ballesta, J. P. G. (1990). The 26S rRNA binding ribosomal protein equivalent to bacterial protein L11 is encoded by unspliced duplicated genes in *Saccharomyces cerevisiae*. *Nucleic Acids Res.* **18**, 4409–4416.

Reddy, R., and Busch, H. (1988). Small nuclear RNAs: RNA sequences, structure, and modifications. *In* "Structure and Function of Major and Minor Small Nuclear Ribonucleoprotein Particles" (M. L. Birnstiel, ed.), pp. 1–37. Springer-Verlag, Berlin.

Redman, K. L., and Rechsteiner, M. (1989). The long ubiquitin extension is ribosomal protein S27a. *Nature (London)* **338**, 438–440.

Reidel, N., Wise, J. A., Swerdlow, H., Mak, A., and Guthrie, C. (1986). Small nuclear RNAs from *Saccharomyces cerevisiae:* Unexpected diversity in abundance, size, and molecular complexity. *Proc. Natl. Acad. Sci. U.S.A.* **83**, 8097–8101.

Remacha, M., Saenz-Robles, M. T., Vilella, M. D., and Ballesta, J. P. G. (1988). Independent genes coding for three acidic proteins of the large ribosomal subunit from *Saccharomyces cerevisiae*. *J. Biol. Chem.* **263**, 9094–9101.

Remacha, M., Santos, C., and Ballesta, J. P. G. (1990a). Disruption of single-copy genes encoding acidic ribosomal proteins in *Saccharomyces cerevisiae*. *Mol. Cell. Biol.* **10**, 2182–2190.

Remacha, M., Ramirez, L., Marin, I., and Ballesta, J. P. G. (1990b). Chromosome location of a family of genes encoding different acidic ribosomal proteins in *Saccharomyces cerevisiae*. *Curr. Genet.* **17**, 535–536.

Rhode, P. R., Sweder, K. S., Oegema, K. F., and Campbell, J. L. (1989). The gene encoding ARS-binding factor I is essential for the viability of yeast. *Genes Dev.* **3**, 1926–1939.

Rosbash, M., Harris, P. K. W., Woolford, J. L., Jr., and Teem, J. L. (1981). The effect of temperature sensitive *RNA* mutants on the transcription products from cloned ribosomal protein genes of yeast. *Cell* **24**, 679–686.

Rose, K. M., Szopa, J., Han, F. S., Cheng, Y. C., Richter, A., and Scheer, U. (1988). Association of DNA topoisomerase I and RNA polymerase I: a possible role for topoisomerase I in ribosomal gene transcription. *Chromosoma* **96**, 411–416.

Rosset, R., and Gorini, L. (1969). A ribosomal ambiguity mutation. *J. Mol. Biol.* **39**, 95–107.

Rotenberg, M. O., and Woolford, J. L., Jr. (1986). Tripartite upstream promoter element essential for expression of *Saccharomyces cerevisiae* ribosomal protein genes. *Mol. Cell. Biol.* **6**, 674–687.

Rotenberg, M. O., Moritz, M., and Woolford, J. L., Jr. (1988). Depletion of *Saccharomyces cerevisiae* ribosomal protein L16 causes a decrease in 60S ribosomal subunits and formation of half-mer polyribosomes. *Genes Dev.* **2**, 160–172.

Sachs, A. B., and Davis, R. W. (1989). The poly(A) binding protein is required for poly(A) shortening and the 60S ribosomal subunit-dependent translation initiation. *Cell* **58**, 857–867.

Sachs, A. B., and Davis, R. W. (1990). Translation initiation and ribosomal biogenesis: Involvement of a putative rRNA helicase and *RPL46*. *Science* **247**, 1077–1079.

Saffer, L., and Miller, O. L., Jr. (1986). Electron microscopic study of *Saccharomyces cerevisiae* rDNA chromatin replication. *Mol. Cell. Biol.* **6**, 1148–1157.

Sánchez-Madrid, F., Juan-Vidales, F., and Ballesta, J. P. G. (1981). Effect of phosphorylation on the affinity of acidic proteins from *Saccharomyces cerevisiae* for the ribosome. *Eur. J. Biochem.* **114**, 609–613.

Santangelo, G. M., and Tornow, J. (1990). Efficient transcription of the glycolytic gene *ADH1* and three translational component genes requires the *GRC1* product, which can act through TUF/GRF/RAP binding sites. *Mol. Cell. Biol.* **10**, 859–862.

Schaap, P. J., Molenaar, C. M. T., Mager, W. H., and Planta, R. J. (1984). The primary structure of a gene encoding yeast ribosomal protein L34. *Curr. Genet.* **9**, 47–52.

Scheer, U., and Benavente, R. (1990). Functional and dynamic aspects of the mammalian nucleolus. *BioEssays* **12**, 14–21.

Schimmang, T., Tollervey, D., Kern, H., Frank, R., and Hurt, E. C. (1989). A yeast nucleolar protein related to mammalian fibrillarin is associated with small nucleolar RNA and is essential for viability. *EMBO J.* **8**, 4015–4024.

Schindler, D., Grant, P., and Davies, J. (1974). Trichodermin resistance-mutation affecting eukaryotic ribosomes. *Nature (London)* **248**, 535–536.

Schmidt-Zachmann, M. S., and Franke, W. W. (1988). DNA cloning and amino acid sequence determination of a major constituent protein of mammalian nucleoli: correspondence of the nucleoplasmin-related protein NO38 to mammalian protein B23. *Chromosoma* **96**, 417–426.

Schmidt-Zachmann, M. S., Hügle, Dörr, B., and Franke, W. W. (1987). A constitutive nucleolar protein identified as a member of the nucleoplasmin family. *EMBO J.* **6**, 1881–1890.

Schultz, L. D., and Friesen, J. D. (1983). Nucleotide sequence of the *tcm1* gene (ribosomal protein L3) of *Saccharomyces cerevisiae*. *J. Bacteriol.* **155**, 8–14.

Schwindinger, W. F., and Warner, J. R. (1987). Transcriptional elements of the yeast ribosomal protein gene *CYH2*. *J. Biol. Chem.* **262**, 5690–5695.

Shore, D., and Nasmyth, K. (1987). Purification and cloning of a DNA-binding protein that binds to both silencer and activator elements. *Cell* **51**, 721–732.

Shore, D., Stillman, D. J., Brand, A. H., and Nasmyth, K. A. (1987). Identification of silencer binding proteins from yeast: Possible roles in *SIR* control and DNA replication. *EMBO J.* **6**, 461–467.

Shulman, R. W., Sripati, C. E., and Warner, J. R. (1976). Noncoordinated transcription in the absence of protein synthesis in yeast. *J. Biol. Chem.* **252**, 1344–1349.

Sillevis-Smitt, W. W., Vlak, J. M., Molenaar, I., and Tozijn, T. H. (1973). Nucleolar function of the dense crescent in the yeast nucleus. A biochemical and ultrastructural study. *Exp. Cell Res.* **80**, 313–321.

Skogerson, L., McLaughlin, C., and Wakatama, E. (1973). Modification of ribosomes in cryptopleurine-resistant mutants of yeast. *J. Bacteriol.* **116**, 818–822.

Smith, N., Matheson, A. T., Yaguchi, M., Willick, G. E., and Nazar, R. N. (1978). The 5S RNA protein complex from an extreme halophile, *Halobacterium cutirubrum*. *Eur. J. Biochem.* **89**, 501–509.

Sollner-Webb, B., and Tower, J. (1986). Transcription of cloned eukaryotic ribosomal RNA genes. *Annu. Rev. Biochem.* **55**, 801–830.

Sommerville, J. (1986). Nucleolar structure and ribosome biogenesis. *Trends Biochem. Sci.* **11**, 438–442.

Song, J. M., and Liebman, S. W. (1987). Allosuppressors that enhance the efficiency of omnipotent suppressors in *Saccharomyces cerevisiae*. *Genetics* **115**, 451–460.

Spector, D. L., Ochs, R. L., and Busch, H. (1984). Silver staining, immunofluorescence, and immunoelectron microscopic localization of nucleolar phosphoproteins B23 and C23. *Chromosoma* **90**, 139–148.

Steitz, J. A., Berg, C., Hendrick, J., LaBranche-Chabot, H., Metspalu, A., Rinke, J., and Yario, T. (1988). A 5S rRNA/L5 complex is a precursor to ribosome assembly in mammalian cells. *J. Cell Biol.* **106**, 545–556.

Stern, S., Powers, T., Changchien, L.-M., and Noller, H. F. (1989). RNA–protein interactions in 30S ribosomal subunits: Folding and function of 16S rRNA. *Science* **244**, 783–790.

Stocklein, W., and Piepersbeg, W. (1980). Altered ribosomal protein L29 in a cycloheximide resistant strain of *Saccharomyces cerevisiae*. *Curr. Genet.* **1**, 177–183.

Stöffler-Meilicke, M., and Stöffler, G. (1990). Topography of the ribosomal proteins from *Escherichia coli* within the intact subunits as determined by immunoelectron microscopy and protein–protein crosslinking. *In* "The Ribosome—Structure, Function, and Evolution" (W. Hill, A. Dahlberg, R. Garrett, P. Moore, D. Schlessinger, and J. R. Warner, eds.), pp. 123–159. Am. Soc. Microbiol., Washington, D.C.

Stroke, I. L., and Weiner, A. M. (1989). The 5' end of U3 snRNA can be crosslinked *in vivo* to the external transcribed spacer of rat ribosomal RNA precursors. *J. Mol. Biol.* **210**, 497–512.

Suzuki, K., and Otaka, E. (1988). Cloning and nucleotide sequence of the gene encoding yeast ribosomal protein YS25. *Nucleic Acids Res.* **16**, 6223.

Suzuki, K., Hashimoto, T., and Otaka, E. (1990). Yeast ribosomal proteins. XI. Molecular analysis of two genes encoding YL41, an extremely small and basic ribosomal protein, from *Saccharomyces cerevisiae*. *Curr. Genet.* **17**, 185–190.

Sweder, K. S., Rhode, P. R., and Campbell, J. L. (1988). Purification and characterization of proteins that bind to yeast ARSs. *J. Biol. Chem.* **263**, 17270–17277.

Tai, P.-C., Kessler, D. P., and Ingraham, J. (1969). Cold-sensitive mutations in *Salmonella typhimurium* which affect ribosome synthesis. *J. Bacteriol.* **97**, 1298–1304.

Teem, J. L., Abovich, N., Kaufer, N. F., Schwindinger, W. F., Warner, J. R., Levy, A., Woolford, J., Leer, R. J., van Raamsdonk-Duin, M. M. C., Mager, W. H., Planta, R. J., Schultz, L., Friesen, J. D., Fried, H., and Rosbash, M. (1984). A comparison of yeast ribosomal protein gene DNA sequences. *Nucleic Acids Res.* **12**, 8295–8312.

Tollervey, D. (1987). A yeast small nuclear RNA is required for normal processing of preribosomal RNA. *EMBO J.* **6**, 4169–4175.

Tollervey, D., Lehtonen, H., Carmo-Fonseca, M., and Hurt, E. C. (1991). The small nucleolar RNP protein NOP1 (fibrillarin) is required for pre-rRNA processing in yeast. *EMBO J.* **10**, 573–583.

Trapman, J., Retel, J., and Planta, R. J. (1975). Ribosomal precursor particles from yeast. *Exp. Cell Res.* **90**, 95–104.

Traut, R. R., Tewari, D. S., Sommer, A., Gavino, G. R., Olson, H. M., and Glitz, D. C. (1986). Protein topography of ribosomal functional domains: Effects of monoclonal antibodies to different epitopes in *Escherichia coli* protein L7/L12 on ribosome function and structure. *In* "Structure, Function, and Genetics of Ribosomes" (B. Hardesty and G. Kramer, eds.), pp. 286–308. Springer-Verlag, New York.

Tsay, Y.-F., and Woolford, J. L., Jr. (1991). In preparation.

Tsay, Y.-F., Thompson, J. R., Rotenberg, M. O., Larkin, J. C., and Woolford, J. L., Jr. (1988). Ribosomal protein synthesis is not regulated at the translational level in *Saccharomyces cerevisiae:* Balanced accumulation of ribosomal proteins L16 and rp59 is mediated by turnover of excess protein. *Genes Dev.* **2**, 664–676.

Tsay, Y.-F., Shankweiler, G., Lake, J., and Woolford, J. L., Jr. (1991a). In preparation.

Tsay, Y.-F., Deshmukh, M., Paulovich, A., and Woolford, J. L., Jr. (1991b). In preparation.

Tyc, K., and Steitz, J. A. (1989). U3, U8, and U13 comprise a new class of mammalian snRNPs localized in the cell nucleolus. *EMBO J.* **8**, 3113–3119.

Udem, S. A., and Warner, J. R. (1972). Ribosomal RNA synthesis in *Saccharomyces cerevisiae*. *J. Mol. Biol.* **65**, 227–242.

Udem, S. A., and Warner, J. R. (1973). The cytoplasmic maturation of a ribosomal precursor ribonucleic acid in yeast. *J. Biol. Chem.* **248**, 1412–1416.

Underwood, M. R., and Fried, H. M. (1990). Characterization of nuclear localizing sequences derived from yeast ribosomal protein L29. *EMBO J.* **9**, 91–100.

Ursic, D., and Davies, J. (1979). Cold-sensitive mutant of *Saccharomyces cerevisiae* defective in ribosome processing. *Mol. Gen. Genet.* **175**, 313–323.

Vázquez, D. (1979). Inhibitors of protein synthesis. *Mol. Biol. Biochem. Biophys.* **30**, 138–144.

Veinot-Drebot, L. M., Singer, R. A., and Johnston, G. C. (1988). Rapid initial cleavage of nascent pre-rRNA transcripts in yeast. *J. Mol. Biol.* **199**, 107–113.

Veldman, G. M., Klootwijk, J., van Heerikhuizen, H., and Planta, R. J. (1981). The nucleotide sequence of the intergenic region between the 5.8S and 26S rRNA genes of the yeast ribosomal RNA operon. Possible implications for the interaction between 5.8S and 26S rRNA and the presence of the primary transcript. *Nucleic Acids Res.* **9**, 4847–4862.

Vignais, M. L., Woudt, L. P., Wassenaar, G. M., Mager, W. H., Sentenac, A., and Planta, R. J. (1987). Specific binding of TUF factor to upstream activation sites of yeast ribosomal protein genes. *EMBO J.* **6**, 1451–1457.

Vioque, A., and Palacian, E. (1985). Partial reconstitution of 60S ribosomal subunits from yeast. *Mol. Cell. Biochem.* **66**, 55–60.

Wang, C. K., and Weil, P. A. (1989). Purification and characterization of *Saccharomyces cerevisiae* transcription factor IIIA. *J. Biol. Chem.* **264,** 1092–1099.

Warner, J. R. (1971). The assembly of ribosomes in yeast. *J. Biol. Chem.* **246,** 447–454.

Warner, J. R. (1989a). Synthesis of ribosomes in *Saccharomyces cerevisiae. Microbiol. Rev.* **53,** 256–271.

Warner, J. R. (1989b). A marriage of convenience or necessity? *Nature (London)* **338,** 379.

Warner, J. R. (1990). The nucleolus and ribosome formation. *Curr. Opinion Cell Biol.* **2,** 521–527.

Warner, J. R., and Gorenstein, C. (1978a). Yeast has a true stringent response. *Nature (London)* **275,** 338–339.

Warner, J. R., and Gorenstein, C. (1978b). The ribosomal proteins of *Saccharomyces cerevisiae. Methods Cell Biol.* **20,** 45–60.

Warner, J. R., Mitra, G., Schwindinger, W. F., Studeny, M., and Fried, H. M. (1985). *Saccharomyces cerevisiae* coordinates the accumulation of yeast ribosomal proteins by modulating mRNA splicing, translational initiation, and protein turnover. *Mol. Cell. Biol.* **5,** 1512–1521.

Wittekind, M., Kolb, J. M., Dodd, J., Yamagishi, M., Memet, S., Buhler, J.-M., and Nomura, M. (1990). Conditional expression of *RPA190,* the gene encoding the largest subunit of yeast RNA polymerase I: Effects of decreased rRNA synthesis on ribosomal protein synthesis. *Mol. Cell. Biol.* **10,** 2049–2059.

Woese, C. R., Gutell, R., Gupta, R., and Noller, H. F. (1983). Detailed analysis of the higher-order structure of 16S-like ribosomal ribonucleic acids. *Microbiol. Rev.* **47,** 621–669.

Wool, I. G., Endo, Y., Chan, Y.-L., and Glück, A. (1990). Structure, function, and evolution of mammalian ribosomes. *In* "The Ribosome—Structure, Function, and Evolution" (W. Hill, A. Dahlberg, R. Garrett, P. Moore, D. Schlessinger, and J. R. Warner, eds.) pp. 203–214. Am. Soc. Microbiol., Washington, D.C.

Woolford, J. L., Jr. (1989). Nuclear pre-mRNA splicing in yeast. *Yeast* **5,** 439–457.

Woolford, J. L., Jr. (1991). In preparation.

Woolford, J. L., Jr., and Warner, J. R. (1991). The ribosome and its synthesis. *In* "The Molecular and Cellular Biology of the Yeast *Saccharomyces:* Genome Dynamics, Protein Synthesis, and Energetics" (J. Broach, E. Jones, and J. Pringle, eds.). Cold Spring Harbor Laboratory, Cold Spring Harbor, NY. In press.

Woolford, J. L., Jr., Hereford, L. M., and Rosbash, M. (1979). Isolation of cloned DNA sequences containing ribosomal protein genes from *Saccharomyces cerevisiae. Cell* **18,** 1247–1259.

Woudt, L. P., Smit, A. B., Mager, W. H., and Planta, R. J. (1986). Conserved sequence elements upstream of the gene encoding yeast ribosomal protein L25 are involved in transcription activation. *EMBO J.* **5,** 1037–1040.

Woudt, L. P., Mager, W. H., Nieuwint, R. T. M., Wassenaar, G. M., van der Kuyl, A. C., Murre, J. J., Murre, M. F. M., Hoekman, M. F. M., Brockhoff, P. G. M., and Planta, R. J. (1987). Analysis of upstream activation sites of yeast ribosomal protein genes. *Nucleic Acids Res.* **15,** 6037–6048.

Yang, C. H., Lambie, E. J., Hardin, J., Craft, J., and Snyder, M. (1990). Higher order structure is present in the yeast nucleus: autoantibody probes demonstrate that the nucleolus lies opposite the spindle pole body. *Chromosoma* **98,** 123–128.

Zagorski, J., Tollervey, D., and Fournier, M. J. (1988). Characterization of an *SNR* gene locus in *Saccharomyces cerevisiae* that specifies both dispensable and essential small nuclear RNAs. *Mol. Cell. Biol.* **8,** 3282–3290.

EVOLUTIONARY GENETICS OF FISH

Dennis A. Powers

Hopkins Marine Station, Department of Biological Sciences, Stanford University, Pacific Grove, California 93950

ADVANCES IN GENETICS, Vol. 29

I. Introduction

Fish are the oldest and most diverse representatives of the vertebrates. They began to evolve around 540 million years before the present (540 MyBP). The first group that emerged was the "jawless" fishes of the class Agnatha, whose fossil remains first appeared in the late Cambrian period. The Agnatha included the ostracoderms, which were bony-skinned jawless fishes, a major group in the fossil record until the Devonian period (about 350 MyBP). Present-day members of the jawless fishes are represented by hagfish and lamprey species. A major evolutionary advance took place during the Ordovician period (435 MyBP), when the jawed fishes began to evolve. Fishes with jaws were not limited to filter feeding as were their ancestors. Rather, a vast array of prey became available and, as a result, this major evolutionary advance transformed the entire ecology of the oceans, lakes, and rivers. The evolution of jaws was followed by major structural changes in swimming appendages, including tails and fins. During the Silurian and Devonian periods (340–445 MyBP), three major groups of fishes began to evolve: the Chondrichthyes (cartilaginous fish), the Actinopterygii (spiny-finned fish), and the Sarcopterygii (fleshy-finned fish). These three groups gave rise to all the present-day fishes and other vertebrate taxa. One of the ancient jawed, armored fishes, Placodermi, was the ancestor of the Chondrichthyes that today are represented by the sharks, skates, and rays. Approximately 200–300 MyBP, ancestors of the modern-day sturgeon and gar pike began to evolve from the Actinopterygii, and during the early Cretaceous period (140 MyBP) the bony fish (Teleostei) emerged. The bony fish rapidly diverged and radiated into essentially every type of aquatic habitat. The Sarcopterygii were the ancestors of the Rhipidistians, which, in turn, were responsible for the evolution of present-day coelacanths, lungfish, and "higher" vertebrates, whose radiation began around 350 MyBP (Fig. 1).

Although the higher vertebrates have been very successful, today there are many more fish species than all the other vertebrates combined. Research on fish, therefore, provides a conceptual framework and evolutionary reference point for all other vertebrate studies. Fish have a fossil record that is relatively well characterized, and there are a

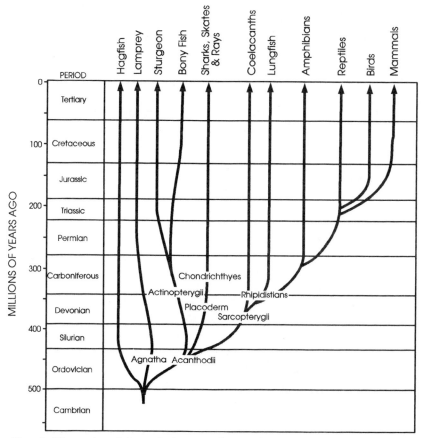

Fɪɢ. 1. Illustration of the evolutionary radiation of chordate groups during the past 600 million years.

number of "living fossils" that are particularly useful in comparative biochemical and physiological studies. Fish live in a wide variety of habitats that range from freshwater to saltwater, cold polar seas to warm tropical reefs, and shallow surface waters to the intense pressures of the ocean's abyss. Elucidating the evolutionary strategies and genetic mechanisms that fish use to adapt to these diverse environments is one of the most exciting challenges for modern evolutionary biologists.

Fish are also excellent experimental models for genetic and evolutionary studies. Many fish species are amenable to both laboratory and field experiments and are easily raised and bred under laboratory conditions. There is extensive animal husbandry information available that has been established during hundreds of years of practical experience by fish farmers, hobbyists, and aquaculturists. Many fish are much less expensive to buy and raise than their mammalian, avian, reptilian, or amphibian counterparts. They are generally the most fecund, some producing hundreds of eggs on a periodic basis, others producing thousands. These eggs are usually large, externally fertilized, and, because some are transparent, development can be easily followed. Historically, these advantages and the economic importance of some fish have made them favored models for genetic and developmental studies.

Fish are particularly useful for many kinds of genetic manipulations. There are several highly homozygous strains and general methods for obtaining new strains and mutants have been established. Inbred strains of medaka (*Oryzias latipes*), top minnows (*Poeciliopsis lucida*), and others have been produced by classical repetitive inbreeding. In addition, naturally occurring hermaphroditic (*Rivulus marmoratus*) and gynogenetically reproducing fish are available and some scientists have successfully produced homozygous diploid fish by experimental manipulation (see Powers, 1989, and references therein).

The purpose of this review is to provide an overview of the evolutionary genetics of fish and to demonstrate how studies on fish provide critical links in understanding the evolution of other vertebrate classes. In addition, using selected examples, I will point out where genetic studies on fish have required a reevaluation of evolutionary models that were previously based solely on data from higher vertebrates.

Although morphological and physiological genetic characters are important in the evolution of fish, they will not be addressed in this paper. Rather, I will focus on protein characters and the genes that encode them, including DNA sequences when they are available. I will also cover DNA techniques that are being used to study subtle genetic variation within and among individuals, populations, and species.

I will begin with the general methods used to detect genetic variation in fish systems and then will present the current fish genetic nomenclature for genes encoding proteins. Afterward, the evolution of higher order genomic structures will be covered, including genome size, karyotype, isochore structures, and linkage relationships. I will discuss gene duplication and multigene families and then provide some examples of fish genes that respond to environmental parameters. Other sections will cover genes expressed in the nervous, immune, and endocrine systems.

II. Detection of Genetic Variation in Fish

For over 100 years, evolutionary studies have utilized qualitative and quantitative morphological characters to differentiate between taxa. During the past several decades, researchers have added cytological techniques to their repertoire of systematic tools. More recently, the use of protein and DNA techniques has allowed the discrimination between variants of specific genes or gene products on the basis of protein and DNA sequence similarities and differences. This approach is leading to an entirely new understanding of evolutionary processes that impact fish populations and species.

A. Protein-Coding Loci

During the better part of three decades, electrophoresis coupled with histochemical staining for the identification of protein electromorphs has uncovered a wealth of genetic variation at the molecular level, both among species and within species. Variations in electrophoretic mobility of homologous proteins reflect their amino acid sequence differences, which, in turn, usually indicate differences in nucleotide sequences of the genes that encode them. Such electrophoretic variations are reflected as either multilocus isozymes or allelic isozymes. Multilocus isozymes usually indicate one or more ancient gene duplications followed by evolutionary divergence of the duplicated locus. These multilocus isozymes are most often expressed within all the members of a given species, but the level of expression may vary among tissues of the same individual (e.g., heart, brain, skeletal muscle, eye, and gut). In some cases, the tissue-specific expression of these multilocus isozymes has been shown to complement the metabolic needs of the tissue.

When there is no genetic variation at a particular locus within a species, but substantial variation among species, multilocus isozymes can be used to detect species differences among larvae or other life-history stages that may be ambiguous from a morphological perspective. For example, the white perch, *Morone americana,* is extremely difficult to distinguish from *Morone saxatilis* in early larval stages and thus studies of larval recruitment of these species are difficult. Biochemical methods have been developed to assess the relative portion of each species in a given collection of larval fish (Morgan *et al.*, 1973; Morgan, 1975; Sidell *et al.*, 1978, 1980). These methods provide relatively fast and unambiguous species identifications, whereas morphological identification has a significant associated error.

Perhaps even more importantly, isozymes have also revealed cryptic species that were not morphologically distinguishable. The most striking example of this is the work of Shaklee and Tamaru (1981) with Hawaiian bonefish (*Albula*). They identified two sympatric sibling species that were isozymically distinct at 58 out of 84 loci. Other examples of isozymically detected cryptic species have been described in clupeids, lizardfish, and mackerels (reviewed in Shaklee, 1983).

Hybridization is another example of the increased power of isozyme methods to identify species. Natural hybridization is much more common in fish than in other vertebrates (review in Campton, 1987). The detection of hybridization by morphological criteria suffers from many shortcomings. The basic problem is that interspecific hybrids of fishes are often not morphologically intermediate to their parents. The analysis of isozymes encoded by multiple diagnostic loci is the most sensitive and reliable method to identify hybridization. Hybridization is apparently not as common in marine fish as it is in freshwater species. However, the use of these and other molecular techniques (e.g., mitochondrial DNA) in marine species is likely to reveal more hybridization than has previously been thought to exist (see, e.g., She *et al.*, 1987).

Whereas morphology, life-history characteristics, and other variables have been useful in population and ecological studies of fish species, the analysis of isozymes and their allelic variants has also been widely employed in the identification and analysis of fish population structures and breeding "stocks." Moreover, it has often helped resolve problems that could not be resolved by conventional approaches.

The advantages of using isozymes over morphological and other classical variables are that (1) the biochemical phenotype is essentially unaffected by the environment, (2) the biochemical phenotype of each individual is stable through time, and (3) the observed genetic variation is usually due to a single gene whose alleles are codominantly expressed (Ayala, 1975).

Allelic isozymic description of the stock composition of marine fishes has become routine since the pioneering review of de Ligny (1969). A book on population genetics and fisheries management (Ryman and Utter, 1987) extensively reviews the voluminous literature on this subject. The ingeniously entitled paper "Which Witch Is Which?" by Fairbairn (1981) exemplifies the value of these studies. Isozyme analysis of samples from three management areas of witch flounder revealed a total of six genetically distinct stocks that differed with respect to age structure, time of spawning, individual growth rate, and temperature and depth at which the fish were captured. Previous practices had managed these fish as a large homogeneous stock.

An extension of this approach also allows estimating the geographical origin of fish caught in mixed-stock fisheries. It is essential to be able to identify the origin and proportional contribution of different stocks to a mixed fishery. However, this approach has been very difficult to put into practice (Larkin, 1981). Statistical techniques recently have been developed that allow the use of allelic isozyme variants to estimate the contribution of different stocks to mixed-stock fisheries (review in Pella and Milner, 1987).

Other researchers have also shown the utility of using these techniques to describe the transport of organisms by physical features of the ocean environment. For example, Heath and Walker (1987) have used allelic isozymes to describe the pattern of drift and to identify the geographical spawning origin of larval herring (*Clupea harengus*) caught in the North Sea.

The potential for genetic differentiation among populations of a species depends upon a number of variables, including migration rate, the number of individuals within a population, and natural selection at different loci. Determination of genetic exchange among populations has been estimated by a number of experimental and theoretical approaches. Release/recapture studies have been used to examine the migration of individuals, but there are a number of practical restrictions, questionable assumptions, and theoretical constraints that have limited the usefulness of this approach.

In addition to describing the genetic architecture of fish species, allelic isozymes can be used to estimate the amount of gene flow among populations. Allendorf and Phelps (1981) used population genetic theory (Wright, 1969) and computer simulation to show that the amount of allelic divergence, as measured by Wright's F_{st}, among subpopulations is a function of the absolute number rather than the fraction of migrants exchanged. This is an important finding because it emphasizes the need to know the population size in order to estimate reproductive isolation from allozyme data. They also cautioned that the use of larval data to draw conclusions about divergence of reproducing adults could be greatly misleading.

Slatkin (1985) has developed a powerful method for using the frequency of rare alleles to estimate gene flow among populations by determining the average number of migrants exchanged. This approach is both useful and relatively insensitive to changes in any parameter except the number of migrants exchanged and the number of individuals sampled per population.

Waples (1987) has used Wright's F_{st} and Slatkin's (1985) method to estimate gene flow in 10 species of marine shore fishes. Estimates of gene flow were highly correlated with the dispersal ability of the species. Waples concluded that genetic differentiation among these fishes was primarily determined by gene flow and genetic drift, rather than by natural selection.

Sometimes the gene frequencies of certain enzyme-synthesizing loci that are correlated with directional changes in specific environmental variables such as temperature, salinity, and oceanic circulation are found to be the result of natural selection. In such cases, studies have been launched in order to elucidate the detailed mechanisms driving the selection process (reviews in Powers, 1990; Powers *et al.*, 1991).

Although detection of species his historically been directed toward specific gene products (e.g., isozymes, allelic isozymes, and other proteins), developments in the area of molecular biology have begun to focus attention at the DNA and RNA level.

B. Genetic Variation in Mitochondrial DNA

Though multilocus isozymes and allelic isozymes are useful for characterizing some species and populations, the lack of observable genetic variation in other species has restricted the application of this technique. This has been partly due to the fact that isozyme methods underestimate the extent of genetic variability arising from changes in isopolar amino acids and in nucleotides that are not reflected in corresponding changes in protein sequence.

Recent molecular "tools" employed in population studies have led to the discovery of genetic variability that was unexpected on the basis of isozyme data. Not only do these methods permit analysis of a broader array of genetic diversity, but the sensitivity of these methods permits the study of egg and juvenile stages, tissue biopsies of adults, and even single cells.

Endonuclease restriction digests of mitochondrial DNA (mtDNA) in marine and freshwater fish are now beginning to be routinely employed. The general approach is as follows: DNA is isolated from a given taxonomic unit (individual, species, etc.), each sample is divided into a series of test tubes to which is added one or more DNA sequence-specific endonuclease restriction enzymes, the fragmented DNA is subjected to electrophoresis, and the resulting electrophoretic patterns are visualized by one of several methods. These electrophoretic patterns are referred to as restriction fragment-length polymorphisms (RFLPs). The RFLP patterns can be compared directly or these types of data can be used to construct restriction maps. Because mtDNA is usually between 16 and 19 kb in length, it is relatively easy to map with an array of restriction enzymes (Maniatis *et al.*, 1982).

Because mtDNA is generally maternally inherited, the variation within and among populations can be studied and matriarchal lineages can be traced. This variation is reflected both as differences in restriction sites and/or differences in the size of the mtDNA. Although RFLP patterns of mtDNA reflect varying degrees of natural selection and historically relevant evolutionary incidents, they may prove extremely valuable for identifying the geographical origin of individuals and populations. Such information can assist in stock identification, fisheries management, transport studies of larvae, and evolutionary studies (Avise *et al.*, 1987; Bermingham, 1990; Avise, 1991).

There are a number of examples wherein mtDNA analysis has already provided insight concerning a marine species' population structure that could not be resolved by isozyme studies. For example, *Anquilla* are known to spawn in the Sargasso Sea and the leptocephalus larvae migrate thousands of kilometers to metamorphose in estuarine waters. Given this life history, it would seem a foregone conclusion that genetic uniformity would be expected over vast regions of the Americas and Europe. However, this has been a debatable point for many years.

The evidence from isozyme studies has been equivocal. Williams *et al.* (1973) found little interlocality variation among elvers but some interlocality differences among adults in North American eels. In more extensive studies (Koehn and Williams, 1978; Williams and Koehn, 1984), it was argued that the small gene frequency differences among populations were due to natural selection. European scientists argued to the contrary.

Comparini and Rodino (1980) have concluded on the basis of allozyme frequency differences that North American and European eels should be considered separate species. However, Williams and Koehn (1984) have argued that their work with North American eels suggests that the amount of allele frequency divergence among European and North American eels indicates only partial reproductive isolation among eels from the two continents.

Avise and his colleagues (Avise *et al.*, 1986) resolved this conflict with their classic paper on mtDNA differentiation in North Atlantic eels. Their restriction site polymorphism study of mtDNA showed no genetic divergence among the eels (*Anquilla rostrata*) along the coast of North America and suggested they were all members of a single panmictic population. However, they found that samples of the European eel, which they referred to as *Anquilla anquilla*, were significantly different than those studied along the North American coast.

Bermingham and Avise (1986) used mtDNA RFLPs to study the zoogeography of four species of freshwater fish: *Amia calva, Lepomis punctatus, Lepomis gulosus,* and *Lepomis microlophus.* They found that within each species, major mtDNA phylogenetic discontinuities distinguished populations from different geographical areas. From these data, they concluded that dispersal and gene flow were inadequate to override the historically driven geographical changes in sea level and morphology. Similarly, Gonzalez-Villasenor and Powers (1990) used mtDNA restriction fragment data to show that a previous barrier to gene flow existed among two groups of the teleost *Fundulus heteroclitus*. This finding helped them to distinguish between two alternative evolutionary models (Powers *et al.*, 1986), which helped explain the existence of a series of allelic isozyme gene frequency clines along the east coast of North America.

Thomas *et al.* (1986) used mtDNA to study intra- and interspecific variation for rainbow trout and five species of salmon. Though an inadequate sampling of populations limited the intraspecies studies, interesting interspecific divergences were observed. Similar intra- and interspecific mtDNA studies have been performed on three trout species. Wilson *et al.* (1985) demonstrated significant divergence among all populations and the expected evolutionary divergence among trout species.

On the other hand, Kornfield and Bogdanowicz (1987) studied the mtDNA of Atlantic herring, *C. harengus,* from the Gulf of Maine and the Gulf of St. Lawrence. They concluded that their data did not support the notion that these were separate genetic stocks.

In addition to the analysis of RFLPs of mtDNA, the use of direct DNA sequence analysis is being increasingly employed to study the phylogenetic relationships among fish taxa. Though this approach has been slow and rather tedious in the past, the introduction of the polymerase chain reaction (described in Section II,D) is dramatically increasing the applicability of this approach by reducing the time and material required for analysis.

C. DNA FINGERPRINTING

Individual-specific "fingerprints" of human DNA have been successfully employed for parenthood verification. Tandem repetitive regions of DNA, called minisatellites, are dispersed throughout the genome of a number of organisms. Jeffreys *et al.* (1985) showed that a subset of human minisatellites shared a common 10 to 15-bp core that had hypervariable regions. Later they demonstrated that a hybridization probe could detect highly polymorphic minisatellites that could be used as DNA fingerprints specific to an individual. DNA fingerprinting is now commonplace in biomedical research and is routinely employed in a variety of legal situations. This methodology is now being extensively applied to the analysis of genomic DNA of a variety of marine and freshwater fishes (see, e.g., Avise *et al.*, 1989; Fields *et al.*, 1989; Whitmore *et al.*, 1990). For example, Whitmore *et al.* (1990) used DNA fingerprinting to study sibling largemouth bass (*Micropterus salmoides*). They showed that Southern blots of bass DNA hybridized to human minisatellite DNA probes yielded patterns that were different for each individual but that sibs were more similar than were fish from wild stocks. Taggart *et al.* (1990) isolated hypervariable single locus probes from an Atlantic salmon, *Salmo salar*, genomic library. They are using these probes, and some of those developed for human DNA fingerprinting, to study the population structure of salmon from several regions of Ireland. A Canadian group (J. L. Goodier and W. S. Davidson, personal communication) have identified a 450 bp tandemly repeated component in the genome of Atlantic salmon which they cloned and sequenced. This element contains several recognition sites for restriction enzymes that will make them useful for the analysis of population structure. Others (P. Bentzen and J. W. Wright, personal communication) have cloned and sequenced a variety of highly polymorphic salmon minisatellites of 9-65 bp and microsatellites that are four or less base pair. These salmon clones as well as those being developed for other species should be very useful in analyzing the genetic architecture of fish populations and help in the difficult practical problem of fish stock assessment and related management issues. Recent coupling of DNA "fingerprinting" with the polymerase chain reaction promises to greatly expand the use of this methodology for studying the genetic architecture of fish populations (see below).

D. DNA AMPLIFICATION EMPLOYING THE POLYMERASE CHAIN REACTION

Although analyses of mtDNA and genomic DNA offer very powerful approaches for addressing fundamental problems in the population and evolutionary biology of fishes, these methods usually require significant amounts of material for each analysis. When very small organisms or only a few cells are available, obtaining enough DNA can be a limitation. Under such conditions, the desired DNA is usually cloned and analyzed directly or used as a molecular probe.

When a significant amount of a specific DNA sequence is needed, it is cloned into an active replicon, identified by a specific method, and produced in large quantities in bacteria. However, the initial cloning and identification methods can often be very time consuming, especially when the target sequence is not abundant and the starting sample is a complex mixture of DNAs.

The detection and characterization of specific DNA sequences employing the polymerase chain reaction (PCR) are simple, less expensive, and less time consuming alternatives to the cloning of specific genes. The current procedure employs a thermostable bacterial DNA polymerase and specific oligonucleotide primers to replicate a target DNA sequence *in vitro*. From as little as a single molecule of the target sequence, enough material for standard analytical procedures such as restriction mapping, hybridization, or DNA sequencing is produced in about 3 hours. A commercially available microprocessor-controlled device automatically takes the reaction through multiple cycles of DNA denaturation/primer annealing/DNA synthesis. The target sequence may be amplified from many samples in parallel through this automated process.

Problems that can be addressed by the PCR method include (1) rapid detection and identification of individual fish eggs and larvae, (2) rapid analysis of individual genomes for population studies, (3) detection and analysis of "rare events," e.g., gene rearrangements that occur in a small fraction of cells in a tissue sample or field collection, (4) analysis of a rare DNA sequence in a complex sample mixture, (5) examination of symbiotic and parasitic relationships, and (6) estimation of water quality by detection of pathogenic viruses, bacteria, and/or parasites. The application of the PCR technique to terrestrial and aquatic organisms and populations was recently reviewed by Arnheim *et al.* (1990). They provide many examples of the use of PCR technology in biosystematics, population biology, conservation biology, ecology, developmental biology, and experimental genetics. Highly conserved regions of mtDNA—such as 12S rRNA, cytochrome *b* genes, and other loci—are routinely being amplified via PCR technology to generate fragments of DNA that can then be studied for population and species variation by RFLP and/or analysis of the DNA sequences.

A recent variation of the PCR technique is beginning to be used to study the genetic architecture of populations and species. The method involves the use of PCR primers of arbitrary nucleotide sequences of 10 to 20 bases in length that are used to amplify discrete loci. The major advantage this method has over the more conventional approach is that there is no need for prior knowledge of species-specific DNA sequences for the construction of PCR primers. This method was used only on a very limited basis until recently when Williams *et al.* (1990) described a suite of PCR primers, termed random amplified polymorphic DNA (RAPD) markers, that are available on a commercial basis. The amplification protocol is the same as that for the conventional approach but only a single primer is used instead of a pair to amplify the DNA. Although one does not know what region is being amplified, the DNA "fingerprint" can be used to study the genetic architecture of populations and species and can be used in gene mapping studies.

Because PCR techniques appear to work on a variety of preserved samples and even on partially degraded samples obtained from gut contents of predators, it is possible not only to analyze fresh specimens, but also to analyze samples fixed in the field or even museum specimens collected 100 years or more ago. Once amplified, the DNA can be studied by RFLP mapping or DNA sequencing (see e.g., Gyllenstein and Ehrlich, 1988; Higuchi and Ochman, 1989).

E. PROTEIN AND DNA SEQUENCING

Electrophoresis of proteins underestimates the total amount of genetic variation because it relies on charged differences. Although a number of other electrophoretic methods have been developed to detect isopolar amino acid differences, none has been entirely satisfactory. The obvious way to determine all the amino acid differences among proteins from different taxa is to isolate and sequence the proteins in question. Though this has been used for some evolutionary studies, the method is too time consuming and expensive to be routinely employed in most evolutionary analyses. In those cases in which the same protein has been sequenced in a variety of taxonomic groups, the information has been extremely valuable, but even in those cases the actual DNA sequence that encodes the protein remains a mystery because most amino acids have more than one codon. Ultimately, it is preferable to isolate and sequence the cDNA or genomic DNA encoding the protein that is being used in an evolutionary study. It goes without saying that sequencing of mtDNA or genomic fragments (e.g., those generated by the PCR) is also preferable to RFLP and mapping studies.

III. Fish Genetic Nomenclature

Over the past several decades, researchers working in fish biochemical genetics have used a variety of genetic nomenclatures. The lack of a standard genetic nomenclature has hampered the field and made it difficult to draw comparisons within and among fish species. In 1987, the Fish Genetics Section of the American Fisheries Society established the Committee on Fish Genetics Nomenclature. The Committee's charge was to review existing nomenclature systems and devise a standard for describing genetic variation among fishes. In 1989, the Committee drafted a document that proposed guidelines for the genetic nomenclature of protein-coding loci. This draft was published and the readers were asked to comment directly to the Committee's chair. After reviewing the comments by the fish biochemical genetics community at large, the recommendations were published in 1990 (Shaklee *et al.*, 1990).

The Committee's recommendations were to (1) standardize the designations of loci, alleles, and proteins, (2) provide a basis for journal editorial policy, and (3) establish a common nomenclature that will promote communications among geneticists, fishery scientists, evolutionary biologists, and related fields. The fish nomenclature uses the enzyme names recommended by the International Union of Biochemistry Nomenclature Committee (IUBNC) and some of the conventions used in human genetics (Shows *et al.*, 1987).

A. ENZYMES AND PROTEINS

The recommended names for enzymes are the same as those adopted by the IUBNC with the exception of the cytosolic aminopeptidases and the malic enzyme. The five well-studied fish cytosolic aminopeptidases are referred to as dipeptidase, tripeptide aminopeptidase, peptidase-C, proline dipeptidase, and peptidase-S (Frick, 1983, 1984). The last of these five, peptidase-S, has maintained the same nomenclature as used in the human system because it has been shown to be orthologous among fish and mammals (Frick, 1984). Although the IUBNC uses the name malate dehydrogenase for all four enzymes that use malate and NAD (or NADP) as cofactors, the Fish Nomenclature Committee has opted to preserve that name for the classical dimeric malate dehydrogenase enzyme. The other four enzymes, which are tetrameric and require Mg^{2+} or Mn^{2+} for catalysis, are referred to as malic enzymes.

When enzymes are known to occur in two or more subcellular compartments, the Committee recommends that these enzymes be identified with appropriate prefixes in order to minimize possible confusion (e.g., mitochondrial malate dehydrogenase and cytoplasmic malate dehydrogenase).

It is recommended that proteins that are not enzymes should be referred to by their common names (e.g., hemoglobin and transferrin). However, if no common name exists, then they should simply be referred to as protein-1, protein-2, etc.

The recommended abbreviations for proteins commonly analyzed by fish geneticists are to be presented in uppercase without underlining or italics. When Greek prefixes are commonly used with a protein name, it is either preserved in the abbreviation or replaced with a Roman surrogate (i.e., a = alpha, b = beta, g = gamma, d = delta, and e = epsilon). If the protein is found in two or more subcellular compartments, a lowercase subcellular prefix is used to identify the compartment (e.g., l = lysosomal, m = mitochondrial, p = peroxisomal, and s = cytosolic or supernatant or soluble protein form). When there are two or more forms of a substrate-specific dehydrogenase that use different cofactors (i.e., NAD or NADP), the NADP-dependent form adds P to the end of the abbreviation. For example, the abbreviation for the NAD-dependent isocitrate dehydrogenase is IDH but the abbreviation for the NADP-dependent isocitrate dehydrogenase is IDHP.

When two or more forms of the same enzyme are known (multilocus isozymes), the isozyme abbreviations are followed by a hyphen and an Arabic number or uppercase letter (e.g., IDHP-1 and IDHP-2; LDH-A, LDH-B, and LDH-C). Letters are only used when orthology with isozymes in other taxa are well established (e.g., LDH-A, LDH-B, and LDH-C). The Fish Nomenclature Committee differentiates between orthology and paralogy as follows: orthology reflects descent of species and paralogy reflects descent of loci. For example, LDH-A is orthologous in vertebrate species but LDH-A, LDH-B, and LDH-C within a particular fish species are paralogous. Paralogous gene loci coexist in the same species but orthologous gene loci are found in different species. To date, orthology has only been established for four multilocus enzyme-coding loci: creatine kinase, glucose-6-phosphate isomerase, L-lactate dehydrogenase, and cytosolic malate dehydrogenase.

B. GENES

The standard nomenclature for genes employs the same alphanumeric symbols used for abbreviations of the proteins they encode but they are either underlined or italicized and include an asterisk (e.g., IDHP-1*, LDH-A*, and mAAT-1*). These differences are used to clearly distinguish gene loci (genotypes) from gene products (phenotypes).

Recently duplicated loci, such as those common in tetraploid fishes, are handled in either of two manners. When not much information is available about the evolutionary relationship of the loci in question, multiple loci encoding the same enzyme are distinguished by Arabic numerals (e.g., EST-1*, EST-2*, and EST-3*). However, when orthology has been clearly established (e.g., LDH-A*, LDH-B*, and

LDH-C*), paralogies among recent duplicates are identified by the addition of Arabic numerals (e.g., *LDH-A1** and *LDH-A2*; LDH-B1** and *LDH-B2**). Recently duplicated loci whose products are not electrophoretically different (isoloci) are distinguished by the use of a comma between the alphanumeric isolocus pair (e.g., s*AAT-1,2** and *GPI-B1,2**).

Loci that either directly or indirectly affect the expression of specific genes are often referred to as regulatory loci. These loci are identified by a lowercase italicized *r* suffix attached to the symbol of the locus it regulates. For example, *LDH-Ar** would be a gene that regulates the expression of the *LDH-A** gene. When more than one regulatory locus is involved, each is assigned an Arabic numeral in order of its discovery (e.g., *LDH-Ar1**, *LDH-Ar2**, and *LDH-Ar3**, or *PGM-1r1**, *PGM-1r2**, and *PGM-1r3**).

Pseudogenes are identified by a lowercase italicized *p* suffix that is attached to the gene symbol (e.g., *LDH-Ap** is a pseudogene of *LDH-A**). However, if information about the homology is not known, then an alternative approach is recommended (Shaklee *et al.*, 1990).

Alleles may be identified by the addition of italicized Arabic numerals (allele **1*, allele **2*, etc.), lowercase letters (allele **a*, allele **b*, etc.), or relative electrophoretic mobilities (allele **50*, allele **100*, allele **150*, etc.). The asterisk precedes the allele symbol as opposed to the asterisk that follows the Arabic numerals or the uppercase letters used to identify multiple loci (e.g., *LDH-B*a* and *LDH-B*b*, *EST-2*1* and *EST-2*2*, or *EST-1*50* and *EST-1*100*). The preferred method is the use of the allele number codes. When alleles are identified by the relative electrophoretic mobility of their protein products, a series of detailed recommendations have been suggested by the Fish Nomenclature Committee (Shaklee *et al.*, 1990). Quantitative allelic variants are identified by one of three different codes that use uppercase letters: QO = null allele or no enzyme activity or gene product, QE = elevated activity or elevated product, and QL = lower than normal activity or product level. For example, three quantitative alleles representing no activity, elevated activity, and low activity for *LDH-B** might be designated as *LDH-B*aQO*, *LDH-B*bQE*, and *LDH-B*cQL*, respectively.

C. Differentiating between Phenotypes and Genotypes

As was the case for genes, genotypes are underlined or italicized whereas phenotypes are not. When genotypes involve more than one allele, the alleles are separated by a forward slash (e.g., *MPI*1/2*,

LDH-B*a/b, and *EST-1*100/150).* Similarly, phenotypes are treated with slashes but they are neither underlined not italicized (e.g., MPI 1/2, LDH-B a/b, and EST-1 100/150).

IV. Evolution of Nuclear Genomic Structures

The genetic material of vertebrates is located within the nucleus of cells and in mitochondria. Mitochondrial DNA is relatively small (16 to 18 kb) and circular whereas nuclear DNA is larger and organized into higher order complex structures (e.g., chromosomes). In this section we shall focus on the evolution of nuclear DNA. Evolutionary changes in nuclear DNA can occur as a result of increases or decreases in genome size, changes in the structure and organization of genetic material within genomes, recombination, gene duplication, and changes arising from point mutations.

A. GENOME SIZE

Changes in the concentration of cellular DNA is believed to have played an important role in evolution (reviews in Ohno, 1970; Hinegardner and Rosen, 1972; Smith, 1974; Hinegardner, 1976; Gold, 1979; Gold and Amemiya, 1987; Cavalier-Smith, 1985a,b,c). The DNA content determined from over 1000 species varies from 0.007 to over 100 pg of DNA per haploid cell (Fig. 2A). Although there is great variation among species, typical prokaryotes have around 10^{-2} pg per haploid cell whereas most eukaryotes have between 1 and 5 pg or approximately 300 times more DNA per cell than prokaryotes. In addition to variations in DNA concentrations among taxa that are evolutionarily distant from each other, there is also significant variation within taxonomic groups. Within major taxa such as a phylum or an order, the DNA content per cell is neither uniform nor normally distributed. For example, in teleost fishes, the DNA content per haploid cell has been found to vary between 0.5 and 4.5 pg, with the majority of species clustered around 1 pg of DNA, but the distribution is significantly skewed toward higher concentrations (Fig. 2B). Fishes with large amounts of DNA per cell generally have more chromosomes (Hinegardner and Rosen, 1972; Hinegardner, 1976), but in mammals and many other organisms, there is no apparent correlation between DNA content and chromosome number. Even among the fishes, there are examples in which chromosome numbers differ among closely related species but

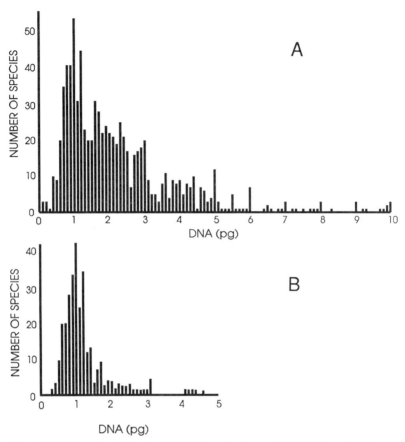

Fɪɢ. 2. Distribution of the haploid DNA content per cell: (A) Eukaryotes in general; (B) Teleost fishes. [From Hinegardner (1976).]

there is no significant difference in DNA concentration. This can be accounted for by chromosomal fusion, fission, inversion, and/or translocation, which are genetic rearrangements that do not require the addition or deletion of DNA.

Evolutionary changes in genome size can arise as a result of the duplication of single loci, the duplication of a large section of DNA within a chromosome (polyteny), or the duplication of an entire genome (polyploidy). Although tetraploidy has been established for some fish taxa, it is not absolutely clear whether differences in the genome sizes of other fish taxa are the result of numerous small increases in DNA or losses following polyteny or polyploidy events. However, it is generally agreed that the evolutionary trend is toward smaller genome size. Speculation about the mechanisms responsible for this phenomenon and its evolutionary significance is extensive (review in Gold, 1979).

B. Chromosome Number and Morphology

The number and morphology of chromosomes of an organism is often referred to as the *karyotype*. The general approach to karyotype analyses involves comparisons of chromosome size, shape, symmetry, centromere location, chromosome numbers, and the presence of sex-determining characters. There are four general chromosome morphologies: (1) acrocentric chromosomes that are rod shaped with the centromere at the end of the arm, (2) metacentric chromosomes that are V shaped with the centromere at the crux between two relatively symmetrical arms, (3) telocentric chromosomes that have the centromere near the middle but usually with one arm shorter than the other, and (4) sex chromosomes that have morphologies that vary widely but which carry sex-associated characters. These types of karyotype differences within and among species have been used as major systematic and evolutionary tools for several decades.

Of the 20,000–30,000 living fish species, chromosome numbers have only been studied for less than 2000 species, and complete karyotypes are only known for less than 1000. Chromosome numbers in fish range from 8 to 86 chromosome pairs (see e.g., Post, 1965; Calton and Denton, 1974; Potter and Rothwell, 1970; Arkhipohuk, 1988; Gold, 1979; Viktorovsky *et al.*, 1985). However, 80% of all fish species have between 20 and 28 chromosome pairs and half of them have 24 pairs. Approximately 6% of the fishes, including the Salmonidae, Cyprinidae, Catostomidae, and Corbitidae teleosts as well as a few lampreys and skates, have between 40 and 52 chromosome pairs; a few lamprey species have between 82 and 84 chromosome pairs. In these latter cases, the larger number of chromosomes is apparently the result of genomic duplication (polyploidy) because there is a concomitant and multiplicative increase in the DNA content per cell. For example, the salmonids, catostomids, and others have approximately twice the DNA per cell as do fish with 24 chromosome pairs. It has been suggested that the ancestral chromosome number of modern fishes was 24 pairs, and it may have been the primordial chromosome number that gave rise to all vertebrates (Ohno *et al.*, 1968; Ohno, 1974). Although there are data to support this hypothesis in some primitive fishes (Nogusa, 1960; Taylor,

1967), other species do not appear to conform to this hypothesis (Denton, 1973; Chiarelli and Capanna, 1973).

Several hundred studies have employed karyotype differences to address fish systematic and evolutionary questions, thus I will not attempt to survey that literature here. Rather, a few selected examples will be mentioned and some general references cited for those who wish to pursue the subject. The best review of fish cytogenetics was written by Gold (1979), wherein he also surveys many of the more critical fish karyotype studies prior to 1979. Therefore, I will only mention a few selected papers published since Gold's review.

Cano *et al.* (1982) analyzed a large group of Mediterranean fishes using chromosome number, morphology, and nuclear DNA content in an attempt to address the evolutionary mechanisms responsible for the radiation of this group. Hartley and Horne (1984) studied the chromosomes of a variety of salmonid species in an attempt to derive information about the ancestral tetraploidization event that gave rise to the salmonid radiation between 25 and 100 million years ago. Feldberg and Bertollo (1985) analyzed the karyotype and nucleolar organization regions of 10 neotropical teleost species and concluded that the nucleolar organization regions associated with the first pair of chromosomes indicated the most primitive evolutionary state of this taxonomic group. Gold and colleagues (1986) examined chromosomal heterochromatin differentiation among the North American cyprinid fishes and established a powerful case for the evolution of this group. Arkhipchuk (1988; Arkhipchuk and Berdyshev, 1987) studied the karyotypes of 1500 fish species. Arkhipchuk and Berdyshev, (1987) concluded that an increase in the chromosome variability is correlated ($r = 0.99$) with an increase in the variability of exterior morphological characters. Arkhipohuk (1988) estimated evolutionary rates from variations in morphology, chromosome number, and the generation time of different taxa. He concluded that there was a tendency for a decrease in the number of generations and generation time during the evolution from older to younger orders of teleosts. Banerjee *et al.* (1988) studied the karyotype and cell volume of selected *Channa* fish species and, on the basis of those data, proposed a model for the evolution of the genus and the basis for chromosomal rearrangement within the genus. Aref'ev (1989) studied the karyotypes of the common bass, *Dicentrarchus labrax,* which has 24 chromosome pairs per cell, and showed that this group had one of the most conservative karyotypes.

The identification of sex-determining chromosomes is an important karyotypic characteristic. Although many fish species do not have identifiable sex chromosomes (reviews in Gold, 1979; Price, 1984; Kallman,

1983), some researchers have successfully studied sex chromosomes in salmonids and other fish species (Thorgaard, 1977, 1978, 1983; Thorgaard and Allen, 1987; Wright *et al.*, 1987; Gellman *et al.*, 1987; Allendorf *et al.*, 1991).

The notion that chromosomal rearrangements are involved in the process of speciation is well entrenched in the evolutionary literature (see e.g., Dobzhansky, 1951; White, 1968; Mayr, 1973). White (1973) suggested that chromosomal rearrangement may be important for speciation in the absence of geographical isolation because it could provide a mechanism by which postmating isolation could be achieved. Others (see, e.g., Stebbins, 1969; Wilson *et al.*, 1974) have suggested that rearrangements could affect changes in the regulation of genes that control important biological processes, such as metabolism, reproduction, development, and life-history characteristics. Although these are two very interesting and thought-provoking mechanisms, the first— speciation in the absence of isolation—is complicated by the fact that hybridization among species is fairly common in fishes (Hubbs, 1955). This fact and the conservation of karyotypes among some of the most speciose fish taxa (Denton, 1973) make the "isolation without separation hypothesis" less than compelling. The second chromosomal rearrangement-driven speciation mechanism is difficult and perhaps impossible to test experimentally. Although Wilson and colleagues have used selected karyotype and fossil data to estimate rates of chromosomal change in teleost fishes, Gold (1979) has pointed out flaws in those estimates and has provided arguments that many speciations in fish are not associated with gross chromosomal changes. In fact, Avise and Gold (1977) studied the karyotypes of several North American fishes and concluded that the rates of regulatory change associated with gross chromosomal rearrangements are not more associated with speciose taxa than with species-poor taxa. These and other studies suggest that speciations in fishes can arise in the absence of chromosomal rearrangements. However, the present technology used in such studies cannot rule out the possibility of rearrangements that cannot be detected by present cytological techniques.

On the other hand, changes in regulatory genes that do not require chromosomal rearrangements could be important in the genetic differentiation process that may eventually lead to speciation. A selective advantage in a particular environment could be achieved by the modification of a regulatory gene that affects the level or timing of gene expression, in the absence of chromosomal rearrangements. Crawford and Powers (1989) provided evidence for differential gene expression among natural populations of *F. heteroclitus* living at different environmental temperatures that resulted in different enzyme concentrations consistent with the metabolic demands imposed by their thermal regimes. These and related studies (Place and Powers, 1979, 1984a,b; DiMichele and Powers, 1982a,b, 1991; 1984; DiMichele *et al.*, 1986; Powers *et al.*, 1986; Powers, 1989, 1990; Ropson and Powers, 1988; Van Beneden and Powers, 1989; Ropson *et al.*, 1990; Paynter *et al.*, 1991) are consistent with a selective advantage in relation to environmental temperature at the extremes of the species range, and are in concordance with evidence from mitochondrial DNA studies that supports the segregation of two subspecies of *F. heteroclitus* (Gonzalez-Villasenor and Powers, 1990; Smith *et al.*, 1991). If the extent of this regulatory mechanism was extended to several metabolic loci, as preliminary studies suggest (D. A. Powers, unpublished data), then a modified version of Wilson's hypothesis would seem both reasonable and feasible.

C. Isochores and Genome Organization

Although there is an international effort underway to sequence the human genome, it is not generally appreciated that only a tiny fraction of the coding sequences has been determined, and even less is known about the noncoding sequences. Because the known coding sequences only account for about 0.04% of the genome, if all the coding sequences had been determined, the majority of the human genome (approximately 98%) would still be a mystery. Because so little is known about the eukaryotic genome, it is not surprising that many modern biologists maintain the notion that its structure is essentially a collection of genes or gene clusters randomly scattered over an expanse of evolutionarily meaningless DNA. On the other hand, some evolutionary geneticists have asserted that the eukaryotic genome is a highly integrated structure whose organization is of both functional and evolutionary significance (review in Bernardi, 1985, 1989). This position is based on the analysis of compositional patterns of large DNA fragments and their associations with specific sequences.

Fractionation of DNA via equilibrium centrifugation allows the identification of a limited number of DNA families or components characterized by similar base compositions. These fractions comprise major, minor, and satellite families of highly repeated DNA. The human genome is composed of families in the 30- to 100-kb size range that are referred to as L1 and L2, which are GC-poor families that represent about two-thirds of the genome, and H1, H2, and H3, which are GC-rich components that represent the remaining one-third (Fig. 3). Though this distribution of fragments appears to be shared by other warm-blooded vertebrates, the fragments are more restricted in the cold-blooded vertebrates, as illustrated in Fig. 3. Within specific DNA families, there are compositional homogeneities that extend over large areas of the DNA that are considered relatively equal regions and they are therefore referred to as *isochores* (Bernardi *et al.*, 1985).

Bernardi (1989) has noted that hybridization of major compositional DNA fragments with gene probes from warm-blooded species reveals that (1) the GC levels of genes are correlated with those of the larger DNA component in which they are contained, (2) most of the human genes are localized in the H3 component, which represents less than 5% of the genome, and (3) these genes tend to be localized in the telomeres (Gardiner *et al.*, 1988).

Differences in chromosomal banding have been used in karyotype analyses for decades. Classical Giemsa staining of chromosomes produces positively stained bands (G-bands) and those that are not stained (R-bands). The genomes of warm-blooded vertebrates show extensive compositional heterogeneity of DNA fragments and strong banding, whereas cold-blooded vertebrates have weak heterogeneity and poor banding (Medrano *et al.*, 1988; Schmid and Guttenbach, 1988; Bernardi and Bernardi, 1990a,b, 1991). The GC-rich isochores are associated with the R-bands, and GC-poor isochores are associated with G-bands (see e.g., Cuny *et al.*, 1981), and genes identified with R- and G-bands

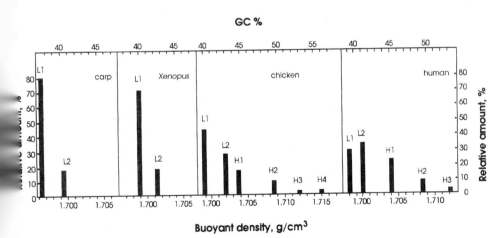

FIG. 3. Histograms showing the relative amounts, modal bouyant densities, and GC content of the major DNA components from teleost (carp), amphibian (*Xenopus*), avian (chicken), and mammalian (human) species, respectively. (From Bernardi, 1989; reproduced with permission from the *Annual Review of Genetics*, vol. 23, © 1989 by Annual Reviews Inc.)

are GC-rich and GC-poor, respectively (Ikemura and Aota, 1988). The timing of G- and R-band replication (Comings, 1978), the replication of specific genes associated with these bands, and the GC content of these genes and their associated isochores are consistent with the view that isochores represent a new structural level of genome organization that bridges the gap between the gene and the chromosome.

Bernardi and colleagues (review in Bernardi, 1989) have suggested that isochores are not only important structural elements, but they provide insight concerning vertebrate genome evolution. Two general modes of genome evolution were proposed: the *conservative mode,* which prevails in warm-blooded animals, and the *shifting mode,* which predominates in cold-blooded animals. In the *shifting mode* hypothesis, characteristic of fishes and other cold-blooded vertebrates, there are compositional changes in isochores and genes that apparently reflect parallel events. Bernardi and Bernardi (1990a,b) have suggested that these compositional changes are not consistent with the molecular clock hypothesis (Zuckerkandl and Pauling, 1965). Rather, Bernardi and colleagues (Bernardi and Bernardi, 1986; Barnardi *et al.,* 1985, 1988; Mouchiroud *et al.,* 1987, 1988; Perrin and Bernardi, 1987) have concluded that compositional changes are the result of fixation of point mutations driven by selection.

In addition, they suggest that evolution has selected for higher thermal stability of proteins, RNA, and DNA in relation to body temperature (i.e., for warm-blooded vertebrates). The difference in the genomic compositional patterns (see Fig. 3) for warm- and cold-blooded vertebrates suggests that optimization of genome function is associated with the transition between cold- and warm-blooded life styles. The L and H components, which are GC-poor and GC-rich, respectively, are referred to as the *paleogenome* and the *neogenome,* and are characterized by a number of similarities and differences in warm- and cold-blooded vertebrates. Warm-blooded vertebrates have both the paleogenome and neogenome (L and H components), whereas cold-blooded vertebrates only have the paleogenome. The characteristics of the paleogenome are conserved among cold- and warm-blooded animals, whereas those of the neogenome distinguish between these groups of organisms. These conclusions require constraints on isochore evolution and imply functional roles for these high-level genomic structures.

V. Evolutionary Conservation of Linkage Groups

Morizot (1990) has recently reviewed the evolutionary conservation of linkage groups across vertebrate taxa. In that paper he reviewed

(1) the current status of fish gene maps, (2) map homologies among fish species, (3) the comparisons of fish gene maps with those of other vertebrates, and (4) the various hypotheses concerning the origins and evolution of vertebrate gene arrangements. The data available for fish gene maps are rather meager compared to the extensive genetic information available for human and mouse maps. Nevertheless, a number of very interesting observations can be made when the genetic maps of vertebrates are compared (review in Morizot, 1990).

Using classical genetic approaches that involve the construction of genetic crosses and backcrosses, more than 50 loci have been studied in a variety of fish species. Because many fish species, unlike mammals, produce fertile interspecies hybrids, this approach has been combined with conventional genetic approaches to delineate genetic groups within and among closely related taxa. Most of the information has been generated in three different fish orders, Atheriniformes, Salmoniformes, and Perciformes, which include the poeciliid fishes, salmonid fishes, and sunfishes, respectively.

Gene mapping of representatives of the genus *Xiphophorus* has been the subject of extensive efforts by a number of groups for more than 20 years (Siciliano *et al.*, 1976; Ahuja *et al.*, 1980; Morizot and Siciliano, 1983; Morizot *et al.*, 1991). This fish group has been particularly interesting because two representatives of the genus, swordtails and platyfishes, have been excellent models for the study of malignant melanomas (review in Vielkind and Vielkind, 1982). Gene mapping studies in this group have facilitated the identification of regulatory genes controlling the melanoma phenotype (Siciliano *et al.*, 1976; Ahuja *et al.*, 1980; Morizot and Siciliano, 1983). The elucidation of a large number of protein-encoding loci and the ability to hybridize species have facilitated gene-mapping studies, which have led to the establishment of multipoint linkage groups that involve over 50 protein-encoding loci, distributed over two-thirds of the 24 chromosome pairs (Morizot, 1990). In addition, hybridizations of restriction fragment-length polymorphisms with oncogene probes have facilitated the localization of these genes within RFLP fragments (Vielkind and Dippel, 1984; Schartl *et al.*, 1982, 1985; Schartl and Barnekow, 1984; Mauler *et al.*, 1988; Harless *et al.*, 1990).

The other well-studied fish group is that of Salmonidae. Because of their economic importance, the ability to create hybrids among closely related groups, and interest in the tetraploidization event that took place somewhere between 25 and 100 million years ago (Allendorf and Thorgaard, 1984), genetic analysis of this group has yielded some of the most extensive molecular and morphological genetic information of any fish. The synthetic gene map of this group includes 18 classical linkage groups and six pseudolinkages—many of which have been identified in several different species within the Salmonidae (Wright *et al.*, 1987; Johnson *et al.*, 1987; Allendorf *et al.*, 1991). In addition, over 50 polymorphic enzyme-encoding loci have been mapped in relation to their chromosome's centromere (Allendorf *et al.*, 1986; Thorgaard *et al.*, 1983; Wright *et al.*, 1987).

Another genus for which linkage information is available is that of *Poeciliopsis* (Leslie and Vrijenhoek, 1977, 1980; Leslie, 1982; Leslie and Pontier, 1980; Morizot *et al.*, 1990). There has also been a series of elegant evolutionary and ecological studies on these fishes (see, e.g., Schultz, 1967, 1969, 1973, 1977, 1982; Vrijenhoek, 1978, 1979, 1984, 1985; Vrijenhoek *et al.*, 1977, 1978). At present, studies have identified five linkage groups in *Poeciliopsis* (review in Morizot, 1990). Because both *Xiphophorus* and *Poeciliopsis* are poeciliid fishes, it should not be surprising that linkage groups identified in both genera are conserved. For example, the linkage among loci is conserved in both groups, but the distance is not identical. In all cases, linkage groups identified in both of these genera (*G6PD** and *PGD**, *GPI1** and *PEPD**, and *LDH-C** and *ES4**) are conserved. As a result, Morizot (1990) has combined these maps to generate a common poeciliid map (Fig. 4).

Utilizing hybridization to establish single-locus inheritance and linkage relationships, members of the fish genus *Lepomis* have also been studied for a few linkage relationships (Wheat *et al.*, 1973; Childers, 1967; Philipp *et al.*, 1979, 1983; Whitt, 1981, 1983; Whitt *et al.*, 1973, 1977; Pasdar *et al.*, 1984).

Genetic studies have been done on over 20 enzyme-encoding loci in the teleost *F. heteroclitus*, and two linkage groups have been identified (*FUM-A** and *PGM-A** and *H6PDH** and *PGM-B**), the latter pair of which is only loosely linked (Brown *et al.*, 1988).

Considering the extensive divergence in karyotype, genomic structure, and genome sizes alluded to earlier in this paper, it is quite surprising that Morizot and colleagues (Morizot, 1983, 1986, 1990; Morizot and Siciliano, 1983, 1984) found that some genetic linkages or chromosomal syntenies have been conserved for more than 400 million years. In spite of the paucity of data, there are several linkage groups that appear to have been conserved for several 100 million years (Fig. 4). Because the conservation of linkage groups among lower vertebrates is discussed in detail elsewhere (Morizot, 1990), only a few groups will be mentioned. As would be expected, the portion of conserved linkage groups decreases in direct proportion to the genetic distance between the taxa being compared. However, a few linkage groups that apparently persist in every vertebrate class have been examined. For example, *PEP-D** and *GPI** as well as *PEP-B** and *LDH-B** loci are apparently syntenic in mammals, amphibians, and fishes (Fig. 4). In addition, the human *mIDH** and *PK** and *MPI** linkage group on chromosome 15 is reflected in both poeciliid and salmonid fishes. There are several other linkage groups that also appear to have been conserved in each of these vertebrate classes, but the precise identification of the

Poeciliid fish	Salmonid fish	Frogs (*Rana*)	Mouse	Mouse lemur	Human
II	13		1		2
GP12	MDH	HK2	IDH1	LDHA	ACP1
IDH-M	IDH	MANA	2		IDH-S
LDHA	GPI	PEPB	ACP2	HEXA	MDH1
LDHC	LDHA	LDHB	SORD	PKM2	10
PK2	LDHC	MPI	9	MPI	GOT-S
ENO2	GOT		PK3	NP	HK
MPI	MPI	GPI	MPI	CKBB	11
III	3	GOT2(M?)	7	SORD	ACP2
GUK2	GPI	PEPD	PEPD		HBB
GAPD1	PEPD	GOT1(S?)	GPI	PEPB	LDHA
ME	SORD	TPI	IDH-M	LDHB	12
IV	7		HBB	CS	PEPB
PK1	LDHB	IDH1	LDHA	TPI	LDHB
GPI1	PEPB	HB	8	GAPD	CS
IDH1	1		GOT-M	ENO2	ENO2
GOT-M	GOT		19		GAPD
PEPD	MDH		GOT-S	GPI	TPI
V			6	PEPD	14
MDH2			LDHB		NP
GLYDH			GAPD		CKBB
VI			TPI		15
NP2			14		IDH-M
GLNS			NP		MANA
TF			11		PKM2
UMPK			HBA		HEXA
GUK3			10		SORD
AMY			CS		MPI
VII			HK		16
GALT2			APK		GOT-M
IDH2					HBA
U3					19
GOT3					GPI
MDH1					PEPD
U4					MANB
PEPA					CKMM
TPI1					
GAPD3					

FIG. 4. Linkage groups of several vertebrates postulated to have been derived from duplication of a single chromosome of a vertebrate ancestor. Poeciliid, salmonid, and frog syntenic groups are composited from gene maps from several related species. [From Morizot (1990).]

locus in question has not always been delineated. Unlike the case for mammals, in which only single loci have been well characterized for several biochemical loci, in fish, polyploidy and other types of gene duplication have resulted in several loci at specific enzyme-encoding loci—thereby complicating the intepretation of any linkage relationship. As the cDNAs and genes of various loci are cloned and unambiguously identified by DNA sequencing, the relationships of these loci should become more obvious. In addition, the use of restriction mapping of fish genomes and the use of specific gene probes will be particularly useful in expanding the potential of this approach. Although these approaches are beginning to be used in fish gene mapping, to date the vast majority of the data have been derived from classical genetic techniques.

Because the possibility that convergent evolution is responsible for similar linkage groups in each class of vertebrates does not seem compelling, one must question how these linkages could be maintained for hundreds of millions of years. Morizot (1990) has hypothesized that the conservation of some genetic linkages for more than 400 million years could be explained by (1) strong natural selection that preserves specific genetic linkages because of functional and/or positional evolutionary constraints, or (2) the gene duplication strategy, commonly employed by vertebrates, that resulted in one or more specialized meiotic mechanisms that require chromosomes to retain specific gene arrangements. Perhaps as more genetic linkage information becomes available in a variety of "lower vertebrates," the mechanisms responsible for this important evolutionary phenomenon will become clear.

VI. Gene Duplication and the Evolution of Multigene Families

Gene duplication has been a fundamental mechanism in the evolution and biochemical diversification of plants and animals. Gene duplication can be accomplished by replicating a portion of a gene, an entire gene, a series of genes, or an entire genome (polyploidy).

Polyploidy has arisen in fish as a result of chromosomal replication without cell division within a species (autoploidy) or by combining chromosomes from two different allopatric taxa as a result of interspecies hybridization (alloploidy). Incidences of both of these mechanisms can be distinguished by karyotype and electrophoretic analyses. In the first case, the chromosomes are from identical sources, whereas in the second case, the karyotype of the hybrid is a combination of two different karyotypes. Allendorf and Thorgaard (1984) have shown that salmonids are autotetraploids, and Ferris (1984) has presented convincing evidence that catostomids are allotetraploids. Triploidy is produced in some poeciliid species by an interesting and very useful mechanism (Schultz, 1977).

Duplication of a single gene probably arises by some error in cell division, such as unequal crossing-over, which results in duplicated genes that are in tandem. These duplicated genes sometimes diverge in function but in other cases they do not. If genes are amplified many times, they will yield a higher concentration of the gene product unless the duplicated gene(s) is not expressed. Sequential gene duplication followed by evolutionary divergence (but with similar physiological function) is illustrated by the classic cases of the vertebrate hemoglobin and lactate dehydrogenase gene families.

A. EVOLUTION OF VERTEBRATE HEMOGLOBINS

Myoglobin and hemoglobin are excellent molecules to illustrate gene duplication followed by evolutionary divergence. The primary function of hemoglobin is to carry oxygen from the gas-exchange organs to the metabolizing tissues. When that tissue is red muscle, myoglobin binds the oxygen and passes it on to the cytochrome system, where it becomes the final electron acceptor in the oxygen transport chain. The physiological function of both myoglobin and hemoglobin depends on their ability to form a reversible complex between oxygen and the ferrous iron in a hematoporphyrin prosthetic group that is buried in a hydrophobic pocket of the protein (i.e., globin). The amino acid residues that hold the heme in its hydrophobic pocket have been highly conserved for over 400 million years of evolution. The globin, with its associated hematoporphyrin, is approximately 16 kDa and constitutes either the myoglobin molecule or one of a subunit of the hemoglobin molecule, which is a tetramer of four globin chains (about 64 kDa).

Although some species have hemoglobins that are composed of identical globin subunits, most have at least two different types. In adult vertebrates these polypeptides are usually referred to as the α and β chains. Some of the earliest indications that myoglobin and hemoglobin were derived from a common evolutionary source arose from structural studies. Extensive studies over the past several decades have confirmed this notion, which was generated several decades ago.

In humans, both α chains are identical and consist of 141 amino acids each, whereas the hemoglobins of some fish species have two or more α chains with slightly different amino acid sequences (see e.g., Gillen and Riggs, 1971; Powers and Edmundson, 1972; Mied and Powers, 1978;

Takeshita *et al.*, 1984). The heme group is covalently bound between the iron and the imidazole side chain of a histidine at or near the 87th amino acid, which is called the proximal histidine of the α chain. The human β chains are slightly larger than the α chains, approximately 146 amino acids, and the proximal histidine is at or near the 92nd amino acid. Although the teleost β chains are also about 146 residues, the shark α and β chains are both about the same size (approximately 142 amino acid residues) (Nash *et al.*, 1976; Fisher *et al.*, 1977). As was the case for the α chains, human β chains are identical within the human hemoglobin tetramer, but duplicated β chains in some fish species vary in primary structure.

The primary structures of myoglobins and the subunits of hemoglobin from a variety of species have been used to estimate ancestral relationships among taxa (review in Goodman *et al.*, 1982). Figure 5 summarizes some of that information for myoglobins and α- and β-hemoglobin subunits from a few selected vertebrate species. This tree supports the hypothesis that several gene duplications gave rise to the globin multigene family. It has been agreed for many years that a monomeric globin ancestral gene was duplicated approximately 500 million years ago, and that divergence of structure and function followed. The functional divergence probably involved restriction of one molecule to muscle tissues (myoglobin) and the other to the circulation (hemoglobin). Myoglobin evolved a higher oxygen affinity than hemoglobin, enabling it to receive oxygen from the latter. Due to osmotic and oxygen affinity requirements, cooperativity evolved that facilitated the binding of oxygen at the respiratory surface and its delivery to the tissues. In the lamprey, a tetramer of identical hemoglobin subunits will form a tetramer when deoxygenated, but will disassociate into monomers upon oxygenation. This is perhaps one of the first steps in the generation of a cooperative hemoglobin tetramer in vertebrates. Subsequent to the divergence of myoglobin and the monomeric-like hemoglobin, there was another gene duplication about 450 million years ago, just before the divergence of the ancestors of the Elasmobranchii and Teleostei. After duplication, the α and β chains arose by evolutionary divergence. The tetrameric hemoglobin molecule that evolved would "relax" when oxygenated instead of "falling apart" (i.e., dissociation into monomers), as was the case with the lamprey hemoglobin. About 350 million years ago, an α chain gene duplication gave rise to α chain alternatives, including ζ chain of human hemoglobin and the π chain of birds. A number of gene duplications over the last 250 million years yielded a series of β chain derivatives, including human δ, τ, and ϵ chains. Another example of β chain divergence is that expressed in the

◇ **Gene Duplication**

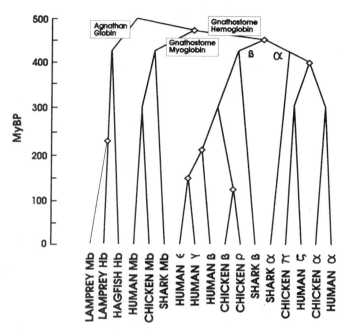

FIG. 5. Representative vertebrate lineages in the globin gene family as a function of millions of years before the present (MyBP); Mb, myoglobin; Hb, hemoglobin. [After Goodman *et al.*, 1982).]

adult frog and its larvae. These two β chains are thought to have diverged about 400 million years ago—well before the evolution of anuran amphibians per se.

Kimura (1981) attributed the tremendous sequence divergence of myoglobin and hemoglobin chains to a single origin of myoglobin from an ancient duplication. Goodman *et al.* (1982) points out that according to the molecular clock hypothesis, that event would have to have been approximately a billion years ago. Goodman's cladistic analysis (Goodman *et al.*, 1982) suggests that myoglobins arose independently from a general globin ancestor at least three times during metazoan evolution, including two times during vertebrate evolution. He points out that lamprey heart muscle myoglobin has a much greater homology with the two known sequences of lamprey hemoglobin than with any other sequence, whereas the myoglobins of jawed vertebrates are closer to the hemoglobin subunits of Gnathostomata than to any other sequences. In fact, they go further and suggest that this duplication was an important factor favoring the successful radiation of jawed vertebrates (Goodman *et al.*, 1982). As stated above, the evolution of α and β chains created the possibility for a heterotetrameric hemoglobin that eventually yielded a molecule with enhanced cooperativity that facilitated the binding of oxygen at the organism–environment interface and better delivery of the oxygen to the tissues.

In general, globins have eight helical segments designated A through H. The D helix is missing from the α chains and from both the α and β chains of shark hemoglobins (Nash *et al.*, 1976; Fisher *et al.*, 1977). Nonhelical regions between helical segments are designated by the helices on either side (e.g., EF and FG). Globins have clusters of hydrophobic residues on the outside of some helices. Studies of the three-dimensional structures of these molecules have shown that in monomeric myoglobin, hydrophobic residues are pointing toward the interior of the molecule, whereas in hemoglobin they are either pointing toward the interior or are located at interfaces with the other subunits of the hemoglobin polymer and thus are not exposed to solvent. These subunit–subunit contacts are very important in (1) stabilizing the tetrameric structure, (2) controlling oxygen-binding capability, and (3) the cooperative binding of oxygen.

The α and β chains of tetrameric vertebrate hemoglobins are arranged as a dimer of dimers—i.e., a tetramer of two identical α chains and two β chains. One dimer is designated $\alpha_1\beta_1$ and the other dimer, $\alpha_2\beta_2$. Together these form the $\alpha_1\beta_1 : \alpha_2\beta_2$ tetramer. The contacts between these various polypeptides are thus referred to as the $\alpha_1\beta_1$ (or $\alpha_2\beta_2$) and $\alpha_1\beta_2$ (or $\alpha_2\beta_1$) contacts, respectively. Comparisons of the oxy- and deoxyhemoglobin three-dimensional structures indicate that, upon oxygenation, the hemoglobin tetramer relaxes and the β chains move apart by approximately 7 Å. This is associated with a change in the position of the β chains relative to the α chains. These and other structural alterations upon oxygenation involve the movement of the subunits relative to each other such that there are changes in the amino acid contacts between complementary α and β subunits. When one compares homologous sequences of elasmobranchs and teleosts with those of higher vertebrates, it becomes obvious that evolutionary pressures have conserved critical $\alpha_1\beta_2$ contact residues as well as certain portions of the $\alpha_1\beta_1$ contacts. This observation was initially made many years before the sequences of elasmobranch α and β chains and teleost β chains were available (Powers and Edmundson, 1972). As these and other lower vertebrate sequences have become available, that initial observation has stood the test of time.

The energy changes that take place during the breaking and remaking of bonds at the $\alpha_1\beta_2$ interface are responsible for most of the subunit cooperativity of hemoglobin–oxygen binding. Among the $\alpha_1\beta_2$ contacts, evolutionary substitutions have been very limited in number and are generally conservative isopolar changes (Table 1). Residues conserved in one chain tend to be somewhat different in the other chain, but complementary contacts tend to be conserved across taxa (Table 1). The $\alpha_1\beta_2$ contacts, presumed by the evolutionary conservation of these residues, have been shown to be very important in subunit cooperativity. It is reasonable to assume that rapid evolution of these subunit contacts took place following gene duplication and the divergence of α and β subunits, and that natural selection for subunit cooperativity generated complementary $\alpha_1\beta_2$ contacts that have been conserved over evolutionary time (Table 1). Similar arguments could be made for other parts of the hemoglobin molecule that are involved in allosteric modulation, such as the organophosphate-binding site, residues involved in the Bohr effect, and those involved in the heme pocket.

B. LACTATE DEHYDROGENASE EVOLUTION

Lactate dehydrogenase (LDH) is a tetrameric enzyme that reversibly converts pyruvate to lactate and NADH to NAD^+. There are at least three LDH isozymes in vertebrates: LDH-A (muscle form), LDH-B (heart form), and LDH-C (Holbrook et al., 1975; Markert et al., 1975; Whitt et al., 1975). LDH-A and LDH-B tend to have specific biochemical functions and tissue distributions (Everse and Kaplan, 1975; Markert et al., 1975; Whitt et al., 1975). LDH-A is best suited for pyruvate reduction in anaerobic tissues, whereas LDH-B is superior for lactate oxidation in aerobic tissues. In lower teleost fishes, LDH-C has a generalized tissue distribution, but it is either eye or liver specific in advanced teleosts (Shaklee et al., 1973; Markert et al., 1975; Kettler and Whitt, 1986). In mammals and birds, LDH-C is expressed only in mature testes (Blanco et al., 1975; Wheat and Goldberg, 1983). It is surprising that LDH-C has only been found in one family of birds, Columbidae (Matson, 1986).

The LDH isozymes were thought to have arisen from a single LDH-A*-like locus (Markert et al., 1975). This primordial locus was presumably duplicated to form LDH-A* and LDH-B*; then LDH-B* was duplicated to form LDH-B* and LDH-C* (Fig. 6A) (Markert et al., 1975; Whitt et al., 1975). Support for this theory is based on many types of evidence. There appear to be only two LDH isozymes in lower vertebrates (reptiles and below) (Fisher et al., 1980). Advanced teleosts are

TABLE 1

The $\alpha_1\beta_2$ (or $\alpha_2\beta_1$) Interchain Contacts in Mammalian and Nonmammalian Hemoglobins[a]

Position in horse hemoglobin	α Chains					β Chains				
	Horse	Chicken	Frog	Carp	Shark	Horse	Chicken	Frog	Carp	Shark
C2	Pro	Pro	Tyr	Pro	Ala	Pro	Pro	Pro	Pro	Pro
C3	Thr	Thr	Thr	Glu	Ala	Trp	Trp	Trp	Trp	Trp
C5	Lys	Lys	Lys	Lys	Lys	Gln	Gln	Gln	Gln	Thr
C6	Thr	Thr	Thr	Thr	Ser	Arg	Arg	Arg	Arg	Arg
C7	Tyr	Tyr	Tyr	Tyr	Tyr	—	—	—	—	—
CD2	Pro	Pro	Ala	Ala	Lys	—	—	—	—	—
FG3	Leu	Leu	Leu	Leu	Asp	—	—	—	—	—
FG4	Arg	Arg	Arg	Arg	Lys	His	His	His	His	His
FG5	Val	Val	Val	Val	Val	Val	Val	Val	Val	Val
G1	Asp	Asp	Asp	Asp	Asp	Asp	Asp	Asp	Asp	Asp
G2	Pro	Pro	Pro	Pro	Pro	Pro	Pro	Pro	Pro	Val
G3	Val	Val	Val	Ala	Ala	Glu	Glu	Ala	Asp	Glu
G4	—	—	—	—	—	Asn	Asn	Asn	Asn	Ser
H23	Tyr	Tyr	Tyr	Tyr	Tyr	Tyr	Tyr	Tyr	Tyr	Tyr
H24	—	—	—	—	—	His	His	His	His	His

[a] Aligned by homology with horse globins.

an exception in that they have three LDH isozymes (Shaklee et al., 1973; Markert et al., 1975; Whitt et al., 1975; Fisher et al., 1980). The two isozymes that occur in most vertebrates are thought to be LDH-A and LDH-B because of their tissue-specific distribution, biochemical parameters, and immunoaffinity (Wilson et al., 1964; Holmes, 1972; Shaklee et al., 1973; Holmes and Scopes, 1974; Markert et al., 1975; Whitt et al., 1975; Whitt, 1984). The existence of LDH-A prior to tetrapod divergence is indicated by the similarity of the primary structures of the dogfish LDH-A (class Chondrichthyes) and mammalian LDH-A (Li et al., 1983). LDH-B is thought to be the second LDH isozyme (i.e., other than LDH-A) in lower vertebrates, and its gene (LDH-B*) was presumably duplicated and diverged to form LDH-B* and LDH-C* in advanced teleosts (Markert et al., 1975; Whitt et al., 1975). Finally, the enzyme kinetics for the mammalian LDH-C are more similar to those of the LDH-B isozyme than to those of LDH-A (Blanco et al., 1975). Because the mammalian and teleostean LDH-C isozymes are not functionally similar to phylogenetically older LDH isozymes, they appear to have evolved by independent gene duplications. A recent and independent evolution of the teleostean and mammalian LDH-C is also suggested by its limited taxonomic distribution, specialized tissue distributions, and differential developmental regimes (Shaklee *et al.*, 1973; Champion *et al.*, 1975; Millan *et al.*, 1987). Both the taxonomic distribution of these three LDH isozymes and other evidence suggest that LDH-C evolved independently in teleosts and mammals.

On the other hand, a variety of structural data suggest that the primordial vertebrate LDH is more similar to mammalian LDH-C than to LDH-A (Li *et al.*, 1983; Rehse and Davidson, 1986; Baldwin and Lake, 1987; Crawford *et al.*, 1989; Li, 1990; Hiraoka *et al.*, 1990). This suggestion is primarily based on computer analyses of LDH amino acid sequences from a variety of species (Li *et al.*, 1983; Crawford *et al.*, 1989) (see Fig. 7). Although some portions of the evolutionary scheme illustrated in Fig. 6A are supported by the computer analysis illustrated in Fig. 7, other parts are not. For example, the conclusion that LDH-A and LDH-B in lower vertebrates are homologous to the avian/mammalian LDH-A and LDH-B, respectively, is supported by the computer analysis. However, a recent and independent origin of LDH-C is not as readily supported. If LDH-C was recently derived, then it should have the greatest similarity to the locus from which it originated, i.e., either *LDH-A** or *LDH-B**. Instead, the mammalian LDH-C is the least similar, suggesting either that it is closer to the ancestral isozyme or that it

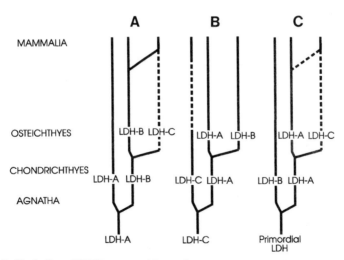

FIG. 6. Evolution of LDH isozymes. Three alternative patterns of LDH isozyme evolution are represented: (A) the scheme of LDH evolution according to Markert *et al.* (1975); (B) the model of LDH evolution as the synthesis of information presented in Crawford *et al.* (1989); and (C) modification of pattern A.

has evolved so rapidly that the expected similarity is obscure. Consistent with the hypothesis that LDH-C is ancestral, Baldwin and Lake (1987) showed that, relative to the other teleostean LDH enzymes, both the single isozyme in lampreys and the heart-type isozyme in hagfish have the greatest immunoaffinity to teleostean LDH-C. In addition, Baldwin *et al.* (1988) showed that the amino acid composition and immunocharacteristics of the only LDH in a lower chordate (subphylum Urochordata, *Pyura stoloifera*) are most similar to the teleostean LDH-C. The concept that LDH-C is similar to the primordial LDH is, therefore, a major departure from the theory advanced by Markert *et al.* (1975), in two fundamental ways: (1) the evolutionary order from which the isozymes arose must be different and (2) the primordial isozyme (i.e., LDH-C) has maintained its structural but not its functional similarity.

An alternative evolutionary scheme is presented in Fig. 6B. As seen in the figure, LDH-C is suggested to be most like the ancestral LDH isozyme. The ancestral *LDH** locus was duplicated to form *LDH-C** and *LDH-A**. Then *LDH-A** in turn was duplicated to yield *LDH-B**. Within this scheme, another pathway would be *LDH-C** as a precursor of *LDH-B**. Although the computer analysis (Fig. 7) does not support this alternative pathway, other investigators have shown that teleost LDH-B is immunologically more similar to teleost LDH-C than is LDH-A (Whitt, 1969; Shaklee *et al.*, 1973; Whitt *et al.*, 1975).

The major problem with an LDH-C-like isozyme being ancestral is the extensive information on the taxonomic distribution of LDH isozymes (Markert *et al.*, 1975), which is not consistent with that hypothesis. For example, there is no evidence for an observable third isozyme in amphibians, reptiles, and most birds. The two LDH isozymes in amphibians and reptiles have the conserved biochemical and physiological functions of LDH-A and LDH-B. This presents a logical dilemma because taxonomically older and younger groups contain LDH-C, and there is evidence from both groups that these isozymes are most similar to the ancestral LDH. If an LDH-C-like protein is ancestral, then the current taxonomic distribution would have to be the result of (1) LDH-B evolving independently in advanced teleost and terrestrial vertebrates, (2) LDH-C in mammals and fish evolving independently, as suggested by Markert *et al.* (1975), but with LDH-C evolving much more rapidly than LDH-A or LDH-B and in a direction that obscures its evolutionary origin, or (3) all three LDH isozymes being present prior to the divergence of teleost and terrestrial vertebrates but with the LDH-C "turned off" or cryptically expressed in some lower vertebrates. Both of the latter two cases would require differential evolutionary rates for the LDH isozymes in different vertebrate classes.

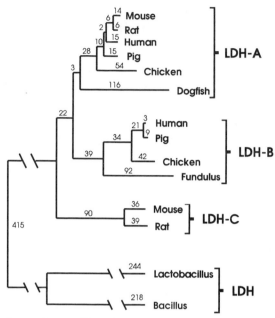

FIG. 7. Phylogenetic tree. The phylogenetic relationship between the 14 LDH iso-zymes according to a computer-generated dendrogram based on protein sequence information. [After Crawford *et al.* (1989).]

Our work on *F. heteroclitus* LDH-B can be used to reject the first hypothesis (Crawford *et al.*, 1989) because it clearly indicates that the fish LDH-B was homologous to the mammalian and avian LDH-B. This analysis (Fig. 7) also indicates that the branch lengths of the two lower vertebrate LDHs were longer than those of higher vertebrates, suggesting that the rate of evolution is different in these vertebrate taxa. If that suggestion is correct, then it would be consistent with the second and third hypotheses alluded to above. However, rapid evolution of LDH in lower vertebrates is contrary to the accepted paradigm that lower vertebrates have a slower rate of evolution (Bush *et al.*, 1977). Either our computer analysis is misleading or the paradigm of Bush *et al.* (1977) needs closer scrutiny. Other work presented in this review and current work on other fish LDHs, strongly support the notion that several loci are evolving rapidly in lower vertebrates and that the rate of evolution is variable. Those data are not consistent with the hypothesis of Bush *et al.* (1977) and do not support the constant "molecular clock" hypothesis.

If it is assumed that the evolutionary scheme in Fig. 6B is correct, then there are at least two alternatives that could account for the

missing third isozyme. First, if LDH-C is similar to the primordial
isozyme and LDH-A occurs in primitive vertebrates, then the two isozymes in primitive fishes and lower tetrapods should be LDH-A and
LDH-C, not LDH-A and LDH-B. As stated above, we can reject this
hypothesis because it implies that LDH-B evolved independently in
advanced teleosts and mammals, and all the available data indicate
that the LDH-B isozymes from all vertebrate classes have a common
origin. Second, if the three isozymes in teleosts have homologues in
mammals, then all three isozymes should occur in lower tetrapod vertebrates and in the Sarcopterygii (the fish from which tetrapods were
derived; see Fig. 1). However, to date, a third isozyme has not been
found in sarcopterygian fish. Though this may be due to the scarcity of
tissue samples from these fish, as suggested by Markert *et al.* (1975), the
absence of a third LDH isozyme in amphibians, reptiles, and most birds
(Fisher *et al.*, 1980; Matson, 1986) cannot be easily explained by such
reasoning. Because it is unlikely that a silent locus could maintain its
functional and structural similarity over the 330 million years during
which the tetrapods evolved, perhaps the third LDH isozyme has been
overlooked or misidentified in lower tetrapods.

Recently, two *LDH-B** pseudogenes have been identified in the teleost, *Fundulus heteroclitus* (G. Bernardi and D. A. Powers, in preparation). Both of the pseudogenes were identified by the presence of mRNA
that did not produce active enzyme. One of the two has a single base
change that resulted in a termination codon and the other had a large
deletion—both precluded the formation of active enzyme. The presence
of *LDH-A** pseudogenes in mammals (S. Lee, personal communication)
and *LDH-B** pseudogenes in fish present the possibility that *LDH-C**
pseudogenes may exist in lower vertebrates. Studies on fish genomic
*LDH** genes are needed to address this possibility.

The lack of an observable third LDH isozyme in lower terrestrial
vertebrates could be explained by the technical difficulty in detecting it.
LDH-C in teleosts has the greatest variability in both tissue distribution and electrophoretic mobility, relative to other LDH isozymes
(Shaklee *et al.*, 1973; Champion *et al.*, 1975; Whitt *et al.*, 1975; Whitt,
1984). In addition, in mammals, LDH-C is expressed only in breeding
males (Millan *et al.*, 1987). This variation and the temporal expression
may explain why it has not been found in some lower tetrapods. Further
studies are needed to test this hypothesis.

The potential homology between the mammalian and lower vertebrate LDH-C is suggested by the ancestral origin of this locus, as
presented in Fig. 6B. Although the immunochemical and amino acid
characterizations of the single LDH in lampreys and tunicates indicate

that it is most similar to the teleostian LDH-C, there is no corroborating evidence that these LDH isozymes are orthologous to the mammalian LDH-C. There is a need to determine the LDH sequences from tunicates and jawless fishes, and it is equally important to sequence at least one teleost LDH-C in order to determine if the mammalian and teleost diverged from the same source or if they arose independently. Current work on Tunicate LDH cDNA sequencing (J. Quattro and D. A. Powers, in preparation) suggests that it may reflect a primordial LDH with some amino acid sequence similarities to each of the three LDH isozymes. Comparison of the Tunicate LDH sequence with that of LDH-A, LDH-B, and LDH-C from other vertebrates, including fish, should provide a better understanding of the evolution of these important enzymes. On the basis of the available sequence data, the conservation of the LDH-A*/LDH-C* linkage group, and an apparent GC-codon bias in fish DNA, a third scheme for the evolution of LDH in vertebrates is presented in Fig. 6C. The actual evolutionary scheme will be much more complex that that presented in any of the schemes in Fig. 6, but delineating the appropriate details will require extensive cDNA and genomic DNA sequence studies from a variety of fish taxa and representative invertebrates. Those studies are currently underway in several laboratories.

C. Protamine Genes

Protamines are small argine-rich proteins that are only found in the nuclei of sperm (Gedamu et al., 1977; Jatrou et al., 1978; Dixon et al., 1986). They are synthesized during spermiogenesis and replace somatic histones in the nucleus. The trout protamine multigene family was the first to be properly characterized and has acted as the model system for mammalian protamine genes until relatively recently, when mammalian protamines were characterized. The trout system contains approximately 20 different protamine genes with at least six different sequences (Aiken et al., 1983; McKay et al., 1986a), whereas mammals apparently only have two genes, which are referred to as P1 and P2, respectively (Kleene et al., 1985; McKay et al., 1986b; Yelick et al., 1987; Krawetz et al., 1987; Krawetz and Dixon, 1988; Bellvé et al., 1988).

Dixon and colleagues (1986) have examined the distribution of protamines among teleost fishes and found that only a limited number of fish suborders express the smallest protamines. This has led to the hypothesis that the protamine multigene family evolved by horizontal transmission, possibly involving retroviral integration (Jankowski *et al.*, 1986). An alternative model has been proposed based on data obtained from mammalian protamines (Krawetz *et al.*, 1987). This model referred to as the regional assembly model, requires the joining of a "species-specific" variable region with the highly conserved "protamine core" region, to form the mammalian P1 protamine gene. Krawetz *et al.* (1987) also proposed that the highly conserved poly(arginine)-rich segment, referred to as the protamine core, reflects a primordial gene from which the multigene family arose. Although the existence of a common protamine core could be explained by convergent evolution, Dixon and his colleagues (Krawetz *et al.*, 1987; Krawetz and Dixon, 1988) have argued that the arginine codons are also highly conserved, favoring divergent evolution.

Krawetz and Dixon (1988) searched GenBank sequences for similarities to the trout, bovine, and mouse protamine sequences and found that the poly(arginine)-coding core sequences were conserved in a variety of species. For example, they found similarities in hepatitis B virus core antigen from several mammals and the *Escherichia coli* P protein (Altman *et al.*, 1981). Particularly interesting was their suggestion that the shark protamine, which contained a poly(arginine) core similar to that of microorganisms and mammals, represented an intermediate evolutionary form. These and other findings (Krawetz and Dixon, 1988) led to the conclusion that the arginine-rich core represents a primordial sequence from which the protamine gene family arose.

VII. Genes That Respond to Environmental Changes

Comparative physiologists and biochemists are interested in the mechanisms that organisms use to adapt to environmental stress. Fish are particularly good models because they live in a variety of habitats and must adapt to environmental parameters such as temperature, pressure, oxygen, pH, and salinity, which are easily measured and controlled under laboratory conditions. Hochachka and Somero (1984) nicely capture the flavor of this research area and illustrate many of the adaptive mechanisms and strategies employed by aquatic animals.

Temperature is a particularly useful parameter to illustrate biochemical adaptation. Fish are cold-blooded organisms and their success involves adaptations to changes in environmental temperature. This is accomplished by a host of metabolic, physiological, and behavioral changes that are genetically determined.

A. Heat-Shock Protein Genes

When stressed, organisms employ a broad repertoire of biochemical, physiological, and behavioral strategies in order to maintain homeostatic functions. Molecular adaptation to a given stress usually involves the induction of one or more specific proteins that provide cellular protection. For example, in response to an elevation in ambient temperature, a family of heat-shock genes is expressed resulting in a rapid synthesis of heat-shock proteins (hsps) (reviews in Schlesinger *et al.*, 1982; Atkinson and Walden, 1985; Burdon, 1986; Lindquist, 1986). Heat-shock proteins are expressed in all organisms (prokaryotes, eukaryotes, plants, and animals) in response to a variety of physical and chemical stresses. A particularly remarkable feature of this phenomenon is the high degree of evolutionary conservation of heat-shock gene and protein structure across diverse taxa (Schlesinger *et al.*, 1982; Atkinson and Walden, 1985), suggesting that they are an ancient set of genes whose function(s) is both general and fundamental. Although all the functions of hsps are not known with any certainty, there is compelling evidence that some of these proteins protect cells from heat damage and may be involved in the acquisition of thermotolerance (Lindquist, 1986). This stems primarily from the observation that a thermal stress that is sufficient to induce synthesis and accumulation of hsps will later provide transient thermotolerance, allowing cells to survive a temperature that would otherwise be lethal in the absence of hsps (Li and Laszlo, 1985). This is not a firm rule, because there are numerous examples of heat-shock-induced development of thermotolerance in the absence of hsp synthesis (Lindquist, 1986). In either case, the molecular mechanisms by which the thermoprotection occurs are not known. Heat-shock genes have also been implicated in a variety of other biological functions, including the renaturation of proteins, the mediation of protein–protein exchange, protein interactions, chaperoning proteins to and from organelles, the development of malignancy, receptor/hormone interactions, and receptor activation.

Because heat-shock genes are selectively and rapidly activated, this phenomenon has proved to be an excellent molecular model to study gene expression and regulation. A more holistic approach to the study of heat shock is also gaining favor. Analysis of the importance of hsps in the thermal ecology of a natural animal population and determining if hsps have a role in acute and evolutionary adaptation of organisms to high-temperature stress may eventually provide a means by which the function of heat-shock genes in cellular physiology can be determined. The heat-shock response of the model teleost, *F. heteroclitus,* has been studied because it is one of the most heat-tolerant fishes (Umminger, 1975; Bulger and Tremain, 1985) and can adapt to a very wide range of temperatures. Moreover, it experiences rapid and substantial temperature changes diurnally and seasonally in its habitat of salt marshes and estuaries. Koban *et al.* (1991) have described some of the unusual features of the heat-shock response of *F. heteroclitus* that are related to the evolutionary adaptation of this fish to its highly variable thermal environment.

The span of temperatures that constitute a stressful condition and result in induction of the heat-shock response varies tremendously among poikilothermic vertebrates. For example, antarctic fishes living at $-1.6°C$ will die of heat stress when the temperature is raised to only $6°C$ (Somero and DeVries, 1967), but the desert pupfish, normally living at $35°C$ or more, has an upper lethal temperature of $45°C$ (Bulger and Tremain, 1985). In addition to interspecies differences, responses to temperature stress vary depending upon the thermal history of an organism. What this means is that the upper lethal temperature usually is not fixed. Often it can be extended upward, but within genetically defined limits, by adaptation near the lethal limit (Hochachka and Somero, 1984; Prosser, 1986).

Many of the molecular mechanisms by which poikilotherms adapt to changes in the thermal environment have been elucidated (Hochachka and Somero, 1984; Prosser, 1986). What is less understood is how thermotolerance is achieved. An intriguing aspect of thermal biology and physiological ecology is the role of heat-shock genes in short-term and evolutionary adaptation to heat stress. Of particular interest is whether the heat-shock response of thermotolerant organisms is more effective or more efficient than it is in organisms that are heat intolerant. Eventually, such studies may help explain the relationship between geographical distributions of organisms and environmental temperature.

Numerous studies of the heat-shock response of organisms representing diverse taxa have shown that the major hsps of the 70-kDa class may be composed of one, two, or more protein species (Schlesinger *et al.*, 1982; Atkinson and Walden, 1985). The family of proteins of this class generally ranges in molecular mass from about 68 to 76 kDa, with hsp70 being the most evolutionarily conserved and ubiquitous. hsp70 is not expressed by *F. heteroclitus;* rather, the fish has two major hsps of 76 and 74 kDa that are expressed differentially among tissues (Koban *et al.*, 1991). The heat-shock response of *F. heteroclitus* resembles that of channel catfish (Koban *et al.*, 1987). Although these fish are not related taxonomically, both species express hsp76 and hsp74, and the temperature profiles for synthesis of these hsps are nearly identical. However, the liver of channel catfish expresses both hsp76 and hsp74, whereas liver of *F. heteroclitus* synthesizes only hsp76. Nevertheless, the heat-shock response may be similar because their thermal ecology is comparable—both fish are eurythermal and readily adapt to a wide range of temperatures (Koban, 1986; Kent *et al.*, 1988), and can encounter heat stresses in excess of 40°C in their natural habitats. Interestingly, the fat-head minnow (FHM) is taxonomically closely related to *F. heteroclitus* and occupies similar habitats, but FHM cells primarily express hsp70 (Merz and Laudien, 1987); in ovary cells of the semitropical fish *Tilapia*, hsp70 is the only 70-kDa class hsp that is synthesized (Chen *et al.*, 1988). Among stenothermal fish, salmonids fare poorly when the temperature approaches 25°C, and the predominant hsp that is synthesized is hsp70 (Kothary and Candido, 1982; Heikkila *et al.*, 1982; Gedamu *et al.*, 1983). These examples illustrate that expression of a specific hsp of the 70-kDa class cannot be correlated to the relative thermotolerance of organisms. Clearly, the evolutionary forces that dictate the expression of different hsps of the 70-kDa class even among closely related organisms, and the selective biological advantages (if any) of these differences, remain tantalizing questions. Nevertheless, one relationship that appears to hold is that the threshold temperature for hsp induction and the temperature of maximal hsp synthesis are strongly correlated to the range of temperatures normally encountered by an organism. Hence, organisms native to cold environments, such as salmonid fish, will induce synthesis of hsps at 24–27°C (Heikkila *et al.*, 1982; Kothary and Candido, 1982). By contrast, organisms adapted to warm or hot climates do not express hsps until stress temperatures reach 30–40°C or more (Koban *et al.*, 1991). These and other studies suggest that the span of temperature for initiation of the heat-shock response may be fixed according to evolutionary adaptation to a thermal habitat (Koban *et al.*, 1987, 1991).

Hightower and Schultz (1991) have examined the isoforms of two major families of heat shock proteins in poecliid fishes of the genus *Poeciliopsis* and found substantial variation in both hsp 70s and hsp 30s among the six species studied. The hsp 30s were particularly variable even within species, and some evidence was also found for hsp 70 variation within species.

Studies of the molecular biology of the heat-shock response have shown the regulation of heat-shock gene expression to be quite complex. The level of transcriptional and translational control exerted varies among organisms. Primary control at the level of transcription occurs in *E. coli* (Yamamori and Yura, 1980) and yeast (Lindquist, 1981), whereas dominance of translational control is found in *Xenopus* oocytes (Bienz and Gurdon, 1982). With most organisms, regulation resides at both transcription and translation, but in fish it appears that gene regulation also differs among tissues (Koban et al., 1991). Because many of the hsp genes have been highly conserved for hundreds of millions of years, perhaps the main focus of evolutionary geneticists should be on the evolution of hsp gene regulation rather than on the evolution of the coding regions of homologous members of this environmentally sensitive multigene family.

B. ANTIFREEZE GENES

Although fish invoke heat-shock gene expression in response to elevated temperatures (Koban et al., 1987, 1991), in response to extreme cold some fish species have evolved a novel set of antifreeze genes that encode proteins that keep their blood from freezing. DeVries (1969, 1971), who discovered antifreeze proteins (AFPs), found that polar fish express these genes all year whereas temperate species, such as winter flounder, express AFPs only in winter (reviews in DeVries, 1971, 1988, Feeney and Yeh, 1978; Feeney, 1988; Davies et al., 1982, 1984). This seasonal variation is an excellent system to study the role of environmentally regulated gene expression.

Antifreeze proteins of Antarctic fish are composed of repeating units of Ala-Ala-Thr with a disaccharide, galactosyl-N-acetylgalactosamine, glycosidically linked to the threonine (Raymond et al., 1989). Winter flounder AFPs differ in that they do not have disaccharides. The flounder cells express an alanine-rich helical protein whose primary, secondary, and tertiary structures have been determined (Lin et al., 1972; Raymond et al., 1989; Yang et al., 1988), and the elegant mechanism by which these proteins bind microice crystals and lower the blood's freezing point has been formulated (see, e.g., DeVries et al., 1971; DeVries and Lin, 1977; Chakrabartty et al., 1988; Knight et al., 1991). The DNA sequences encoding these genes have been elucidated (see, e.g., Lin and Gross, 1981; Davies et al., 1982, 1984; Gourlie et al., 1984; Scott et al., 1985, 1986, 1988), and microinjection of the gene into other species has also been successful (Fletcher et al., 1988). In addition, AFPs from a variety of other fish species have also been purified and sequenced and in some cases the cDNA or genomic genes have also been characterized.

The antifreeze protein genes are clustered in tandemly arranged groups (Scott et al., 1985) with extensive sequence homology (see, e.g., Lin and Gross, 1981; Davies et al., 1982, 1984; Gourlie et al., 1984; Scott et al., 1985, 1986, 1988). The number of gene copies (gene dose) appears to be directly related to the winter serum levels of antifreeze protein

(Scott *et al.*, 1988). For example, the winter flounder has higher levels of AFP than does yellowtail flounder and has a concomitantly higher number of gene copies. Higher levels of AFP are directly related to freeze protection, and the winter flounder is exposed to consistently lower winter temperatures than is the yellowtail flounder. Though the timing of gene expression is related to environmentally induced factors, it appears that maximum AFP serum concentration is also related to gene dosage. The evolution of the regulatory mechanisms that control AFP gene expression and the amplification of these genes within and between species have probably been important to the survival and radiation of several fish species into frigid waters during past glacial events and to expansion of home ranges.

Scott *et al.* (1986) combined evidence from paleoclimatology, the teleost fossil record, AFP protein and DNA sequences, and the genomic organization of AFPs from several fish groups to conclude the Cenozoic cooling was an important evolutionary force that helped shape the distribution of AFPs among teleost taxa. They conclude that Cenozoic glaciation in the Southern Hemisphere, which preceded glaciation in the Northern Hemisphere by 25 million years, affected the present distribution of AFPs among teleost suborders, families, genera, and species. They suggested that the AFP gene organization and amplification, mentioned above, are consistent with that hypothesis. Such a hypothesis would require convergent evolution for alanine-rich AFPs in both Northern and Southern Hemisphere species. Although Scott *et al.* (1986) present a reasonable and logical case for convergent evolution, further evidence is necessary to confirm or reject this interesting theory. Their hypothesis requires the development of some of the AFP multigene families that date back only a few million years, which, if correct, would provide an opportunity to study a multigene family in the process of evolution. In any case, the time is ripe to address the detailed molecular mechanisms responsible for the regulation of this multigene family, delineate the modes by which information is transferred from the environment to the fish's target tissue, and clarify the evolutionary constraints operating on this important genetic mechanism of environmental adaptation.

C. Enzyme-Synthesizing Loci

The potential adaptive role of genetic variation of enzyme-synthesizing loci has been the subject of intense investigation for almost three decades. Indeed, few subjects in biology have been more debated than the evolutionary significance of protein polymorphisms

(Lewontin, 1974). Most of the debate centered around two contrasting views: the "selectionist" view and the "neutralist" view. Proponents of the former school assert that natural selection maintains protein polymorphisms, whereas those of the latter persuasion argue that the vast majority of such variation is selectively neutral. Lewontin (1974) summarized the failure of evolutionary biologists to resolve this important controversy by biogeographical and mathematical approaches alone. Stimulated by Lewontin's book (Lewontin, 1974), a few evolutionary biologists, including myself, developed experimental approaches to the neutralist/selectionist controversy.

Since the neutralist hypothesis implies that most genetic variation is functionally equivalent, it can be rejected for specific loci whenever functional nonequivalence can be established between allelic alternatives. The major advantage of an experimental strategy is the ability to generate and test hypotheses. If functional analysis of allelic isozymes leads to predictable differences in cell physiology, organism response, etc. that can be substantiated by experimentation, then the neutralist hypothesis can be rejected for that locus. Experiments designed to test these cellular predictions should yield results that allow one to make other testable predictions at higher levels of biological organization. As each new cycle of predictions is followed by experimental testing, one can ultimately be led to accept either the selectionist or neutralist paradigm. If predictions can be followed by experimental validation, then the selectionist viewpoint would be supported; otherwise, the neutralist position would be favored. It is this cycle of *a priori* predictions, coupled with testing those predictions, that provides the power of the experimental approach.

My colleagues and I have been using this approach to address the evolutionary significance of genetic variation within species. We are studying allelic variants of an array of enzyme synthesizing loci in the model teleost *Fundulus heteroclitus*, an abundant Atlantic coast fish ranging from the Mantanzas River in Florida to Port au Port Bay in Newfoundland, Canada. *Fundulus heteroclitus* maintain a very high level of protein polymorphism (reviews in Powers *et al.*, 1986; Powers, 1990; Powers *et al.*, 1991). Biogeographical examination of those loci have uncovered significant directional changes in gene frequency (i.e., clines) and genetic diversity in relation to latitude. Directional changes in genetic characters with geography (i.e., clines) have classically been described by two general models: primary and secondary intergradation. In the primary intergradation model, adaptation to local conditions along an environmental gradient or genetic drift may lead to genetic differences along the gradient. Gene flow may not eliminate these differences, either because it is too small or because of nonrandom dispersal along the gradient. In the secondary intergradation model, populations are first separated by some barrier that prevents gene flow. Next, adaptation to local conditions and/or genetic drift produces genetic differences between these disjunct populations. When the isolating barrier is removed, the formerly disjunct populations interbreed, producing a cline in gene frequencies between them. The main difference between these two models, therefore, is the need for the previous existence of isolating barriers to gene flow in the latter.

Evidence from mtDNA and other studies support the secondary intergradation model for the present day spatial gene frequency patterns of *Fundulus heteroclitus* (Gonzalez-Villasenor and Powers, 1990; Powers, 1990; Smith *et al.*, 1992). While these biogeographical studies are useful for placing the genetic clines into a historical context, they do not provide insight concerning the relative contributions of chance (e.g., genetic drift) and adaptive (e.g., natural selection) forces that shaped the genetic divergence between allelic alternatives prior to, during, and/or after an isolation event. Yet, it is the relative roles of chance and adaptive forces that strike at the very heart of the neutralist/selectionist controversy. Thus, additional approaches must be undertaken to determine the role of natural selection, if any, as a driving force for generating and/or maintaining gene diversity. In an attempt to address these issues, we have taken the experimental approach alluded to above.

Since *Fundulus heteroclitus* is found in one of the steepest thermal gradients in the world, if temperature affects, or has affected, the differential survival of fish with specific allelic isozymes, then natural selection could be, or may have been, acting to change the gene frequency of populations that experience different thermal regimens along the East Coast. Using temperature and other environmental variables (e.g., oxygen, salinity, pH, etc.) that change over the species' natural distribution, we have employed an experimentally based strategy in an attempt to falsify the hypothesis that natural selection was (or is) a major driving force responsible for the observed gene diversity in *Fundulus heteroclitus*. Our strategy begins with a detailed biochemical study of the allelic isozymes and progresses through higher levels of biological organization by a linked series of predictions followed by experimental testing of those predictions.

We have examined over 50 loci for electrophoretic variation within and between populations and inheritance studies have been done on 20 of the polymorphic loci (Place and Powers, 1978; Van Beneden *et al.*, 1981; Brown *et al.*, 1988). Of these 20 loci, we have examined the allelic isozymes of seven loci for differences in steady-state kinetics, thermal stability, and *in vivo* enzyme concentration. The enzymes that we have examined are encoded by the lactate dehydrogenase "heart" locus (*LDH-B**), a cytoplasmic malate dehydrogenase locus (*MDH-A**), a cytoplasmic NADP-dependent isocitrate dehydrogenase (*IDHP-B**), hexose-6-phosphate dehydrogenase (*H6PDH**), glucosphosphate isomerase (*GPI-B**), phosphoglucomutase (*PGM-A**), and a cytoplasmic aspartate amino transferase locus (*AAT-A**). Steady-state kinetic analysis and thermal stability differences have been found for the allelic isozymes of *LDH-B*, *IDHP-B*, *H6PDH**, and *GPI-B**. While thermal stability differences were apparent for the allelic isozymes of *AAT-A**, there was no obvious kinetic variation. *In vivo* concentrations of LDH-B and MDH-A were found to be much higher for fish living in cold northern waters than their southern counterparts but no differences were found for PGM-A and GPI-B (see, e.g., Crawford and Powers, 1989; Crawford *et al.*, 1990; Powers *et al.*, 1991).

Based on the functional differences between allelic isozymes alluded to above, experiments were designed to explore differences at higher levels of biological organization, including genotype-specific cellular metabolism, oxygen consumption, swimming ability, developmental rates, and hatching times (see, e.g., DiMichele and Powers, 1982a,b, 1984; Paynter *et al.*, 1991; DiMichele *et al.*, 1991). Results of those experiments were used to predict heterochrony and mortality differences between phenotypes. Our selection experiments demonstrated hatching time and mortality differences for both single and multilocus phenotypes in relation to temperature (DiMichele *et al.*, 1986; DiMichele and Powers, 1991). Moreover, those fish that survived the highest temperature regime were also the most common phenotypes at the warm southern extreme of the species natural distribution. The molecular mechanism responsible for this differential survivorship is currently being elucidated. Although this multidiscipline approach is just beginning to bear fruit, it already appears that some enzyme loci are maintained by natural selection but that others are not.

Another example of this approach is the work of Vrijenhoek and colleagues, who have shown dramatic differences in survival among populations of the fish genus *Poeciliopsis* (Quattro and Vrijenhoek, 1989; R. C. Vrijenhoek, personal communication). In addition, laboratory and field selection experiments reveal the action of natural selection on genetic variants marked by four enzyme-encoding loci. Using acute cold, heat, and anoxia—variables that mimic seasonal environmental stress—they demonstrated that enzyme heterozygosity and survival were intrinsically linked (R. C. Vrijenhoek, personal communication). It will be exciting to explore the biochemical and molecular basis for this phenomenon in the future.

Elucidating the array of molecular mechanisms that animals use to adapt to diverse environments in one of the exciting challenges for modern biology; again fish provide excellent models to meet that challenge.

D. Cytochrome P-450 Genes

The cytochrome P-450-dependent monooxygenases are known to be involved in the metabolism of steroids, prostaglandins, fatty acids, and other naturally occurring biomolecules. In addition, these proteins in fish catalyze the biotransformation of aquatic-borne environmental contaminants such as pesticides, carcinogens, and other xenobiotics (Stegeman and Kloepper-Sams, 1987; Jewell et al., 1989). The genes expressing these proteins are part of a multigene superfamily composed of a dozen or more families of closely related genes whose products have similar substrate specificities. Although sequence information is available on several of the genes and/or their proteins from mammalian sources, comparatively little structural information is known about homologues from fish and other lower vertebrates. In the absence of adequate sequence information from lower vertebrates, the postulated evolutionary relationships among vertebrates are based entirely upon mammalian sequences (Gonzalez et al., 1989; Nebert et al., 1989). Proteins functionally similar to rat cytochrome P-450IA1 have been isolated for several fish species (Klotz et al., 1983; Williams, and Buhler, 1983; Goksoyr, 1985). Some researchers have used antibodies directed against mammalian P-450 proteins to probe tissues of fish and other lower vertebrates (see, e.g., Ronis et al., 1989; Stegeman, 1989).

Ronis et al. (1989), for example, have used polyclonal antibodies, directed against mammalian cytochrome P-450c (P-450IA1), P-450d (P-450IIB1), P-450h (P-450IIC11), and P0450j (P-450IIE1), to probe liver microsomes prepared from a variety of vertebrate groups, including jawless fish (hagfish), elasmobranchs (shark), bony fish (perch), and reptiles (caimen and alligators), as well as several birds and a mammal. Cross-reactivity was used to examine the expression of cytochrome P-450 isozymes in an attempt to provide insight about the evolution of the cytochrome P-450 gene families I and II and their regulation in lower vertebrates. Although a general lack of cross-reactivity was apparent for some antibodies, others reactions provided evidence that certain families of cytochrome P-450 are present in lower vertebrates.

The general properties of P-450 proteins in various fish species have been reviewed by Bend and James (1978) and Stegeman (1981). These enzymes have been characterized in 10 teleost fish families including

characterization of the specificity and concentrations of microsomal
P-450 in fish livers, factors that vary depending upon species, strain,
and sex (Pedersen *et al.*, 1976; Stegeman and Woodin, 1984; Stegeman,
1989).

Multiple *P*-450 proteins have been described in a number of fish
species with distinct chemical, physical, and catalytic characteristics
(review in Stegeman and Kloepper-Sams, 1987). Using immunological
techniques, cross-reactions between the various proteins have been
characterized for several teleosts (see, e.g., Park *et al.*, 1986; Kloepper-
Sams *et al.*, 1987; Goksoyr *et al.*, 1989). Induction studies have been
done in these teleosts and have suggested that a member of the aromatic hydrocarbon-inducible *P*-450IA family is present in all fish species examined. The use of an antibody for a teleost *P*-450IA1 protein
confirmed that hypothesis.

Heilmann *et al.* (1988) cloned and sequenced a cDNA from a trout
BNF-inducible *P*-450. The sequence similarity to that of the mammalian *P*-450IA forms was adequate enough to suggest that the trout
cDNA encoded a member of the *P*-450IA protein family. This finding
was consistent with an earlier suggestion by Stegeman and Kloepper-
Sams (1987) that was based on BNF induction and immunological data.
Jaiswal *et al.* (1985) had previously speculated that the divergence of
mammalian *P*-450IA1 and *P*-450IA2 genes took place subsequent to the
divergence of the teleost and mammalian ancestral forms. Consistent
with that hypothesis, Heilmann *et al.* (1988) have shown that the trout
P-450 cDNA shows 57–59% sequence similarity with the mammalian
P-450IA1 and 51–53% similarity with *P*-450IA2. On the basis of the
combined data, Stegeman (1989) concluded that the teleost *P*-450IA
gene was orthologous to the mammalian *P*-450IA1 and *P*-450IA2 genes.

Stegeman (1989) reviewed the evidence for and against multiple
forms of *P*-450 genes in teleosts and suggested that multiple forms of
*P*450IA genes are not only present in teleosts, but they may be evolving
differently than in their mammalian counterparts. Recently, T. T. Chen
and colleagues (personal communication) have shown that 3-
methylcholathrene induces at least two *P*-450 genes in trout. This has
been demonstrated by the direct sequencing of cDNA generated from
mRNA extracted from induced fish. The amino acid sequences of the
gene products appear to be about 96% similar. T. T. Chen and colleagues (personal communication) have also mapped the two trout
P-450 genomic genes. Future studies on the sequences of *P*-450 genes
from teleosts and elasmobranchs should provide important insights
concerning the evolution of this important multigene family.

E. Metallothionein Genes

Many metals are highly toxic to both terrestrial and aquatic organisms. Some organisms are better adapted than others to survive in the presence of high concentrations of metals. One reason for this phenomenon may be the induction of a series of metal-binding proteins that sequester these metal toxicants. This potential detoxification mechanism would allow tissue metal concentrations many orders of magnitude greater than are found in the external environment. Though this mechanism may be advantageous to some organisms, the excess metals may be concentrated as they are moved up the food chain. Pathological consequences that can result from consuming excess metals have been shown to include damage to the kidney and reproductive systems. Heavy metals cause DNA breakage and alter the fidelity and efficiency of cellular enzymes. These damages to DNA may lead to informational errors and affect genetic integrity. Moreover, if this DNA damage occurs in germ-line DNA, it will be passed on to subsequent generations. An understanding of this toxicity–detoxicity cycle is a critical element in understanding the physiological ecology of marine organisms and related public health problems. An understanding of the genetic mechanisms that regulate these processes will provide insight concerning the ability of some fish species to survive heavy metal contamination while others do not.

When vertebrates are exposed to certain transition metals, they respond by increasing the synthesis of a unique class of proteins in the liver, kidney, intestine, and other organs. These proteins, termed metallothioneins, are low-molecular-weight, cystein-rich proteins that bind metals with high affinity (review in Kagi and Nordberg, 1979). These proteins were first isolated from mammalian tissue and they have been found in numerous lower vertebrates as well (Kagi and Nordberg, 1979). Each metallothionein molecule binds up to seven atoms of transition metals. Metallothioneins have molecular masses around 10 kDa and the amino acid sequences are somewhat conserved in an evolutionary sense.

There are two major families of metallothioneins, referred to as MT-I and MT-II. The MT-I group can be resolved into several molecular forms (MT-IA, MT-IB, etc.) that have slightly different metal-binding constants. The proteins are encoded by a multigene family and their differential induction is dependent upon their promoter elements.

Animals exposed to chronic levels of transition metals accumulate large amounts of metallothionein. Organisms exposed to sublethal initial doses of transition metals are subsequently able to tolerate toxic doses, even though such doses are lethal to animals that do not receive an initial exposure (see, e.g., Webb and Verschoyle, 1975). Similarly, metal toxicity may be abated by direct administration of metallo-thionein. These data suggest that the induction of metallothionein protects organisms by complexing the metal toxins, thereby reducing the concentrations of toxic free metals.

During the past decade, a number of investigators have studied the induction of metallothionein proteins in various fish species in relation to environmental metals, including cadmium, copper, mercury, and zinc, among others. Though most of those studies were conducted at the whole organism level, Gedamu and colleagues (Price-Haughey et al., 1987) developed trout hepatoma cell lines that could be used as models to study metal-induced synthesis of metallothioneins. They found that trout cell lines were more responsive to some metals than to others and that the time course of gene expression was different for the different metals, suggesting that the various metals may differentially regulate gene expression at the posttranscriptional level. These and other stud-ies have used fish metallothionein cDNA (MT-cDNA) to quantitate the levels of the specific MT-mRNA. Fletcher and colleagues (Chan-King et al., 1989) have studied heavy metal metabolism in winter flounder using an antisense-MT-RNA that allowed them to quantitate precisely the concentration of MT-mRNA in various tissues in response to an assortment of heavy metals. They have also recently finished a detailed evolutionary study of the structure of metallothionein genes and proteins in fish and higher vertebrates.

F. ONCOGENES

Protooncogenes are highly conserved across taxa. In mammals, am-plification, rearrangement, and changes in gene expression of cellular oncogenes have been associated with certain kinds of tumors and other types of malignant conditions. Tumors in a variety of fish species have been noted for many years. Russell and Kotin (1957) were the first to suggest a correlation between environmental pollution and incidence of fish tumors. Those correlations were emphasized when an outbreak of liver cancers in cultured rainbow trout was traced to the presence of an aflatoxin in their food (review in Mix, 1986). Hepatocellular carcinomas have been found to be significantly elevated in the winter flounder (*Pseudopleuronectes americanus*) from Boston Harbor (Murchelano and Wolke, 1985) and in the English sole (*Pleuronectes vetulus*) from Puget Sound (Malins et al., 1985). The latter study suggested that the tumors might be the result of excess polycyclic aromatic hydrocarbons in the sediments. The elegant studies of Hendricks *et al.* (1985) demonstrated that, indeed, the polyclyclic aromatic hydrocarbon, benzo[*a*]pyrene, was capable of inducing hepatomas. In fact, the induction of fish tumors has been demonstrated in a variety of fish and with many different types of carcinogens (see, e.g., Sinnhuber *et al.*, 1977; Schultz and Schultz, 1982a,b, 1985; Stanton, 1965; Aoki and Matsudaira, 1977; Hyodo-Taguchi and Matsudaira, 1984). In a particularly important paper, Schultz and Schultz (1988) demonstrated that wild fish populations contained enough genetic diversity in their response to carcinogens to account for the presence of resistant phenotypes as a direct result of natural selection. They identified intraspecies differences in the incidence and types of tumors, as well as, the rate of tumor development. The ability to induce neoplastic lesions in fish tissues has inspired innovative methods for detecting chemical carcinogens, and some researchers have suggested that fish might be preferable for such studies (reviews in Hendricks, 1982; Hendricks *et al.*, 1984; Klaunig *et al.*, 1984; Bailey and Hendricks, 1988; Couch *et al.*, 1981; Simon and Lapis, 1984; Dawe and Couch, 1981; Hawkins *et al.*, 1988).

In addition to chemical carcinogens, viruses have been suggested as potential causes of fish neoplasms. For example, Papas and colleagues (1976, 1977) suggested that lymphosarcomas in the Northern pike were the result of a C-type virus. Kimura *et al.* (1981) indicated that lesions or tumors in salmon could be induced upon exposure to some types of herpes viruses.

The discovery that melanomas could be generated in hybrid crosses between swordtails (*Xiphophorus helleri*) and platyfish (*Platypoecilus maculatus*) opened an entire new area of melanoma research. Following this discovery, hundreds of scientists analyzed the genetic basis of this interesting phenomenon (see, e.g., Anders, 1967; Anders *et al.*, 1973; Anders and Anders, 1978; Ozato and Wakamatsu, 1981; Perlmutter and Potter, 1988; Vielkind *et al.*, 1989). Playtfish have melanin pigment patterns that are coded by specific color genes. For example, one strain has a black-pigmented spot or spots on the dorsal fin, the expression of which is controlled by an allele of a sex-linked locus. If a female is crossed with a melanin-lacking male swordtail, the offspring will have abnormal melanization that will often lead to melanomas. Anders *et al.* (1984) described the color gene as an oncogene and suggested that it was correlated with c-*src*. This color oncogene is controlled by at least one regulatory locus and a host of environmental and physiological factors.

There have been other oncogenes studied in fish and some have been analyzed at the molecular level. The c-*myc* gene was isolated and characterized from rainbow trout (Van Beneden *et al.*, 1986) and the *ras* genes have been cloned and sequenced from goldfish (Nemoto *et al.*, 1986) and trout (Mangold *et al.*, 1991). Each of these genes showed a remarkable similarity to their mammalian and avian counterparts. For example, Van Beneden *et al.* (1988) compared the c-*myc* gene sequence of trout with those of other species and found very interesting results that increase our understanding of the evolution and function of cellular oncogenes in neoplasia. The intron regions between trout exons II and III were found to be shorter than those of chicken or human. Van Beneden and colleagues (1988) suggested that the smaller intron size in the c-*myc* gene was evolutionarily more primitive. The c-*myc* gene of trout showed extensive homology to exons II and III of the c-*myc* gene of chicken and human, but exon III was more highly conserved. The most extensive homology was identified in a particular part of exon II, where unique inserted regions were also found for each of these species. The other exons appeared to vary as a result of accumulated point mutations. Comparisons of the vertebrate c-*myc* oncogene sequences caused Van Beneden *et al.* (1986, 1988) to conclude that the human and chicken sequences were more similar to each other than either were to the fish sequence. They concluded that this was consistent with the evolutionary model in which birds and mammals share a common lineage that diverged relatively early from the line that led to modern fishes.

For many years, trout has been a particularly good model for carcinogenesis (reviews in Hendricks *et al.*, 1984; Bailey *et al.*, 1984, 1987). However, until recently, c-*myc* was the only protooncogene studied at the molecular level. Yet, members of the *ras* gene family are more often implicated in tumorigenesis (review in Bos, 1989). Recently, Bailey and colleagues have undertaken a detailed analysis of trout *ras* genes (Mangold *et al.*, 1991; Chang *et al.*, 1991). They found two *ras* genes (*ras-1* and *ras-2*) expressed in the livers of rainbow trout. Sequence comparisons with human *ras* indicated a homology of between 76.8 and 87.1%. The majority of the base differences between the fish and human *ras* genes resided in changes that did not require alterations in the protein sequence. In fact, the predicted amino acid sequence of the trout *ras-1*-encoded protein differed by only one residue out of the first 172 amino acids of the human c-*Ki-ras*-encoded protein, but it varied by 17–18 residues from the human proteins encoded by c-*N-ras* and c-*H-ras*, respectively. These highly conserved sequences caused Mangold *et al.* (1991) to conclude that the *ras*-encoded p21 protein has the same function in normal and neoplastic cells among the various vertebrate classes.

Information gained during the study of the trout *ras* genes identified by Mangold *et al.* (1991) was used by Chang *et al.* (1991) to identify chemically induced *ras-1* mutants in liver tumors of trout. They analyzed DNA isolated from aflatoxin B1-induced liver tumors from trout by screening exon 1 of both *ras-1* and *ras-2* genes. Of the samples screened, over 70% of the aflatoxin B1-induced liver tumors showed evidence of activating point mutations in the trout c-*Ki-ras* gene, and the majority of those point mutations were codon 12 GGA-to-GTA transversions, whereas the others were either codon 12 GGA-to-AGA or codon 14 GGT-to-GTT transversions. This elegant paper was the first experimental study on fish that clearly demonstrated the induction of *ras* point mutations. These classic papers demonstrate the utility of fish as model systems and the evolutionary and functional linkage of fish protooncogenes with those of higher vertebrates.

Schartl and Peter (1988) demonstrated that malignant melanotic melanoma tissue from the swordtail fish *Xiphophorus* transplanted into thymus-aplastic nude mice showed progressive growth of the fish tumors. Moreover, while the tumor adapted to the physiological conditions of the mammalian host, it retained its fish-specific morphology and biochemical specificity. In a recent study, winter flounder tissues that contained histopathological lesions were assayed for oncogenes by transfection of the DNA into mouse fibroblasts. The transfected fibroblasts induced subcutaneous sarcomas when transferred into nude mice, and Stegeman has suggested that those sarcomas may contain fish c-*Ki-ras* oncogenes.

VIII. The Evolution of Genes Involved with Development

Modern developmental biology tends to focus on (1) embryonic pattern formation, including the movement and eventual fate of specific cells, (2) the mechanisms responsible for developmental stability, (3) the expression of specific genes during development, including their regulatory mechanisms, (4) agents responsible for initiating new developmental programs and shifting the timing of developmental events, (5) sex determination, (6) the mechanisms of cellular and tissue differentiation, and (7) the mechanisms that control organ system development. Although many of these topics can be addressed by using a variety of model organisms, clearly a vertebrate is needed for questions relating to typical vertebrate development, and fish have continued to be favorite models for over a century. An excellent review on fish developmental genetics addressed many of these foci from an evolutionary perspective (Thorgaard and Allendorf, 1988). They emphasized the underlying theme that gene regulation is intrinsically tied to evolutionary adaptation and from that perspective, fish provide a unique vantage point. Because that review is relatively recent, only a few points will be mentioned here.

In the absence of an extensive array of laboratory mutants, geneticists have taken advantage of interspecific fish hybrids, unisexual fish, and species derived from polyploid ancestors to address fish developmental and evolutionary genetic questions. The use of interspecific fish hybrids to study the fate of alleles and gene regulation is an *in vivo* analog to the *in vitro* somatic cell hybrid technique commonly employed to study gene regulation in mammalian cell culture. The application of this approach has been reviewed by Whitt (1983). He has shown that the greater the evolutionary distance between the parental stocks of hybrids, the greater the frequency of expression of abnormal characters; also, maternal alleles are generally expressed at their normal time but paternal alleles are delayed. With the recent advances in genetic techniques to manipulate fish genomes, the time is ripe to address the mechanisms responsible for these interesting observations.

Shifts in the timing of developmental events (heterochrony) have also been studied using fish models. These shifts, which are evolutionarily important, can sometimes be traced to a single locus. For example, Kallman (1983) has shown that differences in the time required to reach sexual maturity in the swordtail *Xiphophorus maculatus* is a function of a single locus that regulates luteinizing hormone-releasing hormone.

Some investigators have shown that the developmental rate and time required for hatching are correlated with specific enzyme-encoding loci that presumably play an important role in the timing of developmental events. For example, DiMichele and Powers (1982a, 1984, 1991) showed that developmental rate and hatching in the killifish *F. heteroclitus* was highly correlated with genetic variation of the "heart" locus of lactate dehydrogenase (*LDH-B**) and other loci (DiMichele *et al.*, 1986). The homozygote for one allele, *LDH-B*a,* consumed oxygen faster and hatched earlier than did the homozygote with the other allele, *LDH-B*b.* Recently, it has been shown that oxygen consumption was altered in a predictable way by the type of lactate dehydrogenase enzyme microinjected into fertilized eggs, indicating that the enzyme had a direct effect on development (DiMichele *et al.*, 1991). Developmental rate and hatching differences have also been observed for other loci in *Fundulus* (DiMichele *et al.*, 1986; DiMichele and Powers, 1991). In addition, Allendorf and colleagues (1983) have shown that the amount of phosphoglucomutase in rainbow trout livers was correlated with developmental rate and hatching. The concentration of this enzyme was regulated by a gene, *PGM1-tr*,* that affects the liver tissue specificity of one phosphoglucomutase locus that, in turn, affects development. Other studies have reported delays in the expression of allelic isozymes encoded by a lactate dehydrogenase locus (Wright *et al.*, 1975) and an isocitrate dehydrogenase locus (Danzmann *et al.*, 1985) in rainbow trout. Finally, Knudsen *et al.* (1984) have shown that the tetraploid rainbow trout can be used to study the effect of null alleles of a lactate dehydrogenase locus (*LDH3**) on developmental stability (Thorgaard and Allendorf, 1988). Because these fish were derived from tetraploid ancestors, they have two or more copies of many enzyme loci—making the detection of null alleles possible.

One of the major drawbacks to using vertebrates for developmental studies has been the paucity of mutants. The cryptic nature of mammalian development and the problems associated with identifying and isolating these mutants have been both costly and difficult. On the other hand, the zebrafish has been an unusually successful model for generating and analyzing developmental mutants. The success of the zebrafish system is largely the result of methods that allow (1) developmental mutants to be identified in a single generation, (2) the generation of completely isogenic stocks in a single generation, (3) the cryopreservation of gametes, (4) the ability to artificially generate mutants, and (5) the ability to create transgenic fish (see Powers, 1989, and references therein). Streisinger and his colleagues, for example, introduced methods for large-scale production of homozygous diploid zebrafish, *Brachydanio rerio* (Streisinger *et al.*, 1981; Streisinger, 1984). This simple technique involves the activation of eggs by sperm whose DNA had been inactivated by UV irradiation, followed by duplication of the maternal haploid genome. The first cell division is then prevented by heat stress or hydrostatic pressure; however, subsequent cell divisions are allowed to proceed without intervention. Thus, the offspring is a diploid homozygote with the maternal genome. Due to the unusual sex-determination characteristics, the offspring are both males and females, so that normal breeding can ensue for the next generation. This general approach has been applied to other fish, but some require hormones to produce males. A novel variation on Streisinger's theme uses active sperm to initiate development of trout eggs whose DNA had been photoinactivated (Thorgaard *et al.*, 1985).

The movement and eventual fate of cells during development can be studied by direct observation of unmarked or marked cells. The latter is usually accomplished by introducing one of several nontoxic "tags" that facilitate observation. Kimmel and colleagues have illustrated how a combination of direct observation of unmarked cells, cells tagged with fluorescent dyes, and genetic mosaics can be used to study the lineages and eventual fates of embryonic cells (review in Kimmel and Warga,

1988). They demonstrate that substantial indeterminacy exists in blastomere lineages, but considerable lineage restriction exists after gastrulation. However, it is not clear that postgastrula cells are irrevocably committed. This is an important developmental and evolutionary question that needs to be resolved.

The studies of Grunwald and collaborators illustrate the power of Streisinger's approach for isolating and analyzing developmental mutants (Grunwald *et al.*, 1988). One of Grunwald's mutants causes degeneration of later-developing central nervous system components, but does not affect early primary neural tissue. This and other studies on zebrafish are providing important insights about vertebrate development and such studies are not as easily approachable employing other vertebrate systems. Clearly, zebrafish are becoming a powerful tool to study vertebrate development, and recent molecular studies on fish neuropeptides (see, e.g., Kitahara *et al.*, 1988), hormones (see Section XI), and homeobox genes (Eiken *et al.*, 1987; Njolstad and Fjose, 1988) coupled with the ability to make transgenic zebrafish (Stuart *et al.*, 1988) promise an expanded role for zebrafish in biology and an enhanced understanding of the developmental mechanisms that play key roles in the evolutionary genetics of fish and other vertebrates.

IX. Genes Involved with the Nervous System

For decades, neurobiologists have found fish to be excellent model systems for experimental and evolutionary studies. In fact, most biologists and physicians over 40 years of age had their first exposure to vertebrate neuroanatomy when they dissected the brain and cranial nerves of the dogfish shark. Classical comparative neurobiology has provided important insights concerning the evolution of the nervous system and a deeper understanding of the role the human system plays in health-related issues. These insights can come from the use of fish as models to understand vertebrate neurobiology in general and from the perspective provided by their fundamental evolutionary relationship with other vertebrates. Bullock accentuated the fact that Hughlings Jackson emphasized this point almost 100 years ago (Bullock, 1983; Lassek, 1970). In fact, it has been asserted that certain progressive neurological diseases are best understood in the context of the evolutionary states of the nervous system, in which evolutionarily higher central nervous system functions are lost first, then sequentially lower evolutionary states, with the order being reversed during recovery. Bullock has provided several examples that are consistent with that hypothesis (Bullock, 1983). In addition, several studies on fish sensory systems at the cellular and molecular levels have contributed significantly to the advancement of neurobiology of higher vertebrates. Our present concept of vertebrate color vision, for example, has been significantly influenced by a number of classical studies on fish retina (see, e.g., Daw, 1968; Powers and Easter, 1983). The fish visual system continues to be an excellent model for vertebrate vision, as was apparent during a special symposium at the European Neuroscience Association meeting in Oristano, Italy, during August, 1989. The topics ranged from optics to retinal functions and central processing to visually guided behavior. Studies on the molecular cloning and sequencing of fish eye crystallin genes (Chang and Chang, 1987; Chang et al., 1988) have furthered our understanding of the evolution of lens proteins and other molecular studies have added to our understanding of vertebrate color vision, including the evolution of color vision pigments.

A. EVOLUTION OF COLOR VISUAL PIGMENT GENES

Vision has a very important impact on an organism's ability to survive. It is critical in many aspects of an organism's life, including mating behavior, predator/prey relationships, and migration. An organism's visual pigments are characterized by the wavelength at which they absorb light. Human color vision is characterized by one short-wavelength blue-sensitive (420 nm) pigment and two long-wavelength pigments that are green sensitive (530 nm) and red sensitive (560 nm), respectively. The human genes for these pigments have been cloned and sequenced (Nathans et al., 1986). The long-wavelength pigments are very similar to each other and probably diverged from a common ancestral gene about 30 million years ago, and it is suspected that the short- and long-wavelength genes probably diverged several hundred million years ago (Nathans et al., 1986; Yokoyama and Yokoyama, 1988). Recent molecular work on the evolution of a fish green-sensitive color vision gene (Yokoyama and Yokoyama, 1990) revealed approximately 70% identity with both the human red-sensitive and green-sensitive genes. Even though the fish gene was isolated from a blind cave fish (Astyanax fasciatus), it had a sequence that should encode a functional gene product. When the DNA sequence of the fish green-sensitive gene was compared with the human color vision genes, it appeared that the fish gene was more similar to human red- and green-sensitive genes than to the blue-sensitive gene. Moreover, the analysis also suggested a higher rate of nucleotide substitution in the fish gene than in the human genes, which was suspected to reflect accumulated nucleotide substitutions during the past 400 million years. Because one could explain this apparent rapid evolution by an accelerated evolutionary rate of pseudogenes, sequence analyses of other fish color vision genes will be necessary to test more rigorously the evolutionary hypothesis proposed by Yokoyama and Yokoyama (1990).

Two other examples particularly worth mentioning are studies on the acetylcholine receptor and the Na^+ channel.

B. ACETYLCHOLINE RECEPTOR GENES

Prosser described neurobiology as the neuronal basis of animal behavior, which is determined by neural circuits that are controlled by cell–cell communications, including chemical coupling through neurotransmitters (Prosser, 1986). Most neurotransmitters are amino acids, their derivatives, or peptides. Acetylcholine (ACh) is a combination of choline (from serine) and acetyl-CoA. ACh is perhaps the most universally recognized neurotransmitter by nonneurobiologists. It is widespread among most taxa and performs a variety of important functions. Research on the ACh receptor and the Na^+ channel of fish has played a critical role in the development of neurobiology.

Approximately one-third of vertebrate neurons respond to ACh. In the brain, there are at least two types of ACh or cholinergic receptors, muscarinic and nicotinic. The most important studies on the nicotinic receptor have used fish models. The electric organ of the ray, *Torpedo californica,* contains cholinergic neurons that innervate electrocytes that develop from myotubes but have 1000 times more ACh receptors than do muscle cells (review in Whittaker, 1987). Due to its abundance, the ACh receptor has been extensively characterized, including the cloning and sequencing of all four of its protein subunits (Numa *et al.,* 1983; Devillers-Thiery *et al.,* 1983; Noda *et al.,* 1983; Mishima *et al.,* 1984; Raftery *et al.,* 1980). Moreover, this receptor has been reconstituted in artificial membranes and its role in the disease myasthenia gravis has been elucidated. These studies on the fish ACh receptor are one of the most important successes in molecular neurobiology. In fact, it has become the model approach to which other studies aspire, and the use of the fish model system was critical to its development.

C. SODIUM CHANNEL GENES

Another example in which research on fish has paved the way for molecular approaches to neurobiology is provided by the studies on the voltage-controlled Na^+ channel. This integral membrane protein is responsible for the extremely rapid depolarization associated with propagated action potentials in nerve and muscle cells of animals from many phyla. Studies of Na^+ channels have guided researchers addressing other voltage-controlled channels, such as K^+ and Ca^{2+} channels, which are even more widespread and functionally diverse.

The Amazonian electric eel, *Electrophorus electricus,* like the electric ray, *T. californica,* is well endowed with electroplax tissue for delivering strong electric shocks to both predators and prey. Extensive research during the 1950s and 1960s on the electric organ of this fish resolved a bitter conflict between bioelectrical and biochemical interpretations of the nervous system. Since that time, this fish has been a favorite model for other neurochemical studies. For example, because the electric organ is such a rich source of Na^+ channels, it was used as a tissue source for the purification of the first Na^+ channel (Agnew *et al.,* 1978). This Na^+ channel was also the first from which essentially normal functional activity was successfully reconstituted (Rosenberg *et al.,* 1984a). Those studies on fish Na^+ channels have become the model for studies on other channels (Flockerzi *et al.,* 1986).

As was the case for the ACh receptor, a fish Na^+ channel was the first of such molecules to be cloned (Noda *et al.,* 1984). The primary structure revealed four repeating homologous units, each of which contained a unique sequence in which five to seven positively charged lysine or arginine residues occurred at every third position, with mostly other polar residues at intervening positions (Fig. 8). Because of the similarity between this sequence and the hypothetical structure of the voltage-dependent gating machinery for the channel (Armstrong, 1981; Gilly and Armstrong, 1982), it was proposed that this macromolecular machine was a transmembrane structure that underlies the intermembrane charge movement that triggers opening of the channel, referred to as gating current. This concept is central to all proposed structural models that attempt to account for Na^+ channel function (Catterall, 1988).

The S4 sequence identified in the eel Na^+ channel has apparently been conserved for hundreds of millions of years because nearly identical structures have now been identified in essentially every other voltage-controlled channel that has been cloned and sequenced: the Na^+ channels from rat brain (Noda *et al.,* 1986) and *Drosophila* (Salkoff *et al.,* 1987a,b), the Shaker K^+ channel from *Drosophila* (Tempel *et al.,* 1987), and the dihdyropyridine receptor from rabbit skeletal muscle, a putative Ca^{2+} channel (Ellis *et al.,* 1988). The presence of an S4-like sequence has become diagnostic for identifying genes coding for voltage-controlled ion channels (Fig. 8). Clearly, this evolutionarily

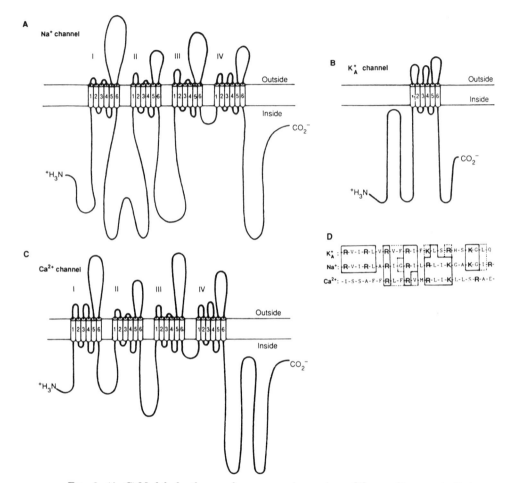

FIG. 8. (A–C) Models for the membrane-spanning regions of three voltage-controlled ion channels. The S4 region of each domain is segment 4. (D) Conservation of the S4 region among voltage-controlled channels described in the text and pictured in A–C. Positively charged amino acids (arginine = R; lysine = K) are regularly spaced with two intervening residues. Solid lines enclose identical amino acids; dotted lines denote conservative replacements (standard single-letter designations for amino acids are used). This figure is adapted from Catterall (1988) (© 1988 by the AAAS) and was previously presented in a paper by Powers (1989).

important work on the electric eel has directly shaped our present understanding of the molecular structure and function of these and perhaps all channels gated by membrane voltage. Clearly, evolutionary studies involving fish have much wider impacts on our understanding of biological phenomena and processes than simply expanding details of evolutionary genetics of fish systems.

X. Evolution of Genes Involved with the Immune System

A. The Immunoglobulin Gene Superfamily

The immunoglobulins and T cell receptors are multisubunit proteins that are key elements in the immune response. They are involved in the self versus non-self recognition and have the capacity of effecting highly specific recognition of a diversity of foreign molecules (i.e., antigens). The cellular, molecular, and evolutionary origins of this specificity have been a major focus of a large number of scientists for the better part of this century. As a result of extensive sequence analyses of proteins and DNA and elegant cellular studies, a general understanding of this important biological phenomenon has begun to emerge.

Immunoglobulins (Ig) are found in vertebrate serum as circulating antibodies and on the surface of B cells (bone marrow-derived lymphocytes) as receptors for antigens. The T cell receptor (TCR) is the immunoglobulin counterpart found on the surface of T cells (thymus-derived lymphocytes). Many other molecules show some structural similarity to one or more parts of the immunoglobulins and are therefore considered members of the immunoglobulin gene superfamily (reviews in Marchalonis and Schluter, 1990; Hunkapiller and Hood, 1989).

The typical circulating antibody is composed of two identical small polypeptides and two larger identical polypeptides, referred to as light and heavy chains, respectively. The light chains have two disulfide-bonded domains, and the heavy chains have four, in which the cysteines are separated by approximately 60 amino acid residues. The four chains are joined together by interchain disulfide bridges (see Fig. 9). The antigen specificity of antibodies resides in a particular portion of the molecule called the variable (V) region, which shows tremendous amino acid sequence heterogeneity. It has been shown that the differences in amino acid sequence are responsible for the antigen-binding specificity. Other portions of the molecule are less variable and referred to as constant (C) regions, these regions mediate effector functions. The V

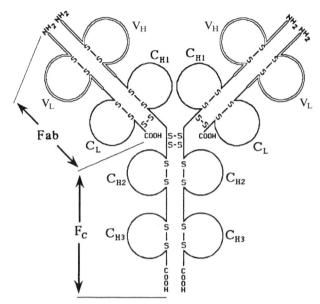

Fɪɢ. 9. Illustration of a circulating immunoglobulin. The light chains are identified by V_L and C_L and the heavy chains are identified by V_H and C_H (i.e., C_{H1}, C_{H2}, and C_{H3}). The disulfide bridges are represented (S—S) and the Fab and Fc fragments are identified. [After Hood *et al.* (1984).]

region is formed by the amino-terminal half the light chain (V_L) and one-quarter of the heavy chain (V_H).

Protein sequence studies have shown that the different regions of these chains have evolved from a common ancestor. For example, the variable portion of the light chain (V_L) is homologous with the variable portion of the heavy chain (V_H). The constant region of the heavy chain has three equal domains (C_{H1}, C_{H2}, and C_{H3}), which are homologous to each other and to the constant region of the light chain (C_L). In addition, there is considerable structural similarity among the V and C regions. X-Ray crystallographic studies have shown that each of these regions form a unique compact structure called an immunoglobulin fold. The obvious implication of these homologies is that they arose via gene duplication and diversification of a primordial gene that encoded a peptide of approximately 100 amino acid residues.

There are several classes of immunoglobulins (IgM, IgG, IgA, IgD, and IgE) and within each class there are two general types of light chains (κ or λ), but one major type of heavy chain. However, each class or subclass of macromolecule is represented by several hundred unique sequences. The sequence variability found among different immuno-globulin molecules arises primarily from the translocation and joining of separate DNA fragments. Elucidating the mechanism by which this process is achieved has been one of the most exciting scientific achieve-ments of the twentieth century.

It is now clear that the V and C regions of an antibody molecule are encoded by distinct genes that become joined during cellular differenti-ation. There are several hundred V_L and V_H genes but a much smaller number of C_L and C_H genes. Although combining these various ele-ments can account for thousands of antibodies, it is still inadequate to encompass the entire repertoire of antigen–antibody specificities. For some immunoglobulin families, V genes can recombine with diversity (D) and joining (J) segments to provide additional genetic variability. The light chain is encoded by V, J, and C genes, whereas the heavy chain is encoded by V, D, J, and C genes. The V_L region is encoded by light chain-specific V–J rearranged segments whereas the V_H region is encoded by heavy chain-specific V–D–J rearranged segments.

In mammalian germ-line cells, the V, D, J, and C gene segments for each immunoglobulin chain are clustered and tandemly arranged along the same stretch of DNA (Fig. 10A). However, in some lower vertebrates (e.g., shark) these genes are linked as separate V, D, J, and C gene units (Fig. 10B). During cellular differentiation, a mammalian functional light chain gene is formed by the translocation of a V gene to a J gene segment, which is upstream of the C gene. The DNA region between the V–J gene and the C gene is removed by splicing at the RNA level. Similarly, a functional heavy chain gene is formed by the translocation of a V gene to a D gene to a J gene segment upstream of the C gene cluster (Fig. 10A). Additional genetic diversity is provided by allowing the V and J genes to be rearranged in slightly different joining frames. Also, immunoglobulin variable regions have a high somatic mutation rate, generating even more genetic diversity. As a result of these genetic rearrangements, the various gene segments are joined together to form functional light chain and heavy chain genes that, after splicing of exons and translation, yield the immunoglobulin light and heavy chain polypeptides, which form a functional antibody.

The different classes of antibodies (IgM, IgG, IgA, IgD, and IgE) are generated within a cell by a rearrangement process that is referred to as C_H switching. In this case, the V region is maintained but the C_H region is changed, which means that all the classes of immunoglobulins gener-ated by one cell have the same antigen specificity. The genes that encode the C regions of different antibody classes are next to each other, which facilitates the switching process, which is sequential and non-

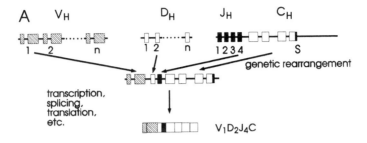

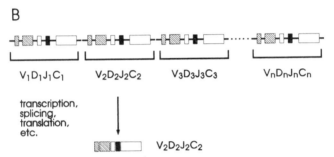

FIG. 10. The genetic arrangement and rearrangement schemes for the heavy chains of mammalian (A) and shark (B) genes. (A) Illustration in mammalian germ-line genes of the many V_H genes at some distance from the D_H and J_H–C_H complex, during genetic rearrangement, a V_H gene and a D_H gene are translocated to a J_H–C_H gene, where they fuse to form a VDJC somatic gene, but there is a host of combinations with various V and D genes. (B) The shark genes are tandemly arranged as predetermined $V_iD_iJ_iC_i$ genes and there is no rearrangement; rather, the gene product is a copy of the germ-line gene in question. [After Hood et al. (1984).]

reversible. For example, before the cell stops making IgM and starts making IgA, the C gene for IgM is removed, leaving the rearranged V_H–J_H gene upstream from the C gene for IgA. Because the constant region controls effector functions, C_H switching allows antibody specificity to be maintained when other effector functions are needed.

In summary, the immune system combines germ-line variability, somatic recombination, and somatic mutation to provide the required antibody variability for survival in a variable and often hostile environment. The genes that code for immunoglobulin polypeptide chains have an elaborate organization that requires at least one rearrangement to form a functional gene that specifies a particular light chain, heavy chain, or T cell receptor. Somatic recombination of a large number of germ-line V genes and a limited number of D and J genes with the C genes accounts for a significant portion of the variability within some immunoglobulin classes, whereas somatic mutations play an important part in others.

B. EVOLUTION OF IMMUNOGLOBULINS

Even though the vast majority of structural information on the V, D, J, and C genes has been derived from a few mammalian species, recent application of recombinant DNA techniques to the genes of lower vertebrates is beginning to provide critical information for meaningful evolutionary comparisons, which are important for estimating evolutionary divergence and conservation across taxa. A few years ago, a complete protein sequence of a bird light chain immunoglobulin was derived from the nucleotide sequence of a chicken λ light chain (Reynaud et al., 1985, 1987). More recently, sequence information has become available for amphibian immunoglobulin light chains (Mikoryak and Steiner, 1988) and heavy chains (Schwager et al., 1988). Genes encoding teleost fish immunoglobulin heavy chains have also been reported (Wilson et al., 1988; Ghaffari and Lobb, 1989a; Litman et al., 1990). However, the most recent and evolutionarily important sequence information on lower vertebrate immunoglobulins comes from work on shark light and heavy chains (Litman et al., 1984; Hinds and Litman, 1986; Kokubu et al., 1987, 1988; Schluter et al., 1990). Comparisons of these sequences have provided important insights concerning the evolution of the rearranging immunoglobulins.

Although inadequate evidence is available for certain critical taxa (cyclostomes and protochordates) on the basis of comparisons of the shark immunoglobulin sequences with those of other species, Marchalonis and Schluter (1989) concluded that the distinction between the light and heavy chains of immunoglobulins is very ancient and that the general structure of vertebrate immunoglobulins has been generally conserved throughout vertebrate evolution.

Marchalonis and Schluter (1989) compared the sequences of the shark C_L regions with constant regions of other vertebrate immunoglobulins and human T cell receptor chains. The sequences of the shark light chain were so similar to human λ light chain that it was predicted to have a three-dimensional structure virtually identical to that of human protein. Figure 11A graphically illustrates the phylogenetic relationships for the light chain constant regions. The figure emphasizes the fact that the shark λ chain is more similar to the bird and mammalian λ chains than to the amphibian and mammalian κ chains. However, the shark λ chain is more similar to the κ chains than are any of the λ chains from other species.

The C_H regions of shark μ chains (those which encode IgM) are more

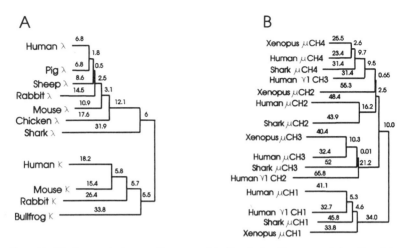

FIG. 11. Phylogenetic trees of immunoglobulin chains from a variety of vertebrate species. (A) Phylogenetic tree for immunoglobulin light chain constant regions. (B) Phylogenetic tree for immunoglobulin heavy chain constant region domains. [From Marchalonis and Schluter (1989).]

similar to homologous C_H regions of μ and γ (IgG encoding) immunoglobulins of other vertebrates than to other shark C_H regions (Fig. 11A). Although Fig. 11B appears to suggest that the evolutionary relatedness of the C_H regions is from oldest to youngest C_{H1}, C_{H2}, and C_{H3}, then C_{H4}, the division between the C_{H2} and C_{H3} branchpoints is too close to make an unambiguous determination. As C_{H2} and C_{H3} sequences of more primitive chordate immunoglobulins become available, the evolutionary relatedness of these structural domains should become clearer.

Kokubu et al. (1987) used a C_H-specific probe to screen a shark genomic library and found that V, D, and J segments were associated with different C_H genes, which is somewhat different than the typical arrangement in mammals. They later determined the complete genomic sequence of one shark C_H gene (Kokubu et al., 1988) and found that the exons were equivalent to those found in higher vertebrates but that the introns were larger. This is similar to the case for the fish versus the mammalian C_H genomic gene system discussed earlier. The shark gene had two poly(adenylation) signals in the C_{H4} secretory exon instead of the one in the mammalian gene. Perhaps most interesting was the fact that the transmembrane sequence of the shark gene was very similar (at both the DNA and protein levels) to that of mammals. The conservation of this sequence should prove useful in isolating homologous genes from distantly related taxa.

The variable regions of all known light and heavy chains are encoded by V–J and V–D–J DNA segments, respectively. Clustering analyses of variable region sequences show that the V_L and V_H are distinct from each other and the κ and λ V_L subclasses are also different. Moreover, the V regions of T cell receptors (TCRs) cluster between the V_H and V_L clusters, which suggests that the evolutionary divergence of V_H and V_L took place prior to the divergence of the V region genes of the TCR (Beaman et al., 1987; Marchalonis and Schluter, 1989).

Comparisons of nucleotide and inferred amino acid sequences of teleost (Carassius auratus; gold fish) heavy chain variable regions (V_H) with those of other vertebrate V_H genes indicate that the teleost fish genes generally have the same regulatory and structural features common to other vertebrate taxa, including the 5'-putative promoter region, the split hydrophobic leader sequence, three framework regions (FRs), (areas of relatively low variability), and two complementarity-determining regions (CDRs) (regions of high variability which interact with antigens), and the 3' recombination signals for V_H joining (Wilson et al., 1988). Although Wilson et al. (1988) showed that V_H genes existed as distinct gene families in teleost fish, the number of such gene families varied widely within and among individuals. Litman et al. (1990) analyzed immunoglobulin genes from a more primitive teleost (Elops). Using hybridization, they found closely linked V_H genes within 15- to 16-kb chromosomal fragments. However, sequence analysis of those linked genes indicated that some were pseudogenes. Their initial studies with C_H-specific DNA probes indicated that the multiple V_H genes were probably associated with a single C_H gene (unpublished data, referenced in Litman et al., 1990). Other DNA sequence studies and evolutionary analyses have been done on the catfish heavy chain cDNA (Ghaffari and Lobb, 1989b), and more recently on the heavy chain variable region germ-line genes of rainbow trout (Matsunaga et al., 1990). In the former case, Ghaffari and Lobb (1989b) found that the catfish C_H gene is represented by a single genomic copy. Because that finding was so different from that reported for shark, the authors concluded that the phylogeny of single-copy C_H genes was probably established during the evolution of the bony fishes. They also present evidence for additional gene copies. Matsunaga et al. (1990) focused their attention on the variable region of the heavy chain gene and found species-specific residues in the V_H regions of several species and an unusual amino acid in the CDR of the trout V_H. In general, the efforts with teleost V_H and C_H genes are consistent with a hypothesis that the general gene structure of teleost fish immunoglobulin genes is similar to those found in other vertebrates and emphasizes the conservation of gene organization during vertebrate evolution.

Litman *et al.* (1985, 1990) also presented data from a more primitive fish, the horned shark, that indicated that their V_H regions were similar to those of higher taxonomic groups. Not only did they identify extensive homology among shark and some mammalian V_H genes (60%), but they also showed that horned shark had approximately 200 V_H genes (including allelic variants). However, the arrangement of the shark V_H genes is quite different than that found in mammals, birds, amphibians, and teleost fish (Amemiya and Litman, 1990). Although the V_H genes of higher vertebrates are known to occur in rearranging clusters at some unknown distance from the D_H, J_H, and C_H gene clusters (see Fig. 10A), in the shark the heavy chain genetic elements occur in discrete clusters in which the V_H, D_H, J_H, and C_H genes that encode a particular immunoglobulin are linked (V_H–D_H–J_H–C_H) (Fig. 10B).

C. Major Histocompatibility Complex

The major histocompatability complex (MHC) is a cluster of genes that codes for self versus nonself recognition at the tissue level. It is best known for its role in the control of rejection of tissue grafts and transplanted organs. In higher vertebrates, the MHC encodes two classes of proteins that serve as cell surface antigens for T cells in response to foreign tissues as well as pathogens, such as viruses (review in Hood *et al.*, 1985). The MHC antigens share structural similarity with immunoglobulins and are therefore members of the Ig gene superfamily. The amino-terminal domains of MHC class I and II proteins apparently form low-affinity interactions with the T cell receptor on the T cells (Buus *et al.*, 1987).

The MHC system has been conserved, to some extent, during the evolution of mammals, but this is less clear in lower vertebrates. The MHC genes have been identified in mammals, birds, frogs, and bony fishes, but studies on primitive fishes have not unambiguously identified the MHC molecules. In general very little is known about the evolution of MHC and MHC-like molecules. Kaufman *et al.* (1990) recently reviewed the present understanding of the MHC molecules in nonmammalian vertebrates. Although the data are rather sketchy, there are some interesting and provocative possibilities that should be considered in an evolutionary context.

There has been considerable speculation concerning the functional evolution of the MHC and MHC-like molecules, especially their role in tissue graft rejection (Du Pasquier *et al.*, 1989). Although tissue graft rejection has been demonstrated in essentially all major vertebrate groups, the details of the process differ substantially among taxa (review in Kaufman *et al.*, 1990).

A major tenet of MHC genes is that there is extensive genetic variability within a population, which forms the basis of the graft rejection response. A major question that arises is "What is the evolutionary origin of the MHC?" Some think that MHC molecules evolved as a response to environmental pathogens or species–species competition (Zinkernagel and Doherty, 1979; Weissman, 1988). Klein (1987a,b) has suggested that pathogen recognition is not a sufficient selective pressure to explain the level of polymorphisms at the MHC in some species. Rather, Klein (1987b) suggested that only a few alleles are adequate to protect a population, and point mutations, genetic drift, and selective neutrality are responsible for most of the MHC variants. This hypothesis asserts that the majority of genetic diversity, within a species, arises during rapid radiation associated with speciation events. However, a number of studies have shown that different species often possess similar MHC genes. Moreover, several laboratory and theoretical studies clearly indicate that the MHC genes are under strong selective pressures (Nathenson *et al.*, 1986; Hughes and Nei, 1988, 1989).

Another possibility is that the very high levels of MHC polymorphisms in vertebrates are due to something other than pathogenic defense (Flaherty, 1987). Some of those potential functional roles might be kin recognition, mate selection, competition for space, etc. Another possibility would be some combination of these and other factors (see other examples in Kaufman *et al.*, 1990).

Functional studies are ambiguous concerning the evolutionary origin of the MHC immune system. To date, there is no molecular evidence to indicate that the vertebrate immune system, including the MHC, is in any way evolutionarily related to invertebrate allorecognition systems. Even among the vertebrates, there is variability in the cellular immune response—making it difficult to place into an evolutionary context. For example, the evidence of T cell function in jawless and cartilaginous fishes is not compelling, but the immune system in teleosts appears to be clearly related to that of higher vertebrates. Recently, Hashimoto *et al.* (1990) reported the isolation of MHC genes from a teleost fish. They identified two MHC antigen-encoding sequences, one of which was homologous to MHC class I heavy chains and the other homologous to MHC class II β chains of mammalian and avian species. Evolutionarily conserved amino acid residues were not evenly distributed throughout the sequences. Rather, they tended to be clustered in specific regions. In addition, these investigators provide a logical strategy for isolating homologous genes from even more primitive species and lay the foundation for a detailed evolutionary analysis of MHC molecules.

XI. Evolution of Genes Involved with the Endocrine System

Vertebrate endocrine organs are either multipurpose, such as the kidney and pancreas, or exclusive for hormone secretion, such as the thyroid and pituitary. Because the hypothalamus secretes a number of hormones that control pituitary functions, it is included as part of the vertebrate endocrine system. The pituitary gland is composed of the anterior (hypophysis) and posterior (neurohypophysis) lobes. The anterior lobe arises from mouth epithelium during development and the posterior lobes of the pituitary and hypothalamus are derived from brain tissue. Due to its embryonic origins, and because the neurohypophysis and hypothalamus secrete a number of neuropeptides, they are considered neuroendocrine glands whereas the hypophysis is not.

The pituitary hypophysis secretes at least eight hormones: thyrotropic hormone, follicle-stimulating hormone (FSH), luteinizing hormone (LH), adrenocorticotropic hormone (ACTH), melanophore-stimulating hormone (MSH), melanophore-concentrating hormone (MCH), lipotropin (LT), prolactin (Prl), and growth hormone (GH). These hormones are involved in the control of reproduction, growth, osmoregulation, and other functions. The neurohypophysis secretes arginine vasotocin, oxytocin, isotocin, and/or other peptides involved in osmoregulation. The hypothalamus synthesizes some of the hormones that are secreted by the neurohypophysis. In addition, the hypothalamus secretes hormones and hormone inhibitors that control endocrine functions, including thyroxin-releasing hormone, corticotropic release-inhibiting hormone, gonadotropin-releasing hormone, prolactin release-inhibiting hormone, melanophore-stimulating hormone release-inhibiting hormone, growth hormone-releasing hormone, and growth hormone release-inhibiting hormone. The physiology, molecular biology, and regulation of several of these polypeptide hormones have been studied in mammals but only a few aspects have been studied in fish and other lower vertebrates; however, data on fish systems are critical to our understanding of the evolution of the endocrine system.

A. Selected Genes of the Anterior Pituitary

Osmoregulation

Osmoregulation has been an extremely important physiological mechanism that has influenced the radiation of new fish species into freshwater and saltwater habitats. Several hormones of the anterior pituitary are involved in this important evolutionary process.

Fish invaded freshwater streams and lakes several hundred MyBP, and the ancestors of both the Chondrichthyes (sharks, skates, and rays) and Osteichthyes (bony fish) migrated from freshwater habitats into the ocean. Eventually, several species of bony fish reinvaded freshwater habitats. Today, some fish species are restricted to either freshwater or saltwater (stenohaline) environments, and still others spend part of their life in each environment (euryhaline). In fresh habitats, fish are in a Na^+-poor environment and have evolved mechanisms to retain salt. Although they do not drink water and their skin is relatively impermeable to water, a significant influx of water occurs across the gills and is eliminated as a dilute urine via the kidney. The salt that is lost in the feces and urine is replaced from food and via active Na^+ uptake at the gills. The opposite situation exists in saltwater habitats, where the fish must conserve water and exclude salt. Marine fish drink water and eliminate the excess ions either at the gills or via feces—urine output is minimized. Fish that migrate between saltwater and freshwater environments must therefore change these mechanisms in order to survive. Osmoregulation appears to be very important in the evolutionary radiation of fish species. Therefore, the genes expressed in the pituitary and hypothalamus that affect osmoregulation and other functions in fish continue to be a focus of study by both physiologists and evolutionary biologists. A few selected examples will be discussed below.

a. Growth Hormone and Prolactin. Growth hormone (GH) and prolactin (Prl) are, perhaps, the most well-studied fish pituitary polypeptides. Growth hormone is a single polypeptide chain that is required for growth and development of all preadult vertebrates. As in other vertebrates, growth enhancement is a major function of fish GH, but it has also been shown to be involved in osmoregulation by aiding in the adaptation to saltwater habitats by some fish species. In mammals, prolactin functions to induce milk production whereas in some fish species prolactin is involved in osmoregulation.

Prolactin simulates active Na^+ uptake, inhibits Cl^- excretion, helps retain Ca^{2+}, enhances production of dilute urine by inhibiting water reabsorption, and facilitates Na^+ retention by the suppression of a Na^+, K^+-ATPase (see Powers, 1989, and references therein). In salmonids, GH functions just the opposite to Prl in osmoregulation; it enhances Na^+,K^+-ATPase activity and Na^+ exclusion at the gills. When salmonids migrate from saltwater to freshwater environments, Prl increases, GH decreases, and Na^+ is retained by reducing Na^+,K^+-ATPase activity. When salmonids migrate from freshwater to saltwater habitats, the opposite is true.

The detailed mechanisms of this Prl/GH control and their general applicability to other species are not known, but the availability of large quantities of biosynthetic GH and Prl from cloned cDNAs (see, e.g., Sekine *et al.*, 1985; Agellon and Chen, 1986; Gonzalez-Villasenor *et al.*, 1988; Yasuda *et al.*, 1986; Agellon *et al.*, 1988b; Rentier-Delrue *et al.*, 1989a,b), should provide adequate material to study these mechanisms in the future. The elucidation of fish GH and Prl gene structures provide the basic material for elucidating the genetic mechanisms controlling gene regulation of these and other genes involved in osmoregulation. These molecular studies as well as similar efforts on other pituitary hormones (hormones from the hypothalamus and other endocrine hormones; see below) signal that a new phase in fish endocrinology has begun.

 b. Evolution of the GH/Prl/PL/SL Multigene Family. The GH polypeptides isolated from mammals, birds, reptiles, and amphibians have shown remarkable similarities (Li *et al.*, 1973; W. W. Farmer *et al.*, 1974, 1976). In recent years, GH polypeptides have also been purified from a variety of fish species, including tilapia, carp, chum salmon, eel, sturgeon, winter flounder, and yellowtail flounder (S. W. Farmer *et al.*, 1976, 1981; Cook *et al.*, 1983; Kawauchi *et al.*, 1986; Watahiki *et al.*, 1989). Though some GH domains are somewhat conserved among fish and mammalian GHs, other domains are not. Amino acid sequences of fish Prl show homologies not only with other vertebrate Prls, but also with GH and other pituitary hormones. For example, comparisons of the primary structures of GH and Prl from mammals and fish reveal the presence of four conserved structural domains in GH and three in Prl. Three of the four conserved domains in GH are homologous to the three conserved domains in Prl (residues 10–48, 53–95, and 147–195), but the fourth (residues 113–132) is only conserved among the GH gene family, which suggests that it may be involved with the unique biological function of GH.

 On the basis of sequence information from a variety of mammalian growth hormone, prolactin, and placental lactogen (PL) polypeptides, it has been concluded that they evolved from a common ancestor (reviews in Miller and Eberhardt, 1983; Slater *et al.*, 1986). Niall and colleagues (1971) proposed that the genes that encode these peptides arose by repeated duplication of a smaller primordial gene or coding region (Phase I in Fig. 12A). Several investigators expanded on this idea to generate the current model for the evolution of this gene family (Fig. 12A). Subsequent duplication and divergence of the precursor gene (Phase II in Fig. 12A) are presumed to have led to the evolution of GH, Prl, and PL.

 Because a majority of the data used to generate this model were

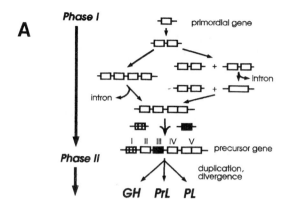

A

Phase I

Phase II

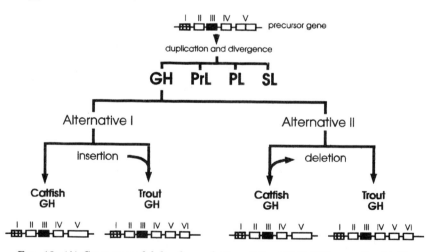

B

Revised Phase II Evolution

FIG. 12. (A) Current model for the evolution of the GH/Prl/PL gene family (from Agellon *et al.*, 1988a). (B) Revised or modified Phase II of the evolutionary model illustrated in Phase II shown in A.

provided by mammalian protein and DNA sequences, the sequence of the first fish GH gene (Agellon *et al.*, 1988a) raised serious doubts concerning the validity of some of Phase I of this evolutionary model.

Much of the rationale for Phase I is based on the existence of apparent internally homologous regions with GH, Prl, and PL (Niall *et al.*, 1971). In human GH, for example, the first two of the four regions of internal homology are each encoded by separate exons (exons II and IV), but the last two regions are encoded by one larger exon (exon V). The latter exon may have been generated after the deletion of the intervening sequence that separated the two reduplicated coding domains either prior to or after its incorporation into the gene. The two other exons (exon I and III) of the human gene are thought to have separate origins. Exon I, which eventually took over the controlling functions of the gene, was incorporated at the 5' upstream region, and exon III, which conferred the hormone with carbohydrate-regulating properties, was incorporated between the originally duplicated regions. Imperfect direct repeats have also been found flanking exons I, III, and V of rat GH, rat Prl, human GH, and human PL genes. This observation was taken as further evidence that these regions arose by separate insertion events by a mechanism analogous to DNA transposition. The formation of the precursor gene marks the end of Phase I. At the beginning of Phase II, the entire precursor structure was duplicated and subsequent divergence gave rise to the genes that encode GH and Prl (Phase II in Fig. 12A).

The existence of an additional intron (intron 5) in the trout GH gene is a notable difference of the fish and mammalian GH genes. The presence of intron 5 in the trout GH gene might be considered as support of Phase I of the model, but Agellon *et al.*, (1988a) have suggested that intron 5 might be a relatively recent introduction into the salmonid GH gene structure (Fig. 12B, Alternative I). They presented several observations that support this hypothesis. For example, the event that gave rise to GH and Prl genes (Phase II) occurred around 350–400 million years ago, well before the divergence of fish and tetrapods. The existence of GH and Prl in these two groups of animals attests to this notion. Mammalian genes for GH and Prl are organized in a similar manner—i.e., both genes have five exons and four introns. Thus, intron 5 of the trout GH gene could not have existed prior to the divergence of fish and tetrapods or the line that led to tetrapods might have deleted intron 5 before divergence (Fig. 12B; Alternative II). In addition, comparisons of regions in the trout GH polypeptide sequence, equivalent to those described by Niall *et al.* (1971), do not show the existence of internally homologous regions. Moreover, direct repeats similar to those flanking exons I, III, and V of the rat GH, rat Prl, human GH, and human PL genes are not found in the trout GH gene (Agellon *et al.*, 1988a). Therefore, although the similarity between the polypeptide sequences of fish GH and Prl is consistent with Phase II of the model (Fig. 12), the trout GH gene structure is inconsistent with Phase I.

In human GH, the apparent internal repeats share 30% identical amino acid residues and 51.3% similarity when conservative substitutions are taken into account. By comparison, the equivalent regions in the trout GH have only 10.9% identical residues and 39.1% similarity. Furthermore, the groups of similar amino acid residues among the selected regions in trout GH are not in the same category of acceptable substitutions as those found in the apparent internally repetitive regions of human GH. Significant sequence similarity, however, is observed among equivalent regions of trout and human GH. These comparisons suggest that the presumed internal repeats in the human GH are not present in trout GH.

Nicoll *et al.* (1987) have shown that similarity between randomly selected regions in human GH, human PL, or ovine Prl can be demonstrated by the introduction of appropriate gaps in the sequence. In their example, the selected regions have at least the same extent of similarity as those described by Niall *et al.* (1971). Our analysis of the trout GH structure and that of Nicoll *et al.* (1987) do not support the hypothesis that internally repeated regions in GH, Prl, or PL arose from a small primordial gene (Phase I in Fig. 12A).

Recent cloning and sequencing of carp and catfish genomic genes (T. T. Chen, personal communication) have shown that the carp and catfish GH genes span about 2.5 kb and have five exons and four introns that are similar to the GH gene structures of mammals (Seeburg, 1982; Evans *et al.*, 1982; Dobner *et al.*, 1981; Barlow *et al.*, 1986; Lavin *et al.*, 1988), whereas the trout GH gene spans approximately 4.5 kb and has six exons and five introns (Agellon *et al.*, 1988a). These important new data are consistent with the hypothesis that intron 5 was a relatively recent introduction that was inserted into exon V of the ancestral salmonid growth hormone gene (Fig. 12B; Alternative I). On the other hand, an ancestor within the fish line that led to catfish and carp may have deleted intron 5 (see Alternative II, Fig. 12B). In order to test this hypothesis, it is necessary to explore the existence of intron 5 in a variety of fish taxa. That can be accomplished by developing PCR primers from cDNA sequences that flank intron 5 and using PCR amplification to test for its presence. There is a need for a GH gene structure from at least one organism, common to both branches leading to teleostean and mammalian lines. In addition, GH and Prl gene structures from shark and hagfish would be particularly interesting as would the elucidation of the structures from some of the invertebrates (e.g., abalone and oyster) in which GH has been recently identified.

  c. Somatolactin, a part of the GH/Prl/PL Multigene Family. Recently, a new 28-kDa glycoprotein cDNA, cloned and sequenced from flounder pituitaries (Ono *et al.,* 1988), appeared homologous to members of the GH/Prl fish multigene family. The novel hormone, designated somatolactin (SL), appears to be more evolutionarily conserved than either GH or Prl. Although its biological function is yet to be determined, further study of the structure and function of this exciting new hormone will have a dramatic impact on our understanding of the evolution of pituitary hormones. For example, studies on the gene structure of SL could provide insight concerning the evolution of fish GH genes. Recall that the GH genes of rainbow trout (Agellon *et al.,* 1988a) and Atlantic salmon (Johansen *et al.,* 1989) have five introns instead of the four introns in mammalian GH genes. As stated above, the fifth intron could be interpreted to support the evolutionary model of Niall *et al.* (1971) or it could be the result of a more recent insertion in the fifth exon (Fig. 12B; Alternative I) or intron 5 may have been deleted in the fish line that led to higher vertebrates. When the SL gene is eventually sequenced, it would be expected to have four introns if the insertion hypothesis is correct (see Fig. 12B).

  The molecular genetic studies alluded to above as well as recent efforts on other fish pituitary hormones (Kitahara *et al.,* 1988) and hormones from the hypothalamus (Okawara *et al.,* 1988), suggest that an explosion of molecular endocrinology in fish has begun. Moreover, the recently developed ability to transfer these genes into fish eggs with high efficiency (review in Chen and Powers, 1990) opens the door to study the gene regulation and tissue specificity of these endocrine hormones in a way that was previously unapproachable. Such studies will not only greatly facilitate our understanding of growth, reproduction, and physiological adaptation, but the analyses of DNA sequences that code for these hormone polypeptides will provide a new understanding about the evolutionary genetics of vertebrates.

B. GENES EXPRESSED IN THE HYPOTHALAMUS

1. The Vasotocin/Isotocin Gene Family

  The vasopressin/oxytocin hormone gene family is widespread throughout the animal kingdom and probably arose from the duplication of a single ancestral gene (Acher and Chauvet, 1988). This gene family consists of a dozen or more genes that code for nonapeptides (i.e., peptides of nine amino acids) that contain a disulfide bridge between two evolutionarily conserved cystines. The general peptide structure is Cys-X-X-X-Asn-Cys-Pro-X-Gly, where X represents variable amino acid residues. In mammals, vasopressin and oxytocin control water retention and smooth muscle contraction, respectively. In teleost fish, vasotocin and isotocin are the counterparts of mammalian vasopressin and oxytocin, respectively.

Several cDNAs coding for mammalian vasopressin and oxatocin precursors have been cloned and sequenced (Rehbein et al., 1986). The data indicate that the vasopressin precursor encodes three peptides: vasopressin, neurophysin, and copeptin. Neurophysin acts as a carrier protein and helps in the transport of vasopressin from the hypothalamus to the neurohypophysis. On the other hand, copeptin appears to act as a prolactin-releasing factor (Nagy et al., 1988). The oxytocin precursor is similar to the vasopressin counterpart except the neurophysin region is shorter and the copeptin-encoding sequence is absent.

Recent sequences of cloned cDNAs encoding the precursors of teleost vasotocin and isotocin indicate the presence of a hormone moiety and a neurophysin-like molecule (Heierhorst et al., 1989). The teleost neurophysins are significantly longer peptides than their mammalian counterparts, having approximately 30 more amino acid residues at the carboxy-terminal end. This extension of the neurophysin region appears similar to the copeptin present in the mammalian vasopression precursor, suggesting that copeptin was derived from the carboxy terminus of an ancestral neurophysin-like molecule (Heierhorst et al., 1989).

Mammalian vasopressin and oxytocin genes contain two introns that separate three exons. These exons, in turn, code for the hormone precursor (Richter, 1986). The first exon encodes the hormone. The second and part of the third exon encode neurophysin and the remainder encodes copeptin in the vasopressin gene but not the oxytocin gene (Acher and Chauvet, 1988). Isotocin genes of the white sucker, *Catostomus commersoni* (Figueroa et al., 1989) apparently do not have the introns characteristic of the mammalian vasopressin/oxytocin gene family, but the fish vasotocin gene (Morley et al., 1990), which is the mammalian vasopressin counterpart, does have the introns in the appropriate position (unpublished data, cited in Figueroa et al., 1989). The lack of introns in the fish isotocin genes is probably the result of a deletion event subsequent to evolutionary divergence.

2. Corticotropin-Releasing Factor

Corticotropin-releasing factor (CRF) is a neuropeptide that is synthesized in the hypothalamus of mammals. It stimulates the secretion of pituitary adrenocorticotropic hormone (ACTH), which, in turn, controls the secretion of steroids, such as cortisol, from the adrenal cortex. Because cortisol increases branchial water fluxes across the gills of fish, CRF and ACTH effect osmoregulation by participating in the control of cortisol concentration.

Peptides structurally similar to mammalian CRF have been isolated from the neurosecretory system of several fish species (Lederis *et al.*, 1982; Ichikawa *et al.*, 1982; McMaster *et al.*, 1988). These peptides, often referred to as urotensin (UI), have been shown to effect fish osmoregulation (Bern *et al.*, 1985). Lederis *et al.* (1982, 1985a,b) have shown that UI has corticotropin-releasing activity in both mammals and fish, suggesting that UI functions as a CRF in fish.

The cDNAs of CRF and UI were isolated and sequenced from rat hypothalamus and carp spinal cord, respectively (Furutani *et al.*, 1983; Ishida *et al.*, 1986). Because immunological and peptide separation studies indicated that the teleost *C. commersoni* had a pituitary CRF in addition to nervous system UI (Yulis and Lederis, 1986, 1987), Okawara and colleagues (1988) cloned and sequenced a CRF cDNA that they isolated from the fish's hypothalamus. This CRF sequence was more similar to the mammalian CRF than to the carp UI. At the nucleotide level, the fish and mammalian CRF-encoding regions were approximately 80% similar but the noncoding regions were less similar (Okawara *et al.*, 1988). The fish and mammalian CRF peptide sequences were identical except for two amino acid residues. The primary structure of CRF and UI hormone precursors from mammals and fish indicate that they are part of a gene family that probably evolved from a common origin as a result of gene duplication and divergence.

3. Somatostatin Gene Family

Somatostatin is a small peptide that inhibits the secretion of several peptide hormones. In the pituitary, somatostatin inhibits growth hormone secretion. In addition to its effect on growth hormone, somatostatin can inhibit other peptide hormones. For example, in the pancreas it is an inhibitor of insulin and glucagon, and in the intestine somatostatin can inhibit the secretion of gastrin, secretin, and choleocystokinin.

The classical somatostatin tetradecapeptide was first purified from ovine hypothalamus (Brazeau *et al.*, 1973). The 14-amino acid somatostatin peptide (somatostatin-14) was later isolated from porcine hypothalamus (Schally *et al.*, 1976), pigeon pancreas (Spiess *et al.*, 1979), and angelfish pancreas (Noe *et al.*, 1979). In addition to the decatetrapeptides, a somatostatin of 22 amino acids has also been found to be synthesized in the channel catfish endocrine pancreas (Magazin *et al.*,

1982). Similarly, additional somatostatins of 25 and 28 amino acid residues are synthesized in ovine hypothalamus (Esch *et al.*, 1980) and porcine intestine (Pradayrol *et al.*, 1978). In the cow (Esch *et al.*, 1980), the two larger hormones have the same sequence except the largest one has three additional residues at the amino-terminal end of the peptide.

Somatostatin is part of a much larger precursor molecule (i.e., preprosomatostatin) that is processed to yield the bioreactive hormone (Hobart *et al.*, 1980; Taylor *et al.*, 1981; Shen *et al.*, 1982; Argos *et al.*, 1983). These precursor peptides are usually between 100 and 125 amino acid residues in length. The cDNA sequences of preprosomatostatin have been studied in angelfish, catfish, bovine, rat, and human cells (Hobart *et al.*, 1980; Taylor *et al.*, 1981; Magazin *et al.*, 1982; Shen *et al.*, 1982; Funckes *et al.*, 1983; Su *et al.*, 1988). The nucleotide sequences of the angelfish somatostatin cDNAs indicated at least two forms; a 121-amino acid somatostatin-I precursor and a 125-residue somatostatin-II precursor. Both precursors contain the 14-amino acid hormone at the carboxy-terminal region and they differ by only 2 of the 14 amino acids, i.e., Tyr/Phe and Gly/Thr at positions 7 and 10, respectively. Moreover, different somatostatins may have distinct biological activities (Hobart *et al.*, 1980). In addition to the somatostatin-14, the catfish has a pancreatic somatostatin-22 that is homologous to somatostatin-14 in 7 of the 14 amino acids, including a classical Phe-Tyr-Lys sequence. Evolutionary studies of these and other somatostatins suggest that the two fish somatostatin genes are the result of a gene duplication event that is of common ancestry to both angelfish and catfish (Su *et al.*, 1988) (Fig. 13).

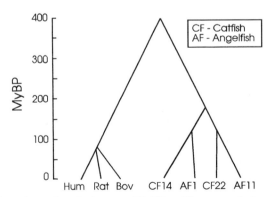

FIG. 13. A hypothetical evolution tree (MyBP, million years before the present) for the somatostatin genes of human (Hum), rat, bovine (Bov), catfish (somatostatin-14, CF14; somatostatin-22, CF22), and angelfish (AF1 and AF11) cells. [From Su *et al.* (1988).]

As was the case for the fish somatostatin precursors, sequences of cDNAs encoding the mammalian preprosomatostatins indicate somatostatin-14 and somatostatin-28 are also located near the carboxy-termini of the prepropeptide. In addition to the cDNA, the human somatostatin-I genomic gene has been cloned and sequenced (Shen and Rutter, 1984). The gene is interrupted by a single intron in the propeptide region but the intron does not appear to separate functional domains of the molecule. In recent years, two different alleles of the human genomic gene have been sequenced and, although they differ by only a few nucleotides, both code for identical somatostatin peptide hormones.

Evolutionary studies of fish growth hormone genes and the vasopressin/oxytocin complex have alerted us to the fact that evolutionary schemes based only on mammalian structures can be misleading. Therefore, it will be interesting to see what new insights are provided as the structure of fish somatostatin genes are elucidated.

4. Melanin-Concentrating Hormone Genes

Fish have the ability to change their body color or shading to match more closely their environmental background. This is accomplished by moving melanin granules within the melanophores. At least two melanocyte-stimulating hormones (MSHs) are responsible for this pigment dispersal in fish. Fish also have an MSH antagonistic hormone called melanin-concentrating hormone (MCH). Kawauchi and colleagues (1983) were the first to isolate MCH from fish pituitaries (i.e., the chum salmon, *Oncorhynchus keta*). A number of studies have clearly indicated that MCH is synthesized in the hypothalamus and is then transferred to the pituitary (Baker and Rance, 1983; Rance and Baker, 1979; Naito *et al.*, 1985; Kawazoe *et al.*, 1987). Moreover, these and other studies have clearly indicated that MCH activity is also present in a variety of other vertebrate species. Takayama *et al.* (1989) have cloned and sequenced two genes encoding the MCH hormones of chum salmon in order to help elucidate the regulatory mechanisms controlling production. These were shown to be intronless genes with an exon of 0.63 kb that coded for a 132-amino acid peptide hormone. These two MCH genes shared 86% of their nucleotide sequences. Although homologous genes could be detected in other fish species, the MCH genes of higher vertebrates were too different to detect by nucleic acid hybridization. However, the use of cross-reactive antibodies and the ability to detect MCH activity in mammalian hypothalamic fractions ensure that the MCH genes of higher vertebrates should be cloned in the near future.

XII. Conclusions

Darwin's *The Origin of Species* emphasized the importance of systematic and zoogeographic studies. In pursuing this approach, ichthyologists such as David Starr Jordan and others became major figures in early American evolutionary thought. Because fish represent the largest and most diverse group of vetebrates, they should continue to be key elements in the analysis of vertebrate evolution. Their evolutionary position relative to other vertebrates, their relatively well-characterized fossil record, the existence of "living fossils," and their ability to adapt to a wide variety of environmental conditions make them ideal for studying both organismic and molecular evolution. In addition to their critical role in vertebrate evolutionary studies, they have played an important role in the development of several other scientific disciplines, including neurobiology, developmental biology, endocrinology, and immunology, just to name a few. Fish have contributed significantly to our understanding of many important biological phenomena in each of these and other disciplines and, for the many reasons cited in this review, they will continue to be important in the future. The ability to clone and sequence specific fish genes and gene families, to make isogenic lines of fish in a single generation, to create and maintain mutants in the laboratory, to culture and manipulate fish cell lines, to follow cell lineages during development, to transfer cloned genes into embryos and do genetic analyses of transgenic offspring, and a host of other sophisticated techniques signal an increasing and exciting new role for fish as vertebrate models. The recent explosion of DNA sequencing efforts on fish systems enumerated in this review attests to the emergence of fish as important evolutionary and experimental models that will significantly contribute to our understanding of vertebrate evolutionary genetics in the coming decades.

In this review we have mentioned only a few of the many fish gene systems that could have been addressed. Others that could have been cited include the central nervous system myelin proteins, the fibrinogens, the insulin and insulin-like growth factors, the actins, the homeobox genes, the gonadotropins, the calcitonins, the glucons, and the creatine kinases, just to name a few. This review has repeatedly demonstrated how information gained by studying fish evolutionary genetics has improved our understanding of molecular evolution and provided insight concerning the pitfalls of generating vertebrate evolutionary models in the absence of information on fish taxa. By the time this review is published, there will be many new fish cDNA and genomic DNA sequences available that will cause evolutionary geneticists to reevaluate the tenets upon which their evolutionary hypotheses are based.

Although the future efforts of some researchers will continue to focus on DNA sequencing and molecular systematics, the elucidation of the molecular basis of evolutionary mechanisms will be an exciting new frontier for the twenty-first century. Particular emphasis should be given to the elucidation of the detailed mechanisms that regulate fish gene expression and their biological role and evolutionary significance in the control of intermediate metabolism, reproduction, development, environmental adaptation, behavior, the nervous system, the endocrine system, and other organ systems.

REFERENCES

Acher, R., and Chauvet, J. (1988). Structure, processing and evolution of the neurohypophysial hormone-neurophysin precursors. *Biochimie* **70,** 1197–1207.
Agellon, L. B., and Chen, T. T. (1986). Rainbow trout growth hormone: molecular cloning of cDNA and expression in *Escherichia coli*. *DNA* **5,** 463–471.
Agellon, L. B., Davies, S. L., Chen, T. T. and Powers, D. A. (1988a). Structure of a fish (rainbow trout) growth hormone gene and its evolutionary implications. *Proc. Natl. Acad. Sci. U.S.A.* **85,** 5136–5140.
Agellon, L. B., Davies, S. L., Lin, C. M., Chen, T. T., and Powers, D. A. (1988b). Rainbow trout has two genes for growth hormone. *Mol. Reprod. Dev.* **1,** 11–17.
Agnew, W. S., Levinson, S. R., Brabson, J. S., and Raftery, M. A. (1978). Purification of the tetrodotoxin-binding component associated with the voltage-sensitive sodium channel from *Electrophorus electricus* electroplax membranes. *Proc. Natl. Acad. Sci. U.S.A.* **75,** 2606–2610.
Ahuja, M., Schwab, M., and Anders, F. (1980). Linkage between a regulatory locus for melanoma cell differentiation and an esterase locus in *Xiphophorus*. *J. Hered.* **71,** 403–407.
Aiken, J. M., McKenzie, D., Zhao, H. Z., States, J. C., and Dixon, G. H. (1983). Sequence homologies in the protamine gene family of rainbow trout. *Nucleic Acids Res.* **11,** 4907–4992.
Allendorf, F. W., and Phelps, S. R. (1981). Use of allelic frequencies to describe population structure. *Can. J. Fish. Aquat. Sci.* **38,** 1507–1514.
Allendorf, F. W., and Thorgaard, G. H. (1984). Tetraploidy and the evolution of salmonid fishes. *In* "Evolutionary Genetics of Fishes" (B. J. Turner, ed.), pp. 1–53. Plenum, New York.
Allendorf, F. W., Knudsen, K. L., and Leary, R. F. (1983). Adaptive significance of differences in the tissue-specific expression of a phosphoglucomutase gene in rainbow trout. *Proc. Natl. Acad. Sci. U.S.A.* **80,** 1397–1400.
Allendorf, F. W., Seeb, J. E., Knudsen, K. L., Thorgaard, G. H., and Leary, R. F. (1986). Gene-centromere mapping of 25 loci in rainbow trout. *J. Hered.* **77,** 307–312.
Allendorf, F. W., Gellman, W. A., and Thorgaard, G. H. (1991). Sex-linkage of two enzyme loci in rainbow trout. Unpublished paper, Univ. of Montana, Missoula.
Altman, S., Model, P., Dixon, G. H., and Wosnick, M. A. (1981). An *E. coli* gene coding for a protamine-like protein. *Cell* **26,** 299–304.

Amemiya, C. T., and Litman, G. W. (1990). The complete nucleotide sequence of an immunoglobulin heavy chain gene and analysis of immunoglobulin gene organization in a primitive teleost species. *Proc. Natl. Acad. Sci. U.S.A.* **87**, 811–815.

Anders, A., and Anders, F. (1978). Etiology of cancer as studied in a platyfish-swordtail system. *Biochim. Biophys. Acta* **516**, 61–95.

Anders, A., Anders, F., and Klinke, K. (1973). Regulation of gene expression in the Gordon–Kosswig melanoma system. *In* "Genetics and Mutagenesis in Fish" (J. H. Schroeder, ed.), pp. 33–52. Springer-Verlag, New York.

Anders, F. (1967). Tumor formation in platyfish–swordtail hybrids as a problem of gene regulation. *Experientia* **23**, 1–10.

Anders, F., Schartl, M., Barnekow, A., and Anders, A. (1984). Xiphophorus: An *in vivo* model for studies on normal and defective control of oncogenes. *Adv. Cancer Res.* **42**, 191–275.

Aoki, K., and Matsudaira, H. (1977). Induction of hepatic tumors in a teleost (*Orysias latipes*) after treatment with methylazoxy-methanol acetate: Brief communication. *J. Natl. Cancer Inst.* **59**, 1747–1749.

Aref'ev, V. A. (1989). Cytogenetic analysis of the common bass, Dicentrarchus labrax, and the structure of the nucleolar organizer regions in fish. *Vopr. Ikhtiol.* **29**, 812–822.

Argos, P., Taylor, W. L., Minth, C. D., and Dixon, J. E. (1983). Nucleotide and amino acid sequence comparisons of preprosomatostatins. *J. Biol. Chem.* **258**, 8788–8793.

Arkhipchuk, V. V. (1988). Effect of generation time on karyotype evolution in fish. *Gidrobiol. Zh.* **24**, 92–94.

Arkhipchuk, V. V. and Berdyshev, G. D. (1987). *Vopr. Ikhtiol./J. Ichthyol.* **27**, 151–154.

Armstrong, C. M. (1981). Sodium channels and gating currents. *Physiol. Rev.* **61**, 644–683.

Arnheim, N., White, T., and Rainey, W. E. (1990). Application of PCR: Organismal and population biology. *BioScience* **40**, 174–182.

Atkinson, B. G., and Walden, D. B. (1985). Effects of stress on the gene expression of amphibian, avian, and mammalian red blood cells. *In* "Changes in Eukaryotic Gene Expression in Response to Environmental Stress" (B. G. Atkinson and D. B. Walden, eds.), pp. 159–181. Academic Press, Orlando, Florida.

Avise, J. C. (1991). Molecular population structure and the biogeographical history of a regional fauna: A case history with lessons for conservation biology. *Oikos* (in press).

Avise, J. C., and Gold, J. R. (1977). Chromosomal divergence and rates of speciation in two families of North American fishes. *Evolution* **31**, 1–13.

Avise, J. C., Helfman, G. S., Saunders, N. C., and Hales, S. (1986). Mitochondrial DNA differentiation in North Atlantic Eels: Population genetic consequences of an unusual life history pattern. *Proc. Natl. Acad. Sci. U.S.A.* **83**, 4350–4354.

Avise, J. C., Arnold, J., Ball, R. M., Bermingham, E., Lamb, T., Neigel, J. E., Reeb, C. A., and Saunders, N. C. (1987). Intraspecific phylogeography: The mitochondrial DNA bridge between population genetics and systematics. *Annu. Rev. Ecol. Syst.* **18**, 489–522.

Avise, J. C., Bowen, B. W., and Lamb, T. (1989). DNA Fingerprints from hypervariable mitochondrial genotypes. *Mol. Biol. Evol.* **6**, 258–269.

Ayala, F. J. (1975). "Molecular Evolution." Sinauer, Sunderland, Massachusetts.

Bailey, G., and Hendricks, J. (1988). Environmental and dietary modulation of carcinogenesis in fish. *Aquat. Toxicol.* **11**, 69–75.

Bailey, G. S., Hendricks, J. D., Nixon, J. E., and Pawlowski, N. E. (1984). The sensitivity of rainbow trout and other fish to carcinogens. *Drug Metab. Rev.* **15**, 725–750.

Bailey, G. S., Selivonchick, D., and Hendricks, J. (1987). Initiation, promotion, and inhibition of carcinogenesis in rainbow trout. *Environ. Health Perspect.* **71,** 147–153.

Baker, B. I., and Rance, T. A. (1983). Further observations on the distribution and properties of teleost melanin concentrating hormone. *Gen. Comp. Endocrinol.* **50,** 423–431.

Baldwin, J., and Lake, P. S. (1987). Lactate dehydrogenase homopolymer of hagfish heart and the single lamprey display greater immunochemical similarity to $LDHC_4$ than to $LDHB_4$ of teleost fish. *J. Exp. Zool.* **242,** 99–120.

Baldwin, J., Mortimer, K., and Pathak, A. (1988). Do ascidians possess the ancestral subunit type of vertebrate lactate dehydrogenase? *J. Exp. Zool.* **246,** 109–114.

Banerjee, S. K., Misra, K. K., Banerjee, S., and Ray-Chaudhuri, S. P. (1988). Chromosome numbers, genome sizes, cell volumes and evolution of snake-head fish (family Channidae). *J. Fish. Biol.* **33,** 781–789.

Barlow, J. W., Voz, M. L. J., Eliard, P. H., Nathy-Hartert, M., DeNayer, P., Economidis, I. V., Belayew, A., Martial, J. A., and Rouseau, G. G. (1986). Thyroid hormone receptors bind to defined regions of the growth hormone and placental lactogen genes. *Proc. Natl. Acad. Sci. U.S.A.* **83,** 8925–9021.

Barstow, D. A., Black, G. W., Sharman, A. F., Scawen, M. D., Atkinson, T., Li, S. S., Chia, W. N., Clarke, A. R., and Holbrook, J. J. (1990). Expression of the copy DNA for human A4 and B4 L-lactate dehydrogenases in *Escherichia coli. Biochim. Biophys. Acta* **1087,** 73–79.

Batra, A., Richards, R. I., Baxter, D. J., and Shine, J. (1981). Primary structure and evolution of rat growth gene. *Proc. Natl. Acad. Sci. U.S.A.* **78,** 4867–4871.

Beaman, K. D., Barker, W. C., and Marchalonis, J. J. (1987). Molecular biology of T lymphocyte recognition elements. *In* "Antigen-Specific T Cell Receptors and Factors" (J. J. Marchalonis, ed.), Vol. 2, pp. 105–126. CRC Press, Boca Raton, Florida.

Bellvé, A. R., McKay, D. J., Renaux, B. S., and Dixon, G. H. (1988). Purification and characterization of mouse protamines P1 and P2. Amino acid sequence of P2. *Biochemistry* **27,** 2890–2897.

Bend, J. R., and James, M. O. (1978). Xenobiotic metabolism in marine and freshwater species. *In* "Biochemical and Biophysical Perspectives in Marine Biology" (D. C. Malins and J. R. Sargent, eds.), pp. 61–81. Academic Press, New York.

Berlot-Picard, F., Vodjdani, G., and Doly, J. (1986). Nucleotide sequence of a cDNA clone encoding *Scylliorhinus caniculus* protamine Z2. *Eur. J. Biochem.* **160,** 305–310.

Bermingham, E. (1990). Mitochondrial DNA and the analysis of fish population structure. *In* "Electrophoretic and Isoelectric Focusing Techniques in Fisheries Management" (D. H. Whitmore, ed.), pp. 197–222. CRC Press, Boca Raton, Florida.

Bermingham, E., and Avise, J. C. (1986). Molecular zoogeography of freshwater fishes in the southeastern United States. *Genetics* **113,** 939–965.

Bern, H. A., Pearson, D., Larson, B. A., and Nishioka, R. S. (1985). Neurohormones from fish tails: The caudal neurosecretory system. 1. Urophysiology and the caudal neurosecretory system of fishes. Proceedings of the 1984 Laurentian Hormone Conference. *Recent Prog. Horm. Res.* **41,** 533–552.

Bernardi, G. (1985). The organization of the vertebrate genome and the problem of the CpG shortage. *In* "Chemistry, Biochemistry and Biology of DNA Methylation" (G. L. Cantoni and A. Razin, eds.), pp. 3–10. Alan R. Liss, New York.

Bernardi, G. (1989). The isochore organization of the human genome. *Annu. Rev. Genet.* **23,** 637–661.

Bernardi, G., and Bernardi, G. (1986). The human genome and its evolutionary context. *Cold Spring Harbor Symp. Quant. Biol.* **51,** 479–487.

Bernardi, G., and Bernardi, G. (1990a). Compositional transitions in the nuclear genomes of cold-blooded vertebrates. *J. Mol. Evol.* **31**, 282–293.

Bernardi, G., and Bernardi, G. (1990b). Compositional patterns in the nuclear genome of cold-blooded vertebrates. *J. Mol. Evol.* **31**, 265–281.

Bernardi, G., and Bernardi, G. (1991). Compositional properties of nuclear genes from cold-blooded vertebrates. *J. Mol. Evol.* (in press).

Bernardi, G., Olofsson, B., Filipski, J., Zerial, M., Salinas, J., et al. (1985). The mosaic genome of warm-blooded vertebrates. *Science* **228**, 953–958.

Bernardi, G., Mouchiroud, D., Gautier, C., and Bernardi, G. (1988). Compositional patterns in vertebrate genomes: Conservation and change in evolution. *J. Mol. Evol.* **28**, 7–18.

Bienz, M., and Gurdon, J. B. (1982). The heat-shock response in *Xenopus* oocytes is controlled at the translational level. *Cell* **29**, 818–819.

Blanco, A., Zinkham, W. H., and Walker, D. G. (1975). LDH-X: Cellular localization, catalytic properties, and genetic control of synthesis. *In* "Isozymes: Developmental Biology" (C. L. Markert, ed.), Vol. 4, pp. 297–312. Academic Press, New York.

Bos, J. L. (1989). Ras oncogenes in human cancer: A review. *Cancer Res.* **49**, 4682–4689.

Brazeau, P., Vale, W., Burgus, R., et al. (1973). Hypothalamic polypeptide that inhibits the secretion of immunoreactive pituitary growth hormone. *Science* **179**, 77–79.

Brown, D. C., Ropson, I. J., and Powers, D. A. (1988). Biochemical genetics of *Fundulus heteroclitus* (L): Inheritance of 10 biochemical loci. *J. Hered.* **79**, 359–365.

Bulger, A. J., and Tremain, S. C. (1985). Magnitude of seasonal effects of heat tolerance in *Fundulus heteroclitus*. *Physiol. Zool.* **58**, 197–204.

Bullock, T. H. (1983). Why study fish brains. *In* "Fish Neurobiology" (R. G. Northcutt and R. E. Davis, eds.), Vol. 2, pp. 362–368. Univ. of Michigan Press, Ann Arbor.

Burdon, R. H. (1986). Heat shock and the heat shock proteins. *Biochem. J.* **240**, 313–324.

Bush, G. L., Case, S. M., Wilson, A. C., and Patton, J. L. (1977). Rapid speciation and chromosomal evolution in mammals. *Proc. Natl. Acad. Sci. U.S.A.* **74**, 3942–3946.

Buus, S., Setle, A., Colon, S. M., et al. (1987). The relation between major histocompatibility complex (MHC) restriction and the capacity of Ia to bind immunogenic peptides. *Science* **235**, 1353–1358.

Calton, M. S., and Denton, T. E. (1974). Chromosomes of the chocolate gourami: A cytogenetic anomaly. *Science* **185**, 618–619.

Campton, D. E. (1987). Natural hybridization and introgression in fishes: Methods of detection and genetic interpretations. *In* "Population Genetics and Fisheries Management" (N. Ryman and F. M. Utter, eds.), pp. 161–192. Univ. of Washington Press, Seattle.

Campton, D. E. (1990). Application of biochemical and molecular genetic markers to analysis of hybridization. *In* "Electrophoretic and Isoelectric Focusing Techniques in Fisheries Management" (D. H. Whitmore, ed.), pp. 241–264. CRC Press, Boca Raton, Florida.

Campton, D. E., and Utter, F. M. (1985). Natural hybridization between steelhead trout (*Salmo gairdneri*) and coastal cutthroat trout (Salmo clarki clarki) in two Puget Sound streams. *Can. J. Fish. Aquat. Sci.* **42**, 110–123.

Cano, J., Thode, G., and Alvarez, M. C. (1982). Karyoevolutive considerations in 29 Mediterranean teleost fishes. *Vie Milieu* **32**, 21–24.

Catterall, W. A. (1988). Structure and function of voltage-sensitive ion channels. *Science* **242**, 50–61.

Cavalier-Smith, T. (1985a). Cell volume and the evolution of eukaryote genome size. *In*

"The Evolution of Genome Size" (T. Cavalier-Smith, ed.), pp. 105–184. Wiley, Chichester, England.

Cavalier-Smith, T. (1985b). Eukaryotic gene numbers, non-coding DNA, and genome size. In "The Evolution of Genome Size" (T. Cavalier-Smith, ed.), pp. 69–103. Wiley, Chichester, England.

Cavalier-Smith, T. (1985c). Introduction: The evolutionary significance of genome size. In "The Evolution of Genome Size" (T. Cavalier-Smith, ed.), pp. 1–36. Wiley, Chichester, England.

Chakrabartty, A., Hew, C. L., Shears, M., and Fletcher, G. (1988). Primary structures of the alanine-rich antifreeze polypeptides from grubby sculpin, Myoxocephalus aenaeus. Can. J. Zool. 66, 403–408.

Champion, M. J., Shaklee, J. B., and Whitt, G. S. (1975). Developmental genetics of teleost isozymes. In "Isozymes: Developmental Biology" (C. L. Markert, ed.), Vol. 4, pp. 417–437. Academic Press, New York.

Chan-King, M., Davidson, W. S., Hew, C., and Fletcher, G. L. (1989). Molecular cloning of metallothionein cDNA and analysis of metallothionein gene expression in winter flounder tissues. Can. J. Zool. 67(10), 2520–2527.

Chang, T. N., and Chang, W. C. (1987). Cloning and sequencing of carp beta sub(s)-crystallin cDNA. Biochim. Biophys. Acta 910, 89–92.

Chang, T., Jiang, Y. J., Chiou, S., and Chang, W. C. (1988). Carp gamma-crystallins with high methionine content: Cloning and sequencing of the complementary DNA. Biochim. Biophys. Acta 95, 226–229.

Chang, Y.-J., Mathews, C., Mangold, K., Marien, K., Hendricks, J., and Bailey, G. (1991). Analysis of ras gene mutations in rainbow trout liver tumors initiated by aflatoxin B1. Mol. Carcinog. 4(2), 1–8.

Chen, J. D., Hew, F. H., and Li, G. C. (1988). Thermal adaptation and heat shock response of Tilapia ovary cells. J. Cell. Physiol. 134, 189–199.

Chen, T. T., and Powers, D. A. (1990). Transgenic fish. Trends Biotechnol. 8, 209–216.

Chiarelli, A. B., and Capanna, E. (1973). Checklist of fish chromosomes. In "Cytotaxonomy and Vertebrate Evolution" (A. B. Chiarelli and E. Capanna, eds.), pp. 206–232. Academic Press, New York.

Childers, W. F. (1967). Hybridization of four species of sunfishes (Centrarchidae). Bull.—Ill. Nat. Hist. Surv. 29, 158–214.

Chiou, C. S., Chen, H. T., and Chang, W. C. (1989). The complete nucleotide sequence of the growth hormone gene from the common carp (C. carpio). Biochim. Biophys. Acta 1087, 91–94.

Clark-Walker, G. D. (1985). Basis of diversity in mitochondrial DNAs. In "The Evolution of Genome Size" (T. Cavalier-Smith, ed.), pp. 277–297. Wiley, Chichester, England.

Comings, D. E. (1978). Mechanisms of chromosome banding and implications for chromosome structure. Annu. Rev. Genet. 12, 25–46.

Comparini, A., and Rodino, E. (1980). Electrophoretic evidence for two species of Anguilla leptocephali in the Sargasso Sea. Nature (London) 287, 435–437.

Cook, A. F., Wilson, S. W., and Peter, R. E. (1983). Development and validation of a carp growth hormone radioimmunoassay. Gen. Comp. Endocrinol. 50, 335–347.

Couch, J. A., Courtney, L. A., and Foss, S. S. (1981). Laboratory evaluation of marine fishes as carcinogen assay subjects. In "Phyletic Approaches to Cancer" (C. J. Dawe, J. C. Harshbarger, S. Kondo, T. Sugimura, and S. Takayama, eds.), pp. 125–139. Japan Sci. Soc. Press, Tokyo.

Crawford, D. L., and Powers, D. A. (1989). Molecular basis of evolutionary adaptation at the lactate dehydrogenase-B locus in the fish Fundulus heteroclitus. Proc. Natl. Acad. Sci. U.S.A. 86, 9365–9369.

Crawford, D. L., Costantino, H. R., and Powers, D. A. (1989). Lactate dehydrogenase-B cDNA from the teleost *Fundulus heteroclitus:* Evolutionary implications. *Mol. Biol. Evol.* **6,** 369–383.

Crawford, D. L., Place, A. R., and Powers, D. A. (1990). Clinial variation in the specific activity of lactate dehydrogenase-B from the teleost *Fundulus heteroclitus. J. Exp. Zool.* **255,** 110–113.

Cuny, G., Soriano, P., Macaya, G., and Bernardi, G. (1981). The major components of the mouse and human genomes. 1. Preparation, basis properties, and compositional heterogeneity. *Eur. J. Biochem.* **111,** 227–233.

Danzmann, R. G., Ferguson, M. M., and Allendorf, F. W. (1985). Allelic differences in initial expression of paternal alleles at an isocitrate dehydrogenase locus in rainbow trout. *Dev. Genet.* **5,** 117–127.

Davies, P. L., Roach, A. H., and Hew, C. L. (1982). DNA sequence coding for an antifreeze protein precursor from winter flounder. *Proc. Natl. Acad. Sci. U.S.A.* **79,** 335–339.

Davies, P. L., Hough, C., Scott, G. K., Ng, N., white, B. N., and Hew, C. L. (1984). Antifreeze protein genes of the winter flounder. *J. Biol. Chem.* **259,** 9241–9247.

Daw, N. W. (1968). Colour-coded ganglion cells in the goldfish retina: Extension of their receptive fields by means of new stimuli. *J. Physiol. (London)* **197,** 567–592.

Dawe, C. J., and Couch, J. A. (1981). Debate: Mouse versus minnow: The future of fish in carcinogenicity testing. *Nat. Cancer Inst. Monogr.* No. 65, 223–227.

de Ligny, W. (1969). Serological and biochemical studies on fish populations. *Oceanogr. Mar. Biol.* **7,** 411–513.

Denton, T. E. (1973). "Fish Chromosome Methodology." Thomas, Springfield, Illinois.

Denton, T. E., and Howell, W. M. (1969). A technique for obtaining chromosomes from the scale epithelium of teleost fishes. *Copeia* No. 2, 392–393.

Devillers-Thiery, A., Giraudat, J., Bentaboulet, M., and Changeux, J. P. (1983). Complete mRNA coding sequence of the acetylcholine binding alpha-subunit of Torpedo marmorata acetylcholine receptor: A model for the transmembrane organization of the polypeptide chain. *Proc. Natl. Acad. Sci. U.S.A.* **80,** 2067–2071.

DeVries, A. L. (1969). Freezing resistance in fishes of the Antarctic Peninsula. Ph.D. Thesis, Stanford Univ., Stanford, California.

DrVries, A. L. (1971). Glycoproteins as biological antifreeze agents in antarctic fishes. *Science* **172,** 1152–1155.

DeVries, A. L. (1988). The role of antifreeze glycopeptides and peptides in the freezing avoidance of Antarctic fishes. *Biochem. Physiol. B* **90B,** 611–621.

DeVries, A. L., and Lin, Y. (1977). Structure of a peptide antifreeze and mechanism of adsorption to ice. *Biochim. Biophys. Acta* **495,** 388–392.

DeVries, A. L., Vandenheede, J., and Feeney, R. E. (1971). Primary structure of freezing point-depression glyco-proteins. *J. Biol. Chem.* **246,** 305–308.

DiMichele, L., and Powers, D. A. (1982a). LDH-B genotype- specific hatching times of *Fundulus heteroclitus* embryos. *Nature (London)* **296,** 563–564.

DiMichele, L., and Powers, D. A. (1982b). Physiological basis for swimming endurance difference between LDH-B genotypes of *Fundulus heteroclitus. Science* **216,** 1014–1016.

DiMichele, L., and Powers, D. A. (1984). Developmental and oxygen consumption rate differences between Ldh-B genotypes of *Fundulus heteroclitus* and their effect on hatching time. *Physiol. Zool.* **57,** 52–56.

DiMichele, L., and Powers, D. A. (1991). Developmental heterochrony and differential mortality in the model teleost, *Fundulus heteroclitus. Physiol. Zool.* (in press).

DiMichele, L., Powers, D. A., and DiMichele, J. A. (1986). Developmental and physiologi-

208 DENNIS A. POWERS

cal consequences of genetic variation at enzyme synthesizing loci in *Fundulus hetero-clitus. Am. Zool.* **26,** 201–208.

DiMichele, L., Paynter, K., and Powers, D. A. (1991). Lactate dehydrogenase-B allozymes directly affect development of *Fundulus heteroclitus. Science* **253,** 898–900.

Dixon, G. H., Aiken, J. M., Jankowski, J. M., McKenzie, D. I., Moir, R., and States, J. C. (1986). Organization and evolution of the protamine genes of salmonid fishes. *In* "Chromosomal Proteins and Gene Expression" (G. R. Reeck, G. A. Goodwin, and P. Puigdomenech, eds.), pp. 287–314. Plenum, New York.

Dobner, P. R., Kawasaki, E. S., Yund, L. Y., and Bancroft, F. C. (1981). Thyroid or glucocorticoid hormone induces pre-growth hormone mRNA and its probable nuclear precursor in rat pituitary cells. *Proc. Natl. Acad. Sci. U.S.A.* **78,** 2230–2234.

Dobzhansky, T. (1951). "Genetics and the Origin of Species," 3rd Ed. Columbia Univ. Press, New York.

Du Pasquier, L., Schwager, J., and Flajnik, M. (1989). The immune system of *Xenopus. Annu. Rev. Immunol.* **7,** 251.

Eiken, H. G., Njolstad, P. R., Molven, A., and Fjose, A. (1987). A zebrafish homeobox-containing gene with embryonic transcription. *Biochem. Biophys. Res. Commun.* **149,** 1165–1171.

Ellis, S. B., Williams, M. E., Ways, N. R., Brenner, R., *et al.* (1988). Sequence and expression of mRNAs encoding the alpha 1 and alpha 2 subunits of a DHP-sensitive calcium channel. *Science* **24,** 1661–1664.

Esch, F., Bohlen, P., Ling, N., Benoit, R., Brazeau, P., and Guillemin, R. (1980). Primary structure of ovine hypothalamic somatostatin-28 and somatostatin-25. *Proc. Natl. Acad. Sci. U.S.A.* **77,** 6827–6831.

Evans, R. M., Birnberg, N. C., and Rosenfield, M. G. (1982). Glucocorticoid and thyroid hormones transcriptionally regulate growth hormone gene expression. *Proc. Natl. Acad. Sci. U.S.A.* **79,** 7659–7663.

Everse, J., and Kaplan, N. O. (1975). Mechanism of action and biological functions of various dehydrogenase isozymes. *In* "Isozymes: Physiological Function" (C. L. Markert, ed.), Vol. 3, pp. 29–43. Academic Press, New York.

Fairbairn, D. J. (1981). Which witch is which? A study of the stock structure of witch flounder (*Glyptocephalus cynoglossus*) in the Newfoundland region. *Can. J. Fish. Aquat. Sci.* **38,** 782–794.

Farmer, S. W., Papkoff, H., Hayashida, T., Bewley, T. A. Bern, H. A., and Li, C. H. (1976). Purification and properties of teleost growth hormone. *Gen. Comp. Endocrinol.* **30,** 91–100.

Farmer, S. W., Hayashida, T. M., Papkoff, H., and Polenov, A. L. (1981). Characteristics of growth hormone isolated from sturgeon (*Aceipenser guldenstadti*) pituitary. *Endocrinology (Baltimore)* **108,** 377–381.

Farmer, W. W., Papkoff, H., and Hayashida, T. (1974). Purification and properties of avain growth hormones. *Endocrinology (Baltimore)* **95,** 1560–1565.

Farmer, W. W., Papkoff, H., and Hayashida, T. (1976). Purification and properties of reptilian and amphibian growth hormones. *Endocrinology (Baltimore)* **99,** 692–700.

Feeney, R. E. (1988). Inhibition and promotion of freezing: Fish antifreeze proteins and ice-nucleating proteins. *Comments Agric. Food Chem.* **1,** 147–181.

Feeney, R. E., and Yeh, Y. (1978). Antifreeze proteins from fish bloods. *Adv. Protein Chem.* **32,** 191–282.

Feldberg, E., and Bertollo, L. A. C. (1985). Nucleolar organizing regions in some species of neotropical cichlid fish (*Pisces, Perciformes*). *Caryologia* **38,** 319–324.

Ferguson, M. M., and Allendorf, F. W. (1991). Evolution of the fish genome. *In* "The

Biochemistry and Molecular Biology of Fishes. Vol. 1: Phylogenetic and Biochemical Perspectives" (P. W. Hochachka and T. P. Mommsen, eds.). ■■, ■■. In press.

Ferris, S. D. (1984). Tetraploidy and the evolution of the catostomid fishes. In "Evolutionary Genetics of Fishes" (B. J. Turner, ed.), pp. 55–93. Plenum, New York.

Fields, R. D., Johnson, K. R., and Thorgaard, G. H. (1989). DNA fingerprints in rainbow trout detected by hybridization with DNA of bacteriophage M13. Trans. Am. Fish. Soc. 118, 78–81.

Figueroa, J., Morley, S. D., Heierhorst, J., Krentler, C., Lederis, K., and Richter, D. (1989). Two isotocin genes are present in the white sucker Catostomus commersoni both lacking introns in their protein coding regions. EMBO 8, 2873–2877.

Fisher, S. E., Shaklee, J. B., Ferris, S. D., and Whitt, G. S. (1980). Evolution of five mutilocus isozyme systems in the chordates. Genetica 52/53, 73–85.

Fisher, W. K., Nash, A. R., and Thompson, E. O. P. (1977). Haemoglobins of the shark, Heterodontus portusjacksoni. III. Amino acid sequence of the β-chain. Aust. J. Biol. Sci. 30, 487–506.

Flaherty, L. (1987). MHC complex polymorphism: A nonimmune theory for selection. Hum. Immunol. 21, 3.

Fletcher, G. L., Shears, M. A., King, M. J., Davies, P. L., and Hew, C. L. (1988). Evidence for antifreeze protein gene transfer in atlantic salmon (Salmo salar). Can. J. Fish. Aquat. Sci. 45, 352–357.

Flockerzi, V., Oeken, H. J., Hormann, F., et al. (1986). Purified dihydropyridine-binding site from skeletal muscle t-tubules is a functional calcium channel. Nature (London) 232, 66–68.

Frail, D. E., Mudd, J., and Merliev, J. P. (1990). Nucleotide sequence of an intermediate filament cDNA from Torpedo californica. Nucleic Acids Res. 18, 1910.

Frick, L. (1983). An electrophoretic investigation of the cytosolic di- and tripeptidases of fish: Molecular weights, substrate specificities, and tissue and phylogenetic distributions. Biochem. Genet. 21, 309–322.

Frick, L. (1984). Isolation and characterization of five cytosolic di- and tripeptidases from the skipjack tuna (Katsuwonus pelamis). Comp. Biochem. Physiol., B: Comp. Biochem. 77, 533–540.

Fryer, J. N., and Lederis, K. (1985). Urotensin I and corticotropin secretion: Comparative actions in fishes and mammals. In "Neurosecretion and the Biology of Neuropeptides" (H. Kobayashi, H. A., Bern, and A. Urano, eds.), pp. 464–470. Academic Press, New York.

Funckes, C. L., Minth, C. D., Deschenes, A., Magazin, M., et al. (1983). Cloning and characterization of a mRNA-encoding rat preprosomatostatin. J. Biol. Chem. 268, 8781–8787.

Furutani, Y., Morimoto, Y., Shibahara, S., Noda, M., et al. (1983). Cloning and sequence analysis of cDNA for ovine corticotropin–releasing factor precursor. Nature (London) 301, 537–540.

Gardiner, K., Watkins, P., Münke, M., Drabkin, H., Jones, C., and Patterson, D. (1988). Partial physical map of human chromosome 21. Somatic Cell Mol. Genet. 14, 623–638.

Gedamu, L., Davies, P. L., and Dixon, G. H. (1977). Identification and isolation of protamine messenger ribonucleoprotein particles from rainbow and trout testis. Biochemistry 16, 1383–1391.

Gedamu, L., Culham, B., and Heikkila, J. J. (1983). Analysis of the temperature-dependent temporal pattern of heat-shock-protein synthesis in fish cells. Biosci. Rep. 3, 647–658.

Gellman, W. A., Allendorf, F. W., and Thorgaard, G. H. (1987). Hexosaminidase is sex linked in rainbow trout. *Isozyme Bulletin*, **20**, 14.

Ghaffari, S. H., and Lobb, C. J. (1989a). Cloning and sequence analysis of channel catfish heavy chain cDNA indicate phylogenetic diversity within the IgM immunoglobulin family. *J. Immunol.* **142**, 1356–1365.

Ghaffari, S. H., and Lobb, C. J. (1989b). Nucleotide sequence of channel catfish heavy chain cDNA and genomic blot analyses: Implications for the phylogeny of Ig heavy chains. *J. Immunol.* **143**, 2730–2739.

Gillen, R. G., and Riggs, A. (1971). The hemoglobins of the freshwater teleosts *Cichlasoma cyanoguttatum:* The effects of phosphorylated organic compounds upon the oxygen equilibria. *Comp. Biochem. Physiol. B* **38B**, 585–591.

Gilly, W. F., and Armstrong, C. M. (1982). Divalent cations and the activation kinetics of potassium channels in squid giant axons. *J. Gen. Physiol.* **79**, 965–996.

Goksoyr, A. (1985). Purification of hepatic microsomal cytochromes P-450 from β-naphthoflavone-treated Atlantic cod (*Gadus morhua*), a marine teleost fish. *Biochim. Biophys. Acta* **840**, 409–417.

Goksoyr, A., Andersson, T., Buhler, D. R., Stegeman, J. J., Williams, D. E., and Forlin, L. (1991). An immunological comparison of β-naphthoflavone-inducible microsomal cytochrome P-450 in different fish species and rat. *Fish Physiol. Biochem.*, (In press).

Gold, J. R. (1979). Cytogenetics. *In* "Fish Physiology" (W. S. Hoar, D. J. Randall, and J. R. Brett, eds.). Vol. 8, pp. 353–405. Academic Press, New York.

Gold, J. R., and Amemiya, C. T. (1987). Genome size in North American minnows (*Cyprinidae*). II. Variation among 20 species. *Genome* **29**, 481–489.

Gold, J. R., Amemiya, C. T., and Ellison, J. R. (1986). Chromosomal heterochromatin differentiation in North American cyprinid fishes. *Cytologia* **51**, 557–566.

Gonzalez, F. J., Skoda, R. C., Kimura, S., *et al.* (1988). Characterization of the common genetic defect in humans deficient in debrisoquine metabolism. *Nature (London)* **331**, 442–446.

Gonzalez, F. J., Matsunaga, T., and Nagata, K. (1989). Structure and regulation of P-450s in the rat P450IIA gene subfamily. *Drug Metab. Rev.* **20**, 827–837.

Gonzalez-Villasenor, L. I., and Powers, D. A. (1990). Mitochondrial DNA restriction site polymorphisms in the teleost *Fundulus heteroclitus* supports secondary intergradation. *Evolution* **44**, 27–37.

Gonzalez-Villasenor, L. I., Zhang, P., Chen, T. T., and Powers, D. A. (1988). Molecular cloning and sequencing of coho salmon growth hormone cDNA. *Gene* **65**, 239–246.

Goodman, M., Weiss, M. L., and Czelusniak, J. (1982). Molecular evolution above the species level: Branching pattern, rates, and mechanisms. *Syst. Zool* **31**, 376–399.

Gordon, M. (1931). The hereditary basis of melanosis in hybrids of Mexican killifishes. *Proc. Natl. Acad. Sci. U.S.A.* **17**, 276–280.

Gourlie, B., Lin, Y., Price, J., DeVries, A., Powers, D. A., and Huang, R. C. (1984). Winter flounder antifreeze proteins: A multigene family. *J. Biol. Chem.* **259**, 14960–14965.

Grunwald, D. J., Kimmel, C. B., Westerfield, M., *et al.* (1988). A neural degeneration mutation that spares primary neurons in the zebrafish. *Dev. Biol.* **126**, 115–128.

Gyllensten, U. B., and Ehrlich, H. A. (1988). Generation of single-stranded DNA by the polymerase chain reaction and its application to direct sequencing of the HLA-DQA locus. *Proc. Natl. Acad. Sci. U.S.A.* **85**, 7652–7656.

Harding, F. A., Cohen, N., and Litman, G. W. (1990). Immunoglobulin heavy chain gene organization and complexity in the skate, *Raja erinacea. Nucleic Acids Res.* **18**, 1015–1020.

Harless, J., Svensson, R., Kallman, K. D., Moritzot, S.C., and Nairn, R. S. (1990). Assignment of an erbB-like DNA sequence to linkage group VI in fishes of the genus *Xiphophorus* (Poeciliidae). *Cancer Genet. Cytogenet.* **50**, 45–51.

Hartley, S. E., and Horne, M. T. (1984). Chromosome relationships in the genus Salmo. *Chromosoma* **90**, 229–237.

Hashimoto, K., Nakanishi, T., and Kurosawa, Y. (1990). Isolation of carp genes encoding major histocompatibility complex antigens. *Proc. Natl. Acad. Sci. U.S.A.* **87**, 6863–6867.

Hawkins, W. E., Overstreet, R. M., and Walker, W. W. (1988). Carcinogenicity tests with small fish species. *Aquat. Toxicol.* **11**, 113–128.

Heath, M. R., and Walker, J. (1987). A preliminary study of the drift of larval herring (*Clupea harengus* L.) using gene-frequency data. *J. Cons. Cons. Int. Explor. Mer* **43**, 139–145.

Heierhorst, J., Morley, S. D., Figueroa, J., Krentler, C., Lederis, K., and Richter, D. (1989). Vasotocin and istocin precursors from the white sucker, *Catostomus commersoni:* Cloning and sequence analysis of the cDNAs. *Proc. Natl. Acad. Sci. U.S.A.* **86**, 5242–5246.

Heierhorst, J., Mahlmann, S., Morley, S. D., Coe, I. R., *et al.* (1990). Molecular cloning of two distinct vasotocin precursor cDNAs from chum salmon (*Onchorhynchus keta*) suggests an ancient gene duplication. *FEBS Lett.* **260**, 301–304.

Heikkila, J. J., Schultz, B. A., Iatrou, K., and Gedamu, L. (1982). Expression of a set of fish genes following heat or metal ion exposure. *J. Biol. Chem.* **257**, 12000–12005.

Heilmann, L. J., Sheen, Y.-Y., Bigelow, S. W., and Nebert, D. W. (1988). Trout P450IA1 : cDNA and deduced protein sequence, expression in liver, and evolutionary significance. *DNA* **7**, 379–387.

Hendricks, J. D. (1982). Chemical carcinogenesis in fish. *Aquat. Toxicol.* **1**, 149–211.

Hendricks, J. D., Wales, J. H., Sinnhuber, R. O., *et al.* (1980). Rainbow trout (*Salmo gairdneri*) embryos: A sensitive animal model for experimental carcinogenesis. *Fed. Proc.* **39**, 3222–3229.

Hendricks, J. D., Meyers, T. R., Casteel, J. L., *et al.* (1984). Rainbow trout embryos: Advantages and limitations for carcinogenesis research. *Nat. Cancer Inst. Monogr.* No. 65, 129–137.

Hendricks, J. D., Meyers, T. R., Shelton, D. W., Casteel, J. L., and Bailey, G. S. (1985). Hepatocarcinogenicity of Benzo[a]pyrene to rainbow trout by dietary exposure and intraperitoneal injection. *Natl. Cancer Inst.* **74**, 839–851.

Hightower, L. E., and Schultz, R. J. (1991). *Poeciliopsis:* A fish model for evaluating genetically variable responses to environmental hazards. *Biol. Criteria: Research and Regulations* (in press).

Higuchi, R. G., and Ochman, H. (1989). Production of single-stranded DNA templates by exonuclease digestion following the polymerase chain reaction. *Nucleic Acids Res.* **17**, 5865.

Hinds, K. R., and Litman, G. W. (1986). Major reorganization of immunoglobulin V_H segmental elements during vertebrate evolution. *Nature (London)* **320**, 546–549.

Hinds, K., Murphy, K., Litman, R., Berger, L., and Litman, G. (1985). Evolutionary conservation of both immunoglobulin heavy chain gene structure and functional reorganization in a primitive shark, *Heterodontus*. *In* "Short Reports. Vol. 2: Advances in Gene Technology: Molecular Biology of the Immune System" (J. W. Streilein *et al.* eds.), pp. 183–184. Cambridge Univ. Press, New York.

Hinegardner, R. (1976). Evolution of genome size. In "Molecular Evolution" (F. Ayala, ed.), pp. 179–199. Sinauer, Sunderland, Massachusetts.

Hinegardner, R., and Rosen, D. E. (1972). Cellular DNA content and the evolution of teleost fishes. Am. Nat. 106, 621–644.

Hiraoka, B. Y., Sharief, F. S., Yang, Y., Li, W., and Li, S. S. (1990). The cDNA and protein sequences of mouse lactate dehydrogenase B: Molecular evolution of vertebrate lactate dehydrogenase genes A (muscle), B (heart) and C (testis). Eur. J. Biochem. 189, 215–220.

Hobart, P., Crawford, R., Shen, L., Pictet, R., and Rutter, W. J. (1980). Cloning and sequence analysis of cDNAs encoding two distinct somatostatin precursors found in the endocrine pancreas of anglerfish. Nature (London) 288, 137–141.

Hochachka, P. W., and Somero, G. N. (1984). Temperature adaptation. In "Biochemical Adaptation," pp. 355–449. Princeton Univ. Press, Princeton, New Jersey.

Holbrook, J. J., Liljas, A., Steindel, S. J., and Rossmann, M. G. (1975). Lactate dehydrogenase. In "The Enzymes. Vol. 11: Oxidation-Reduction," Part A: Dehydrogenases(I) Electron Transfer(I)" (P. Boyer, ed.), pp. 191–292. Academic Press, New York.

Holmes, R. S. (1972). Evolution of lactate dehydrogenase genes. FEBS Lett. 28, 51–55.

Holmes, R. S., and Scopes, R. K. (1974). Immunochemical homologies among vertebrate lactate dehydrogenase isozymes. Eur. J. Biochem. 43, 167–177.

Honjo, T., Alt, F. W., and Rabbitts, T. H., ed. (1989). "Immunoglobulin Genes." Academic Press, San Diego, California.

Hood, L., Weissman, I. L., Wood, W. B., and Wilson, J. H. (1984). "Immunology." Benjamin/Cummings, Menlo Park, California.

Hood, L., Kronenberg, M., and Hunkapiller, T. (1985). T Cell antigen receptors and the immunoglobulin supergene family. Cell 40, 225–229.

Hubbs, C. L. (1955). Hybridization between fish species in nature. Syst. Zool. 4, 1–20.

Hughes, A. L., and Nei, M. (1988). Pattern of nucleotide substitution at major histocompatibility complex class I loci reveals overdominant selection. Nature (London) 335, 167.

Hughes, A. L., and Nei, M. (1989). Nucleotide substitution at major histocompatibility complex class II loci: Evidence for overdominant selection. Proc. Natl. Acad. Sci. U.S.A. 86, 958.

Hunkapiller, T., and Hood, L. (1989). Diversity of the immunoglobulin gene superfamily. Adv. Immunol. 44, 1–63.

Hyodo-Taguchi, Y., and Matsudaira, H. (1984). Induction of transplantable melanoma by treatment with N-methyl-N'-nitro-nitrosoguanidine in an inbred strain of the teleost Oryzias latipes. J. Natl. Cancer Inst. 73, 1219–1227.

Ichikawa, T., McMaster, D., Lederis, K., and Kobayashi, H. (1982). Isolation and amino acid sequence of urotensin I, a vasoactive and ACTH-releasing neuropeptide from carp (Cyprinus carpio) urophysis. Peptides 3, 859–867.

Ichikawa, T., Ishida, I., Ohsako, S., and Deguchi, T. (1988). In situ hybridization demonstrating coexpression of urotensins I, II-alpha, and II-gamma in the caudal neurosecretory neurons of the carp, Cyprinus carpio. Gen. Comp. Endocrinol. 71, 493–501.

Ikemura, T., and Aota, S.-I. (1988). Global variation in G+C content along vertebrate genome DNA. Possible correlation with chromosome band structures. J. Mol. Biol. 203, 1–13.

Ishida, I., Ichikawa, T., and Deguchi, T. (1986). Cloning and sequence analysis of cDNA encoding urotensin I precursor. Proc. Natl. Acad. Sci. U.S.A. 83, 308–312.

Jaiswal, A. K., Gonzalez, F. J., and Nebert, D. W. (1985). Human dioxin-inducible cytochrome P-450: complementary DNA and amino acid sequences. *Science* **228**, 80–83.

Jankowski, J. M., States, J. C., and Dixon, G. H. (1986). Evidence of sequences resembling avian retrovirus long terminal repeats flanking the trout protamine gene. *J. Mol. Evol.* **23**, 1–10.

Jatrou, K., Spira, A. W., and Dixon, G. H. (1978). Protamine messenger RNA: Evidence for early synthesis and accumulation during spermatogenesis in rainbow trout. *Dev. Biol.* **64**, 82–98.

Jeffreys, A. J., Wilson, V., and Thein, S. L. (1985). Individual-specific "fingerprints" of human DNA. *Nature (London)* **316**, 76–79.

Jewell, C. S., Lee, R. F., and Winston, G. W. (1989). Purification and properties in hepatopancreas and green gland cytosolic glutathione *S*-transferases of the red swamp crayfish, *Procambarus clarkii*. *Mar. Environ. Res.* **28**, 81–85.

Johansen, B., Johnsen, O. C., and Valla, S. (1989). The complete nucleotide sequence of the growth-hormone gene from Atlantic salmon (*Salmo salar*). *Gene* **77**, 317–324.

Johnson, K. R., Wright, J. E., and May, B. (1987). Linkage relationships reflecting ancestral tetraploidy in salmonid fish. *Genetics* **116**, 579–591.

Kagi, J. H. R., and Nordberg, M. (1979). "Metallothionein," pp. 41–116, 261–271. Birkhaeuser, Basel.

Kallman, K. D. (1983). The sex determining mechanism of the poeciliid fish, *Xiphophorus montezumae*, and the genetic control of the sexual maturation process and adult size. *Copeia* pp. 755–769.

Kaufman, J., Skjoedt, K., and Salomonsen, J. (1990). The MHC molecules of nonmammalian vertebrates. *Immunol. Rev.* **113**, 83–117.

Kawauchi, H., Kawazoe, I., Tsubokawa, M., Kishida, M., and Baker, B. I. (1983). Characterization of melanin-concentrating hormone in chum salmon pituitaries. *Nature (London)* **305**, 321–323.

Kawauchi, H., Moriyama, S., Yasuda, A., Yamaguchi, K., Shirahata, K., Kubota, J., and Hirano, T. (1986). Isolation and characterization of chum salmon growth hormone. *Arch. Biochem. Biophys.* **244**, 542–552.

Kawazoe, I., Kawauchi, H., Hirano, T., and Naito, N. (1987). Characterization of melanin concentrating hormone in teleost hypothalamus. *Gen. Comp. Endocrinol.* **65**, 423–431.

Kent, J. D., Koban, M., and Prosser, C. L. (1988). Protein hypertrophy as a mechanism of cold adapatation by liver of channel catfish and green sunfish. *J. Comp. Physiol.* **158**, 185–198.

Kettler, M. K., and Whitt, G. S. (1986). An apparent progressive and recurrent evolutionary restriction in tissue expression of a gene, the lactate dehydrogenase-C gene, within a family of bony fish (salmoniformes: Umbridae). *J. Mol. Evol.* **23**, 95–107.

Kimmel, C. B., and Warga, R. M. (1988). Cell lineage and developmental potential of cells in the zebrafish embryo. *Trends Genet.* **4**, 68–73.

Kimmel, C. B., Kane, D. A., Walker, C., *et al.* (1989). A mutation that changes cell movement and cell fate in the zebrafish embryo. *Nature (London)* **337**, 358–362.

Kimura, M. (1981). Was globin evolution very rapid in the early stages? A dubious case against the rate constancy hypothesis. *J. Mol. Evol.* **17**, 110–113.

Kimura, T., Yoshimizu, M., and Tanaka, M. (1981). Fish viruses: Tumor induction in *Onchorhynchus keta* by the herpesvirus. *In* "Phyletic Approaches to Cancer" (C. J.

Dawe, J. C. Harshbarger, S. Kondo, *et al.*, eds.), pp. 59–68. Japan Sci. Soc. Press, Tokyo.

Kitahara, N., Nishizawa, T., Gatanaga, T., *et al.* (1988). Primary structure of two mRNAs encoding putative salmon alpha-subunits of pituitary glycoprotein hormone. *Comp. Biochem. Physiol.* **91**, 551–556.

Klaunig, J. E., Barut, B. A., and Goldblatt, P. J. (1984). Preliminary studies on the usefulness of medaka, *Oryzias latipes,* embryos in carcinogenicity testing. *Natl. Cancer Inst. Monogr.* No. 65, 155–161.

Kleene, K. C., Distel, R. J., and Hecht, N. B. (1985). Nucleotide sequence of a cDNA clone encoding mouse protamine 1. *Biochemistry* **24**, 719–722.

Klein, J. (1987a). "Natural History of the Major Histocompatibility Complex." Wiley, New York.

Klein, J. (1987b). Origin of major histocompatibility complex polymorphism: The transspecies hypothesis. *Hum. Immunol.* **19**, 155.

Kloepper-Sams, P. J., Park, S., Gelboin, H., and Stegeman, J. (1987). Immunochemical specificity and cross-reactivity of monoclonal and polyclonal antibodies to cytochrome P-450E of the marine fish scup. *Arch. Biochem. Biophys.* **253**, 268–278.

Klotz, A. V., Stegemen, J. J., and Walsh, C. (1983). An aryl hydrocarbon hydroxylating hepatic cytochrome P-450 from the marine fish *Stenotomus chrysops. Arch. Biochem. Biophys.* **226**, 578–592.

Knight, C. A., Cheng, C. C., and DeVries, A. L. (1991). Adsorption of α-helical antifreeze peptides on specific ice crystal surface planes. *Biophys. J.* **59**, 409–418.

Knudsen, K. L., Leary, R. F., and Talluri, M. (1984). Reduced developmental stability of null allele heterozygotes at two lactate dehydrogenase loci in rainbow trout. *Genetics* **107**, s57.

Koban, M. (1986). Can cultured teleost hepatocytes show temperature acclimation? *Am. J. Physiol.* **250**, R211–R220.

Koban, M., Graham, G., and Prosser, C. L. (1987). Induction of heat-shock protein synthesis in teleost hepatocytes: Effects of acclimation temperature. *Physiol. Zool.* **60**, 290–296.

Koban, M., Yup, A. A., Agellon, L. B., and Powers, D. A. (1991). Molecular adaptation to the thermal environment. Heat-shock response of the eurythermal teleost *Fundulus heteroclitus. Mol. Mar. Biol. Biotechnol.* **1**, 1–17.

Kocan, R. M., Landolt, M. L., and Sabo, K. M. (1979). *In vitro* toxicity of eight mutagens/carcinogens for three cell lines. *Bull. Environ. Contam. Toxicol.* **23**, 269–274.

Koehn, R. K., and Williams, G. C. (1978). Genetic differentiation without isolation in the American eel, *Anquilla rostrata.* II. Temporal stability of geographic patterns. *Evolution* **32**, 624–637.

Kokubu, F., Hunds, K., Litman, R. *et al.* (1987). Extensive families of constant region genes in a phylogenetical primitive vertebrate indicate additional level of immunoglobulin complexity. *Proc. Natl. Acad. Sci. U.S.A.* **84**, 5868–5872.

Kokubu, F., Litman, R., Shamblott, M. J., *et al.* (1988). Diverse organization of immunoglobulin V_H gene loci in a primitive vertebrate. *EMBO J.* **7**, 3413–3422.

Kornfield, I., and Bogdanowicz, S. M. (1987). Differentiation of mitochondrial DNA in Atlantic herring, Clupea harengus. *Fish. Bull.* **85**, 561–568.

Kothary, R. K., and Candido, E. P. M. (1982). Induction of a novel set of polypeptides by heat shock or sodium arsenite in cultured cells of rainbow trout, Salmo gairdnerii. *Can. J. Biochem.* **60**, 347–355.

Krawetz, S. A., and Dixon, G. H. (1988). Sequence similarities of the protamine genes: Implications for regulation and evolution. *J. Mol. Evol.* **27**, 291–297.

Krawetz, S. A., Connor, W., and Dixon, G. H. (1987). Cloning of bovine P1 protamine cDNA and the evolution of vertebrate P1 protamines. *DNA* **6**, 47–57.

Larkin, P. A. (1981). A perspective on population genetics and salmon management. *Can. J. Fish. Aquat. Sci.* **38**, 1469–1475.

Lassek, A. M. (1970). "The Unique Legacy of Dr. Hughlings Jackson." Thomas, Springfield, Illinois.

Lavin, T. N., Baxter, J. D., and Horita, S. (1988). The thyroid hormone receptor binds to multiple domains of the rat growth hormone 5'-flanking sequence. *J. Biol. Chem.* **263**, 9418–9426.

Lederis, K., Letter, A., McMaster, D., Moore, G., and Schlesinger, D. (1982). Complete amino acid sequence of urotensin I, a hypotensive and corticotropin-releasing neuropeptide from *Catostomus*. *Science* **218**, 162–164.

Lederis, K., Fryer, J., Rivier, J., *et al.* (1985a). Neurohormones from fish tails. II: Actions of urotensin I in mammals and fishes. *Recent Prog. Horm. Res.* **41**, 553–576.

Lederis, K., Fryer, J. N., and Yulis, C. R. (1985b). The fish neuropeptide urotensin I: Its physiology and pharmacology. *Peptides* **6**, Suppl. 3, 353–361.

Leslie, J. F. (1982). Linkage analysis of seventeen loci in poeciliid fish (genus *Poeciliopsis*). *J. Hered.* **73**, 19–23.

Leslie, J. F., and Pontier, P. J. (1980). Linkage conservation of homologous esterase loci in fish (*Cyprinodontoidei: Poeciliidae*). *Biochem. Genet.* **18**, 103–115.

Leslie, J. F., and Vrijenhoek, R. C. (1977). Genetic analysis of natural populations of *Poeciliopsis monacha*. *J. Hered.* **68**, 301–306.

Leslie, J. F., and Vrijenhoek, R. C. (1980). Consideration of Muller's ratchet mechanism through studies of genetic linkage and genomic compatibilities in clonally reproducing *Poeciliopsis*. *Evolution* **34**, 1105–1115.

Lewontin, R. C. (1974). "The Genetic Basis of Evolutionary Change." Columbia Univ. Press, New York.

Li, C. H., Gordon, D., and Knorr, J. (1973). The primary structure of sheep growth hormone. *Arch. Biochem. Biophys.* **156**, 494–508.

Li, G. C., and Laszlo, A. (1985). Thermotolerance in mammalian cells: A possible role for heat shock proteins. *In* "Changes in Eukaryotic Gene Expression in Response to Environmental Stress" (B. G. Atkinson and D. B. Walden, eds.), pp. 227–254. Academic Press, Orlando, Florida.

Li, S. S. (1990). Human and mouse lactate dehydrogenase genes A (muscle), B (heart), and C (testis): Protein structure, genomic organization, regulation of expression, and molecular evolution. *In* "Isozymes: Structure, Function, and Use in Biology and Medicine," pp. 75–99. Wiley-Liss, New York.

Li, S. S., Fitch, W. M., Pan, Y. E., and Sharief, F. S. (1983). Evolutionary relationship of vertebrate lactate dehydrogenase isozymes A_4 (muscle), B_4 (heart) and C_4 (testis). *J. Biol. Chem.* **258**, 7029–7033.

Lin, Y., and Gross, J. K. (1981). Molecular cloning and characterization of winter flounder antifreeze cDNA. *Proc. Natl. Acad. Sci. U.S.A.* **78**, 2825–2829.

Lin, Y., Duman, J. G., and DeVries, A. L. (1972). Studies on the structure and activity of low molecular weight glycoproteins from an Antarctic fish. *Biochem. Biophys. Res. Commun.* **46**, 87–98.

Lindquist, S. (1981). Regulation of protein synthesis during heat shock. *Nature (London)* **293**, 311–314.

Lindquist, S. (1986). The heat-shock response. *Annu. Rev. Biochem.* **55**, 1151–1191.

Litman, G. W., Berger, L., Murphy, K., Litman, R., Podlaski, F., and Hinds, K. (1984).

Phylogenetic diversification of immunoglobulin V_h genes. *Dev. Comp. Immunol.* **8,** 499–514.

Litman, G. W., Berger, L., Murphy, K., Litman, R., *et al.* (1985). Immunoglobulin V_H gene structure and diversity in *Heterodontus,* a phylogenetically primitive shark. *Proc. Natl. Acad. Sci. U.S.A.* **82,** 2082–2086.

Litman, G. W., Amemiya, C. T., Haire, R. N., and Shamblott, M. J. (1990). Antibody and immunoglobulin diversity. *BioScience* **40,** 751–757.

Magazin, M., Minth, C. D., Funckes, C. L., Deschenes, R., Tavianini, M. A., and Dixon, J. E. (1982). Sequence of a cDNA encoding pancreatic preprosomatostatin-22. *Proc. Natl. Acad. Sci. U.S.A.* **79,** 5152–5156.

Malins, D. C., Krahn, M. M., Brown, D. W., *et al.* (1985). Toxic chemicals in marine sediment and biota from Mukilteo, Washington: Relationships with hepatic neoplasms and other hepatic lesions in English Sole (*Parophyrs vetulus*). *J. Natl. Cancer Inst.* **74,** 487–494.

Mangold, K., Chang, Y.-J., Mathews, C., *et al.* (1991). Expression of *ras* genes in rainbow trout liver. *Mol. Carcinog.* **4,** 1–6.

Maniatis, T., Fritsch, E. F., and Sambrook, J. (1982). "Molecular Cloning: A Laboratory Manual." Cold Spring Harbor Lab. Cold Spring Harbor, New York.

Marchalonis, J. J., and Schluter, S. F. (1989). Evolution of variable and constant domains and joining segments of rearranging immunoglobulins. *FASEB J.* **3,** 2469–2479.

Marchalonis, J. J., and Schluter, S. F. (1990). Origins of Immunoglobulins and immune recognition molecules. *BioScience* **40,** 758–768.

Markert, C. L., Shaklee, J. B., and Whitt, G. S. (1975). Evolution of a gene. *Science* **189,** 102–114.

Matson, R. H. (1986). LDH-X, is it an avian character? *Isozyme Bull.* **19,** 17.

Matsunaga, T., Chen, T., and Törmänen, V. (1990). Characterization of a complete immunoglobulin heavy-chain variable region germ-line gene of rainbow trout. *Proc. Natl. Acad. Sci. U.S.A.* **87,** 7767–7771.

Mauler, W., Raulf, F., and Schartl, M. (1988). Expression of proto-oncogenes in embryonic, adult, and transformed tissue of Xiphophorus (*Teleostei: Poeciliidae*). *Oncogene* **2,** 421–430.

Mayr, E. (1973). "Animal Species and Evolution." Harvard Univ. Press, Cambridge, Massachusetts.

McKay, D. J., Renaux, B. S., and Dixon, G. H. (1986a). Human sperm protamines amino acid sequences of two forms of protamine P2. *Eur. J. Biochem.* **156,** 5–8.

McKay, D. J., Renaux, B. S., and Dixon, G. H. (1986b). Rainbow trout protamines amino acid sequences of six distinct proteins from a single testis. *Eur. J. Biochem.* **158,** 361–366.

McMaster, D., and Lederis, K. (1988). Urotensin I and CRF like peptides in *Catostomus commersoni* brain. *Peptides* **9,** 1043–1048.

McMaster, D., Rivier, J., and Lederis, K. (1988). Isolation, amino acid sequence and synthesis of urotensin I from *Hippoglossoides elassodon. In* "Peptide Chemistry" (T. Shiba and S. Sakakibara, eds.), pp. 145–148. Protein Res. Found., Osaka, Japan.

Medrano, L., Bernardi, G., Couturier, J., Dutrillaux, B., and Bernardi, G. (1988). Chromosome banding and genome compartmentalization in fishes. *Chromosoma* **96,** 178–183.

Merz, R., and Laudien, H. (1987). Two types of heat tolerance in FHM-cells. Induction by heat-shock versus elevated culturing temperature. *J. Therm. Biol.* **12,** 281–288.

Mied, P. A., and Powers, D. A. (1978). Hemoglobins of the killifish *Fundulus heteroclitus:* Separation, characterization and a model for subunit composition. *J. Biol. Chem.* **253,** 3521.

Mikoryak, C. A., and Steiner, L. A. (1988). Amino acid sequence of the constant region of immunoglobulin light chains from *Rana catesbeiana. Mol. Immunol.* **25**, 695–703.

Millan, J. L., Driscoll, C. E., Le Van, K. M., and Goldberg, E. (1987). Epitopes of human testis-specific lactate dehydrogenase deduced from a cDNA sequence. *Proc. Natl. Acad. Sci. U.S.A.* **84**, 5311–5315.

Miller, W. C., and Eberhardt, N. L. (1983). Structure and evolution of the growth hormone gene family. *Endocr. Rev.* **4**, 97–130.

Mishina, M., Tobimatsu, T., Imoto, K., *et al.* (1985). Location of functional regions of acetylcholine receptor α-subunit by site-directed mutagenesis. *Nature (London)* **313**, 364–369.

Mix, M. C. (1986). Cancerous diseases in aquatic animals and their association with environmental pollutants: A critical literature review. *Mar. Environ. Res.* **20**, 1–141.

Moir, R. D., and Dixon, G. H. (1988). A repetitive DNA sequence in the salmonid fishes similar to the retroviral long terminal repeat. *J. Mol. Evol.* **27**, 1–7.

Morgan, R. P., II (1975). Distinguishing larval white perch and striped bass by electrophoresis. *Chesapeake Sci.* **16**, 68–70.

Morgan, R. P., II, Koo, T. S. Y., and Krantz, G. E. (1973). Electrophoretic determination of populations of striped bass, *Morone saxatilis,* in the Chesapeake Bay. *Trans. Am. Fish. Soc.* **102**, 21–32.

Morizot, D. C. (1983). Tracing linkage groups from fishes to mammals. *J. Hered.* **74**, 413–416.

Morizot, D. C. (1986). Comparative gene mapping evidence for chromosome duplications in chordate evolution. *Isozyme Bull.* **19**, 9–10.

Morizot, D. C. (1990). Use of fish gene maps to predict ancestral vertebrate genome organization. *In* "Isozymes: Structure, Function, and Use in Biology and Medicine," pp. 207–234. Wiley-Liss, New York.

Morizot, D. C., and Siciliano, M. J. (1983). Comparative gene mapping in fishes. *Isozymes: Curr. Top. Biol. Med. Res.* 10, 261–285.

Morizot, D. C., and Siciliano, M. J. (1984). Gene mapping in fishes and other vertebrates. *In* "Evolutionary Genetics of Fishes" (B. J. Turner, ed.), pp. 173–234. Plenum, New York.

Morizot, D. C., Schultz, R. J., and Wells, R. S. (1990). Assignment of six enzyme loci to multipoint linkage groups in fishes of the genus *Poeciliopsis (Poeciliidae)*: Designation of linkage groups III–V. *Biochem. Genet.* **28**, 83–95.

Morizot, D. C., Calhoun, S. W., Clepper, L. L., and Schmidt, M. E. (1991). Multispecies hybridization among native and introduced Centrarchid basses in central Texas. *Trans. Am. Fish Soc.* **120**, 283–289.

Morley, S. D., Schönrock, C., Heierhorst, J., *et al.* (1990). Vasotocin genes of the teleost fish *Catostomus commersoni:* Gene structure, exon-intron boundary and hormone precursor organization. *Biochemistry* **29**, 2506–2511.

Morley, S. D., Schönrock, C., Okawara, Y., *et al.* (1991). Corticotropin-releasing factor (CRF) gene family in the brain of the teleost fish *Catostomus commersoni* (White Sucker): Molecular analysis predicts distinct precursors for two CRFs and one urotensin I peptide. *MMBB* **1**, 48–57.

Mouchiroud, D., Fichant, G., and Bernardi, G. (1987). Compositional compartmentalization and gene composition in the genome of vertebrates. *J. Mol. Evol.* **26**, 198–204.

Mouchiroud, D., Gautier, C., and Bernardi, G. (1988). The compositional distribution of coding sequences and DNA molecules in humans and murids. *J. Mol. Evol.* **27**, 311–320.

Murchelano, R. A., and Wolke, R. E. (1985). Epizootic carcinoma in the winter flounder, *Pseudo-pleuronectes americanus. Science* **228**, 587–589.

Nagy, G., Mulchahey, J. J., Smyth, D. G., and Neill, J. D. (1988). The glycopeptide moiety of vasopressin-neurophysin precursor is neurohypophysial prolactin releasing factor. *Biochem. Biophys. Res. Commun.* **151**, 524–529.

Naito, N., Nakai, Y., Kawauchi, H., and Hayashi, Y. (1985). Immuno-cytochemical identification of melanin-concentrating hormone in the brain and pituitary gland of the teleost fishes *Oncorhynchus keta* and *Salmo gairdneri*. *Cell Tissue Res.* **242**, 41–48.

Nash, A. R., Fisher, W. K., and Thompson, E. O. P. (1976). Haemoglobins of the shark, *Heterodontus portusjacksoni*. II. Amino acid sequence of the α-chain. *Aust. J. Biol. Sci.* **29**, 73–97.

Nathans, J., Thomas, D., and Hogness, D. S. (1986). Molecular genetics of human color vision: The genes encoding blue, green, and red pigments. *Science* **232**, 193–202.

Nathenson, S. G., Geliebter, J., Pfaffenbach, G. M., and Zeff, R. A. (1986). Murine major histocompatibility complex class I mutants: Molecular analysis and structure–function implications. *Annu. Rev. Immunol.* **4**, 471.

Nebert, D. W., Adesnik, M., Coon, M. J., *et al.* (1987). The P450 gene superfamily: Recommended nomenclature. *DNA* **6**, 1–11.

Nebert, D. W., Nelson, D. R., Adesnik, M., *et al.* (1989). The P450 superfamily: Updated listing of all genes and recommended nomenclature for the chromosomal loci. *DNA* **8**, 1–13.

Nemoto, N., Kodama, K.-I., Tazawa, A., Masahito, P., and Ishikawa, T. (1986). Extensive sequence homology of the goldfish *ras* gene to mammalian *ras* genes. *Differentiation* **32**, 17–23.

Niall, H. D., Hogan, M. L., Sauer, R., *et al.* (1971). Sequences of pituitary and placental lactogenic and growth hormones: Evolution from a primordial peptide by gene reduplication. *Proc. Natl. Acad. Sci. U.S.A.* **68**, 866–869.

Nicoll, C. S., Steiny, S. S., King, D., *et al.* (1987). The primary structure of coho salmon growth hormone and its cDNA. *Gen. Comp. Endocrinol.* **68**, 387–399.

Njolstad, P. R., and Fjose, A. (1988). In situ hybridization patterns of zebrafish homeobox genes homologous to *HOX-2.1* and *EN-2* of mouse. *Biochem. Biophys. Res. Commun.* **157**, 426–432.

Noda, M., Takahashi, H., Tanabe, T., *et al.* (1983). Structural homology of *Torpedo californica* acetylcholine receptor subunits. *Nature (London)* **302**, 528–532.

Noda, M., Shimizu, S., Tanabe, T., *et al.* (1984). Primary structure of *Electrophorus electricus* sodium channel deduced from cDNA sequence. *Nature (London)* **312**, 121–127.

Noda, M., Ikeda, T., Kayano, T., *et al.* (1986). Existence of distinct sodium channel messenger RNAs in rat brain. *Nature (London)* **320**, 188–192.

Noe, R. D., Fletcher, D., and Spiess, J. (1979). Evidence for the existence of a biosynthetic precursor for somatostatin. *Diabetes* **28**, 724–730.

Nogusa, S. (1960). A comparative study of the chromosomes in fishes with particular considerations on toxonomy and evolution. *Hyogo Noka Daigaku Kiyo, Biol. Ser.* **3**(1), 1–62.

Numa, M., Takahashi, H., Tanabe, T., Toyosato, M., Kikyotani, S., Furutani, Y., Hirose, T., Inayma, S., Miyata, T., and Numa, S. (1983). Structural homology of *Torepedo californica* ACh receptor subunits. *Nature (London)* **302**, 528–532.

Ohno, S. (1970). "Evolution by Gene Duplication." Springer-Verlag, New York.

Ohno, S. (1974). Protochordata, Cyclostomata and Pisces. *In* "Animal Cytogenetics. Vol. 4: Chordata 1" (B. John, ed.), pp. 1–91. Borntraeger, Berlin.

Ohno, S., Wolf, U., and Atkin, N. B. (1968). Evolution from fish to mammals by gene duplication. *Hereditas* **59**, 169–187.

Okawara, Y., Morley, S. D., Burzio, L. O., Zwiers, H., Lederis, K., and Richter, D. (1988). Cloning and sequence analysis of cDNA for corticotropin-releasing factor precursor from the teleost fish *Catostomus commersoni*. *Proc. Natl. Acad. Sci. U.S.A.* **85**, 8439–8443.

Okazaki, K., and Sakano, H. (1988). Thymocyte circular DNA excised from T cell receptor α–δ gene complex. *EMBO J.* **7**, 1669–1674.

Ono, M., Wada, C., Oikawa, I., Kawazoe, I., and Kawauchi, H. (1988). Structures of two kinds of mRNA encoding the chum salmon melanin-concentrating hormone. *Gene* **71**, 433–438.

Ozato, K., and Wakamatsu, Y. (1981). Cellular heterogeneity in the late-onset form of hereditary melanomas in the *Xiphophorus* fish hybrids. *Dev. Growth Differ.* **23**, 273–285.

Papas, T. S., Dahlberg, J. E., and Sonstegard, R. A. (1976). Type C virus in lymphosarcoma in northern pike (*Esox lucius*). *Nature (London)* **261**, 506–508.

Papas, T. S., Pry, T. W., Schafer, M. P., and Sonstegard, R. A. (1977). Presence of DNA polymerase in lymphosarcoma in northern pike (*Esox lucius*). *Cancer Res.* **37**, 3214–3217.

Park, S. S., Miller, H., Klotz, A. V., *et al.* (1986). Monoclonal antibodies to liver microsomal cytochrome P-450E of the marine fish *Stenotomus chrysops* (scup). *Arch. Biochem. Biophys.* **249**, 339–350.

Pasdar, M., Philipp, D. P., and Whitt, G. S. (1984). Linkage relationships of nine enzyme loci in sunfishes (Lepomis: *Centrarchidae*). *Genetics* **107**, 435–446.

Paynter, K. T., DiMichele, L., Hand, S. C., and Powers, D. A. (1991). Metabolic implications of Ldh-B genotype during early development in *Fundulus heteroclitus*. *J. Exp. Zool.* **257**, 24–33.

Pedersen, M. G., Hershberger, W. K., Zachariah, P. K., and Juchau, M. R. (1976). Hepatic transformation of environmental xenobiotics in six strains of rainbow trout (*Salmo gairdneri*). *J. Fish. Res. Board Can.* **33**, 666.

Pella, J. J., and Milner, G. B. (1987). Use of genetic marks in stock composition analysis. *In* "Population Genetics and Fisheries Management" (N. Ryman and F. M. Utter, eds.), pp. 247–276. Univ. of Washington Press, Seattle.

Perlmutter, A., and Potter, H. (1988). Hyperthermic expression of a genetically programmed melanoma in hybrid fishes of the genus *Xiphophorus*. *J. Cancer Res. Clin. Oncol.* **114**, 359–362.

Perrin, P., and Bernardi, G. (1987). Directional fixation of mutations in vertebrate evolution. *J. Mol. Evol.* **26**, 301–310.

Philipp, D. P., Childers, W. F., and Whitt, G. S. (1979). Evolution of patterns of differential gene expression: A comparison of temporal and spatial patterns of isozyme locus expression in two closely related fish species (Northern largemouth bass, *Micropterus salmoides salmoides,* and smallmouth bass, *Micropterus dolomieui*). *J. Exp. Zool.* **210**, 473–488.

Philipp, D. P., Parker, H. R., and Whitt, G. S. (1983). Evolution of gene regulation: Isozymic analysis of patterns of gene expression during hybrid fish development. *Isozymes: Curr. Top. Biol. Med. Res.* **10**, 193–237.

Place, A. R., and Powers, D. A. (1978). Genetic basis for protein polymorphism in *Fundulus heteroclitus*. I. Lactate dehydrogenase, malate dehydrogenase, glucose phosphate isomerase, and the phosphoglucomutase. *Biochem. Genet.* **16**, 577–591.

Place, A. R., and Powers, D. A. (1979). Genetic variation and relative catalytic efficiencies: Lactate dehydrogenase B allozymes of *Fundulus heteroclitus*. *Proc. Natl. Acad. Sci. U.S.A.* **76**, 2354–2358.

Place, A. R., and Powers, D. A. (1984a). The lactate dehydrogenase (LDH-B) allozymes of

Fundulus heteroclitus: I. Purification and characterization. *J. Biol. Chem.* **259,** 1299–1308.

Place, A. R., and Powers, D. A. (1984b). The lactate dehydrogenase (LDH-B) allozymes of *Fundulus heteroclitus:* II. Kinetic analyses. *J. Biol. Chem.* **259,** 1309–1318.

Post, A. (1965). Vergleichende Untersuchungen der Chromosomenzahlen bei Susswasser-Teleosteern. *Z. Zool. Syst. Evolutionsforsch.* **3,** 47–93.

Potter, I. C., and Rothwell, B. (1970). The mitotic chromosomes of the lamprey, *Petromyzon marinus* L. *Experientia* **26,** 429–430.

Powers, D. A. (1989). Fish as model systems. *Science* **246,** 352–358.

Powers, D. A. (1990). Adaptive significance of multiple forms of enzymes. *In* "Electrophoretic and Isoelectric Focusing Techniques in Fisheries Management" (D. H. Whitmore, ed.), pp. 323–339. CRC Press, Boca Raton, Florida.

Powers, D. A., and Edmundson, A. B. (1972). Multiple hemoglobins of catostomid fish. II. The amino acid sequence of the major α chain from *Catostomus* ClarkII hemoglobins. *J. Biol. Chem.* **247,** 6694–6707.

Powers, D. A., Ropson, I., Brown, W. C., Van Beneden, R., Cashon, R., Gonzalez-Villasenor, L. I., and DiMichele, J. (1986). Genetic variation in *Fundulus heteroclitus:* Geographic distribution. *Am. Zool.* **26,** 131–144.

Powers, D. A., Lauerman, T., Crawford, D., and DiMichele, L. (1991). Genetic mechanisms for adapting to a changing environment. *Annu. Rev. Genet.* **25** (in press).

Powers, M. K., and Easter, S. S. (1983). Biological significance of retinal structure and function in fishes. *In* "Fish Neurobiology" (R. G. Northcutt and R. E. Davis, eds.), Vol. 1, pp. 377–404. Univ. of Michigan Press, Ann Arbor.

Pradayrol, L., Chagrialle, J., and Mutt, V. (1978). Pig duodenal somatostatin: extraction and purification. *Metabolism.* **27,** suppl. I, 1197–1200.

Price, D. J. (1984). Genetics of sex determination in fishes: A brief review. *In* "Fish Reproduction: Strategies and Tactics" (G. W. Potts and R. J. Wootton, eds.), pp. 77–89. Academic Press, New York.

Price-Haughey, J., Bonham, K., and Gedamu, L. (1987). Metallothionein gene expression in fish cell lines: Its activation in embryonic cells by 5-azacytidine. *Biochim. Biophys. Acta* **908,** 158–168.

Prosser, C. L. (1986). "Adaptational Biology: Molecules to Organisms." Wiley, New York.

Quattro, J. M., and Vrijenhoek, R. C. (1989). Fitness differences among remnant populations of the Sonoran topminnow, *Poeciliopsis occidentalis. Science* **245,** 976–978.

Ràb, P., Roth, P., and Mayr, B. (1987). Karyotype study of eight species of European Percid fishes (Pisces, Percidae). *Caryologia* **40,** 307–318.

Raftery, M. A., Hunkapiller, M. W., Strader, C. D., and Hood, L. E. (1980). Acetycholine receptor: Complex of homologous subunits. *Science* **208,** 1454–1457.

Rance, T., and Baker, B. I. (1979). The teleost melanin-concentrating hormone—A pituitary hormone of hypothalamic origin. *Gen. Comp. Endocrinol.* **37,** 64–73.

Raymond, J. A., Wilson, P., and DeVries, A. L. (1989). Inhibition of growth of nonbasal planes in ice by fish antifreezes. *Proc. Natl. Acad. Sci. U.S.A.* **86,** 881–885.

Rehbein, M., Hillers, B., Mohr, E., Ivell, R., *et al.* (1986). The neurohypophyseal hormones vasopressin and oxytocin: Precursor structure, synthesis and regulation. *Biol. Chem. Hoppe-Seyler* **367,** 695–704.

Rehse, P. H., and Davidson, W. S. (1986). Evolutionary relationship of a fish C type lactate dehydrogenase to other vertebrate lactate dehydrogenase isozymes. *Can. J. Fish. Aquat. Sci.* **43,** 1045–1051.

Rentier-Delrue, F., Swennen, D., Mercier, L., Lion, M., Benrubi, O., and Martial, J. A. (1989a). Molecular cloning and characterization of two forms of trout growth hormone cDNA: Expression and secretion of tGH-II by *Escherichia coli*. *DNA* **8,** 109–117.

Rentier-Delrue, F., Swennen, D., Prunet, P., Lion, M., and Martial, J. A. (1989b). Tilapia prolactin: Molecular cloning of two cDNAs and expression in *Escherichia coli*. *DNA* **8,** 261–270.

Reynaud, C.-A., and Anquez, V., Dahan, A., and Weill, J.-C. (1985). A single rearrangement event generates most of the chicken immunoglobulin light chain diversity. *Cell* **40,** 283–291.

Reynaud, C.-A., Anquez, V., Grimal, H., and Weill, J.-C. (1987). A hyperconversion mechanism generates the chicken light chain pre-immune repertoire. *Cell* **48,** 379–388.

Richter, D. (1986). Oxytocin and Vasopressin genes: Expression and structure. *In* "Molecular Cloning of Hormone Genes" (J. F. Habener, ed.), pp. 173–206. Humana Press, Clifton, New Jersey.

Ricker, W. E. (1981). Changes in the average size and average age of Pacific salmon. *Can. J. Fish. Aquat. Sci.* **38,** 1636–1656.

Ronis, M. J. J., Andersson, T., Hansson, T., and Walker, C. H . (1989). Differential expression of multiple forms of cytochrome P450 in vertebrates: Antibodies to purified rate cytochrome P-450s as molecular probes for the evolution of P-450 gene families I and II. *Mar. Environ. Res.* **28,** 131–135.

Ropson, I., and Powers, D. A. (1988). A novel dehydrogenase reaction mechanism for hexose-6-phosphate dehydrogenase isolated from the teleost *Fundulus heteroclitus*. *J. Biol. Chem.* **263,** 11697–11703.

Ropson, I., Brown, D., and Powers, D. A. (1990). Biochemical genetics of *Fundulus heteroclitus* (L.) VI. Geographical variation in the gene frequencies of 15 loci. *Evolution* **44,** 16–26.

Rosenberg, R. L., Tomiko, S. A., and Agnew, W. S. (1984a). Single-channel properties of the reconstituted voltage-regulated Na channel isolated from the electroplax of *Electrophorus electricus*. *Proc. Natl. Acad. Sci. U.S.A.* **81,** 5594–5598.

Rosenberg, R. L., Tomiko, S. A., and Agnew, W. S. (1984b). Reconstitution of neurotoxin-modulated ion transport by the voltage-regulated sodium channel isolated from the electroplax of *Electrophorus electricus*. *Proc. Natl. Acad. Sci. U.S.A.* **81,** 1239–1243.

Russell, F. E., and Kotin, P. (1957). Squamous papillomas in the white croaker. *J. Natl. Cancer Inst.* **6,** 857–861.

Ryman, N., and Utter, F., eds. (1987). "Population Genetics and Fisheries Management." Univ. of Washington Press, Seattle.

Salkoff, L., Butler, A., Scavarda, N., and Wei, A. (1987a). Nucleotide sequence of the putative sodium channel gene from *Drosophila:* the four homologous domains. *Nucleic Acid Res.* **15,** 8569–8572.

Salkoff, L., Butler, A., Wei, A., Scavarda, N., Giffen, K., Ifune, C., Goodman, R., and Mandel, G. (1987b). Genomic organization and deduced amino acid sequence of a putative sodium channel gene in *Drosophila*. *Science* **237,** 744–749.

Sato, N., Watanabe, K., Murata, K., Sakaguchi, M., Kariya, Y., Kimura, S., Nonaka, M., and Kimura, A. (1988). Molecular cloning and nucleotide sequence of tuna growth hormone cDNA. *Biochim. Biophys. Acta* **949,** 35–42.

Sawyer, J. R., and Hozier, J. C. (1986). High resolution of mouse chromosomes: Banding conservation between man and mouse. *Science* **232,** 1632–1635.

Schally, A. V., Dupont, A., Arimura, A., *et al.* (1976). Isolation and structure of somatostatin from porcine hypothalami. *Biochemistry* **15,** 509–514.

Schally, A. V., Huang, W., Chang, R. C., Arimura, A., Redding, T. W., Millar, R. P.,

Hunkapiller, M.'W., and Hood, L. E. (1980). Isolation and structure of prosomatostatin: A putative somatostatin precursor from pig hypothalamus. *Proc. Natl. Acad. Sci. U.S.A.* **77,** 4489–4493.

Schartl, M., and Barnekow, A. (1984). Differential expression of the cellular SRC gene during vertebrate development. *Dev. Biol.* **105,** 415–422.

Schartl, M., and Peter, R. U. (1988). Progressive growth of fish tumors after transplantation into thymus-aplastic (nu/nu) mice. *Cancer Res.* **48,** 741–744.

Schartl, M., Barnekow, A., Bauer, H., and Anders, F. (1982). Correlations of inheritance and expression between a tumor gene and the cellular homolog of the Rous sarcoma virus-transforming gene in Xiphophorus. *Cancer Res.* **42,** 4222–4227.

Schartl, M., Schmidt, C. R., Anders, F., and Barnekow, A. (1985). Elevated expression of the cellular SRC gene in tumors of differing etiologies in Xiphophorus. *Int. J. Cancer* **36,** 199–207.

Schlesinger, M. J., Ashburner, M., and Tissieres, A. (1982). "Heat Shock, from Bacteria to Man." Cold Spring Harbor Lab., Cold Spring Harbor, New York.

Schluter, S. F., Beischel, C. J., Martin, S. A., and Marchalonis, J. J. (1990). Sequence analysis of homogeneous peptides of shark immunoglobulin light chains by tandem mass spectrometry: Correlation with gene sequence and homologies among variable and constant region peptides of sharks and mammals. *Mol. Immunol.* **27,** 17–23.

Schmid, M., and Guttenbach, M. (1988). Evolutionary diversity of reverse (R) fluorescent chromosome bands in vertebrates. *Chromosoma* **97,** 101–114.

Schultz, M. E., and Schultz, R. J. (1982a). Diethylnitrosamine-induced hepatic tumors in wild vs. inbred strains of a viviparous fish. *J. Hered.* **73,** 43–48.

Schultz, M. E., and Schultz, R. J. (1982b). Induction of hepatic tumors with 7,12-dimethylbenz[α]anthracene in two species of viviparous fishes (*Genus Poeciliopsis*). *Environ. Res.* **27,** 337–351.

Schultz, M. E., and Schultz, R. J. (1985). Transplantable chemically-induced liver tumors in the viviparous fish *Poeciliopsis*. *Exp. Mol. Pathol.* **42,** 320–330.

Schultz, M. E., and Schultz, R. J. (1988). Differences in response to a chemical carcinogen within species and clones of the live bearing fish *Poecilliopsis*. *Carcinogensis* **9,** 1029–1032.

Schultz, R. J. (1967). Gynogenesis and triploidy in the viviparous fish *Poeciliopsis*. *Science* **157,** 1564–1567.

Schultz, R. J. (1969). Hybridization, unisexuality, and polyploidy in the teleost *Poeciliopsis* (*Poeciliidae*) and other vertebrates. *Am. Nat.* **103,** 605–619.

Schultz, R. J. (1973). Unisexual fish: Laboratory synthesis of a "species". *Science* **179,** 180–181.

Schultz, R. J. (1977). Evolution and ecology of unisexual fishes. *Evol. Biol.* **10,** 277–331.

Schultz, R. J. (1982). Competition and adaptation among diploid and polyploid clones of unisexual fish. *In* "Evolution and Genetics of Life Histories" (H. Dingle and J. P. Hegmann, eds.), pp. 103–119. Springer-Verlag, New York.

Schwager, J., Grossberger, D., and DuPasquier, L. (1988). Organization and rearrangement of immunoglobulin M genes in the amphibian Xenopus. *EMBO J.* **7,** 2409–2415.

Scott, G. K., Hew, C. L., and Davies, P. L. (1985). Antifreeze protein genes are tandemly linked and clustered in the genome of the winter flounder. *Proc. Natl. Acad. Sci. U.S.A.* **82,** 2613–2617.

Scott, G. K., Fletcher, G. L., and Davies, P. L. (1986). Fish antifreeze proteins: Recent gene evolution. *Can. J. Fish. Aquat. Sci.* **43,** 1028–1034.

Scott, G. K., Davies, P. L., Kao, M. H., and Fletcher, G. L. (1988). Differential amplification of antifreeze protein genes. *J. Mol. Evol.* **27**, 29–35.

Seeburg, P. H. (1982). The human growth gene family: nucleotide sequences show recent divergence and predict a new polypeptide hormone. *DNA* **1**, 239–249.

Sekine, S., Miizukami, T., Nishi, T., Kuwana, Y., Saito, A., Sato, M., Itoh H., and Kawauchi, H. (1985). Cloning and expression of cDNA for salmon growth hormone in Escherichia coli. *Proc. Natl. Acad. Sci. U.S.A.* **82**, 4306–4310.

Shaklee, J. B. (1983). The utilization of isozymes as gene markers in fisheries management and conservation. *Isozymes: Curr. Top. Biol. Med. Res.* **11**, 213–247.

Shaklee, J. B., and Tamaru, C. S. (1981). Biochemical and morphological evolution of Hawaiian Bonefishes (ALBULA). *Syst. Zool.* **30**, 125–146.

Shaklee, J. B., Kepes, K. L., and Whitt, G. S. (1973). Specialized lactate dehydrogenase isozymes: The molecular and genetic basis for the unique eye and liver LDHs of teleost fish. *J. Exp. Zool.* **185**, 217–240.

Shaklee, J. B., Allendorf, F. W., Morizot, D. C., and Whitt, G. S. (1990). Gene nomenclature for protein-coding loci in fish. *Trans. Am. Fish. Soc.* **119**, 2–15.

She, J. X., Autem, M., Kotulas, G., Pasteur, N., and Bonhomme, F. (1987). Multivariate analysis of genetic exchanges between Sole aegyptiaca and Solea senegenesis (Teleosts, Soleodae). *Biol. J. Linn. Soc.* **32**, 357–371.

Shen, L., and Rutter, W. J. (1984). Sequence of the human somatostatin I gene. *Science* **224**, 168–171.

Shen, L., Pictet, R. L., and Rutter, W. J. (1982). Human somatostatin I: Sequence of the cDNA. *Proc. Natl. Acad. Sci. U.S.A.* **79**, 4575–4579.

Shows, T. B., and 24 co-authors (1987). Guidelines for human gene nomenclature. An international system for human gene nomenclature (ISGN, 1987). *Cytogenet. Cell Genet.* **46**, 11–101.

Siciliano, M. J., Morizot, D. C., and Wright, D. A. (1976). Factors responsible for platyfish–swordtail hybrid melanoma—many or few? *In* "Melanomas: Basic Properties and Clinical Behavior" (V. Riley, ed.), pp. 47–54. Karger, Basel.

Sidell, B. D., Otto, R. G., and Powers, D. A. (1978). A biomedical method for distinction of striped bass and white perch larvae. *Copei* No. 2, 340–343.

Sidell, B. D., Otto, R. G., Powers, D. A., Karweit, M., and Smith, J. (1980). A reevaluation of the occurrence of sub-populations of striped bass (*Morone saxatilis,* Walbaum) in the upper Chesapeake Bay. *Trans. Am. Fish. Soc.* **109**, 99–107.

Simon, K., and Lapis, K. (1984). Carcinogenesis studies on guppies. *Natl. Cancer Inst. Monogr.* No. 65, 71–81.

Sinnhuber, R. O., Hendricks, J. D., Wales, J. W., and Putnam, G. B. (1977). Neoplasms in rainbow trout, a sensitive animal model for environmental carcinogenesis. *Ann. N.Y. Acad. Sci.* **298**, 389–408.

Slater, E. P., Baxter, J. D., and Eberhardt, N. L. (1986). Evolution of the growth hormone gene family. *Am. Zool.* **26**, 939–949.

Slatkin, M. (1985). Rare alleles as indicators of gene flow. *Evolution* **39**, 53–65.

Smith, M. W., Chapman, R. W., and Powers, D. A. (1992). Mitrochondrial DNA analysis detects a temporally unstable secondary intergradation zone between *Fundulus heteroclitus* subspecies. Submitted.

Somero, G. N., and DeVries, A. L. (1967). Temperature tolerance of some Antarctic fishes. *Science* **156**, 257–258.

Song, S., Trinh, K. Y., Hew, C. L., Hwang, S. J., *et al.* (1988). Molecular cloning and expression of salmon prolactin cDNA. *Eur. J. Biochem.* **172**, 279–285.

Spiess, J., Rivier, J. E., Rodkey, J. A., *et al.* (1979). Isolation and characterization of somatostatin from pigeon pancreas. *Proc. Natl. Acad. Sci. U.S.A.* **76**, 2974–2978.

Stanton, M. F. (1965). Diethylnitrosamine-induced hepatic degeneration and neoplasia in the aquarium fish, *Brachidanio rerio. J. Natl. Cancer Inst.* **34,** 117–130.

Stebbins, G. L. (1969). "The Basis of Progressive Evolution." Univ. of North Carolina Press, Chapel Hill.

Stegeman, J. J. (1981). Polynuclear aromatic hydrocarbons and their metabolism in the marine environment. *In* "Polycyclic Hydrocarbons and Cancer" (H. G. Gelboin and P. O. P. Ts'o, eds.), pp. 1–60. Academic Press, New York.

Stegeman, J. J. (1989). Cytochrome P450 forms in fish: Catalytic, immunological and sequence similarities. *Xenobiotica* **19,** 1093–1110.

Stegeman, J. J., and Kloepper-Sams, P. J. (1987). Cytochrome P-450 isozymes and mono-oxygenase activity in aquatic animals. *Environ. Health Perspect.* **17,** 87–95.

Stegeman, J. J., and Woodin, B. R. (1984). Differential regulation of hepatic xenobiotic and steroid metabolism in marine teleost species. *Mar. Environ. Res.* **14,** 422–425.

Streisinger, G. (1984). Attainment of minimal biological variability and measurements of genotoxicity: Production of homozygous diploid zebra fish. *Natl. Cancer Inst. Monogr.* No. 65, 53–58.

Streisinger, G., Walker, C., Dower, N., Knauber, D., and Singer, F. (1981). Production of clones of homozygous diploid zebra fish (*Brachydanio rerio*). *Nature (London)* **291,** 293–296.

Stuart, G. W., McMurray, J. V., and Westerfield, M. (1988). Replication, integration and stable germ-line transmission of foreign sequences injected into early zebrafish embryos. *Development* **103,** 403–412.

Su, C., White, J. W., Li, W., Luo, C., Frazier, M. L., Saunders, G. F., and Chan, L. (1988). Structure and evolution of somatostatin genes. *Mol. Endocrinol.* **2,** 209–216.

Sudo, K., Maekawa, M., Luedemann, M. M., Deaven, L. L., and Li, S. S. (1990). Human lactate dehydrogenase-B processed pseudogene: Nucleotide sequence analysis and assignment to the x-chromosome. *Biochem. Biophys. Res. Commun.* **171,** 67–74.

Taggart, J. B., Prodohl, P. A., and Ferguson, A. (1990). Isolation of a hypervariable single locus probe from Atlantic salmon, *Salmo salar. J. Fish Biol.* **37,** 991–993.

Takayama, Y., Wada, C., Kawauchi, H., and Ono, M. (1989). Structures of two genes coding for melanin-concentrating hormone of chum salmon. *Gene* **80,** 65–73.

Takeshita, S., Aoki, T., Fukumaki, Y., and Takagi, Y. (1984). Cloning and sequence analysis of a cDNA for the α-globin mRNA of carp, *Cyprinus carpio. Biochim. Biophys. Acta* **783,** 265–271.

Taylor, K. M. (1967). The chromosomes of some lower chordates. *Chromosoma* **21,** 181–188.

Taylor, W. L., Collier, K. J., Deschenes, R. J., Weith, H. L., and Dixon, J. E. (1981). Sequence analysis of a cDNA coding for a pancreatic precursor to somatostatin. *Proc. Natl. Acad. Sci. U.S.A.* **78,** 6694–6698.

Tempel, B. L., Papazian, D. M., Schwarz, T. L., *et al.* (1987). Sequence of a probable potassium channel component encoded at *Shaker* locus of *Drosophila. Science* **237,** 770–777.

Thomas, K., Del Mazo, J., Eversole, P., Bellve, A., Hiraoka, Y., Li, S. S., and Simon, M. (1990). Developmental regulation of expression of the lactate dehydrogenase (LDH) multigene family during mouse spermatogenesis. *Development* **109,** 483–493.

Thomas, W. K., Withler, R. E., and Beckenbach, A. T. (1986). Mitochondrial DNA analysis of Pacific salmonid evolution. *Can. J. Zool.* **64,** 1058–1064.

Thorgaard, G. H. (1977). Heteromorphic sex chromosomes in male rainbow trout. *Science* **196,** 900–902.

Thorgaard, G. H. (1978). Sex chromosomes in the sockeye salmon: A Y-autosome fusion. *Can. J. Genet. Cytol.* **20,** 349–354.

Thorgaard, G. H. (1983). Chromosomal differences among rainbow trout populations. *Copeia* pp. 650–662.

Thorgaard, G. H., and Allen, S. K. (1987). Chromosome manipulation and markers in fishery management. *In* "Population Genetics and Fishery Management" (N. Ryman and F. Utter, eds.), pp. 319–332. Univ. of Washington Press, Seattle.

Thorgaard, G. H., and Allendorf, F. W. (1988). Developmental genetics of fishes. *In* "Developmental Genetics of Higher Organisms: A Primer in Developmental Biology" (G. M. Malacinski, ed.), pp. 363–391. Macmillan, New York.

Thorgaard, G. H., Allendorf, F. W., and Knudsen, K. L. (1983). Gene-centromere mapping in rainbow trout: High interference over long map distances. *Genetics* **103**, 771–783.

Thorgaard, G. H., Scheerer, P. D., and Parsons, J. E. (1985). Residual paternal inheritance in gynogenetic rainbow trout: Implications for gene transfer. *Theor. Appl. Genet.* **71**, 119–121.

Umminger, B. L. (1975). Low temperature resistance adaptations in the killifish *Fundulus heteroclitus. In* "Physiological Ecology of Estuarine Organisms" (F. J. Vernberg, ed.), pp. 59–71. Univ. of South Carolina Press, Columbia.

Van Beneden, R. J., and Powers, D. A. (1989). Glucosephosphate isomerase allozymes from the teleost *Fundulus heteroclitus. Mol. Biol. Evol.* **6**, 155–170.

Van Beneden, R. J., Cashon, R. E., and Powers, D. A. (1981). Biochemical genetics of *Fundulus heteroclitus* (L.). III. Inheritance of isocitrate dehydrogenase (*Idh-A* and *Idh-B*), 6 phosphogluconate dehydrogenase (*6-Pgdh-A*), and serium esterase (*Est-S*) polymorphisms. *Biochem. Genet.* **19**, 701–714.

Van Beneden, R. J., Watson, D. K., Chen, T. T., Lautenberger, J. A., and Papas, T. S. (1986). Cellular *myc* (c-*myc*) in fish (rainbow trout): Its relationship to other vertebrate *myc* genes and to the transforming genes of the MC29 family of viruses. *Proc. Natl. Acad. Sci. U.S.A.* **83**, 3698–3702.

Van Beneden, R. J., Watson, D. K., Chen, T. T., Lautenberger, J. A., and Papas, T. S. (1988). Teleost oncogenes: Evolutionary comparison to other vertebrate oncogenes and possible roles in teleost neoplasms. *Mar. Environ. Res.* **24**, 339–343.

Vassilev, P. M., Scheuer, T., and Catterall, W. A. (1988). Identification of an intracellular peptide segment involved in sodium channel inactivation. *Science* **241**, 1658–1661.

Vielkind, J. R., and Dippel, E. (1984). Oncogene-related sequences in xiphophorin fish prone to hereditary melanoma formation. *Can. J. Genet. Cytol.* **26**, 607–614.

Vielkind, J., and Vielkind, U. (1982). Melanoma formation in fish of the genus *Xiphophorus:* A genetically-based disorder in the determination and differentiation of a specific pigment cell. *Can. J. Genet. Cytol.* **24**, 133–149.

Vielkind, J. R., Kallman, K. D., and Morizot, D. C. (1989). Genetics of Melanomas in *Xiphophorus* fishes. *J. Aquat. Anim. Health* **1**, 69–77.

Viktorovsky, R. M., Makoedov, A. N., and Shevchishin, A. A. (1985). The chromosomal sets of Brachymastax lenok and Hucho taimen and the divergency of the Salmonid genera. *Tsitologiya* **27**, 703–709.

Vrijenhoek, R. C. (1978). Coexistence of clones in a heterogeneous environment. *Science* **199**, 549–552.

Vrijenhoek, R. C. (1979). Genetics of a sexually reproducing fish in a highly fluctuating environment. *Am. Nat.* **113**, 17–29.

Vrijenhoek, R. C. (1984). Ecological differentiation among clones: The frozen niche variation model. *In* "Population Biology and Evolution" (K. Wohrmann and V. Loschke, eds.), pp. 217–231. Springer-Verlag, New York.

Vrijenhoek, R. C. (1985). Homozygosity and interstrain variation in the self-fertilizing fish *Rivulus marmoratus. J. Hered.* **76**, 82–84.

Vrijenhoek, R. C., Angus, R. A., and Schultz, R. J. (1977). Variation and heterozygosity in sexually vs. clonally reproducing populations of *Poeciliopsis. Evolution* **31**, 767–781.

Vrijenhoek, R. C, Angus, R. A., and Schultz, R. J. (1978). Variation and clonal structure in a unisexual fish. *Am. Nat.* **112**, 41–55.

Waples, R. S. (1987). A multispecies approach to the analysis of gene flow in marine shore fishes. *Evolution* **41**, 385–400.

Watahiki, M., Yamamoto, M., Yamakawa, M., Tanaka, M., and Nakashima, K. (1989). Conserved and unique amino acid residues in the domains of the growth hormone. *J. Biol. Chem.* **264**, 312–316.

Webb, M., and Verschoyle, R. D. (1975). Investigation of the role of metallothioneins in protection against the acute toxicity of the cadmium ion. *Biochem. Pharmacol.* **25**, 673–679.

Wei, A., and Salkoff, L. (1986). Occult *Drosophila* calcium channels and twinning of calcium and voltage-activated potassium channels. *Science* **233**, 780–782.

Weissman, I. L. (1988). Was the MHC made for the immune system, or did immunity take advantage of an ancient polymorphic gene family encoding cell surface interaction molecules? A speculative essay. *Int. Rev. Immunol.* **3**, 393–413.

Wheat, T. E., and Goldberg, E. (1983). Sperm-specific lactate dehydrogenase C₄: Antigenic structure and immunosuppression of fertility. *Isozymes: Curr. Top. Biol. Med. Res.* **7**, 113–130.

Wheat, T. E., Whitt, G. S., and Childers, W. F. (1973). Linkage relationships of six enzyme loci in interspecific sunfish hybrids (Genus Lepomis). *Genetics* **74**, 343–350.

White, M. J. D. (1968). Models of speciation. *Science* **159**, 1065–1070.

White, M. J. D. (1973). Chromosomal rearrangements in mammalian population polymorphism and speciation. *In* "Cytotaxonomy and Vertebrate Evolution" (A. B. Chiarelli and E. Capanna, eds.), pp. 95–128. Academic Press, New York.

Whitmore, D. H., Cotton, R., and Sheridan, K. (1990). DNA fingerprinting. *In* "Electrophoretic and Isoelectric Focusing Techniques in Fisheries Management" (D. H. Whitmore, ed.), pp. 81–106. CRC Press, Boca Raton, Florida.

Whitt, G. S. (1969). Homology of lactate dehydrogenase genes: E gene function in the teleost nervous system. *Science* **166**, 1156–1158.

Whitt, G. S. (1981). Developmental genetics of fishes: Isozymic analyses of differential gene expression. *Am. Zool.* **21**, 549–572.

Whitt, G. S. (1983). Isozymes as probes and participants in developmental and evolutionary genetics. *Isozymes: Curr. Top. Biol. Med. Res.* **10**, 1–40.

Whitt, G. S. (1984). Genetic, developmental and evolutionary aspects of the lactate dehydrogenase isozyme system. *Cell Biochem. Funct.* **2**, 134–139.

Whitt, G. S., Childers, W. F., Tranquili, J., and Champion, M. (1973). Extensive heterozygosity at three enzyme loci in hybrid sunfish populations. *Biochem. Genet.* **8**, 55–72.

Whitt, G. S., Shaklee, J. B., and Markert, C. L. (1975). Evolution of lactate dehydrogenase isozymes in fishes. *In* "Isozymes. Vol. 4: Genetics and Evolution" (C. L. Markert, ed.), pp. 381–400. Academic Press, New York.

Whitt, G. S., Philipp, D. P., and Childers, W. F. (1977). Aberrant gene expression during the development of hybrid sunfishes (Perciformes, Teleostei). *Differentiation* **9**, 97–109.

Whittaker, V. P. (1987). Cholinergic function in the nineties: Advantages of work with a model system. *Neurochem. Res.* **12**, 121–128.

Williams, D., and Buhler, D. (1983). Comparative properties of purified cytochrome P-448 from β-naphthoflavone treated rats and rainbow trout. *Comp. Biochem. Physiol.* **75C**, 25–32.

Williams, G. C., and Koehn, R. K. (1984). Population genetics of North Atlantic catadromous eels (*Anquilla*). In "Evolutionary Genetics of Fishes" (B. J. Turner, ed.), pp. 529–560. Plenum, New York.

Williams, G. C., Koehn, R. K., and Mitton, J. B. (1973). Genetic differentiation without isolation in the American eel, *Anquilla rostrata*. *Evolution* 27, 192–204.

Williams, J. G. K., Kubelik, A. R., Livak, K. J., Rafalski, J. A., and Tingey, S. V. (1990). DNA polymorphisms amplified by arbitrary primers are useful as genetic markers. *Nucleic Acids. Res.* 18, 6531–6535.

Wilson, A. C., Kaplan, N. O., Levine, L., et al. (1964). Evolution of lactin dehydrogenase. *Fed. Proc.* 23, 1258–1266.

Wilson, A. C., Maxson, L. R., and Sarich, V. M. (1974). Two types of molecular evolution. Evidence from studies of interspecific hybridization. *Proc. Natl. Acad. Sci. U.S.A.* 71, 2843–2847.

Wilson, G. M., Thomas, W. K., and Beckenbach, A. T. (1985). Intra- and inter-specific mitochondrial DNA sequence divergence in Salmo: rainbow, steelhead, and cutthroat trouts. *Can. J. Zool.* 63, 2088–2094.

Wilson, M. R., Middleton, D., and Warr, G. W. (1988). Immunoglobulin heavy chain variable region gene evolution: Structure and family relationships of two genes and a pseudogene in a teleost fish. *Proc. Natl. Acad. Sci. U.S.A.* 85, 1566–1570.

Wittbrodt, J., Adam, D., Malitschek, B., et al. (1989). Novel putative receptor tyrosine kinase encoded by the melanoma-inducing *Tu* locus in *Xiphophorus*. *Nature (London)* 341, 415.

Wright, J. E., Heckman, J. B., and Atherton, L. M. (1975). Genetic and developmental analysis of LDH isozymes in trout. In "Isozymes. III: Developmental Biology" (C. L. Markert, ed.), pp. 375–410. Academic Press, New York.

Wright, J. E., Johnson, K. R., and May, B. (1987). Synthetic linkage map of salmonids. In "Genetic Maps 1987: A Compilation of Linkage and Restriction Maps of Genetically Studied Organisms" (S. J. O'Brien, ed.), pp. 405–413. Cold Spring Harbor Lab., Cold Spring Harbor, New York.

Wright, S. (1969). "Evolution and the Genetics of Populations. Vol. II: The Theory of Gene Frequencies." Univ. of Chicago Press, Chicago, Illinois.

Yamamori, T., and Yura, T. (1980). Temperature-induced synthesis of specific proteins in Escherichia coli: Evidence for transcriptional control. *J. Bacteriol.* 142, 843–851.

Yang, D. S. C., Sax, M., Chakrabartty, A., and Hew, C. L. (1988). Crystal structure of an antifreeze polypeptide and its mechanistic implications. *Nature (London)* 333, 232–237.

Yasuda, A., Itoh, H., and Kawauchi, H. (1986). Primary structure of chum salmon prolactins: Occurrence of highly conserved regions. *Arch. Biochem. Biophys.* 244, 528–541.

Yelick, P. C., Balhorn, R., Johnson, P. A., et al. (1987). Mouse protamine 2 is synthesized as a precursor whereas mouse protamine 1 is not. *Mol. Cell. Biol.* 7, 2173–2179.

Yokoyama, R., and Yokoyama, S. (1990). Isolation, DNA sequence and evolution of a color visual pigment gene of the blind cave fish *Astyanax fasciatus*. *Vision Res.* 30, 807–816.

Yokoyama, S., and Yokoyama, R. (1988). Molecular evolution of human visual pigment genes. *Mol. Biol. Evol.* 6, 186–197.

Yulis, C. R. and Lederis, K. (1986). The distribution of "estraurophyseal" urotensin I-immunoreactivity in the central nervous system of *Catostomus commersoni* after urophysectomy. *Neurosci. Lett.* 70, 75–80.

Yulis, C. R., and Lederis, K. (1987). Co-localization of the immunoreactivities of corticotropin-releasing factor and arginine vasotocin in the brain and pituitary system of the teleost *Catostomus commersoni. Cell Tissue Res.* **247**, 267–273.

Zinkernagel, R. M., and Doherty, P. C. (1979). MHC-restricted cytotoxic T cells: Studies on the biological role of polymorphic major transplantation antigens determining T cell restriction specificity, function and responsiveness. *Adv. Immunol.* **27**, 52.

Zuckerkandl, E., and Pauling, L. (1965). Evolutionary divergence and convergence in proteins. *In* "Evolving Genes and Proteins" (V. Bryson and H. J. Vogel, eds.), pp. 97–165. Academic Press, New York.

Drosophila TRANSPOSABLE ELEMENTS: MECHANISMS OF MUTAGENESIS AND INTERACTIONS WITH THE HOST GENOME

Patricia A. Smith and Victor G. Corces

Department of Biology, The Johns Hopkins University, Baltimore, Maryland 21218

I. Introduction

Most spontaneous mutations in yeast and *Drosophila* are caused by the insertion of transposable elements (Finnegan and Fawcett, 1986; Boeke, 1989). The relative contribution of this type of mutagenesis to the total mutation rate in higher organisms is unclear at the moment; there are many examples of transposon-induced mutations in verte-

ADVANCES IN GENETICS, Vol. 29

brates (see, e.g., Jenkins *et al.*, 1981; Stoye *et al.*, 1988), and several recent reports have shown *de novo* insertions of transposable elements resulting in inheritable genetic defects or neoplastic transformation in humans (Kazazian *et al.*, 1988; Morse *et al.*, 1988). Therefore, the generation of mutant phenotypes by the insertion of transposable elements may be an evolutionarily general phenomenon that deserves study for both basic and practical considerations.

In *Drosophila*, transposable elements may insert into genes and cause mutant phenotypes by a variety of mechanisms, the nature of which will depend on the location of the insertion site with respect to the different structural and functional domains of the affected gene. For example, insertion into the protein-coding region of a gene may result in an unstable transcript or a truncated or aberrant protein; insertion into splice consensus sequences may affect the processing of the mature message; and insertion into sequences necessary for transcription initiation may affect the rate of transcription of the gene. In addition, the nature of the element is of importance in determining the basis of the phenotype, because transposons carry signals necessary for various aspects of their expression that can act on adjacent genes or interfere with their own transcriptional machinery. For example, transposable elements may contain splice consensus sequences that, when inserted into the transcription unit of a gene, could result in aberrant processing patterns, or they may contain transcription termination signals that could cause premature termination of transcription of the mutant gene; transposable elements also carry sequences necessary for transcription initiation, such as enhancers, that could alter the pattern of expression of adjacent genes. In many cases, transposable element-induced phenotypes can be suppressed or enhanced by second site mutations at various modifier loci (Rutledge *et al.*, 1988). Analysis of the interactions between spontaneous alleles and various suppressor and enhancer mutations suggests the existence of a complex set of interrelations between transposable element-induced alleles and modifier loci in the *Drosophila* genome; these interrelations are now beginning to be unraveled. The genetic behavior of suppressor and enhancer loci and the specificity of their effect on various types of mutations may offer an indication of the respective contribution of the nature of the element, versus its location within the gene, to the phenotype of specific alleles. The understanding of the mechanisms by which insertions of transposable elements result in mutant phenotypes can therefore benefit from the study of the nature of the products encoded by modifier loci and their interaction with specific elements. In addition, the study of these genes, which are identified on the basis of their effect on transposable element-induced mutations, affords the characterization of important cellular functions for which direct genetic selection is not available.

Drosophila is an ideal system to study the molecular basis of transposable element-induced mutagenesis because of the large variety of transposable elements and the wealth of genetic information available in this organism. In many cases these elements have been isolated because they inhabit the middle-repetitive DNA, often in varying genomic locations, suggesting mobility, but they have not yet been proved to be transposons. For the purpose of this review, we will classify transposable elements into two main categories, retrotransposons and nonretrotransposons. Because this classification is based on structural characteristics, which in turn are the basis for the kinds of mutant phenotypes induced by transposable elements, this division also reflects functional properties of these elements and the nature of the mutations they can induce.

II. Retrotransposons

A. STRUCTURE

Most transposable elements described in *Drosophila* show structural features suggestive of a role in transposition via an RNA intermediate and are therefore classified as retrotransposons. A great majority of these elements fall into two classes, which we will call the long terminal repeat (LTR)-containing and the poly(A)-type retrotransposons.

LTR-containing retrotranspons show a series of remarkable structural and functional similarities to the retroviral proviruses of vertebrates (Boeke and Corces, 1989). The DNA consists of two directly repeated LTR sequences flanking a central coding region. The LTRs can be divided into three regions, U3, R, and U5; the full-length transcript initiates at the U3–R boundary and terminates at the R–U5 boundary. Hence the RNA, R–U5–internal domain–U3–R, is terminally repetitious, thus the retrotransposon full-length transcript is analogous to retroviral genomic RNA and retrotransposon DNA is analogous to the retroviral provirus. Other similarities include target site duplications of a conserved size, characteristic reverse transcription priming sites located just adjacent to the LTR sequences, enhancer sequences that can respond to host regulatory systems, and regions of open reading frame (ORF) that correspond to the well-known retroviral genes *gag, pol,* and in some cases possibly *env.* The *pol* gene almost always contains sequences similar to the protease (PR), RNA-dependent DNA polymerase (RT), RNase H (RH), and integrase (IN) functions of metazoan retroviruses.

Members of this group can be subdivided into copia-like and gypsy-like families based on structural differences. Members of the copia family are characterized by the presence of ORFs corresponding to retroviral *gag* and *pol* genes but lack the extra ORF possibly corresponding to retroviral *env* (see below). Unlike retroviruses and other retrotransposons, the order of functional domains in *pol* is PR, IN, RT, RH (Saigo *et al.*, 1984; Mount and Rubin, 1985). The copia element specifies the production of virus-like particles (VLPs) consisting of element-encoded reverse transcriptase, coat proteins, and full-length transcripts (Shiba and Saigo, 1983; Yoshioka *et al.*, 1990). The best characterized members of the gypsy family are gypsy, 17.6, 297, tom, and 412 (Saigo *et al.*, 1984; Inouye *et al.*, 1986; Marlor *et al.*, 1986; Yuki *et al.*, 1986; Tanda *et al.*, 1988). These elements are distinguished from the above group by the retrovirus-like order of functional domains in the *pol* gene: PR, RT, RH, IN. Sequence alignments confirm that these elements form a distinct group (Doolittle *et al.*, 1989). There is evidence that some members of this group exhibit somewhat more target site specificity than do members of the copia group, because several elements in this family prefer alternating purine–pyrimidine as target sequences (Bingham and Zachar, 1989). Direct evidence that these elements form VLPs has not yet been presented. Interestingly, at least four members of this group, gypsy, 17.6, tom, and 297, contain a third ORF 3' to the *pol* gene that corresponds in position and size to retroviral *env* genes. Homology to retroviral *env* genes is not apparent, but retroviral *env* genes are not well conserved in any case. These ORFs are characterized by a potential membrane-spanning domain near the C terminus, suggesting that they may indeed encode membrane proteins (Saigo *et al.*, 1984; Inouye *et al.*, 1986; Marlor *et al.*, 1986; S. Tanda and V. Corces, unpublished data).

The poly(A)-type elements are characterized by a poly(adenylate) sequence of variable length at the 3' end of the element, the lack of an LTR sequence, target site duplications of variable size, and the presence of multiple copies that are truncated at their 5' ends. The latter suggests that their transposition involves reverse transcription, and that (−) strand synthesis is often abortive. The F, G, I, and jockey elements belong to this family of poly(A)-type retrotransposons (DiNocera and Gasari, 1987; Fawcett *et al.*, 1988; Mizrokhi *et al.*, 1988). Their termini are structurally similar. At the 3' end, either a poly(A) stretch or repeats of the sequence TAA (I factor) are found downstream of a consensus poly(adenylation) signal and structural similarities at the 5' end have been implicated as possible internal RNA polymerase II promoter elements (Mizrokhi *et al.*, 1988). The central coding regions of these elements are similar in sequence to the retroviral *gag* core region, with groupings of cysteine and histidine residues that may be related to metal-binding domains and could serve in nucleic acid recognition (Covey, 1986). The *pol* gene products of poly(A)-type retrotransposons, unlike those of the LTR-containing retrotransposons, typically show homology to RT and RH but not to PR and IN (Johnson *et al.*, 1986; DiNocera and Gasari, 1987; Fawcett *et al.*, 1988; Doolittle *et al.*, 1989). The structures of the ends of the poly(A)-type elements resemble processed pseudogenes and short interspersed nuclear elements (SINEs), such as the mammalian Alu sequence (Weiner *et al.*, 1986), more than they do vertebrate retroviruses. Not all members of the poly(A)-type class contain a true 3' poly(A) tail sequence. The I factor, for example, has repeats of the sequence TAA and other elements have only a short oligo(A) tract.

B. EXPRESSION

The ability of retrotransposons to integrate into new positions in the genome of the host depends, among other things, on the availability of full-length RNA as substrate for reverse transcriptase. It is then important to understand the different levels of control that determine the transcription of retrotransposons, because the expression of these elements in the germ line of the host will determine their ability to cause inheritable transpositions. In addition, the expression of some retrotransposons directly correlates with their ability to mutate the genes into which they insert, and, therefore, sequences involved in the transcriptional activation of these elements may also be responsible for their mutagenic effect. The understanding of this pattern of expression will include the characterization of transcription signals, such as promoter and enhancer elements, and the identification of host genes that interact with these signals. In this section we will review transcriptional properties of those retrotransposons for which enough information is available to draw relevant conclusions.

LTR-containing retrotransposons are usually transcribed into a major RNA that extends from transcription initiation signals located in the 5' LTR to a site located 20–30 bp downstream from the AATAAA signal in the 3' LTR (Arkhipova *et al.*, 1986). Because both LTRs are typically identical, the production of a terminally redundant transcript that could serve as a substrate for transposition requires the suppression of termination signals located in the 5' LTR and of promoter components located in the 3' repeat. Transcription signals for these retrotransposons are usually located in the 5' LTR and inside of the transcribed region. Although most elements do not contain a recognizable TATA homology, some of them, such as gypsy, contain sequences similar to the degenerate TATA boxes found in some mammalian retroviruses (Marlor et al., 1986), though the functional significance of these sequences in most retrotransposons has not been determined experimentally. Other transcription signals typical of eukaryotic promoters, such as the CAAT box, cannot be detected in these retrotransposons. In addition, LTR-containing retrotransposons contain sequences homologous to the AATAAA poly(adenylation) and TTGT or TTTT RNA termination signals in their LTRs. Sequences necessary for transcription initiation have been studied in detail in the case of the gypsy element. Jarrell and Meselson (1991) have described a 98-bp region located in the 5' LTR that extends from -38 to $+60$ bp, with respect to the cap site, which is sufficient for accurate normal-level transcription. The gypsy element contains sequences at the transcription initiation site that are homologous to the functional initiator of the mouse terminal deoxynucleotidyltransferase gene and various *Drosophila* genes lacking TATA boxes such as *engrailed (en)* and *Ultrabithorax (Ubx)*. Mutation of these sequences abolishes transcription.

The expression of retrotransposon-encoded full-length transcripts is developmentally regulated, suggesting the existence of host factors that interact with specific sequences of the transposon to cause a determined pattern of temporal expression. Different retrotransposons present varied patterns of developmental expression. For example, B104 is expressed mostly in embryos, whereas transcription of copia is maximal in larvae, and gypsy RNA accumulates at higher levels in pupae (Parkhurst and Corces, 1987). These differences suggest that different host factors and retrotransposon-specific sequences are involved in the transcriptional control of these elements. These two components have been well studied in the case of gypsy (see below). In addition to the full-length transcript, some *Drosophila* retrotransposons also encode smaller RNAs whose origin has not been studied in detail, with the exception of the copia and tom elements. Because these smaller RNAs are expressed with the same pattern of developmental transcription as the full-length transcript, they must be either 5' coterminal or a result of splicing of the larger RNA. The copia element encodes a full-length 5.0-kb RNA and a subgenomic 2.1-kb transcript (Flavell et al., 1980; Schwartz et al., 1982). The smaller RNA arises by processing of the 5.0-kb RNA and this splicing is used to regulate the appropriate levels of *gag* and *pol*. Most of the *pol* region is removed by splicing in the formation of an abundant 2.1-kb mRNA that has recently been shown to be 5' and 3' coterminal with the full-length transcript, but lacks nucleotides 1606–4554 (Miller *et al.*, 1989; Yoshioka *et al.*, 1990). The 2.1-kb *gag* mRNA also encodes the PR region, making copia unique among the retrotransposons but similar to the *gag* genes of avian retroviruses. Analysis of the RNAs encoded by the tom element of *Drosophila ananassae* has revealed the possibility that a subgenomic RNA encodes an *env*-specific transcript, and that similarly sized RNAs produced by other retrotransposons (Parkhurst and Corces, 1987) might actually encode similar products. In addition to the full-length 6.8-kb RNA, the tom element also encodes a 3.0-kb transcript that hybridizes to sequences containing the third open reading frame, which encodes the putative *env* gene product. The 3.0-kb transcript is spliced from the genomic RNA using a donor splice site located 472 bp downstream from the beginning of ORF1, and an acceptor splice site located 16 bp downstream from the beginning of ORF3. ORF1 and ORF3 are in frame in the spliced message, suggesting that the first methionine in ORF1 is used as a translation initiation site to make the *env* gene product. The tom *gag*–*env*-encoded polyprotein may then undergo proteolytic cleavage to make mature *env*-encoded proteins, as is the case in vertebrate retroviruses. These results suggest that the tom element can in fact regulate its expression by splicing of the full-length genomic RNA to give rise to an *env*-specific transcript (S. Tanda and V. Corces, unpublished data). This process is necessary in vertebrate retroviruses for expression of a functional *env*-encoded protein and viral infectivity. The ability of tom to encode an *env*-specific mRNA establishes further parallels between retroviruses and retrotransposons and supports the possibility that elements such as tom may encode infective virus particles that could mediate the horizontal transmission of this class of retrotransposons (see below for a discussion of horizontal transfer of retrotransposon sequences).

The distribution of retrotransposon-encoded transcripts during the development of the fly is likely to be tissue specific. Although this point has not been investigated in detail, it might be inferred from the tissue specificity in the mutagenic effect of some retrotransposons that, as is the case for the yeast Ty element, correlates with their transcriptional activation. For example, the gypsy element seems to cause defects in genes that are expressed in cuticular structures (Parkhurst and Corces, 1986b), whereas the insertion of the tom element of *D. ananassae* results in eye-specific phenotypes (Tanda *et al.*, 1988). The spatial distribution of retrotransposon-encoded transcripts has been directly studied only in the case of the micropia element of *Drosophila hydei;* this element gives rise to a testis-specific 1.2-kb RNA in males, suggesting that this retrotransposon might contain transcriptional enhancers or splice sites that respond to developmental and tissue-specific host factors to give rise to specific patterns of transcription (Huijser *et al.*, 1988; S. Lankenau, personal communication).

The mechanism of transcription of poly(A)-type elements must account for the fact that these elements apparently transpose via an RNA intermediate and this RNA must encompass the total length of the element in order to maintain its integrity through successive transpositions. It has been proposed that transcription of the element might take place from promoters adjacent to the integration site or from an internal promoter located within the element. Mizrokhi *et al.* (1988) have shown that the latter is indeed the case for the jockey element. Transcription of this retrotransposon is sensitive to α-amanitin and therefore is dependent on RNA polymerase II; in addition, a 335-bp fragment from the 5′ end of the jockey element was able to promote transcription of a linked reporter gene. This indicates that these sequences have promoter activity in spite of the fact that no TATA homologies are present. The 335-bp fragment contains sequences conserved among the jockey, I, and F elements (Mizrokhi *et al.*, 1988).

C. Mechanisms and Regulation of Retrotransposon Mobilization

The mechanisms responsible for the mobilization of retrotransposons in *Drosophila*, with the exception of the poly(A)-type I element, are poorly understood. The I element is responsible for the control of I–R hybrid dysgenesis, a syndrome characterized by high rates of sterility and mutation similar to those involving the P and hobo elements (Finnegan, 1989; Bucheton, 1990). *Drosophila melanogaster* strains fall into two categories described as inducer or reactive with respect to the I–R system (Bucheton *et al.*, 1976). I–R hybrid dysgenesis is observed in F_1 females resulting from crosses between reactive females and inducer males. These F_1 females exhibit reduced fertility and their germ lines are highly susceptible to mutations, chromosomal rearrangements, and nondisjunctions. Sterility is due to embryonic lethality during the early cleavage stages. Genetic analysis of the inducer phenotype indicated that it was determined by transposable elements now known as the I elements. Copies of the I element are dispersed in the genome of inducer strains in which they are stable, but they become unstable and transpose at high frequency in the germ line of the female progeny of dysgenic crosses. I factors never transpose in males. Given the general genomic organization of I factors and the similarities between the polypeptides they encode and reverse transcriptase, it is likely that they transpose by reverse transcription of an RNA intermediate (Pélisson *et al.*, 1991). Because I factors do not appear to encode endonuclease-like domains typical of most viral reverse transcriptases, integration of new elements may occur at preexisting staggered nicks in chromosomal DNA; this would explain the variations in length of target site duplications surrounding I elements. Two important questions exist concerning the mechanisms underlying I retrotransposon mobilization. The first one concerns what causes the I element to be stable in inducer strains and to become activated undergoing mobilization in the female progeny of a dysgenic cross. Recent experiments by Chaboissier *et al.* (1990) have shed some light onto this problem. Full-length RNA for the I element can be detected only under conditions in which the I element transposes. This 5.4-kb RNA has all the characteristics of an RNA intermediate and it is not present in somatic tissues, in agreement with the germ-line-specific transposition of the I element. In addition, the 5.4-kb RNA is present at very low levels in inducer strains, suggesting that repression of I element mobilization in these strains takes place at the level of RNA stability or transcription of this message. In contrast, the full-length transcript was found in the ovaries of dysgenic females, suggesting that at least one of the host functions required for I element expression is restricted to the germ line, and that I factor activity is restricted to this tissue because of regulation at the level of initiation of transcription or RNA stability. In addition to this control at the level of transcription, expression of the I element may also be regulated at a posttranscriptional level by inefficient translation of the second open reading frame, which encodes the reverse transcriptase necessary for transposition (Chaboissier *et al.*, 1990). Inefficient translation of ORF2 from the rare full-length transcripts present in I strains could account for the very low level of transposition of I elements in these stocks. The nature of the regulatory molecules controlling these processes is unknown at the time, but it is possible that factors responsible for I element stability in inducer strains could be encoded by the I elements, and could accumulate during oogenesis in such a way that the embryos from inducer females contain enough molecules to repress I element expression and therefore transposition. In the F_1 progeny from crosses between inducer males and reactive females, I factors are placed in a cellular environment devoid of regulatory molecules, allowing transposition to occur and resulting in the genetic abnormalities characteristic of I–R hybrid dysgenesis (Chaboissier *et al.*, 1990).

However, this simple model is not sufficient to explain all aspects of I element activity, and in particular does not account for the fact that the frequency of I element transposition is dependent on a cellular state known as reactivity that is characteristic of the reactive stock used in the cross. Reactivity levels are determined by crossing males from standard inducer strains with females from various reactive stocks. Strongly reactive females give rise to a female progeny that shows a very high frequency of I element transposition, whereas mobilization of this element is less frequent when weakly reactive females are used in the crosses (Bucheton, 1990). It has been proposed that the reactive state is dependent on regulatory molecules produced by defective I elements present in the heterochromatin of reactive strains. These I elements differ from functional I factors and appear to be relics of an I element ancestor, but they still contain most of the sequences corresponding to ORF1 (Simonelig *et al.*, 1988; Crozatier *et al.*, 1988). This open reading frame encodes a potential regulatory molecule, similar to described viral DNA-binding proteins, that could play a role in the control of I element expression. Because at least some heterochromatic I elements are transcribed, the ORF1-encoded protein could play a role in determining the reactive state of various R strains, and the level of reactivity could be a direct consequence of the amounts of this protein present in the strain (Chaboissier *et al.*, 1990). This situation would be similar to that of defective P elements that are able to encode repressor protein and thus regulate P element mobilization (see below).

In spite of the advances in the understanding of the mechanisms underlying I element transposition, much less is known about the factors responsible for the mobilization of LTR-containing retrotransposons. These types of transposable element are quite stable both in somatic tissues and the germ line of normal laboratory strains. Nevertheless, several cases have been described in which LTR-containing retrotransposons are mobilized at high frequency in specific strains or after determined crosses. Gerasimova *et al.* have described "transposition bursts" in which different types of LTR-containing retrotransposons are mobilized simultaneously in the ct^{MR2} strain and its derivatives (Gerasimova *et al.*, 1985; Mizrokhi *et al.*, 1985). This unstable line arose following a dysgenic cross between a wild-type Oregon R female and a male from the P element-containing stock *MRh12/Cy*, suggesting that perhaps transposition of the P element was responsible for the mobilization of LTR-containing retrotransposons. The spontaneous instability of the ct^{MR2} strain declined over a 2-year period, but could be reactivated by crossing to the *MRh12/Cy* stock. Nevertheless, germ-line transformation with intact P elements could not mimic the effect of this cross, suggesting that other factors present in the *MRh12/ Cy* strain are responsible for retrotransposon mobilization (Leigh Brown *et al.*, 1989). The nature of these factors is unknown at present. Other cases of retrotransposon movement during P element hybrid dysgenesis have been reported (Rubin *et al.*, 1982; Lewis and Brookfield, 1987), but P elements do not seem to play a role in the increase in their mobilization frequency (Woodruff *et al.*, 1987; Eggleston *et al.*, 1988).

Several cases have been described recently in which the mobilization of specific LTR-containing retrotransposons takes place under more controlled condition after crosses between particular *Drosophila* strains. High-frequency transposition of the gypsy and copia elements were observed when males from a stock carrying the ovo^D mutation were crossed to females of the strain $y\ v\ f\ mal$, which contains a high copy number of gypsy elements (Mével-Ninio *et al.*, 1989). A second strain (named MS for mutator strain) has been described in which gypsy mobilization takes place at high frequency (10^{-3}–10^{-4}) (Kim *et al.*, 1990). This strain arose by treatment of a stable laboratory strain with ethyl nitrosourea, and the high mutability rate takes place in the absence of outcrossing. Mutations in the MS strain occur in both sexes at premeiotic stages of germ cell development, and are unstable, reverting to wild type at high frequency. Similar high-mobilization frequency of the Stalker retrotransposon takes place in crosses between a $y^2\ sc^1$ w^{aG} stock and an *FM4* strain (Georgiev *et al.*, 1990). This activation of Stalker mobilization does not depend on the direction of the cross and continues for several generations after the initial cross. Mobilization of LTR-containing retrotransposons has also been described in other *Drosophila* species. The tom retrotransposon is mobilized at high frequency in a *D. ananassae* strain, giving rise almost exclusively to dominant eye phenotypes; these mutations occur as single events in both males and females (Hinton, 1984). In addition, a hybrid dysgenesis syndrome similar to those described in *D. melanogaster* occurs in *Drosophila virilis* when an established laboratory stock is crossed to a strain collected from the wild in the USSR. The element responsible for the dysgenic phenomenon has not been characterized yet, but a second element named Ulysses that belongs to the LTR-containing retrotransposon family is mobilized during these crosses and is responsible for many of the mutations obtained in this system (Scheinker *et al.*, 1990). The reproducible mobilization of LTR-containing retrotransposons under controlled conditions in these various systems will allow rapid progress in the understanding of the mechanisms underlying retrotransposon mobilization in *Drosophila*.

The occurrence of closely related retrotransposons in yeast, *Drosophila*, and other species has led to speculations that LTR retrotransposons occasionally invade phylogenetically distant but ecologially related host species by rare horizontal transmission events (Doolittle *et al.*, 1989; Hansen *et al.*, 1988). In the case of *Drosophila*, the possibility of horizontal transfer of retrotransposons has been examined for the I and Jockey elements by detailed molecular phylogenetic studies. The distribution of the I element is confined to the *D. melanogaster* group and it has been suggested that a complete active I element appeared in natural populations of this group in the 1930s (Kidwell, 1983). The origin of this active I element could be the reactivation of inactive elements present in all strains of *D. melanogaster* or transfer from sibling species that contain active elements (Bucheton *et al.*, 1984; Abad *et al.*, 1989). Evidence for horizontal transfer has also been documented for the jockey element, which outside of the *D. melanogaster* group could only be detected in *Drosophila funebris*. The jockey element from *D. funebris* contains two open reading frames highly homologous to those of *D. melanogaster*. In addition, sequences from the promotor region are also highly conserved among both elements. The absence of jockey in other species of the *D. funebris* group suggests that this distribution pattern did not arise by vertical transmission from a common ancestor, and implies that horizontal transmission might be responsible for the presence of this retrotransposon in these two widely separated *Drosophila* species (Mizrokhi and Mazo, 1990). However, the possibility remains that these retrotransposon families were present in a common ancestor, and that some of the descendant species have lost them while others contain conserved copies of these retrotransposons.

D. CIS-ACTING EFFECTS OF RETROTRANSPOSONS

Transposable elements interact with the genome of the host organism in a bidirectional fashion. The temporal and spatial patterns of transcription of retrotransposons are controlled by host genes, and, at the same time, the mutagenic effect of some transposons on the host genes they mutate is dependent on their transcriptional activation, and, therefore, on the interaction with host factors. Thus, the influence of host genes on the transcription and mutagenicity of retrotransposons is directly related. Host factors that interact with *Drosophila* retrotransposons have been identified on the basis of the effect of mutations in the genes encoding these factors on the mutagenic effect of the transposable element. These host genes are termed modifiers in general, and more specifically, suppressors or enhancers if they respectively reverse or augment the phenotypic effect of the transposable element on the mutated genes (Rutledge *et al.,* 1988). Modifier loci might encode proteins involved in different steps (i.e., transcription initiation, RNA processing) of the expression of retrotransposons, and therefore they may offer a handle on the identification of host factors that control the transcription of normal cellular genes.

Cloning and characterization of some of these loci are helping to elucidate the molecular basis of transposable element-induced mutagenesis and to understand the role of suppressor and enhancer genes in the biology of the host cell. Table 1 shows a summary of the effects of modifier genes on various transposable element-induced mutations and the network of interactions among these different loci. In the next sections we will describe our current understanding of the mechanisms by which a few specific elements that have been studied in detail cause mutations and the role of modifier loci in the generation of the mutant phenotype.

1. Effects on Transcription Rate

a. Mutagenesis by the gypsy Element. A large part of our understanding of the mechanisms by which the gypsy element mutates adjacent genes comes from studies carried out with the *yellow* locus and the analysis of the effects of mutations in the *suppressor of Hairy-wing* [*su(Hw)*] gene on *yellow* expression. Recessive mutations in *su(Hw)* reverse the phenotype of the gypsy-induced y^2 allele to almost wild type (Modolell *et al.,* 1983; Parkhurst and Corces, 1986a); mutations in a second modifier recently described, the *modifier of mdg4* [*mod(mdg4)*], have the opposite effect, enhancing the gypsy effect on the *yellow* gene to a coloration identical to that of a *yellow* null allele (Georgiev and Gerasimova, 1989). The X-linked *yellow* gene encodes a 1.9-kb RNA expressed in the late embryo–early larval stages and later during the midpupal stages of development. Pupal expression of *yellow* is responsible for the proper coloration of adult structures such as bristles, hairs, wing blades, and the thoracic and abdominal cuticle. This pattern of temporal and spatial expression of the *yellow* gene is controlled by a series of DNA sequences that act as tissue-specific transcriptional enhancers and independently regulate *yellow* expression in different tissues and stages of development (Geyer and Corces, 1987). The arrangement of these different functional elements involved in the control of *yellow* expression is summarized in Fig. 1. The insertion of the gypsy element into the *yellow* gene in the y^2 allele results in a developmentally and spatially restricted phenotype. The mouth parts and denticle belts of the larva, as well as the bristles of the adult, are wild type,

TABLE 1
Effects of Modifier Genes on Transposable Element-Induced Alleles[a]

Gene	gypsy										copia		412	?				P
	y^2	Hw^1	sc^1	ct^6	ct^K	f^1	f^K	bx^{34e}	bx^3	lz^1	w^a	v^1	pr^1	lz^{34K}	lz^{37}	lz^k	w^e	y^{76428}
$su(Hw)$	S	S	S	S	S	S	S	S	S	S	0	0	0	0	E	0	0	—
$mod(mdg4)$	E	—	S	S	S	0	S	—	—	E	—	—	0	—	—	—	—	—
$su(f)$	0	0	0	0	S	S	S	S	—	S	E	0	—	0	E	0	0	S
$su(s)$	0	—	0	0	E	E	0	E	E	E	0	S	S	E	E	E	—	S
$su(w^a)$	0	0	0	0	E	E	—	E	—	E	S	0	—	E	0	E	0	0
$su(pr)$	0	E	0	0	E	S	S	E	E	S	0	0	S	S	0	S	0	S
$e(w^e)$	0	0	0	0	E	S	S	S	—	S	0	—	—	0	0	S	E	—
$E(lz)$	—	—	0	—	—	0	—	—	—	E	—	—	—	E	0	S	—	—
$su(lz^{34})$	—	—	0	—	—	S	—	—	—	S	—	—	—	S	S	S	—	—
$su(lz^1)$	—	—	S	—	—	S	—	—	—	S	—	—	—	S	E	E	—	—

[a] The various suppressor and enhancer genes are indicated on the left side of the table, and the spontaneous alleles they affect are indicated on top. The transposable elements responsible for the mutant phenotype are indicated above the names of the induced alleles. S indicates suppression, E indicates enhancement, and 0 indicates no effect. Dashes indicate that the particular combination was not tested. Data were obtained from Rutledge et al. (1988). Information on y^{76428} and f^K is from Geyer et al. (1990), and K. K. Hoover and V. G. Corces (unpublished data). Data on the modifiers of lz are from P. Batterham (personal communication).

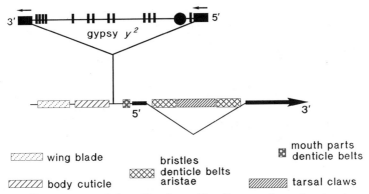

FIG. 1. The structure of the *yellow* locus. The diagram shows the structure of the *yellow* gene, with two exons represented by filled-in boxes separated by an intron. Various transcriptional enhancers involved in the expression of *yellow* in different tissues are represented by boxes. The gypsy element in the y^2 allele is inserted at -700 bp from the start of transcription. Filled boxes represent the LTRs and arrows indicate the direction of transcription. Thick vertical lines represent putative *zeste* binding sites as deduced from sequence homologies to the published target site for the *zeste*-encoded protein (Benson and Pirrotta, 1988). The *su(Hw)* binding site is indicated by a black circle.

whereas the wings and body cuticle of the adult are mutant. Gypsy insertion in the y^2 allele has taken place at -700 bp from the transcription start site, such that the regulatory sequences that control *yellow* expression in the wings and body cuticle are now separated from the *yellow* promoter by the 7.4-kb gypsy element (Fig. 1) (Parkhurst and Corces, 1986a; Geyer and Corces, 1987). One obvious explanation for the mutant phenotype of y^2 flies is that transcriptional enhancers that regulate *yellow* transcription in the two mutant structures are now incapable of acting on the *yellow* promoter due to a 7.4-kb increase in their distance from the TATA box. Analysis of revertants of gypsy-induced mutations indicates that this is not the case (Geyer *et al.*, 1988a,b). In particular, one class of y^2 revertants arose by insertion of the jockey or hobo element into the same region containing an intact gypsy element, suggesting that gypsy sequences where insertion has taken place might be involved in the generation of mutant phenotypes (Geyer *et al.*, 1988b). This region contains 12 copies of a repeated sequence homologous to the octamer motif found in transcriptional enhancers and promoters of eukaryotic genes (see, e.g., Rosales *et al.*, 1987). Revertants of other gypsy-induced mutations in *Hairy-wing* (Geyer *et al.*, 1988b) and *cut* (Mizrokhi *et al.*, 1985; Flavell *et al.*, 1990) are also due to the insertion of other transposable elements in the octamer-like region, and revertants of gypsy-induced *bithoraxoid* alleles contain deletions of some of the copies of the octamer-like repeats (Peifer and Bender, 1988). Furthermore, flies transformed with a *yellow* gene containing only these sequences in the same location where the gypsy element is located in y^2 show a y^2 phenotype, indicating that the 12 copies of the octamer-like repeat can have the same phenotypic effect as does the complete gypsy element and that they are sufficient to generate the mutant phenotype (Corces and Geyer, 1991). The mutagenic effect of these sequences is directional, i.e., only enhancers located distal from the insertion site with respect to the promoter are affected.

Interestingly, sequences responsible for the mutagenic effect of the gypsy element interact with the gene product of the *su(Hw)* locus. Null mutations in the *su(Hw)* gene show a female-sterile phenotype characterized by degeneration of the nurse cells surrounding the developing oocyte when their chromosomes remain condensed, whereas the normal polytene chromosomes of wild-type nurse cells uncoil prior to vitellogenesis. The *su(Hw)* gene encodes a 110,000-Da protein that is present in all stages of development and is in most tissues of the fly. The amino-terminal region contains an acidic domain 48 amino acids long containing 50% Asp and Glu residues. The central portion of the protein includes 12 copies of the zinc finger motif, and the carboxy-terminal portion has several regions of homology with the leucine zipper motif as well as a second acidic domain (Parkhurst *et al.*, 1988). These three classes of motifs have been found in various types of transcription factors in eukaryotes. The zinc finger domain has been shown to be involved in DNA binding (Klug and Rhodes, 1987), whereas acidic and leucine zipper domains might be involved in protein–protein interactions between transcription factors (Hope *et al.*, 1988; Landschulz *et al.*, 1988). The *su(Hw)*-encoded protein is localized in the nucleus and is present at 100–200 different sites on polytene chromosomes from third instar larvae (Spana *et al.*, 1988; Spana and Corces, 1990). These results agree with a putative role for *su(Hw)* as a general transcription factor. In fact, mutations at the *su(Hw)* locus result in up to 25-fold reduction in the accumulation of gypsy RNA, suggesting also a role for this protein in the control of gypsy expression (Parkhurst and Corces, 1986a; Mazo *et al.*, 1989). Partially purified *su(Hw)*-encoded protein binds specifically to gypsy sequences located immediately adjacent to the 5' LTR in the transcribed, untranslated region of the element. The region of gypsy that interacts with *su(Hw)* contains 12 copies of the octamer-like sequence 5'-PyPuTTGCATAC-3' interspersed with AT-rich spacers. This is the same region of gypsy necessary and sufficient to confer the characteristic gypsy-induced phenotype.

The mechanism by which the gypsy element causes a mutant phenotype in the y^2 allele can be rationalized based on the following observations: (1) the *su(Hw)* gene encodes a DNA-binding protein containing acidic and leucine zipper domains that may mediate interactions with other proteins; (2) the *su(Hw)* protein binds to specific sequences in the gypsy element; (3) the *su(Hw)* binding site is necessary and sufficient to induce the same mutant phenotype as the intact gypsy element; and (4) the mutagenic effect of these sequences is directional. The conclusion from these observations is that the gypsy element per se is not responsible for the mutant phenotype in the y^2 allele, and that gypsy is simply a mediator of the effect of the *su(Hw)*-encoded protein, which is the ultimate cause of this mutagenic effect. The reversion of gypsy-induced phenotypes by mutations in the *su(Hw)* gene can then be explained by the absence in these strains of a functional *su(Hw)*-encoded protein that can bind to the gypsy element and cause a mutant phenotype. This protein could exert this effect through its acidic and leucine zipper domains, which may interact with other proteins, particularly the tissue-specific transcription factors responsible for the temporal and spatial pattern of *yellow* expression. Binding of the *su(Hw)*-encoded protein to gypsy sequences may cause interference with the action of enhancer-bound factors on the *yellow* promoter (Fig. 2). The directionality of this effect can be intuitively explained if the *su(Hw)*-encoded protein interacts with these factors and blocks their effect on transcription initiation.

The y^2 allele represents a particular case in which the gypsy element is inserted in the 5' region of the *yellow* gene. The question then arises as to whether this type of mechanism can explain the effects of gypsy in other *Drosophila* genes. A similar case is that of the *bithoraxoid* mutations, which are due to the insertion of gypsy into the upstream regulatory region of the *Ubx* gene (Bender *et al.*, 1985) and may thus be caused by a mechanism analogous to y^2. Nevertheless, other gypsy-induced alleles suppressible by *su(Hw)* are the result of gypsy insertion within the RNA coding region. Independent of the cellular function of the *su(Hw)*-encoded protein, the mutant phenotypes caused by gypsy must be at least in part a direct consequence of the binding of the *su(Hw)*-encoded protein to this element, because the lack of the protein results in a reversion of the mutant phenotype. The question then arises as to the mechanism of gypsy-mediated mutagenesis in these other alleles. In two cases described, insertion of gypsy into an intron or exon of a gene, in the same transcriptional orientation, results in premature termination of transcription. In the dominant *Hairy-wing* mutation Hw^1, gypsy insertion causes termination of transcription of the *achaete* RNA in the gypsy 5' LTR, giving rise to a truncated transcript that

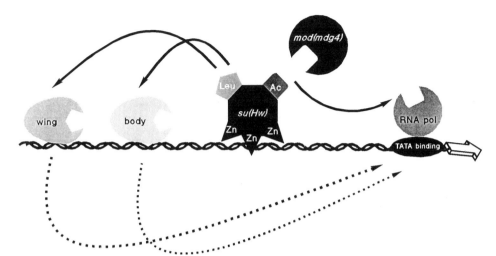

FIG. 2. Mechanism of mutagenesis by the *su(Hw)*-encoded protein. The diagram represents a working model to explain the situation in the case of the y^2 allele, but could be extended to explain other cases discussed in the text. DNA corresponding to the 5' region of the *yellow* gene is depicted, with RNA polymerase and other TATA binding proteins located in the promoter. The direction of transcription is indicated by the arrow on the right. Transcription factors responsible for *yellow* expression in the wing and body cuticle are located distally with respect to the promoter. The *su(Hw)*-encoded protein is bound to gypsy sequences located between the promoter and the wing and body enhancers that interact with the corresponding transcription factors. Several functional domains of the protein are indicated: the zinc (Zn) fingers interact with gypsy DNA and the acidic (Ac) and/or leucine (Leu) zipper domains may interact with transcription factors located upstream. This effect is indicated by solid arrows, whereas the inability of the wing and body transcription factors to act on the promoter as a consequence of the presence of the *su(Hw)*-encoded is indicated by dashed-line arrows. The *mod(mdg4)*-encoded protein may normally interact with the acidic domains of the *su(Hw)*-encoded protein. In a *mod(mdg4)* mutant, these acidic domains may interact with proteins present in the *yellow* promoter, inhibiting transcription and thus enhancing the y^2 phenotype.

encodes a functional protein missing the carboxy terminus (Campuzano *et al.*, 1986). The dominant mutant phenotype of this allele is due to ectopic and increased expression of the truncated *achaete* RNA in the wing imaginal disks (Balcells *et al.*, 1988), perhaps due to the interaction of the *su(Hw)*-encoded protein with regulatory factors controlling the expression of the *achaete* gene. As expected from this hypothesis, mutations in the *su(Hw)* gene restore the normal levels of the truncated *achaete* transcript but do not affect the premature termination of this RNA in the gypsy LTR (Campuzano *et al.*, 1986). Insertion of gypsy into an intron of the *hsp82* gene also results in altered termination of transcription. In this case, the presence of the *su(Hw)* target site in the gypsy element potentiates the use of the poly(adenylation) site located upstream in the 5' LTR, although absence of the protein in *su(Hw)* mutants does not result in an increase of readthrough transcript levels (Dorsett *et al.*, 1989). In two additional cases, insertion of gypsy into the RNA coding region does not result in transcription termination. Gypsy-induced *bithorax* alleles originate from the insertion of this element into different sequences of the third intron of the *Ubx* gene. These insertions cause a monotonic progression in the intensity of the pheno-type that increases as the insertion site approaches the *Ubx* promoter region. For a constant insertion site, the phenotype is more severe when gypsy insertion takes place in the same transcriptional orientation as the *Ubx* gene, i.e., when the *su(Hw)* binding site is closer to the pro-moter of this gene (Peifer and Bender, 1986). These results would be difficult to explain if the *su(Hw)*-encoded protein acts primarily on transcription termination, because truncation of the RNA in different regions of the intron would not have different phenotypic effects. A more likely possibility is that the *Ubx* intron contains different regula-tory regions and, as is the case for *yellow,* only the function of those located distal from the gypsy insertion site with respect to the *Ubx* promoter would be affected by the presence of this element. A similar interpretation would explain the effect of gypsy insertion into an intron of the *forked* locus on the expression of this gene, because the presence of gypsy does not cause truncation of the RNA, but rather lower than wild-type accumulation of the normal transcripts (Parkhurst and Cor-ces, 1985). This effect of gypsy on the rate of transcription initiation could be compounded with secondary effects on transcription termina-tion, RNA stability, and the ability to splice out transposable element sequences when gypsy is inserted into an intron of the gene.

To explain the mechanisms of mutagenesis by the gypsy element in spontaneous alleles as well as the basis for the reversion of the mutant phenotypes by mutations in various modifier loci, one can propose a double action of gypsy on the expression of the mutant gene. First, gypsy causes an effect on the rate of transcription initiation of adjacent genes as a consequence of the interaction of the gypsy-bound *su(Hw)*-encoded protein with transcription factors necessary for the expression of the gene (Fig. 2). This effect could result in a decrease or increase in RNA levels, depending on whether the transcription factors act as positive or negative regulators of gene expression, respectively. Fur-thermore, when gypsy insertion takes place in an intron of the gene, the effect on transcription rate is compounded with an effect on the stability of the precursor transposable element–mutant gene hybrid RNA. This double effect would explain the response of alleles caused by insertions of gypsy in introns to modifiers such as *suppressor of sable, suppressor of white–apricot,* and *suppressor of forked* (Rutledge *et al.,* 1988), some of which are presumed to act at the level of splicing and RNA stability (see below), because the removal of the gypsy-containing intron is a prerequisite for the formation of a stable message.

  b. Mutagenesis by the tom Element.   Genetic instability in a specific strain of *D. ananassae* that carries mutations in the *claret* and *plexus* genes results in a high incidence of mutations that affect almost exclusively eye morphogenesis. These dominant nonpleiotropic *Optic morphology (Om)* mutants arise exclusively in oocytes and they map to at least 25 different euchromatic loci (Hinton, 1984, 1988). *Om* alleles have been shown to be associated with the insertion of the tom transposable element at or in close proximity to the cytogenetic location of the mutation (Shrimpton *et al.,* 1986; Tanda *et al.,* 1989). The tom element of *D. ananassae* is 7060 bp in length and shows structural characteristics typical of retrotransposons, with three open reading frames similar to the *gag, pol,* and *env* genes of retroviruses. Northern blot analysis shows that the expression of the tom element is developmentally regulated. Though a low-level expression of tom is observed during embryogenesis, tom is poorly transcribed during early fly development. However, the level of tom expression begins to increase at late third instar, and the highest accumulation is observed during pupal development, continuing after eclosion. This pattern of expression may be responsible for the types of mutations caused by this element.

  The specificity in the type of effect caused by the tom transposable element constitutes an interesting paradigm to study both eye development and the mechanisms by which transposable elements cause mutations. Two simple mechanisms can be put forward to account for the almost exclusive effect on eye morphogenesis that results from the insertion of the tom retrotransposon. One possibility is that the location of *de novo* insertions of the tom element is highly selective, such that this transposon only moves into regulatory regions that control the expression of a family of genes involved in eye development. A second alternative is that the tom element inserts more or less randomly and the specificity in its mutagenic action could be determined by selective effects of sequences present in the element on adjacent genes. For example, transcriptional regulatory sequences such as tissue-specific transcriptional enhancers present in tom could increase the expression of genes located nearby in certain tissues, such as the eye imaginal disks, thus accounting for both the dominant characteristics and the specificity of the phenotype.

The remarkable specificity of the *Om* hypermutability system has allowed the identification of approximately 25 different genes. The tom-induced mutations in these genes show various degrees of eye morphogenetic defects, including cell death, transformation of eye into antenna tissues, and duplication of eye structures (Hinton, 1984; Tanda *et al.*, 1989). The first gene characterized in this system is *Om(1D)*, which encodes a homeobox protein expressed in the eye imaginal disks (Tanda and Corces, 1991). The tom-induced dominant mutations in *Om(1D)* can be suppressed by tom-induced mutations in the unlinked locus *Om(1K)Su;* such mutations do not show a mutant phenotype but act as dominant suppressors of the Om(1D) phenotype, i.e., *Om(1K)Su/ Om(1D)* flies have wild-type eyes. Mutations in *Om(1K)Su* reverse the phenotype of all tom-induced alleles in the 25 different genes identified so far, suggesting that *Om(1K)Su* acts at a very general level and perhaps on the tom retrotransposon. Because the effect of the tom element on the expression of adjacent genes seems to be limited to the eye imaginal disks (see below), it is possible that *Om(1K)Su* may encode an eye-specific transcription factor involved in the control of tom transcription. The *Om(1D)* locus has been cloned by transposon tagging and was found to encode a 2.7-kb transcript expressed in every developmental stage of *D. ananassae*, albeit accumulation levels are higher in embryos, pupae, and adults, and lower in larvae (Tanda and Corces, 1991). The dominant phenotype of these alleles suggests that the neomorphic function may be the result of the synthesis of an altered protein or aberrant expression of the normal RNA. The latter possibility is more likely in view of the finding that *Om(1D)* alleles contain tom insertions outside of the coding region of the gene, suggesting that the mutant phenotype may be due to ectopic or high levels of expression of the *Om(1D)* RNA. In agreement with this hypothesis, tom-induced *Om(1D)* alleles accumulate 1.7-fold as much transcript as do wild-type flies in third instar and early pupal stages (Tanda and Corces, 1991). Nevertheless, the amount of this 2.7-kb transcript in eye–antenna imaginal disks of mutant animals was found to be seven times that present in wild type. These results suggest that the *Om(1D)* gene is expressed more abundantly in eye–antenna imaginal disks of mutant flies than in other tissues, and therefore the tom element may preferentially activate the *Om(1D)* gene in eye–antenna imaginal disks (Tanda and Corces, 1991). This activation could be the result of the presence in the tom element of tissue-specific transcriptional enhancers that influence the expression of adjacent genes in those particular tissues.

   c. Mutagenesis by other Retrotransposons. An interesting case of the effects of retrotransposons on the initiation of transcription of adjacent genes is that of a variant alcohol dehydrogenase *(Adh)* allele

(RI-42) isolated from a natural population that contains a copia element inserted in the 5' region of the *Adh* gene (Strand and McDonald, 1989). The *Adh* locus encodes two major RNAs that are transcribed from two different promoters. The RNA transcribed from the distal promoter is abundant in adult flies but rare in larvae, whereas the proximal transcript accumulates in early third instar larvae but is present at low levels in adults (Posakony *et al.*, 1985; Savakis and Ashburner, 1985). The copia element present in the RI-42 allele is inserted 240 bp upstream from the distal *Adh* promoter, in the same transcriptional orientation as the adjacent *Adh* gene. The pattern of developmental expression of the *Adh* gene is not affected by this insertion, i.e., *Adh* expression peaks during larval development and again in adults in RI-42 flies. However, the levels of *Adh* transcripts are lower in the RI-42 variant. Furthermore, comparison of the patterns of developmental expression of copia and *Adh* in RI-42 and wild-type flies indicates that the most dramatic reductions in levels of *Adh* transcripts in the RI-42 variant occur at those times of development and in those tissues when copia is abundantly expressed (Strand and McDonald, 1989). For example, *Adh* expression in RI-42 flies is lowest during larval stages in the fat body, where copia is transcriptionally active, but is normal in oocytes, where copia is not expressed. These results are consistent with a model of promoter interference whereby the expression of the upstream copia element actively interferes with the expression of the adjacent *Adh* gene. In fact, transcriptional interference by the distal promoter in adult flies appears to be the mechanism by which the proximal larval promoter is turned off in adults (Corbin and Maniatis, 1989). Alternatively, transcription of the copia element may not be necessary for its effects on *Adh* expression, and these effects might be due to the interaction of tissue-specific transcription factors bound to the copia element with regulatory sequences that control of the expression of the *Adh* gene. Surprisingly, the effect of copia on *Adh* expression is reversed by mutations in both $su(w^a)$ and $su(f)$ through elevation of *Adh* transcript levels (Strand and McDonald, 1989). This effect is at odds with proposed roles for the proteins encoded by these modifier genes in RNA processing events (see below).

A similar effect on the tissue-specific expression is caused by the insertion of B104 into an intron of the *Antennapedia* (*Antp*) gene in the *Antp*[NS] allele. This is a dominant mutation whose phenotype results from ectopic expression of the *Antp* gene in tissues in which it is normally silent. One possible explanation is that this novel pattern of *Antp* expression is the result of activation of the *Antp* promoter by tissue-specific enhancers located on the B104 retrotransposon (Scott *et al.*,

1983). Other cases of transcriptional inactivation by insertion of retro-transposons into regulatory sequences have been reported but were not analyzed in detail. These cases include the insertion of the 17.6 retro-transposon into the TATA box of a histone gene (Inouye *et al.*, 1984), and the insertion of H.M.S. Beagle into the TATA box of the gene encoding cuticle protein 3, which results in inactivation of transcription of this gene (Snyder *et al.*, 1982). Other examples are the insertion of gypsy into the *Beadex* locus, a cis-acting regulatory element of the *heldup* gene (Mattox and Davidson, 1984), and the insertion of B104 into an enhancer-like element causing the w^{sp1} allele at the *white* locus (Davison *et al.*, 1985). A complex case of insertional mutagenesis by transposable elements is that of several *facet* alleles caused by the insertion of various retrotransposons into an intron of the *Notch* gene. Different retrotransposons inserted at almost the same location give rise to very different phenotypes, suggesting that individual properties of the elements rather than the site of insertion are responsible for the mutant phenotype. These phenotypes are probably due to effects of the elements on the pattern of transcription initiation of the *Notch* gene, although additional effects at posttranscriptional levels cannot be dis-counted (Kidd and Young, 1986; Markopoulou *et al.*, 1989).

2. Effects on RNA Processing

a. Mutagenesis by the 412 Element. Insertion of the 412 retrotran-sposon into the *vermilion* locus of *D. melanogaster* results in three different alleles, v^1, v^2, and v^k, whose phenotype is reversed by muta-tions in the *suppressor of sable* [*su(s)*] gene (Searles and Voelker, 1986). In addition, mutations in the *purple* and *speck* loci caused by the 412 element are also suppressed by second-site mutations in *su(s)*. Insights into the mechanisms by which the 412 element causes mutant pheno-types that can be reversed by loss of function of the *su(s)* gene product have come from studies of the *vermilion* locus and its suppressible alleles. The *vermilion* gene encodes a major 1.4-kb mRNA and a minor transcript that initiates 69 bp upstream of the major transcription start site (Searles *et al.*, 1990). The three suppressible *vermilion* alleles men-tioned above are insertions of 412 at the same position in the first exon of the gene, 36 bp downstream of the major initiation site of transcrip-tion. In all three mutants, the transcriptional orientation of 412 is opposite to that of the *vermilion* gene. As a consequence of this inser-tion, only trace amounts of an apparently wild-type 1.4-kb RNA can be detected in these mutations. Nevertheless, in the presence of a muta-tion in the *su(s)* gene, amounts of this transcript increase up to 10–20% compared to amounts present in wild-type flies (Searles and Voelker,

1986; Searles *et al.*, 1990). Characterization of cDNA clones for this RNA has shown that 412 sequences are imprecisely eliminated from *vermilion* mutant transcripts by splicing at donor and acceptor sites located near the ends of the element in what is usually the nontranscribed strand of 412. Four different 5' donor sites are alternatively spliced to a single 3' acceptor site, leaving 10–50 nucleotides of transposable element sequences in the *vermilion* mRNA (Fridell *et al.*, 1990). Because the insertion of 412 has taken place in the transcribed, untranslated region of the *vermilion* gene, a normal protein can be synthesized from this transcript.

Further insights into the mechanisms by which 412 causes mutations have come from the analysis of the *su(s)* locus. The *su(s)* gene has been cloned and found to encode a 5.0-kb message expressed during all stages of development (Voelker *et al.*, 1991). This transcript encodes a 150,000-Da protein that contains an RNA recognition motif and a highly charged region rich in arginine, serine, and aspartic or glutamic acid similar to a region contained in several RNA-processing proteins. Antibodies against this protein detect a product of the predicted size in nuclear fractions from *Drosophila* tissue culture cells and embryos. The structural characteristics of the *su(s)*-encoded protein together with the effects of mutations in the *su(s)* gene on the pattern of *vermilion* RNA expression in 412-induced alleles suggest several possible mechanisms by which the reversion of the 412-induced phenotype in the *vermilion* gene by mutations in *su(s)* could take place (Fridell *et al.*, 1990). Mutations in *su(s)* could affect transcription of the *vermilion* gene, although this possibility is unlikely given the similarity of the *su(s)*-encoded protein to known RNA-processing proteins. More likely possibilities include a decrease in the frequency of random transcription termination within the element that could result in elevated precursor and mRNA levels. Recessive mutations in *su(s)* could also decrease the rate of mRNA turnover and thus increase the stability of precursor and mature RNA. Alternatively, suppressor mutations might elevate mRNA levels by increasing the rate of splicing at the cryptic sites within the 412 element. Because the precursor 412–*vermilion* RNA could not be detected on Northern blots in the experiments described above, a distinction between an effect of the *su(s)*-encoded protein on RNA stability or splicing rate could not be made. Further insights into the role of the *su(s)*-encoded protein and therefore the mechanism of mutagenesis by the 412 retrotransposon were obtained by analyzing P element-induced mutations that can be suppressed by *su(s)* (see Section III).

   b. Mutagenesis by the copia Element.   Many insertions of transposable elements within introns do not cause a mutant phenotype. However, insertion of the copia retrotransposon into the second intron of the *white* gene, in the same transcriptional orientation, results in the *white–apricot* (w^a) allele, which shows a characteristic light orange color intermediate between that of wild-type and null *white* mutations (Levis *et al.*, 1984). Due to the presence of the copia element in the intron, the level of normally spliced *white* RNA is greatly reduced, and the majority of w^a primary transcripts are poly(adenylated) in the 3' copia LTR and are therefore truncated. Four different RNA species are produced from the *white* gene in the w^a allele (Levis *et al.*, 1984; Zachar *et al.*, 1985a; Mount *et al.*, 1988) (Fig. 3). RNA from the locus has been shown to initiate at the *white* promoter and to terminate primarily in the 3' copia LTR, producing a 5.8-kb RNA. A second transcript 1.2 kb in length initiates in the normal *white* promoter and terminates in the 5' copia LTR. In some cases, a third transcript that initiates in the 3' copia LTR and terminates in the normal *white* transcription termination site is also observed (not shown in Fig. 3). Finally, a small amount of a presumptive wild-type 2.6-kb RNA is also seen that probably arises as a consequence of the removal of copia sequences located in the *white* intron via RNA splicing. The presence of this RNA is responsible for the light orange eye coloration of w^a flies. The eye-color phenotype of these flies is then caused by molecular events that lead to the production of these aberrant RNAs at the expense of wild-type transcripts. In addition to these effects on the processing of the *white*–copia precursor

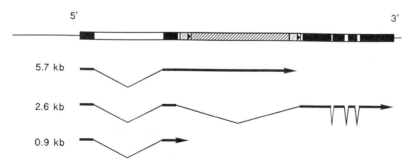

FIG. 3. Structure of the copia-induced w^a allele and encoded transcripts. The DNA structure of the locus is represented in the top of the figure, with *white* exons represented by black boxes and introns represented by empty boxes. The copia element is inserted into the second intron of the *white* gene, in the same transcriptional orientation. The LTRs of the element are represented by shaded boxes, and the central region is hatched. The exon–intron structure of the three main RNAs encoded by the w^a gene are shown in the lower part of the figure. [From Peng and Mount (1990).]

RNA, the insertion of this retrotransposon seems to affect the pattern of developmental expression of the *white* gene (Zachar *et al.*, 1985a*)*. Levels of *white* transcript are reduced in larvae, a time of development when accumulation of copia RNA is highest. Copia is actively transcribed in the larval Malpighian tubules, in which most of the larval transcription of the *white* gene takes place. One interpretation of these results is that expression of the copia element located in the *white* gene in the w^a allele represses expression of the *white* promoter located 3.6 kb upstream, a situation similar to that of the *Adh* gene in the RI-42 variant strain discussed above. The contribution of these effects to the mutant phenotype of the w^a allele is probably not significant. This effect on the pattern of developmental expression of the *white* gene is also observed in a revertant of w^a in which one of the copia LTRs is still present at the copia insertion site, suggesting that regulatory signals necessary for the developmental expression of copia are located in the 5' LTR (Zachar *et al.*, 1985a).

The phenotype of the copia-induced w^a allele can be altered by mutations in various modifier loci, including *suppressor of white–apricot* [*su(w^a)*], *suppressor of forked* [*su(f)*], *Enhancer of white–apricot* [*E(w^a)*], *mottler of white* (*mw*), and *Darkener of apricot* (*Doa*). Mutations in these various modifier loci have different effects on the phenotype of the w^a allele, suggesting that the proteins encoded by these genes may play different roles in those cellular processes necessary for the expression of the *white* gene affected by the insertion of the copia element. For example, mutations in the *su(w^a)* gene reverse the severity of the phenotype, whereas mutations in the *su(f)* and *E(w^a)* genes enhance the effect of copia insertion (Rutledge *et al.*, 1988). These modifiers of the phenotype imparted by w^a probably act to alter the efficiency of rate-limiting steps in the formation of *white* mRNA from the w^a allele. These steps could be the removal of copia sequences by RNA splicing, or steps affecting processes such as RNA stability, poly(adenylation) within the copia element, or termination of transcription. The study of several copia derivatives that alter the severity of the copia-induced phenotype has shed some light on the nature of copia sequences involved in the interactions with modifier genes and the generation of the mutant phenotype. The presence of a copia LTR in various w^a derivatives results in an almost wild-type phenotype that is not affected by any of the modifiers mentioned above (Mount *et al.*, 1988). Nevertheless, the copia LTR contains poly(adenylation) signals that should result in the formation of truncated *white* transcripts similar to those observed in w^a, although sequences located upstream of the 3' LTR in the intact copia element that may affect poly(adenylation) are missing in w^a derivatives containing a solo LTR. In addition, disruption of *white* sequences by copia insertion in the *white* gene in the w^a allele should also take place by the presence of a solo LTR in these w^a derivatives. Finally, the effects of copia on the pattern of *white* developmental expression are also observed when a solo LTR is present (Zachar *et al.*, 1985a). If any of these factors were the basis for the phenotype imparted by w^a and its interaction with the various modifiers, one would expect an effect of these modifiers on w^a derivatives containing a solo LTR. Because none of these modifiers affect the phenotype of these w^a derivatives, one may conclude that sequences located within the central portion of the copia element are responsible for the generation of the mutant phenotype by the copia retrotransposon upon insertion in the second intron of the *white* gene. This conclusion is supported by the finding that insertion of other transposable elements in the central portion of copia results in reversion of the copia-induced phenotype (Mount *et al.*, 1988).

An important clue to the mechanism of this mutagenic effect has come from the isolation and characterization of the $su(w^a)$ gene, which encodes a protein containing an acidic amino-terminal region and a strikingly basic carboxy-terminal domain rich in hydroxylated amino acids. The $su(w^a)$-encoded protein autoregulates its own expression by controlling splicing of its primary transcript (Chou *et al.*, 1987; Zachar *et al.*, 1987). In the presence of mutations in this gene, the levels of the wild-type 2.6-kb *white* RNA increase in w^a $su(w^a)$ with respect to w^a flies. Although a direct influence of the $su(w^a)$-encoded protein on the splicing of w^a RNAs remains to be demonstrated, its effect on the splicing of its own transcripts suggests a possible involvement of this protein in the processing of other RNAs that could explain its effects on the copia-induced phenotype of the w^a mutation and the changes in the accumulation of wild-type *white* mRNA. A similar role in cellular RNA processing may be responsible for the effect of mutations in $su(f)$ on the w^a-encoded phenotype, because the enhancement of the copia-induced phenotype in this mutation correlates with lower levels of the 2.6-kb transcript. A second modifier gene, $E(w^a)$, seems to act at a step different than $su(w^a)$ (Birchler and Hiebert, 1989; Peng and Mount, 1990). Flies carrying homozygous mutations in the w^a and $E(w^a)$ genes show completely white eyes, whereas flies homozygous for w^a and heterozygous for $E(w^a)$ show an eye coloration much lighter than the orange–yellow color of w^a alone. These effects correlate with a corresponding decrease in the levels of wild-type 2.6-kb *white* RNA. The product of the $E(w^a)$ allele behaves as an antimorph and interferes with the effect of the wild-type protein to cause a stimulation of poly(adenylation) in the copia 3′ LTR. These results suggest that the product of the wild-type $E(w^a)$ gene acts to limit poly(adenylation) (Peng and Mount, 1990).

A third modifier that affects the phenotype of the w^a allele is *mottler of white,* which produces a phenotype consisting of nearly white sectors interspersed among those characteristic of w^a. Some *mw* alleles do not show the mottled phenotype and slightly enhance the w^a-encoded phenotype as heterozygotes, and the effect is more extreme as homozygotes (Birchler *et al.,* 1989). In contrast to *su(w^a)* and *E(w^a)*, *mw* is effective on alleles induced by a variety of transposons in the *white* locus. The sites of insertion of these various elements vary, but all are present within the structural portion of the gene. Analysis of RNAs from w^a *mw* flies shows a reduction of the full-length normal *white* RNA with respect to w^a flies, and a concomitant increase in the levels of transcripts that terminate within the copia element. Because the absence of the *mw* gene product increases the degree of termination of *white*-initiated RNAs within the transposable element, these results suggest that the normal product of *mw* might be involved in permitting readthrough of the termination signals present in the respective transposon to give the low level of functional RNA characteristic of the w^a allele (Birchler *et al.,* 1989). An alternative explanation is that the *mw*-encoded protein may be involved in RNA processing within the transposable element, and its elimination removes the processing pathway that leads to a functional *white* message. Another modifier of the w^a-encoded phenotype is *Darkener-of-apricot,* a dosage-sensitive modifier of copia-induced alleles at the *white* locus (Rabinow and Birchler, 1989). *Doa* acts a dominant suppressors of w^a and as an enhancer of w^{sp55}; however, extra wild-type copies of the *Doa* locus enhance w^a. All known *Doa* mutations are recessive lethals during larval development, suggesting that the *Doa*-encoded protein may be important in processes essential to normal cell function. As in the case of other w^a modifiers, the copia LTR alone is insufficient for the interaction, suggesting that the effect takes place through sequences located in the central part of the element. RNA obtained from homozygous w^a;*Doa* escapers show a reduction in the levels of all w^a transcripts initiated at the *white* promoter. Nevertheless, an increase was detected in the amount of wild-type size mRNA in w^a;*Doa* with respect to w^a flies. The evidence available so far suggests that *Doa* mediates its effect by means of other than modulating the quantity of copia transcript accumulation, and the observed phenotypic changes could be due to one or more alterations of w^a synthesis or processing, such as splicing, termination in the LTRs, or initiation within retrotransposon sequences (Rabinow and Birchler, 1989).

Analyses of the effects of modifier loci on the pattern of RNA expression of the w^a allele have given insights into the mechanisms by which the copia element causes mutant phenotypes upon insertion in an intron of a gene. From the effects of $su(w^a)$, $su(f)$, mw, Doa, and $E(w^a)$ on the transcription of the *white* gene in the w^a allele, one might conclude that the mutant phenotype caused by the insertion of copia is the result of a competition between splicing events that remove copia sequences and poly(adenylation) events that produce truncated nonfunctional RNAs. Further analysis of the proteins encoded by these various modifiers will help understand the mechanisms of RNA-processing events involved in the expression of normal cellular genes.

c. *Mutagenesis by other Retrotransposons.*   An interesting case of the effects of a retrotransposon on RNA splicing is that of the insertion of the Springer element into a variably spliced *Drosophila* tropomyosin gene (Karlik and Fyrberg, 1985). This insertion ends up in an exon of the gene when the primary transcripts are spliced in the indirect flight muscles and within an intron when spliced in a mode typical of larval and nonfibrillar adult muscle types. As a consequence of the insertion, this tropomyosin allele fails to direct the synthesis of the flight muscle-specific tropomyosin isoform but is capable of making a second isoform that accumulates in other *Drosophila* muscles. Other examples of these types of effects include the insertion of B104 and blood into an intron of the *white* gene in the w^{bf} and w^{bl} alleles, respectively (Zachar and Bingham, 1982; Bingham and Chapman, 1986). In both cases, processing of the intron results in some full-length transcript, although the presence of poly(adenylation) signals in the LTRs of the elements results in truncated transcripts of various sizes. Insertion of the copia element in the opposite orientation to the adjacent gene in the $w^{hd81b11}$ *white* allele and the Hw^{Ua} *Hairy-wing* allele also results in the formation of truncated transcripts due to poly(adenylation) in retrotransposon sequences (Zachar *et al.*, 1985a; Campuzano *et al.*, 1986). Insertion of B104 into the *glued* locus in the same transcriptional orientation causes poly(adenylation) of *glued* transcripts in the B104 5′ LTR (Swaroop *et al.*, 1985).

E. TRANS-ACTING EFFECTS OF RETROTRANSPOSONS

In addition to cis-acting effects of transposable elements on adjacent genes causing specific mutant phenotypes, some transposons may also be able to mediate effects between copies of a gene located on homologous chromosomes. This type of effect has been observed in the case of the gypsy element, which seems to be responsible for a series of genetic interactions between y^2 and various *yellow* mutations (Geyer *et al.*, 1990). Some *yellow* null alleles give rise to a y^2 phenotype when compounded with y^2, whereas other null mutations, such as y^{59b}, give rise to wild-type y^2/y^{59b} females. This ability of the y^{59b} mutation to complement y^2 is dependent on chromosomal pairing between the two *yellow* alleles, such that disruption of synapsis by translocation of the y^2 locus results in a noncomplementing y^2 phenotype. In addition, this complementation is also affected by mutations at the *zeste* locus. In the presence of a *zeste* null allele such as z^{v77h}, the phenotype of y^2/y^{59b} flies is the same as that of y^2 flies. Interallelic complementation that is dependent upon pairing and upon the allelic state of *zeste* has been termed transvection (Lewis, 1954), and therefore the phenomenon described above represents a description of transvection at the *yellow* locus (Geyer *et al.*, 1990).

Based on the structure of complementing and noncomplementing *yellow* alleles, the molecular mechanism of transvection at *yellow* can be interpreted as the result of the activation of the y^2 promoter by enhancers located in the homologous chromosome in the y^{59b} locus (Geyer *et al.*, 1990) (Fig. 4A). This hypothesis is supported by the behavior of alleles in which the enhancers are not functional, resulting in the inability to complement y^2 (Fig. 4B). Partial inactivation of the enhancers results in an intermediate behavior and only partial complementation. The requirements for transvection at the *yellow* locus are more complex than the simple presence of active enhancers in one of the genes and an intact transcription unit in the other, because several *yellow* mutations examined follow these requirements but are unable to complement y^2. In these noncomplementing alleles, the promoter and enhancer sequences responsible for wing and body cuticle *yellow* expression are functional, and the mutations affect processes downstream from the transcription initiation step, such as RNA stability or protein structure. These results suggest that the presence of an active promoter in cis may be responsible for the inability of these mutations to complement y^2. In agreement with this hypothesis, alleles caused by deletion of promoter sequences or insertions of transposable elements into the promoter region are able to complement y^2, i.e., females carrying each of these mutations in one X chromosome and y^2 in the other show wild-type coloration. This suggests that the wing and body cuticle enhancers might act preferentially on the *yellow* promoter located in cis, and that the cis action prevents trans effects on the promoter located in the homologous chromosome. This ability of enhancers to act in trans has been demonstrated *in vitro* (Müller *et al.*, 1989), and offers important clues on the mechanisms normally employed by these sequences to activate transcription from a distant promoter.

In all pair-wise combinations of alleles tested, at least one of them must contain the gypsy element in order to obtain a complementing

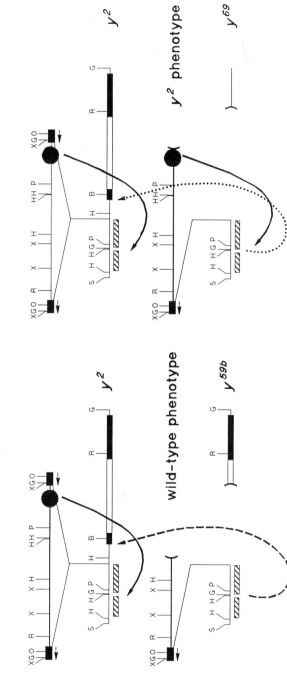

FIG. 4. Interactions between paired *yellow* genes located in different chromosomes. Each panel shows the structure of two *yellow* alleles located in different homologues. (A) A complementing combination of y^2 and y^{59b}; (B) The noncomplementing combination of y^2 and y^{69}. Filled boxes depict *yellow* exons and the empty box represents the intron. Boxes in the 5′ region delineate the wing and body cuticle transcriptional enhancers. The gypsy sequences are shown inserted in the 5′ region of *yellow*. Brackets in the y^{59b} and y^{69} diagrams represent the breakpoints of the deletion that originated both mutations. The *su(Hw)*-encoded protein is represented by a black circle. Solid arrows indicate the negative effect of *su(Hw)* on transcription factors bound to tissue-specific enhancers; a dashed-line arrow indicates the positive effect of enhancers on a promoter in trans, whereas the dotted-line arrow indicates the inability of these enhancers to act on the trans promoter.

wild-type phenotype, raising the question of the putative involvement of gypsy in the transvection phenomenon at *yellow*. A role for gypsy in mediating interchromosomal interactions between the two copies of the *yellow* gene is supported by the fact that an additional copy of the gypsy element at the *scute* locus, located in close proximity to the *yellow* gene, precludes transvection effects, i.e., $y^2 sc^1/y^{59b}$ flies display a y^2-encoded phenotype, suggesting that gypsy–gypsy interactions in cis interfere with interallelic complementation in trans. The role of gypsy in transvection at *yellow* may be to mediate effects of the *zeste* protein (Benson and Pirrotta, 1988), because binding sites for this sequence are present in the gypsy element (Fig. 1).

III. P Elements

A. STRUCTURE

A syndrome of genetic traits called hybrid dysgenesis is characterized by gonadal dysgenesis or the atrophy of gonadal tissues, genetic instability that includes the induction of lethal mutations and the destabilization of the *singed-weak* (sn^w) allele, chromosome rearrangements, male recombination, and segregation distortion and nondisjunction (Kidwell *et al.*, 1977). P elements were shown to be the cause of mutations resulting from a dysgenic cross (Rubin *et al.*, 1982; Bingham *et al.*, 1982). There are two types of P elements: autonomous (or complete) P elements, also known as P factors, and nonautonomous (or defective) elements. Autonomous P elements contain two 31-bp inverse terminal repeats and four open reading frames (ORF0–ORF3), which are required for the production of functional transposase (Fig. 5) (O'Hare and Rubin, 1983). Defective P elements, which range in size from 0.5 to 2.5 kb, are generated via deletions of internal sequences of autonomous P elements in which approximately 150 bp are conserved from each end. These internal deletions are hypothesized to occur as a consequence of an error-prone replication process (O'Hare and Rubin, 1983). Nonautonomous elements cannot transpose unless transposase is provided in trans. An example of a particular defective P element that has been found at a high copy number in certain strains is the 1.1-kb KP element (Black *et al.*, 1987). Approximately 30–50 copies of P elements are scattered throughout the genome; one-third of these are 2.9 kb (Bingham *et al.*, 1982; O'Hare and Rubin, 1983; Rubin *et al.*, 1982). P element-like sequences are found in other species of *Drosophila* but not in closely related species, such as *Drosophila simulans* or *Drosophila*

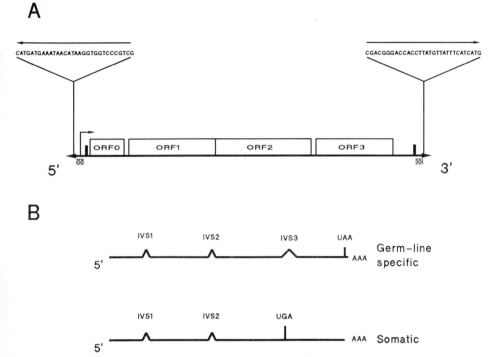

FIG. 5. Diagrams of the 2.9-kb complete P element and the two P element mRNAs. (A) Diagram of the complete P element, sequenced by O'Hare and Rubin (1983). The four open reading frames are represented by the open rectangles. The sequences of the 31-bp inverted repeats are represented by the large arrowheads. The inverted repeat binding protein (IRBP) binds to the terminal 16 bp of the inverted repeats (Rio and Rubin, 1988). The solid rectangles indicate the location of another repetitive sequence, the 11-bp inverted repeats, at nucleotides 126–136 and nucleotides 2763–2773. The P element promoter is located between nucleotides 58 and 103 and P element transcription starts at nucleotide 87, denoted by the small arrow (Kaufman *et al.*, 1989). The cross-hatched rectangles situated below the element represent the two P transposase binding sites, located at nucleotides 48–68 and 2855–2871. The 5′ transposase binding site overlaps the P element promoter (Kaufman *et al.*, 1989). (B) Diagrams of the P element mRNAs. In the germ line, all of the introns (IVS1, IVS2, and IVS3) are spliced. The resulting mRNA encodes an 87-kDa P transposase protein (Laski *et al.*, 1986; Rio *et al.*, 1986). In the soma, only the first two introns are spliced (Laski *et al.*, 1986). This mRNA encodes a 66-kDa repressor protein because translation stops within the third intron (IVS3) due to the presence of a translational stop codon (Robertson and Engels, 1989; Misra and Rio, 1990).

mauritiana (Engels, 1989). There is an insertion site consensus sequence, GGCCAGAC, but it is not the only determinant in the location of P element sequences (O'Hare and Rubin, 1983; Roiha *et al.*, 1988; Engels, 1989). However, independent insertions of P elements in either orientation at the same nucleotide do occur (O'Hare and Rubin, 1983; Roiha *et al.*, 1988). In the target sequence, 8 bp are duplicated upon insertion, although 2- and 9-bp duplications have also been observed (Eissenberg and Elgin, 1987; Williams *et al.*, 1988a).

B. Mechanism and Regulation of P element Transposition

Drosophila strains can be classified into two categories: P strains that contain autonomous and nonautonomous P elements and M strains that do not contain any autonomous P elements (Kidwell *et al.*, 1977). Subsequently, it was determined that M strains can be divided into two types: true M strains that do not contain any P elements and M' strains that may contain many defective P elements (Bingham *et al.*, 1982). Several different assays are used to determine the presence of hybrid dysgenesis. Two of the most common are gonadal dysgenesis (GD) or atrophy of the gonadal tissues, and the hypermutability of the *singed-weak*-encoded phenotype. The *singed-weak* allele is an unstable allele of the *singed* locus located on the X chromosome (Engels, 1979b). Molecular studies have shown that in the *singed-weak* allele, two small, defective P elements (0.95 and 1.15 kb) have inserted into the *singed* locus at the same position but in the opposite orientation (Roiha *et al.*, 1988). This allele is stable in the P cytotype but, under dysgenic conditions, either of the defective P elements will excise. Excision of the 0.95-kb element gives rise to a more extreme bristle phenotype, encoded by the *singed-extreme* allele, and excision of the 1.15-kb element gives rise to a wild-type phenotype (Roiha *et al.*, 1988).

Only progeny from crosses between P males and M females exhibit dysgenic traits. These traits are not seen in the progeny of P × P or M male × P female crosses as P element movement is suppressed. This phenomenon is referred to as the reciprocal cross effect and led to the theory that there are two regulatory states, P and M cytotypes, which govern P element movement (Engels, 1979b; Kidwell, 1981). In addition to cytotype, P element transposition is also regulated by tissue specificity in that P element movement has not been detected in somatic tissues and occurs only in the germ line (Engels, 1983). Therefore, in the P cytotype, P element transposition and excision are suppressed both in the germ line and in somatic cells. The cytotype of an individual is determined by the individual's genotype and the cytotype of the mother. For example, genetic experiments showed that strains that do not contain any P elements have an M cytotype and that as complete P elements are crossed out of a strain, the resultant strains are of the M cytotype (Sved, 1987). Conversely, as strains accumulate P elements, there is an increase in frequency of P cytotype (Engels, 1979a, 1983, 1989; Kidwell, 1981). However, this is a complex process, as different strains with comparable numbers of P elements attain the P cytotype after different numbers of generations (Engels, 1983, 1989; Daniels *et al.*, 1987). The maternal inheritance of P cytotype occurs over many generations. The repressive capability was mapped genetically to certain P strain chromosomes or regions of chromosomes, prompting the speculation that the repressor was encoded by a complete P element (Engels, 1979a; Kidwell *et al.*, 1981). This hypothesis was expanded to propose that both the transposase and repressor are encoded by a complete P element (O'Hare and Rubin, 1983).

O'Hare and Rubin (1983) first proposed that a complete or autonomous P element encodes both a transposase, necessary for the transposition and excision of P elements, and a repressor, which suppresses P element movement. The first step toward elucidating the mechanism of P element transposition was the identification of an autonomous P element. The biological activity of the presumed complete P element was determined by its ability to catalyze the transposition of itself and that of nonautonomous P elements from plasmids into the germ lines of injected M strain embryos (Spradling and Rubin, 1982; Rubin and Spradling, 1982). A single P element was shown to integrate into each insertion site without integration of DNA sequences outside the P element. In addition, the presence of these autonomous P elements caused the destabilization of the *singed-weak* allele. The ability of cloned P elements to provide transposase for the transposition of nonautonomous P elements led to the development of a germ-line transformation system in *D. melanogaster*. In this system, stable transformants are produced when the DNA sequence of interest, which has been cloned into vectors containing defective P elements with their terminal repeats intact, is integrated into the germ line of injected embryos. This event occurs when a "helper plasmid," which provides functional transposase but cannot insert itself into the genome, is coinjected. Stable transformants are identified by the acquisition of the injected stock of phenotypic traits that were originally absent from the parental stock.

Not many details are known about the molecular mechanism of P element transposition, but the structure of the P element suggests that it transposes via a DNA intermediate. While studying the precise loss of a P element from the $w^{hd80k17}$ allele, Engels *et al.* (1990) determined that this process was dependent on the presence of P element transposase and on the presence of a homologue that is wild type at the P element insertion site. From data obtained in this study, it has been proposed that transposition is dependent on the complete excision of the P element. After this event, a double-stranded gap remains and at least one of the target site 8-bp duplication sequences can be removed by exonucleolytic activity. The excised P element can then be inserted into a different position. In the second step of the model, homologous DNA can be utilized as a template to repair the double-stranded gap. In most cases, the sister chromatid can be used for this purpose and the P element is regenerated. However, if the template is a homologous chromosome with wild-type sequences at the insertion site, then the double-stranded gap will be replaced with wild type sequences. The net result of this process will be a reversion. This model has also been suggested to explain the mechanism of P element internal deletions and also to explain the occurrence of male recombination in dysgenic crosses (Engels *et al.*, 1990).

Sequence analyses of defective P elements and germ-line transformation studies indicate that the terminal inverted repeats are required for transposition (Rubin and Spradling, 1982; O'Hare and Rubin, 1983; Karess and Rubin, 1984). Sequences internal to the 31-bp repeats may also be required (Rubin and Spradling, 1982; O'Hare and Rubin, 1983; Mullins *et al.*, 1989). Performing germ-line transformation experiments with *in vitro*-mutagenized 3' ends of P elements, Mullins *et al.* (1989) have found that there is no simple requirement for the cis-acting sequences involved in transposition. These sequences span more than 150 bp at the 3' end and include 11- and 31-bp sequences found repeated in inverted orientation at the 5' end. These experiments also showed that the 5' and 3' inverted repeats are not interchangeable, prompting the hypothesis that a number of factors, including host-encoded ones, were involved in the transposition event. Additional germ-line transformation experiments revealed that all four open reading frames of an autonomous P element are required for the production of a functional transposase (Karess and Rubin, 1984). Karess and Rubin (1984) constructed a P element derivative, Pc[ry], which contained the *rosy* gene placed in a noncoding region of the element. This element functioned as an autonomous P element as assayed by its ability to transpose autonomously into the germ line of M strain embryos, its ability to catalyze the excision of P elements from the *singed-weak* allele, and the restriction of its activity to the germ line. When frameshift mutations in each of the four open reading frames of Pc[ry] were made *in vitro* and were reintroduced into flies, none of the mutagenized constructs exhibited transposase activity, indicating that all four open reading frames are required for the production of functional transposase. The failure of different combinations of the mutagenized derivatives of Pc[ry] to restore transposase activity as assayed by *singed-weak* hypermutability suggests that the four open reading frames encode a single polypeptide.

This idea was supported by *in vitro*-mutagenized derivatives of Pc[ry] in which point mutations in either the 5' or 3' splice junctions of the ORF2–ORF3 intron destroy the ability of the P element to produce transposase as assayed by *singed-weak* destabilization (Laski *et al.*, 1986). Another derivative, P[ry(Δ2–3)], was constructed in which the ORF2–ORF3 intron was deleted, thereby producing an mRNA containing sequences from all four open reading frames. Flies transformed with this construct possess transposase activity in both germ-line and somatic tissues, indicating that the ORF2–ORF3 splice is a germ-line-specific event-Flies transformed with similar constructs in which either the first or second intron was deleted did not affect this observation. This result was supported by the identification of a P element transcript from embryos (somatic tissue) in which the first three open reading frames are spliced together but ORF2 is not spliced to ORF3 (Laski *et al.*, 1986).

The cis-acting sequences necessary for the germ-line specificity *in vivo* of this splicing event were determined to include nucleotides of intron sequences adjacent to the 5' and 3' splice sequences and exon sequences flanking the splice junctions (Laski and Rubin, 1989). To characterize biochemically this tissue-specific splicing event, an *in vitro* splicing system has been developed in which P element pre-mRNA containing the ORF2–ORF3 intron (IVS3) was accurately spliced in a HeLa cell extract but was inhibited in a *Drosophila* somatic Kc cell extract (Siebel and Rio, 1990). Complementation tests indicated that an inhibitory factor in the somatic cell extract prevented the splicing event that occurred in the HeLa cell extract. UV cross-linking experiments showed that this inhibitory factor was a 97-kDa RNA-binding protein whose binding to the IVS3 pre-mRNA can be correlated with the repression of IVS3 pre-mRNA splicing. In addition, the 97-kDa protein-binding sites on the IVS3 pre-mRNA were localized to 5' exon sequences, determined to be important for IVS3 splicing *in vivo* (Laski and Rubin, 1986). The levels of IVS3 splicing intermediates were also diminished when the IVS3 splicing event was inhibited *in vitro,* suggesting that the inhibition by the 97-kDa protein occurred at or before cleavage at the 5′ splice site. The 97-kDa protein may also be important in the regulation of splicing of other germ-line-specific genes (Siebel and Rio, 1990).

Antibodies raised against each of the P element open reading frames immunoprecipitated an 87-kDa protein from *Drosophila* Kc cells transformed with an *hsp*-PΔ2–3 fusion construct in which the P element ORF2–ORF3 intron was removed (Rio *et al.*, 1986). The size of this protein is in agreement with the size predicted from DNA sequence and RNA mapping experiments (O'Hare and Rubin, 1983; Laski *et al.*, 1986). In addition, the biological function of this putative transposase was confirmed when the precise and imprecise excision of a nonautonomous P element was catalyzed in cells transformed with the *hsp*-PΔ2–3 fusion gene. The size of the 87-kDa protein agrees with the predicted size of a protein translated from a mRNA molecule that lacks the third intron (Rio *et al.*, 1986). DNase I footprinting experiments with the purified 87-kDa transposase protein showed that it is a site-specific DNA-binding protein that binds to a 10-bp AT-rich consensus sequence approximately 16 bp from the 5′ inverted repeat and 4 bp from the 3′ inverted repeat (Kaufman *et al.*, 1989). This binding is inhibited when these sites are mutated. The 3′ transposase binding site overlaps a region in the 3′ end that was previously shown to be required for transposition (Mullins *et al.*, 1989). Additionally, the 5′ transposase binding site overlaps the P element promoter, prompting the suggestion that perhaps the 87-kDa transposase protein is involved in the regulation of P element transcription (Kaufman *et al.*, 1989). The 31-bp terminal inverted repeats, which are required for transposition (Rubin and Spradling, 1982; O'Hare and Rubin, 1983; Karess and Rubin, 1984; Mullins *et al.*, 1989), were not protected by transposase binding. The 87-kDa transposase protein also exhibits a significant amount of nonspecific affinity for DNA. Both of these observations lend support to the idea that, like some bacterial transposable element systems, host-encoded proteins are involved in the transposition process. Kaufman *et al.* (1989) have suggested that these proteins may recognize the 31-bp terminal repeats, may stabilize transposase binding, or may direct the transposase to its binding site. In fact, Rio and Rubin (1988), using DNase I footprinting experiments, have isolated a 66-kDa protein (IRBP) from Kc cells that binds to a region of the terminal inverted repeats directly adjacent to the target site duplication sequence. This region has been previously shown to be required for P element transposition (Rubin and Spradling, 1982; O'Hare and Rubin, 1983; Karess and Rubin, 1984; Mullins *et al.*, 1989).

Rio *et al.* (1986) also immunoprecipitated a 66-kDa protein from cells transformed with an *hsp70*–genomic P element construct with antibodies directed against the second open reading frame of the complete P element (Rio *et al.*, 1986). The size of the 66-kDa protein is consistent with it being translated from a mRNA that has been detected in *Drosophila* embryos, in which the first and second but not third introns are removed (Laski *et al.*, 1986). These results agree with a model in which, as a consequence of alternative splicing of pre-mRNA, complete P elements encode two proteins. In the germ-line, the ORF2–ORF3 intron (IVS3) is spliced, resulting in production of an 87-kDa transposase protein that catalyzes P element transposition and excision. The 66-kDa protein is encoded by a mRNA in which only the first two introns are spliced (Laski *et al.*, 1986). This indicates that ORF3 is not required for the P cytotype. This protein is made in somatic and possibly germ-line tissues and can suppress P element transposition in these tissues (Rio *et al.*, 1986; Robertson and Engels, 1989; Misra and Rio; 1990). Additional support for this model is based on the fact that P element activity in somatic tissues due to the presence of the PΔ2–3 element is suppressed in the P cytotype (Engels *et al.*, 1987).

To investigate the idea that the 66-kDa protein was the repressor protein, Misra and Rio (1990) analyzed the repressive ability of a single P element. P element derivatives (Pc[ry$^+$; 66K] and Pc[ry$^+$;hs66k]), in which most of the third intron and all of the third open reading frame were deleted, were injected into an M strain that did not contain any other P elements. These elements, which should only encode the 66-kDa protein, repressed transposase activity as assayed by P element excisions in both germ-line and somatic tissues. Although the amount of 66-kDa protein as well as the repressive ability exhibited by a particular transformed line was influenced by the genomic position of the insertion, these results strongly suggest that the 66-kDa protein is the putative repressor responsible for the P cytotype. In addition, using antibodies that recognize sequences near the carboxy terminus of the 66-kDa protein, this protein was detected in flies transformed with a single modified P element and in an established P strain. Interestingly, the 66-kDa protein was found only in ovaries of females from transformed lines but both in ovaries and in oocytes of the P strain females. The ovaries from P strain females contained a greater amount of the 66-kDa protein than that seen in ovaries from transformed lines. Based on these results, Misra and Rio (1990) hypothesized that the 66-kDa proteins present in the unfertilized germ line of P strain females were responsible for the maternal inheritance of the P cytotype.

These data are consistent with results obtained by analyzing the ability of *in vitro*-modified P elements to duplicate the effects of the P cytotype. Flies transformed with constructs containing either a frame-shift mutation in ORF3 or a mutation in the 5' splice site of the ORF2–ORF3 intron repressed the destabilization of *singed-weak* in the presence of the PΔ2–3 transposase insertion and duplicated the effect of P cytotype on the sterility phenotype of certain *singed* alleles (Robertson and Engels, 1989). In both instances, the protein encoded by these constructs should not contain sequences encoded by the fourth exon and should be analogous to the 66-kDa protein. Although the protein encoded by these constructs was not characterized, these results suggested that a repressor protein responsible for the P cytotype is produced in these fly lines (Robertson and Engels, 1989).

However, the analogy of these two systems to the P cytotype in flies is not complete. For example, the reciprocal cross effect, which is charac-teristic of the maternal inheritance exhibited in the P cytotype, was absent from both systems and repression of P element activity was seen when the PΔ2–3 element was used as a transposase source and not when transposase was provided by an established P strain (Laski *et al.*, 1986; Robertson *et al.*, 1988; Robertson and Engels, 1989). Two expla-nations could account for these discrepancies. The first possibility is that the protein(s) encoded by the *in vitro*-modified P element con-structs utilized in these studies is not the repressor responsible for the P cytotype. The repression of P element activity in fly lines transformed with these constructs argues against this possibility. Alternatively, the 66-kDa protein could be responsible for the P cytotype. In this case, Misra and Rio (1990) have suggested that the number and position of complete P elements in a strain may be important for the establishment of the P cytotype. For example, it is possible that a threshold level of repressor molecules, which would not be accomplished by a single P element, is required in order to see maternal inheritance of P cytotype. Another possibility is that the P element is located in an unfavorable position for its expression and not enough repressor molecules are produced. A variation of this hypothesis suggests that P elements that are inserted into regions where they are expressed during oogenesis may occur with increasing frequency as an M strain becomes a P strain. P cytotype females would possess repressor proteins in their unfer-tilized oocytes and ovaries whereas M cytotype females would not. The position of P elements actively expressed during oogenesis may confer a selective advantage on females of this strain, because their progeny would be fertile, thereby ensuring the maternal inheritance of the P cytotype over several generations (Misra and Rio, 1990).

Several models have also been proposed to explain how the 66-kDa protein may repress transposase activity. First, the 66-kDa protein may actively interfere with transposase by binding to transposase-binding sequences. The 66-kDa protein is thought to be a DNA-binding protein because of its shared structure with the 87-kDa transposase protein and its possible role in the suppression or enhancement of *singed* and *vestigial* alleles, whose phenotype is cytotype dependent (Robertson and Engels, 1989; Williams *et al.*, 1988b). Second, the 66-kDa protein may bind to other P element DNA sequences, thereby prohibiting the binding of host-encoded proteins required for transposition, such as the 66-kDa protein (IRBP) isolated from *Drosophila* Kc cells (Rio and Rubin, 1988). Finally, the 66-kDa protein may inactivate the transposase protein by either complexing with it directly or altering its activity indirectly (Misra and Rio, 1990).

Although the work described in the previous paragraphs indicate that the 66-kDa protein may be responsible for the negative regulation of P element activity, it is not known how nonautonomous P elements contribute to this regulation. For example, a defective P element in which the third intron and most of ORF3 are missing has been isolated from an M' strain. This strain, which contains additional defective elements but lacks complete P elements, possesses the P cytotype as determined by gonadal sterility (Nitasaka *et al.*, 1987). This element is very similar to the P element that encodes the 66-kDa protein (Misra and Rio, 1990; Robertson and Engels, 1989). A 1.1-kb defective element, called the KP element, is present at a high copy number (40–60 copies per cell) in all naturally occurring M' strains. The KP element is missing the entire third exon and part of the second and fourth exons and is transcribed into a 0.8-kb mRNA, which would produce a 207-amino acid polypeptide when translated. Although strains containing KP elements have the M cytotype, the levels of hybrid dysgenesis are reduced when crossed to P strain males (Black *et al.*, 1987). This effect is inherited chromosomally and is presumed to be due to the presence of the KP elements. In fact, it has been suggested that certain characteristics of M' strains indicate that these strains possess a regulatory mechanism other than the P cytotype (Kidwell, 1985; Simmons and Bucholz, 1985; Black *et al.*, 1987; Rasmusson *et al.*, 1990). However, the presence of other P elements on the same chromosomes as the KP elements and the absence of KP elements from other M' strains makes it difficult to assess the role of these elements in an alternate regulatory mechanism (Black *et al.*, 1987; Engels, 1989; Simmons *et al.*, 1990).

C. EFFECTS OF P ELEMENT INSERTION ON GENE EXPRESSION

P elements can generate mutations due to both precise and imprecise excisions, chromosomal rearrangements, and insertions (Engels, 1989). For example, imprecise excisions of P elements can generate mutations by deleting genomic sequences flanking the P insert (Tsubota and Schedl, 1986; Salz et al., 1987; Geyer et al., 1988c; Howes et al., 1988; Williams et al., 1988a). The breakpoints of chromosomal rearrangements occur at the P element insertion sites, thereby mutating genes at or near the breakpoints (Engels and Preson, 1984; Engels, 1989). However, the types of insertional mutations that are generated and their effects on gene expression are varied due to the nature of the target gene, the position of the insertion within the target gene, and the structure of the P element that is inserted. Insertional mutations occur at an approximate rate of 0.0002 mutations per gene per generation (Engels, 1989). However, the *Drosophila* genome contains "hot spots" for P element insertions in which some genes, such as *singed* or *yellow*, are repeatedly the site of P element insertions (Green, 1977; Engels, 1979a; Simmons et al., 1984; Chia et al., 1986; Geyer et al., 1988c; Howes et al., 1988; Robertson et al., 1988) and other genes are refractory to P insertions (Engels, 1989).

The insertion sites within a gene are also diverse. To name a few, P elements have been shown to insert within the coding regions of the *white, yellow, RPII215,* and *forked* genes (O'Hare and Rubin, 1983; Levis et al., 1984; Chia et al., 1986; Searles et al., 1986; Howes et al., 1988; K. K. Hoover and V. G. Corces, unpublished data). A *su(s)* mutation is caused by the insertion of a P element into an intron (Voelker et al., 1990). However, due to the large number of P element insertions isolated in the 5' nontranscribed or 5' transcribed, untranslated region of genes such as *su(s), yellow, rudimentary, Notch, RPII215, Sex-lethal,* and *singed,* it has been suggested that P elements preferentially insert into this region (Voelker et al., 1984, 1990; Tsubota et al., 1985; Chang et al., 1986; Chia et al., 1986; Searles et al., 1986; Tsubota and Schedl, 1986; Kelley et al., 1987; Salz et al., 1987; Geyer et al., 1988c; Howes et al., 1988; Roiha et al., 1988). In fact, this may be due to an altered chromatin structure as detected by the presence of DNase I hypersensitive sites (Tsubota et al., 1985; Tsubota and Schedl, 1986; Eissenberg and Elgin, 1987; Voelker et al., 1990).

The effects of these insertions on gene expression is just as variable as the positions of insertion. Insertions in the coding region of a gene usually result in a null phenotype, as has been shown for *white* and *yellow* genes (O'Hare and Rubin, 1983; Levis et al., 1984; Chia et al., 1986; Howes et al., 1988), but where the insertion lies within the coding region is also important. For example, a P insertion in the 3' end of a *forked* exon results in a mild phenotype, perhaps due to its proximity to an exon–intron junction (K. K. Hoover and V. G. Corces, unpublished data). P element insertions can either increase or decrease the transcription of the affected gene (Tsuboto *et al.*, 1985; Tsubota and Schedl, 1986; Geyer *et al.*, 1988c; Howes *et al.*, 1988). In addition, the heat shock and developmental regulation of Hsp28 is altered when a P element is inserted 5' to the gene (Eissenberg and Elgin, 1987).

The size, structure, and orientation of the P element insertions also affect gene expression (Engels, 1989). When a P element is inserted so that its transcription is in the same orientation as the target gene, the transcription of the target gene terminates within the insertion. Therefore, the resulting effects on gene expression will be more severe than if the P element is oriented in the opposite direction (O'Hare and Rubin, 1983; Levis *et al.*, 1984). Data from *yellow* mutations support these results (Geyer *et al.*, 1988c; Howes *et al.*, 1988). For example, Geyer *et al.* (1988c) have shown that the y^{76d28} allele, in which the P element is oriented in the opposite direction from the *yellow* transcription unit, has a less severe phenotype than does the null mutation $y^{1\#7}$, in which the P element is oriented in the same direction. When inserted in the orientation opposite to that of the *yellow* gene in the allele y^{76d28}, P element sequences can be spliced at a low rate from the P element–*yellow* hybrid RNA to give rise to low levels of a functional *yellow* mRNA and flies with a tan phenotype, slightly darker than y^- but lighter than wild type (Fig. 6). If the P element is inserted in the same orientation as the *yellow* gene in the allele $y^{1\#7}$, P element sequences could not be spliced and the only observed transcript was a 3.0-kb hybrid RNA. These flies show a null y^- phenotype (Fig. 6) (Geyer *et al.*, 1988c, 1991).

In many instances, secondary and tertiary derivatives of P element insertional mutations occur by precise or imprecise excisions of the P element under dysgenic conditions. Often reversions occur via imprecise excision events that result in the internal deletion of the P element (Voelker *et al.*, 1984; Daniels *et al.*, 1985; Chia *et al.*, 1986; Searles *et al.*, 1986; Tsubota and Schedl, 1986; Geyer *et al.*, 1988c; Williams *et al.*, 1988a). Excision events can also result in inversions, the deletion of adjacent genomic sequences, and the deletion of the original P element insert and flanking genomic sequences (Engels, 1979a, Mattox and Davidson, 1984; Daniels *et al.*, 1985; Tsubota and Schedl, 1986; Salz *et al.*, 1987; Williams *et al.*, 1988a). In addition, P element replacement has been observed in the *yellow*, *vestigial*, and *Sex-lethal* genes (Salz *et al.*, 1987; Geyer *et al.*, 1988c; Williams *et al.*, 1988a). For instance, in $y^{1\#7}$, a mutant derivative of the *yellow* revertant y^{+13-11}, a larger P element (1.1 kb) has replaced a 0.4-kb element in y^{+13-11}. These events are believed to be due to homologous recombination or gene conversion between the new element and the preexisting P element (Geyer *et al.*,

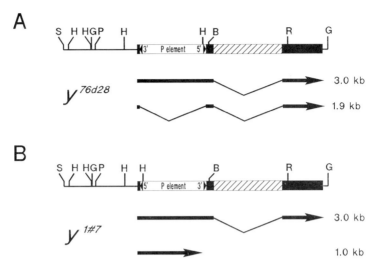

FIG. 6. DNA structure of P element-induced *yellow* mutations. (A) Restriction map of the y^{76d28} allele indicating the position of the insertion of the 1.1-kb P element. The P element is inserted into the *yellow* gene 76 bp downstream of the transcription initiation site, in the opposite transcriptional orientation. P element 31-bp inverted repeats are represented by arrowheads. Dark boxes represent exons and the hatched box indicates the intron. The lower portion within this panel shows the structures of the 3.0- and 1.9-kb poly(A)$^+$ RNAs that accumulate in mid to late pupae. (B) Restriction map of the $y^{1\#7}$ mutation. The same P element is inserted at the same position in the *yellow* gene as in y^{76d28}, but in the opposite transcriptional orientation. The structures of the 3.0- and 1.0-kb RNAs expressed in this mutant are shown in the lower portion. Symbols for restriction enzymes: S, *Sal*I; H, *Hind*III; G, *Bgl*II; B, *Bam*HI; R, *Eco*RI.

1988c; Williams *et al.*, 1988a). Finally, secondary insertions of P elements into existing P elements have been identified in *singed, yellow,* and *Sex-lethal* genes (Salz *et al.*, 1987; Roiha *et al.*, 1988; Engels, 1989) and result in reversion or partial reversion of the phenotype.

The phenotype of several *singed* and *vestigial* mutations generated by P element insertions is influenced by the cytotype of the strain. For example, the bristle phenotype of several *singed* alleles is suppressed in the P cytotype whereas the *singed*-encoded sterility phenotype of other *singed* alleles is enhanced in the P cytotype (Robertson and Engels, 1989). Similar results were obtained with certain *vestigial* alleles in which the phenotypes were suppressed in the P cytotype (Williams *et al.*, 1988b), and with a P transposon containing a modified *white* gene whose expression is dependent on the presence of P chromosomes but curiously not dependent on cytotype (Coen, 1990). As discussed earlier in this review, the effects of the P cytotype on *singed* alleles were duplicated by *in vitro*-modified P elements with mutations in the ORF2–ORF3 intron (Robertson and Engels, 1989). This result suggests that the putative repressor protein encoded by these constructs alters the expression of *singed* by interacting in trans with P sequences in the *singed* locus. In fact, in *singed* alleles whose sterility phenotype is enhanced in the P cytotype, Patterson and O'Hare have detected a female-specific *singed* transcript which is present in the M cytotype, but is missing in the P cytotype (Patterson and O'Hare, cited in Engels, 1989). Why some cytotype-dependent alleles are suppressed and others are enhanced may depend on the nature of the insert and its position within the mutated gene (Williams *et al.*, 1988b).

The insertion of P elements into *yellow* and *singed* genes allows the expression of the mutant genes to be regulated by another gene, *suppressor of sable* [*su(s)*]. *Suppressor of sable* typically modifies the phenotype of mutations caused by retrotransposons (Rutledge *et al.*, 1988). However, the phenotype of the *yellow* allele y^{76d28} is suppressed by *su(s)* (Geyer *et al.*, 1990). In addition, the *singed-weak* bristle phenotype is suppressed by *su(s)*, although the *singed-extreme* phenotype is not affected (M. J. Simmons, unpublished data, cited in Engels, 1989). The two P element-induced alleles described above, y^{76d28} and $y^{1\#7}$, were the basis for an investigation of the mechanisms by which mutations at the *su(s)* locus affect the phenotype of transposable element-induced mutations (Geyer *et al.*, 1991). The effect of the insertion of the P element into the *yellow* gene in these two mutations has essentially resulted in the creation of a *yellow* gene with an additional intron (i.e., the P element). This intron is removed with low efficiency in y^{76d28} and is not removed at all in $y^{1\#7}$ (Fig. 6). Mutations in genes affecting RNA processing, such as *su(s)*, may therefore suppress or enhance the phenotype of these *yellow* alleles. In fact, it has been found that mutations in *su(s)* reverse the phenotype of y^{76d28} but not $y^{1\#7}$. Northern analysis of y^{76d28} flies shows that they contain small amounts of a 3.0-kb RNA that starts at the *yellow* transcription initiation site, is transcribed through P element and *yellow* sequences, and ends at the normal *yellow* termination site. The *yellow* intron is spliced, giving rise to this 3.0-kb transcript that is unstable and present in lower than normal levels. P element sequences are spliced at low efficiency as described above, resulting in small amounts of a 1.9-kb RNA that is functional. The low levels of this 1.9-kb RNA are responsible for the tan phenotype, intermediate between wild type and y^-. On the contrary, y^{76d28} *su(s)* flies show an almost wild-type phenotype, indicating that a mutation in *su(s)* reverses the mutant phenotype induced by the presence of the P element. In y^{76d28} *su(s)* flies, both 3.0 and 1.9-kb RNAs are present at higher levels than in y^{76d28}, explaining the reversion of the mutant phenotype. Nevertheless, the relative amount of 1.9-kb versus 3.0-kb transcripts is the same in y^{76d28} and y^{76d28} $su(s)$ strains, suggesting that the mutation at $su(s)$ does not result in an increased splice rate, but rather in an increased accumulation of the precursor hybrid RNA. This increased accumulation could be due to an elevated transcription rate or to stabilization of the precursor RNA. To differentiate between these two possibilities, the effect of mutations at $su(s)$ on the transcription of the wild-type *yellow* gene as well as $y^{1\#7}$ was analyzed. Mutations in $su(s)$ do not affect the levels of *yellow* RNA in wild-type flies, suggesting that $su(s)$ is not a repressor of normal *yellow* expression. In addition, mutations at $su(s)$ do not affect the pattern or levels of transcription of $y^{1\#7}$. Flies containing the $y^{1\#7}$ mutations accumulate a 3.0-kb hybrid P–*yellow* RNA, but in contrast to y^{76d28}, P element sequences cannot be spliced and no 1.9-kb RNA can be detected in this mutant, thus explaining the null phenotype of these flies (Fig. 6). The presence of the P element in the same orientation as the *yellow* gene does not allow the splicing of P element sequences from the precursor P element–*yellow* RNA. In $y^{1\#7}$ $su(s)$ flies, only the 3.0-kb transcript is expressed, and the levels of this RNA are the same as in $y^{1\#7}$ flies. Therefore, mutations in $su(s)$ do not result in increased transcription initiation even when P element sequences are present in the *yellow* gene. Because this mutation does not increase the rate of splicing as judged from the analysis of y^{76d28} $su(s)$ flies, the $su(s)^-$ background must increase the stability of the precursor RNA. Because levels of this RNA are not higher in $y^{1\#7}$ $su(s)$, this stabilization must be linked to the splicing process. These results give new insights into the role of the $su(s)$-encoded protein, suggesting a function in the processing of cellular RNAs (Geyer *et al.*, 1991).

IV. hobo

A. STRUCTURE

The small transposable element hobo was first identified in an *Sgs-4* allele in *D. melanogaster* (McGinnis *et al.*, 1983). Subsequently, hobo has been found in related species, such as *D. simulans* and *D. mauritiana,* but it may have a very limited distribution among other *Drosophila* species (Streck *et al.*, 1986; Blackman and Gelbart, 1989; Daniels *et al.*, 1990). As shown in Fig. 7, sequence analysis of hobo[108] revealed that it is a 3.0-kb element with short 12-bp inverted repeats

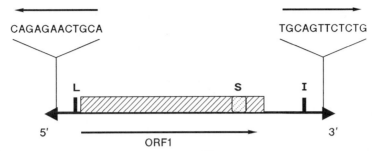

CAGAGAACTGCA   TGCAGTTCTCTG

L   S   I

5'   3'
ORF1

FIG. 7. Diagram of the structure of hobo[108], a 3.0-kb hobo element sequenced by Streck *et al.* (1986). The location of the largest open reading frame, ORF1, between nucleotides 307 and 2250, is indicated by the large hatched rectangle. Additional smaller open reading frames are present in this element but are not shown. The sequences of the 12-bp terminal inverted repeats, represented by the large arrowheads, are shown. Additional repetitive sequences are demarcated by the letters L, S, and I. The I repeat is an inverted duplicate of nucleotides 2771–2786 and, thus, is an imperfect copy of the terminal inverted repeats. The L repeat is a 20-nucleotide repeat found in tandem between nucleotides 249 and 289. The S repeat is a 9-nucleotide sequence. The 10 perfect and 5 imperfect copies of the S repeat are located between nucleotides 1849 and 1983 (small box with dotted lines).

(Streck *et al.*, 1986). Although similar in size and structure, the sequence of hobo is not homologous to an autonomous P element. hobo[108] contains a single 1.9-kb open reading frame that could encode a 75-kDa protein, and several smaller open reading frames.

Some preference is shown by hobo for insertion in the sequence NNNNNNAC or CTTTNNNN, resulting in an 8-bp target duplication (McGinnis *et al.*, 1983; Streck *et al.*, 1986). As in the P—M system, strains have been classified into two types: H strains, which contain hobo elements, and E strains, which do not contain hobo elements of any size (Streck *et al.*, 1986). H strains generally contain 2–10 copies of the 3.0-kb hobo element and approximately 30–75 copies of defective elements, with the copy number and position varying between strains (Blackman *et al.*, 1987; Streck *et al.*, 1986). Defective hobo elements, which appear to be generated from complete elements by internal deletions, exist in H strains and can also generate chromosomal rearrangements (Blackman *et al.*, 1987; Hatzopoulos *et al.*, 1987; Yannopoulos *et al.*, 1987). Unlike P elements, they tend to be of a homogeneous size within a strain. Identification of an insertion site consensus sequence in a hobo element led to the hypothesis that deletion derivatives of intact hobo elements occur by insertion of a second hobo into the first, followed by recombination between the inverted repeats of the two elements (McGinnis *et al.*, 1983; Streck *et al.*, 1986).

Much of the information available about hobo mobilization has been obtained from four systems in which there was a high degree of chromosomal instability. These four systems are the Uc or unstable X chromosome, the 23.5MRF strain, and two *decapentaplegic* (*dpp*) strains, *dpp*[d-blk] and *dpp*[dl]. Genetic analysis has shown that mobilization occurs in H × H and H × E crosses (Blackman *et al.*, 1987; Johnson-Schlitz and Lim, 1987; Laverty and Lim, 1982; Lim, 1979, 1981; Lim *et al.*, 1983; Hatzopoulos *et al.*, 1987; Yannopoulos *et al.*, 1982, 1983a, 1987). The frequency of mobilization is higher when H males are crossed to E females than when E males are crossed to H females, but the difference in frequency between the two crosses is much lower than that seen in the P–M system (Blackman *et al.*, 1987; Blackman and Gelbart, 1989). Unlike the P–M system, hobo regulatory states analogous to P and M cytotypes have not been identified. However, repression of hobo movement was observed in crosses between a hobo strain containing only defective hobo elements and an E strain, supporting the theory that complete 3.0-kb hobo elements provide a transposase function required for hobo movement (Blackman and Gelbart, 1989). Finally, some characteristics of hybrid dysgenesis are exhibited by the four systems, such as atrophy of gonadal tissues and genetic instability, but additional data are needed in order to determine if hobo is involved in this syndrome (Blackman *et al.*, 1987; Lim, 1979; Yannopoulos *et al.*, 1987).

B. MECHANISM AND REGULATION OF HOBO TRANSPOSITION

It has been hypothesized that, because of its size, hobo[108] is an autonomous element that encodes a trans-acting factor necessary for hobo transposition (Streck *et al.*, 1986). However, sequence heterogeneity exists among 3.0-kb hobo elements, indicating that an autonomous hobo element can only be identified with certainty by its ability to catalyze its own transposition and the transposition of defective elements (Lim, 1988; Blackman *et al.*, 1989). A 3.0-kb element, HFL1, is capable of catalyzing the integration of a marked nonautonomous hobo element as well as itself into the germ line of E strain embryos (Blackman *et al.*, 1989). Integration of the marked hobo element occurred when injected into the progeny of an H × E cross but did not occur in the absence of HFL1. The HFL1 element was isolated from an H strain, *dpp*[d-blk], in which hobo instability had previously been identified (Blackman *et al.*, 1987). Unfortunately, the sequence of HFL1 has not been determined so it is not known how it compares to the sequence of hobo[108]. Molecular data obtained from flies transformed with the marked hobo element indicate that a single copy of the element was inserted at each integration site located throughout the genome. Like the P element transformation system, integration occurred at the hobo termini with no integration of flanking sequences and no rearrangement of internal hobo sequences. Once integrated, the marked hobo elements can be subsequently mobilized, presumably by autonomous hobo elements contained in the genome. In addition, transformation frequencies obtained with HFL1 (25%) were similar to those obtained with a P element of comparable size (Blackman *et al.*, 1989; Spradling, 1986).

By analogy to P elements, it is believed that transposition of hobo elements requires the action of a transposase encoded by complete hobo elements as well as host-encoded proteins. However, nothing is currently known about the regulation of transposase activity. Chromosomal rearrangements have been observed in nuclei of salivary gland polytene chromosome squashes in the Uc and 23.5MRF systems, suggesting that somatic instability due to hobo mobilization occurs (Lim, 1979, 1981; Yannopoulos *et al.*, 1983b). These aberrations are believed to be hobo mediated because the locations of preexisting hobo elements have been correlated with the chromosomal breakpoints. However, additional results indicate that hobo mobilization is confined to the germ line (Blackman *et al.*, 1989).

C. HOBO-MEDIATED CHROMOSOMAL REARRANGEMENTS

In all four systems in which hobo mobilization occurs, there is a high degree of instability and a high occurrence of cytologically visible chromosome rearrangements. For example, 40% of the mutations recovered from the $dpp^{d\text{-blk}}$ strain and 30% of the lethal mutations identified in the Uc chromosome are due to chromosomal rearrangements (Blackman *et al.*, 1987; Lim, 1979, 1981). These rearrangements are usually site-specific and often intrachromosomal events. They are often unstable because additional rearrangements may involve existing chromosomal breakpoints (Hatzopoulos *et al.*, 1987; Lim, 1988). In the Uc strain, there is an unusually high reoccurrence of identical chromosomal rearrangements (Johnson-Schlitz and Lim, 1987). The hobo elements have been localized at the breakpoints of the rearrangements, indicating that these events occur between the sites of hobo elements (Yannopoulos *et al.*, 1987; Lim, 1988; Blackman *et al.*, 1987; Hatzopoulos *et al.*, 1987). In a study of a derivative of the Uc chromosome, *Df(1)cm-In*, in which *Notch* mutations are produced at a frequency of 3.5% per generation, it was observed that hobo elements that lie in the same orientation generate deletions and hobo elements that lie in the opposite orientation to each other generate inversions (Johnson-Schlitz and Lim, 1987). This observation suggests that hobo-mediated chromosomal rearrangements can be explained by recombination between paired hobo elements located in the same chromosome (Lim, 1988).

The hobo elements are also associated with small deletions, inversions, and insertions that are not cytologically visible (Blackman *et al.*, 1987; Hatzopoulos *et al.*, 1987; Yannopoulos *et al.*, 1987; Lim, 1988). In fact, while analyzing recessive lethal mutations of the *Df(1)cm-In* chromosome, which did not show any chromosomal aberrations, hobo was localized to the site to which the lethal mutations mapped. Reversions of these lethal mutations did not contain hobo elements at this location (Lim, 1988). There is sparse information on how the insertion of hobo elements affects the expression of the target gene. The most well-studied example is the insertion of hobo into the TATA box of the *Sgs-4* allele. Although the expression of the glue protein decreased 50- to 100-fold, the developmental pattern of expression of this gene is unaffected (McGinnis *et al.*, 1983). In addition, the insertion of a hobo element into the region of gypsy, to which the *su(Hw)* protein binds in y^2 flies, results in a partial y^2 revertant phenotype (Geyer *et al.*, 1988b).

V. mariner

A. STRUCTURE

The mariner element was first identified in *D. mauritiana* when a male with a mutant yellow–orange eye color, subsequently called *white–peach* (w^{pch}), was identified in a Cambridge wild-type strain (Haymer and Marsh, 1986). Molecular analysis revealed that a 1.3-kb transposable element, mariner, had inserted into the 5′ untranslated region of *white* in w^{pch} flies (Jacobson *et al.*, 1986). Approximately 20–30 copies of mariner are located throughout the genome of *D. mauritiana*. This small transposable element is found at a lower copy number among many members of the *D. melanogaster* species subgroup, including *Drosophila simulans, Drosophila yakuba,* and *Drosophila teisseiri* as well as other species, but is not found in *D. melanogaster* (Jacobson *et al.*, 1986; Hartl, 1989). The 1286-bp mariner element inserted into the w^{pch} allele contains 28-bp inverted repeats with four mismatches between them (Fig. 8). Although cDNAs and the putative protein have not been characterized, a single open reading frame of 1035 nucleotides is thought to encode a protein of 345 amino acids

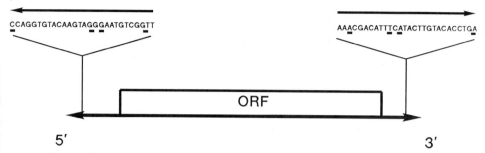

CCAGGTGTACAAGTAGGGAATGTCGGTT   AAACGACATTTCATACTTGTACACCTGA

ORF

5′   3′

Fɪɢ. 8. Diagram of the mariner element. This 1.3-kb mariner element was cloned from the w^{pch} allele in *D. mauritiana* and was sequenced by Jacobson *et al.* (1986). The 28-bp inverted repeats are represented by the large arrowheads. The sequences of the inverted repeats as well as the 4-bp mismatches are shown. The large open rectangle represents the 1.0-kb open reading frame that extends from nucleotides 172–1209.

(Jacobson *et al.*, 1986). Upon insertion, there is a 2-bp duplication of the target site. The dinucleotide TA is the only sequence specificity required for mariner insertion (Jacobson *et al.*, 1986; Bryan *et al.*, 1990). Because smaller mariner elements have been discovered and larger elements have not been identified, the mariner element inserted in the w^{pch} allele is presumed to be a complete element. By analogy to P and hobo elements, the smaller mariner elements that have been characterized are thought to be generated by internal deletions of mariner (Hartl, 1989).

B. Mutations Caused by mariner Insertion and Excision

Mariner has been shown to induce mutations by insertions and excisions, but there is no information on the complex chromosomal rearrangements that have been observed with P, hobo, and FB elements. The w^{pch} allele has been shown to be unstable both in the germ-line and in somatic cells (Jacobson and Hartl, 1985; Haymer and Marsh, 1986). Unlike somatic mutation rates, the germ-line mutation rates differ among the sexes, with a rate of 2×10^{-3} to 4×10^{-3} for males and a twofold lower rate for females (Hartl, 1989). Spontaneous mutations of the w^{pch} allele give rise to either wild-type or bleached-white progeny (Jacobson and Hartl, 1985). Reversion of the phenotype of w^{pch} to wild type results from the imprecise excision of the mariner element, in which the revertant retains the dinucleotide TA and 3 bp from the 3′ end of mariner (Bryan *et al.*, 1990). The bleached-white or null phenotype can arise from deletions of *white* or can occur in double mutants of *white* and *garnet,* suggesting that the *garnet* locus is particularly unstable in the presence of w^{pch} (Jacobson and Hartl, 1985; Bryan *et al.,* 1990).

There are two types of somatic instability of w^{pch}: heritable and nonheritable (Jacobson and Hartl, 1985; Haymer and Marsh, 1986; Bryan *et al.,* 1987). In both instances, this instability is exhibited as a mosaic eye color with non-wild-type pigmented patches on a w^{pch} background. In strains in which the somatic mosaicism is nonheritable, examples of mosaicism are uncommon, occurring at a frequency of 10^{-3} (Haymer and Marsh, 1986). In these individuals, usually only one of the eyes shows a mosaic phenotype. There is a striking variation in the size of pigmented patches, which range from single ommatidia to regions covering 20–30% of the eye. The variation in the size of pigmentation is believed to be due to the excision of mariner from the w^{pch} allele during different developmental stages of the eye (Jacobson and Hartl, 1985). In certain strains of *D. mauritiana,* there is increased instability of w^{pch} both in the germ line and in somatic tissues. For example, in the germ line there is a high incidence of reversion of w^{pch} to a wild-type phenotype, with a frequency exceeding 2% (Bryan *et al.,* 1987). Analysis of the *white* locus in germ-line revertant strains by the polymerase chain reaction indicates that these events are caused by the imprecise excision of mariner from *white,* in which 3 bp from the 5' or 3' end of the transposable element and the flanking dinucleotide TA are left behind (Bryan *et al.,* 1990). Also, in these strains, the mosaic eye phenotype is heritable and occurs in almost every fly (Bryan *et al.,* 1987). Due to a lack of suitable genetic markers in *D. mauritiana,* further genetic analysis of this system was performed in a *D. simulans* strain into which the w^{pch} allele and the "mosaicism" factor had been back-crossed. This analysis indicated that the increase in instability was due to a dominant factor, *Mos1,* on the third chromosome (Bryan *et al.,* 1987). Southern blots of genomic digests of mosaic and nonmosaic flies revealed that the mosaicism was due to the excision of the mariner element from w^{pch} in somatic cells (Bryan and Hartl, 1988). The sequences of somatic revertants of w^{pch} as determined by the polymerase chain reaction indicate that the excision events are imprecise and occur as in the germ line (Bryan *et al.,* 1990). It is not known why the imprecise somatic excision of mariner from w^{pch} results in pigmented sectors that are not wild type in color, whereas the imprecise excision of mariner from the germ line produces eyes that are completely wild type. Additional molecular evidence indicates that *Mos1* promotes the somatic excision of mariner from tissues other than the eye (Medhora *et al.,* 1988; Bryan *et al.,* 1990).

Mariner is capable of mutating genes other than *white*. In a screen for visible mutations in which mariner elements within a somatic mosaic w^{pch} strain were mobilized by the *Mos1* factor, 24 mutations, including *yellow, white, vermilion, prune, garnet,* and *lozenge*, were recovered. Each of the *yellow* and *white* mutations, which showed germ-line and somatic instability in the presence of *Mos1*, were analyzed on a molecular level. The mariner insertions were located in various positions within these two loci, including the large intron of *yellow* and in the introns and 5′ untranslated leader of *white* (Bryan *et al.*, 1990). Partial phenotypic revertants of w^{pch} were also analyzed. The eye color of these revertants is intermediate between w^{pch} and wild type and occurs at a frequency of 0.1% in a w^{pch};*Mos1* strain. These revertants can be categorized into two different types: ones that contain mariner and others in which mariner is missing. In cases in which mariner is present, partial reversion of the phenotype occurs when there is an internal deletion of mariner, when a second mariner element inserts into the first, or when 4 bp of flanking *white* sequence and a single nucleotide from mariner are deleted (Bryan *et al.*, 1990). Analyses of bleached-white or null derivatives of w^{pch} indicate that the null phenotype is generated by imprecise excision of mariner with the concomitant deletion of one or both sides of the *white* sequences flanking the element. In addition, lethal derivatives of w^{pch} were observed in which large deletions of DNA are presumed to occur. Finally, mutants containing rearranged *white* sequences were also observed (Bryan *et al.*, 1990).

C. MECHANISM OF TRANSPOSITION OF MARINER

No molecular information about the mechanism or the regulation of transposition of mariner is known. The *Mos1* factor was first believed to be an autonomous mariner element due to its ability to increase the instability of the mariner element in certain strains (Bryan *et al.*, 1987). The "mosaicism" activity in these stocks is associated with a particular copy of mariner, which is lost from nonmosaic progeny (Medhora *et al.*, 1988). *Mos1* increases the frequency of its own excision, as detected by the appearance of nonmosaic w^{pch} progeny in *Mos1* strains, and of the excision of other mariner elements both in the germ line and in somatic tissues. Transposition of *Mos1* from its site on the third chromosome to other locations in the genome has been observed. Functional assays such as germ-line transformation experiments that prove that *Mos1* is an autonomous mariner element have been performed recently (Garza *et al.*, 1991). Because the *Mos1* factor has not been sequenced, it is not known how it differs molecularly from other copies of mariner. However, the location of *Mos1* in the genome or nucleotide differences among *Mos1* and other mariner elements may account for its excisional and transpositional abilities (Medhora *et al.*, 1988).

A P cytotype phenomenon does not exist in the mariner system. However, in *D. simulans,* a novel form of maternal inheritance exists (Bryan and Hartl, 1988). For example, when *D. mauritiana Mos1* and w^{pch} strains were crossed into *D. simulans,* two classes of offspring were observed when *Mos* heterozygous females were crossed to nonmosaic males. One class was genotypically *Mos/+* and resembled their mothers with respect to somatic mosaicism of the eye. The other class showed a nonheritable maternal effect in which genotypically non-*Mos* offspring possessed mosaic eyes. This effect is not seen when the reciprocal cross (*Mos/+* males × +/+ female) was performed (Bryan and Hartl, 1988). The significance of this maternal effect is not known; it has been observed in *D. simulans* but not in *D. mauritiana.*

VI. foldback Elements

A. STRUCTURE

The foldback (FB) elements are found in *D. melanogaster* and in related species of the *D. melanogaster* subgroup (Brookfield *et al.*, 1984; Silber *et al.*, 1989). FB elements were first identified by the ability of the terminal repeats to "fold back" and form duplex structures under renaturation conditions (Potter *et al.*, 1980). These duplex structures consist of a double-stranded stem composed of the inverted repeats and a single-stranded loop containing a sequence separating the inverted repeats. Approximately 30–40 copies of foldback elements are present per genome, with significant intrastrain and interstrain differences in the locations of the elements (Truett *et al.*, 1981).

This family of transposable elements is characterized by extensive structural heterogeneity. Nevertheless, as shown in Fig. 9, all foldback elements possess inverted terminal repeats that are AT rich and whose size ranges from several hundred base pairs to several kilobases (250 bp–3.4 kb) (Potter, 1982a,b; Truett *et al.*, 1981). The left and right terminal repeats may or may not be identical and may differ substantially in size. Although there is a high degree of homology at the termini, the inverted repeats are composed of many small, tandem repeats that end at the central loop-inverted repeat junctions. For

A

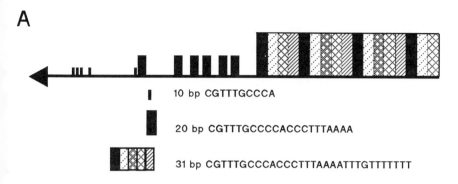

10 bp CGTTTGCCCA

20 bp CGTTTGCCCCACCCTTTAAAA

31 bp CGTTTGCCCACCCTTTAAAATTTGTTTTTTT

B

FIG. 9. Diagrams of an FB4 terminal inverted repeat and the loop sequences of putative complete FB elements. (A) Diagram of the left terminal inverted repeat of FB4, sequenced by Potter (1982b). This 1026-bp inverted repeat consists of several tandem copies of a 10-bp repeat that expands to a 20-bp repeat. The 20-bp repeat extends to a 31-bp repeat. There are five different copies of the 31-bp repeat, represented by the five rectangles of different textures. A set of the five 31-bp repeats comprises a 155-bp repeat. The size heterogeneity of the inverted terminal repeats can be explained by varying numbers of the 31-bp repeats. The loop sequence and the right inverted terminal repeat of the FB4 element are not shown. (B) Comparison of the diagrams of the loop sequences of two FB–NOF elements, putative complete FB elements. The FB terminal inverted repeats are not shown. The upper diagram depicts the loop sequence of an FB element, determined by Templeton and Potter (1989), which is homologous to the FB–w^c element. The bottom diagram shows the loop sequence and 3′ loop–terminal repeat junction of the FB–NOF element from the TE146(Z) element sequenced by Harden and Ashburner (1990). A novel 308-bp inverted repeat, represented by the cross-hatched rectangles, can be seen in both diagrams and is located at the terminal inverted repeat–loop junctions. However, the Templeton and Potter loop sequence contains two open reading frames, represented by the open rectangles. There is a third open reading frame located on the opposite strand that is not pictured here. The Harden and Ashburner loop sequence consists of a single open reading frame that reads through the region separating ORF1 and ORF2 of the Templeton and Potter loop sequence. Also, the amino terminus of the open reading frame is 72 amino acids shorter than the Templeton and Potter loop sequence. Additional differences exist between Harden and Ashburner's single ORF and the C termini of ORF1 and ORF2 (Harden and Ashburner, 1990).

example, the sequence of a complete FB4 element revealed that a 10-bp imperfect repeat is tandemly repeated near the distal termini. This is expanded to a 20-bp repeat that in turn is expanded to a 31-bp repeat. There are five types of 31-bp repeats, which in turn compose a 155-bp repeat that is cut once by $TaqI$. The varying numbers of the 31-bp repeats account for the size variability in the foldback inverted terminal repeats (Truett $et\ al.$, 1981; Levis $et\ al.$, 1982; Potter, 1982a,b). The terminal repeats are apparently noncoding regions, as they contain frequent translational stop codons. The internally repetitious structure of the terminal repeats suggests that these sequences are highly recombinogenic (Potter, 1982a).

The central portions of FB elements are also heterogeneous in structure (Levis $et\ al.$, 1982; Potter, 1982a,b; Truett $et\ al.$, 1981; Templeton and Potter, 1989; Goldberg $et\ al.$, 1982; Harden and Ashburner, 1990; Zachar and Bingham, 1982; Levis and Rubin, 1982; Brierley and Potter, 1985). For example, the majority of FB elements consist only of two copies of the inverted terminal repeats with little or no additional sequence present in the central portion (Truett $et\ al.$, 1981). The single-stranded loop, therefore, may be the result of a duplex structure formed between terminal repeats of unequal sizes. When the loop sequence is present, it may be either a repetitive or unique sequence. For example, the 1.7-kb loop sequence of the FB4 or FB–HB1 element is actually a member of another transposable element family, HB (Brierley and Potter, 1985). Only a few copies of the HB element are present in the genome and its structure is similar to P and hobo elements in that it contains its own short terminal inverted repeats of 29–32 bp. This sequence does not normally associate with FB elements, suggesting that the HB element is inserted between the inverted terminal repeats (Potter, 1982a; Brierley and Potter, 1985).

Another distinctive loop sequence is the one associated with the FB–w^c insertion. The FB–w^c element is a 10-kb insertion consisting of 2.2- and 3.4-kb nonidentical inverted terminal repeats and a 4.0-kb nonhomologous central DNA segment that only associates with FB repeats (Collins and Rubin, 1982; Levis $et\ al.$, 1982; Brierley and Potter, 1985). $In\ situ$ hybridizations and restriction mapping have shown that the central loop sequence of FB–w^c is homologous to a 4.0-kb sequence in the FB–NOF element (Paro $et\ al.$, 1983). FB–NOF flanks TE28, a member of the giant TE (transposing element) family discovered by Ising (Paro $et\ al.$, 1983; Goldberg $et\ al.$, 1982). The NOF sequence is only found in association with FB inverted repeats, whereas only 10% of FB elements have NOF sequences associated with them (Levis $et\ al.$, 1982; Brierley and Potter, 1985). All of the TE elements that have been analyzed have associated FB sequences; a subset of these are FB–NOF sequences (Paro *et al.*, 1983; Gubb *et al.*, 1985; Chia *et al.*, 1985; Harden and Ashburner, 1990). Another interesting finding obtained from *in situ* hybridization experiments is that there are high- and low-copy-number FB–NOF strains, with many lacking any FB–NOF sequences (Harden and Ashburner, 1990).

The structure of two NOF sequences, TE146(Z) and an FB element homologous to FB–w^c, has been determined (Templeton and Potter, 1989; Harden and Ashburner, 1990). First, Templeton and Potter isolated an FB element homologous to FB–w^c from an Oregon-R genomic library. This element contains a 308-bp inverted repeat, which is distinct from the inverted terminal repeats, at the loop–repeat junctions. This repeat is also present in the TE146(Z) element sequenced by Harden and Ashburner (1990). This may indicate that at one time the NOF sequence was a transposable element but has subsequently lost the ability to move without the FB terminal repeats. The central loop or NOF sequence of the FB–w^c homologous element contains three open reading frames, with two on one strand and a third open reading frame on the opposite strand. In contrast, the 3.4-kb central segment of the TE146(Z) element contains a single open reading frame that may encode a protein of 120 kDa. This discrepancy between the two elements is due to 11-bp differences in the non-FB regions and a longer amino terminus in the FB–w^c homologous element (Templeton and Potter, 1989; Harden and Ashburner, 1990). These open reading frames could potentially encode proteins required for the transposition of FB elements. In fact, a 71-kDa protein was localized to nurse cells of *Drosophila* ovaries by an antibody directed against a peptide corresponding to the first open reading frame of the FB–w^c homologous sequence (Templeton and Potter, 1989). This is an important observation, for encoded proteins involved in the transposition of FB elements would be anticipated to function in the germ line. These data as well as the distribution of NOF sequences in different strains suggest that the FB–NOF element is a complete or autonomous FB element and that others, particularly those that are not associated with a central loop sequence, are incomplete. It has been suggested that because FB–NOF elements are very recombinogenic, a mechanism to suppress this recombination would be the absence of functional FB–NOF elements from the genome (Harden and Ashburner, 1990).

FB elements are also capable of forming large, composite transposons whose only common feature is that segments of chromosomal DNA are mobilized by flanking FB elements. Composite transposons can generate insertional translocations. Again, the size of the chromosomal DNA and of the FB elements varies widely. An example of a composite transposon is the w^{DZL} insertion. This 13- to 14-kb element contains a 6.5-kb nonhomologous fragment located between two pairs of inverted repeats (Levis *et al.*, 1982; Zachar and Bingham, 1982). In this instance, a unique DNA sequence normally found on chromosome 2 is mobilized by flanking FB elements and inserted into the *white* locus as a single unit. Other examples of composite transposons belong to the TE element family (Ising and Ramel, 1976; Ising and Block, 1981). The first TE identified was a large DNA segment, consisting of a few hundred kilobases of DNA, including the *white-apricot* allele and the adjacent *roughest* locus, which had transposed from its normal position on the X chromosome to the second chromosome (Ising and Ramel, 1976). All of the TE elements that have been analyzed have FB sequences associated with them; a subset of these are FB–NOF sequences (Paro *et al.*, 1983; Gubb *et al.*, 1985; Chia *et al.*, 1985; Harden and Ashburner, 1990).

B. MECHANISM AND CONTROL OF TRANSPOSITION

Little is known about the actual mechanism or control of FB transposition. The inverted terminal repeats appear to be required in cis for transposition and the data presented in the previous section indicate that a protein or proteins encoded by NOF sequences are involved. There does not appear to be any target site sequence specificity (Truett *et al.*, 1981). Upon insertion, there is a target site duplication of 9 bp, which is similar to the duplications generated by P or hobo (O'Hare *et al.*, 1984; Truett *et al.*, 1981). Because the general structure of FB elements is more similar to that of P elements than that of retrotransposons, FB transposition is unlikely to involve RNA intermediates. Bingham and Zachar have hypothesized that transposition of FB elements occurs via internal recombination between direct repeats contained in the inverted terminal repeats or by DNA cuts at the boundaries of the elements (Bingham and Zachar, 1989). Excision of TE elements occurs by recombination between FB elements, removing any DNA that lies between them (Chia *et al.*, 1985). There are also very few data concerning the regulation of FB transposition, although there is some indirect evidence that this process is actively regulated. For example, stocks containing the w^c and w^{DZL} alleles have become more stable during inbreeding. In addition, the w^{DZL} strain regains its mutability upon outcrossing. These effects are similar to what has been observed with P strains (Bingham and Zachar, 1989). Further investigation of the differences between high- and low-copy-number FB strains may provide additional insights.

C. Chromosomal Rearrangements Mediated by FB Elements

FB elements can generate many chromosomal rearrangements, including deletions, inversions, and reciprocal translocations. FB elements can also generate insertional translocations as discussed previously. In addition, insertions of FB elements have been shown to cause mutations, affecting the expression of genes into which they insert. Much of the information obtained about FB-mediated mutations and rearrangements has been elucidated by the study of the w^c and w^{DZL} alleles, both of which are characteristically unstable alleles of *white*. The w^c allele was first isolated as a partial phenotypic revertant of w^i with an eye color darker than that of the parental w^i mutation (Green, 1967). The w^i mutation is caused by the duplication of 2.9 kb of DNA within the *white* locus (Karess and Rubin, 1982). The w^c allele is unstable, with a mutation frequency of greater than one in 10^3 X chromosomes. In the w^c allele, a 10-kb FB element interrupts the duplication in w^i (Levis *et al.*, 1982; Collins and Rubin, 1982). This FB element contains 2.2- and 3.4-kb inverted repeats and, as previously discussed, the central loop sequence of FB–w^c is homologous to the NOF sequence (Paro *et al.*, 1983). The w^c insertion can also generate chromosomal rearrangements, as large deletions of the *white* sequence flanking the insertion have been observed cytologically (Green, 1967). There are three classes of revertants and mutant derivatives: reversion of w^c to wild type or w^i, and mutation of w^c to w^-. Reversion of w^c to w^i is accompanied by precise excision of the insertion (Collins and Rubin, 1983). Reversion of w^c to wild type involves the excision of both the insertion and one copy of the w^i duplication via recombination between the two copies of the duplication (Collins and Rubin, 1982). Mutant derivatives of w^c, which possess a bleached-white or null phenotype, can either be stable or unstable (Green, 1967). The molecular analyses of deletion derivatives in which sequences to the left of the insertion have been deleted revealed that the w^c chromosome contains an additional FB element insertion approximately 14 kb to the left of the w^c insertion (Collins and Rubin, 1984). The nature of the deletions was consistent with a mechanism in which homologous recombination between two closely situated FB elements resulted in the deletion of sequences located between the FB elements. Presumably recombination occurs at any of the direct tandem repeats contained within the inverted terminal repeats of FB elements. This is thought to be a general mechanism for creating FB element heterogeneity. In addition, the molecular analysis of other bleached-white derivatives indicates that there can be rearrangement of sequences adjacent to or within the

w^c insertion. These may occur in a multistep process. The element-internal rearrangements result in stable derivatives.

The w^{DZL} mutation was first isolated as a yellow-eyed female in an Oregon R strain (Bingham, 1980). A 13.0-kb FB element consisting of a 6.5-kb sequence flanked by two pairs of FB terminal repeats is inserted to the right of the *white* locus in this allele (Bingham and Zachar, 1985; Levis *et al.*, 1982; Zachar and Bingham, 1982). The w^{DZL} allele is also highly mutable, with new mutants arising at a frequency of 0.5–1.5%, or 1 in 10^{-3} X chromosomes (Bingham, 1981). Several classes of new mutants arise, including simple revertants, colorless derivatives of w^{DZL}, and chromosomal rearrangements. The simple revertants possess a wild-type eye color in the presence of other alleles of *white* and *zeste*. They are unstable, give rise to flies with novel eye phenotypes, and are generated by the imprecise excision of the FB element. Specifically, they are characterized by a partial internal deletion of the central 6-kb sequence that presumably occurs via recombination within the tandem direct repeats present in the inverted terminal repeats (Levis *et al.*, 1982; Levis and Rubin, 1982; Zachar and Bingham, 1982). The colorless derivatives of w^{DZL} result from small deletions of the right-most portion of the *white* locus. Deletions of large segments of DNA beginning at the *white* locus as well as inversions and reciprocal translocations have also been observed (Bingham, 1981). The translocation of the central loop sequence in the FB–w^{DZL} from its normal position on the second chromosome to the *white* locus alters the developmental and tissue-specific expression of this unique sequence and is associated with the repression of *white* expression. A novel transcript containing both transposon and *white* sequences is produced in the eye whereas *white* expression occurs normally in other tissues (Bingham and Zachar, 1985; Zachar *et al.*, 1985b).

References

Abad, P., Vaury, C., Pélisson, A., Chaboissier, M.-C., Busseau, I., and Bucheton, A. (1989). A long interspersed repetitive element—the I factor of *Drosophila teissieri*—is able to transpose in different *Drosophila* species. *Proc. Natl. Acad. Sci. U.S.A.* **86**, 8887–8891.

Arkhipova, I. R., Mazo, A. M., Cherkasova, V. A., Gorelova, T. V., Schuppe, N. G., and Ilyin, Y. V. (1986). The steps of reverse transcription of *Drosophila* mobile dispersed genetic elements and U3-R-U5 structure of their LTRs. *Cell* **44**, 555–563.

Balcells, L., Modolell, J., and Ruiz-Gomez, M. (1988). A unitary basis for different *Hairy-wing* mutations of *Drosophila melanogaster*. *EMBO J.* **7**, 3899–3906.

Bender, W., Weiffenbach, B., Karch, F., and Peifer, M. (1985). Domains of *cis*-interaction in the *bithorax* complex. *Cold Spring Harbor Symp. Quant. Biol.* **50**, 173–180.

Benson, M., and Pirrotta, V. (1988). The *Drosophila zeste* protein binds cooperatively to sites in many gene regulatory regions: implications for transvection and gene regulation. *EMBO J.* **7**, 3907–3915.

Bingham, P. M. (1980). The regulation of *white* locus expression: a dominant mutant allele at the *white* locus of *Drosophila melanogaster*. *Genetics* **95**, 341–353.

Bingham, P. M. (1981). A novel dominant mutant allele at the *white* locus of *Drosophila melanogaster* is mutable. *Cold Spring Harbor Symp. Quant. Biol.* **45**, 519–525.

Bingham, P. M., and Chapman, C. H. (1986). Evidence that *white-blood* is a novel type of temperature-sensitive mutation resulting from temperature-dependent effects of a transposon insertion on formation of *white* transcript. *EMBO J.* **5**, 3343–3351.

Bingham, P. M., and Zachar, Z. (1985). Evidence that two mutations, w^{DZL} and z^1, affecting synapsis-dependent genetic behavior of *white* are transcriptional regulatory mutations. *Cell* **40**, 819–825.

Bingham, P. M., and Zachar, Z. (1989). Retrotransposons and the FB transposon from *Drosophila melanogaster*. *In* "Mobile DNA" (D. E. Berg and M. M. Howe, eds.), pp. 485–502. Am. Soc. Microbiol., Washington, D.C.

Bingham, P. M., Kidwell, M. G., and Rubin, G. M. (1982). The molecular basis of P-M hybrid dysgenesis: the role of the P element, a P strain-specific transposon family. *Cell* **29**, 995–1004.

Birchler, J. A., and Hiebert, J. C. (1989). Interaction of the *Enhancer-of-white-apricot* with transposable element alleles at the *white* locus in *Drosophila melanogaster*. *Genetics* **122**, 129–138.

Birchler, J. A., Hiebert, J. C., and Rabinow, L. (1989). Interaction of the *mottler of white* with transposable element alleles at the *white* locus in *Drosophila melanogaster*. *Genes Dev.* **3**, 73–84.

Black, D. M., Jackson, M. S., Kidwell, M. G., and Dover, G. A. (1987). KP elements repress P-induced hybrid dysgenesis in *D. melanogaster*. *EMBO J.* **6**, 4125–4135.

Blackman, R. K., and Gelbart, W. M. (1989). The transposable element hobo of *Drosophila melanogaster*. *In* "Mobile DNA" (D. E. Berg and M. M. Howe, eds.), pp. 523–529. Am. Soc. Microbiol., Washington, D.C.

Blackman, R. K., Grimaila, R., Koehler, M. M. D., and Gelbart, W. M. (1987). Mobilization of hobo elements residing within the *decapentaplegic* gene complex: suggestion of a new hybrid dysgenesis system in *Drosophila melanogaster*. *Cell* **49**, 497–505.

Blackman, R. K., Koehler, M. M. D., Grimaila, R., and Gelbart, W. M. (1989). Identification of a fully-functional hobo transposable element and its use for germ-line transformation of *Drosophila*. *EMBO J.* **8**, 211–217.

Boeke, J. D. (1989). Transposable elements in *Saccharomyces cerevisiae*. *In* "Mobile DNA" (D. E. Berg and M. M. Howe, eds.), pp. 335–374. Am. Soc. Microbiol., Washington, D.C.

Boeke, J. D., and Corces, V. G. (1989). Transcription and reverse transcription of retrotransposons. *Annu. Rev. Microbiol.* **43**, 403–434.

Brierley, H. L., and Potter, S. S. (1985). Distinct characteristics of loop sequences of two *Drosophila* foldback elements. *Nucleic Acids Res.* **13**, 485–500.

Brookfield, J. Y., Montgomery, E., and Langley, C. H. (1984). Apparent absence of transposable elements related to the P elements of *Drosophila melanogaster* in other species of *Drosophila*. *Nature (London)* **310**, 330–332.

Bryan, G. J., and Hartl, D. L. (1988). Maternally inherited transposon excision in *Drosophila simulans*. *Science* **240**, 215–217.

Bryan, G. J., Jacobson, J. W., and Hartl, D. L. (1987). Heritable somatic excision of a *Drosophila* transposon. *Science* **235**, 1636–1638.

Bryan, G. J., Garza, D., and Hartl, D. L. (1990). Insertion and excision of the transposable element mariner in *Drosophila*. *Genetics* **125**, 103–114.

Bucheton, A. (1990). I transposable elements and I–R hybrid dysgenesis in *Drosophila*. *Trends Genet.* **6**, 16–21.

Bucheton, A., Lavige, J. M., Picard, G., and L'Heritier, P. L. (1976). Non-mendelian female sterility in *Drosophila melanogaster:* quantitative variations in the efficiency of inducer and reactive strains. *Heredity* **36**, 305–314.

Bucheton, A., Paro, R., Sang, H. H., Pelisson, A., and Finnegan, D. J. (1984). The molecular basis of I–R hybrid dysgenesis: identification, cloning and properties of the I factor. *Cell* **38**, 153–163.

Campuzano, S., Balcells, L., Villares, R., Carramolino, L., Garcia-Alonso, L., and Modolell, J. (1986). Excess function *Hairy-wing* mutations caused by *gypsy* and *copia* insertions within structural genes of the *achaete-scute* locus of *Drosophila*. *Cell* **44**, 303–312.

Chaboissier, M. C., Busseau, I., Prosser, J., Finnegan, D. J., and Bucheton, A. (1990). Identification of a potential RNA intermediate for transposition of the LINE-like element I factor in *Drosophila melanogaster*. *EMBO J.* **9**, 3557–3563.

Chang, D.-Y., Wisely, B., Huang, S.-M., and Voelker, R. A. (1986). Molecular cloning of *suppressor of sable*, a *Drosophila melanogaster* transposon-mediated suppressor. *Mol. Cell. Biol.* **6**, 1520–1528.

Chia, W., McGill, S., Karp, R., Gubb, D., and Ashburner, M. (1985). Spontaneous excision of a large composite transposable element of *Drosophila melanogaster*. *Nature (London)* **316**, 81–83.

Chia, W., Howes, G., Martin, M., Meng, Y. B., Moses, K., and Tsubota, S. (1986). Molecular analysis of the *yellow* locus of *Drosophila*. *EMBO J.* **5**, 3597–3605.

Chou, T.-B., Zachar, Z., and Bingham, P. M. (1987). Developmental expression of a regulatory gene is programmed at the level of splicing. *EMBO J.* **6**, 4095–4104.

Coen, D. (1990). P element regulatory products enhance *zeste[1]* repression of a P[white[duplicated]] transgene in *Drosophila melanogaster*. *Genetics* **126**, 949–960.

Collins, M., and Rubin, G. M. (1982). Structure of the *Drosophila* mutable allele, *white-crimson* and its *white-ivory* and wild type derivatives. *Cell* **30**, 71–79.

Collins, M., and Rubin, G. M. (1983). High-frequency precise excision of the *Drosophila* foldback transposable element. *Nature (London)* **303**, 259–260.

Collins, M., and Rubin, G. M. (1984). Structure of chromosomal rearrangements induced by the FB transposable element in *Drosophila*. *Nature (London)* **308**, 323–327.

Corbin, V., and Maniatis, T. (1989). Role of transcriptional interference in the *Drosophila melanogaster* Adh promoter switch. *Nature (London)* **337**, 279–282.

Corces, V. G., and Geyer, P. K. (1991). Interactions of retrotransposons with the host genome: The case of the gypsy element of *Drosophila*. *Trends Genet.* **7**, 86–90.

Covey, S. N. (1986). Amino acid sequence homology in *gag* region of reverse transcribing elements and the coat protein of cauliflower mosaic virus. *Nucleic Acids Res.* **14**, 623–633.

Crozatier, M., Vaury, C., Busseau, I., Pélisson, A., and Bucheton, A. (1988). Structure and genomic organization of I elements involved in I–R hybrid dysgenesis in *Drosophila melanogaster*. *Nucleic Acids Res.* **16**, 9199–9213.

Daniels, S. B., McCarron, M., Love, C., and Chovnick, A. (1985). Dysgenesis-induced instability of *rosy* locus transformation in *Drosophila melanogaster:* analysis of excision events and the selective recovery of control element deletions. *Genetics* **109**, 95–117.

Daniels, S. B., Clark, S. H., Kidwell, M. G., and Chovnick, A. (1987). Genetic transformation of *Drosophila melanogaster* with an autonomous P element: phenotypic and molecular analyses of long-established transformed lines. *Genetics* **115**, 711–723.

Daniels, S. B., Chovnick, A., and Boussy, I. A. (1990). Distribution of hobo transposable element in the genus *Drosophila. Mol. Biol. Evol.* **7,** 589–606.

Davison, D., Chapman, C. H., Wedeen, C., and Bingham, P. M. (1985). Genetic and physical studies of a portion of the *white* locus participating in transcriptional regulation and in synapsis-dependent interactions in *Drosophila* adult tissues. *Genetics* **110,** 479–494.

DiNocera, P. P., and Gasari, G. (1987). Related polypeptides are encoded by *Drosophila* F elements, I factors, and mammalian L1 sequences. *Proc. Natl. Acad. Sci. U.S.A.* **84,** 5843–5847.

Doolittle, R. F., Feng, D. F., Johnson, M. S., and McClure, M. A. (1989). Origins and evolutionary relationships of retroviruses. *Q. Rev. Biol.* **64,** 1–30.

Dorsett, D., Viglianti, G. A., Rutledge, B. J., and Meselson, M. (1989). Alteration of *hsp82* gene expression by the gypsy transposon and suppressor genes in *Drosophila melanogaster. Genes Dev.* **3,** 454–468.

Eggleston, W. B., Johnson-Schlitz, D. M., and Engels, W. R. (1988). P–M hybrid dysgenesis does not mobilize other transposable element families in *D. melanogaster. Nature (London)* **331,** 368–370.

Eissenberg, J. C., and Elgin, S. C. R. (1987). *Hsp28^{stl}*: a P-element insertion mutation that alters the expression of a heat shock gene in *Drosophila melanogaster. Genetics* **115,** 333–340.

Engels, W. R. (1979a). Hybrid dysgenesis in *Drosophila melanogaster:* rules of inheritance of female sterility. *Genet. Res.* **33,** 219–236.

Engels, W. R. (1979b). Extrachromosomal control of mutability in *Drosophila melanogaster. Proc. Natl. Acad. Sci. U.S.A.* **76,** 4011–4105.

Engels, W. R. (1983). The P family of transposable elements in *Drosophila. Annu. Rev. Genet.* **17,** 315–344.

Engels, W. R. (1989). P elements in *Drosophila melanogaster. In* "Mobile DNA" (D. E. Berg and M. M. Howe, eds.), pp. 437–484. Am. Soc. Microbiol., Washington, D.C.

Engels, W. R., and Preston, C. R. (1984). Formation of chromosomal rearrangements by P factors in *Drosophila. Genetics* **107,** 657–678.

Engels, W. R., Benz, W. K., Preston, C. R., Graham, P. L., Phillis, R. W., and Robertson, H. M. (1987). Somatic effects of P element activity in *Drosophila melanogaster:* pupal lethality. *Genetics* **117,** 745–757.

Engels, W. R., Johnson-Schlitz, D. M., Eggleston, W. B., and Sved, J. (1990). High-frequency P element loss in *Drosophila* is homolog dependent. *Cell* **62,** 515–525.

Fawcett, D. H., Lister, C. K., Kellett, E., and Finnegan, D. J. (1988). Transposable elements controlling I–R hybrid dysgenesis in *D. melanogaster* are similar to mammalian LINEs. *Cell* **47,** 1007–1015.

Finnegan, D. J. (1989). The I factor and I–R hybrid dysgenesis in *Drosophila melanogaster. In* "Mobile DNA" (D. E. Berg and M. M. Howe, eds.), pp. 503–517. Am. Soc. Microbiol., Washington, D.C.

Finnegan, D. J., and Fawcett, D. H. (1986). Transposable elements in *Drosophila melanogaster. In* "Oxford Surveys in Eukaryotic Genes" (N. Maclean, ed.), Vol. 3, pp. 1–62. Oxford Univ. Press, Oxford.

Flavell, A. J., Ruby, S. W., Toole, J. J., Roberts, B. E., and Rubin, G. M. (1980). Translation and developmental regulation of RNA encoded by the eukaryotic transposable element copia. *Proc. Natl. Acad. Sci. U.S.A.* **77,** 7107–7111.

Flavell, A. J., Alphey, L. S., Ross, S. J., and Leigh Brown, A. J. (1990). Complete reversions of a gypsy retrotransposon-induced *cut* locus mutation in *Drosophila melanogaster* involving jockey transposon insertion and flanking gypsy sequence deletions. *Mol. Gen. Genet.* **220**, 181–185.

Fridell, R. A., Pret, A.-M., and Searles, L. L. (1990). A retrotransposon 412 insertion within an exon of the *Drosophila melanogaster vermilion* gene is spliced from the precursor RNA. *Genes Dev.* **4**, 559–566.

Garza, D., Medhora, M., Koga, A., and Harte, D. (1991). Introduction of the transposable element mariner into the germline of *Drosophile melanogaster*. *Genetics* **128**, 303–310.

Georgiev, P. G., and Gerasimova, T. I. (1989). Novel genes influencing the expression of the *yellow* locus and mdg4 (gypsy) in *Drosophila melanogaster*. *Mol. Gen. Genet.* **220**, 121–126.

Georgiev, P. G., Kiselev, S. L., Simonova, O. B., and Gerasimova, T. I. (1990). A novel transposition system in *Drosophila melanogaster* depending on the Stalker mobile genetic element. *EMBO J.* **9**, 2037–2044.

Gerasimova, T. I., Matjunina, L. V., Mizrokhi, L. J., and Georgiev, G. P. (1985). Successive transposition explosions in *Drosophila melanogaster* and reverse transpositions of mobile genetic elements. *EMBO J.* **4**, 3773–3779.

Geyer, P. K., and Corces, V. G. (1987). Separate regulatory elements are responsible for the complex pattern of tissue-specific and developmental transcription of the *yellow* locus in *Drosophila melanogaster*. *Genes Dev.* **1**, 996–1004.

Geyer, P. K., Green, M. M., and Corces, V. G. (1988a). Reversion of a gypsy-induced mutation at the *yellow* (*y*) locus of *Drosophila melanogaster* is associated with the insertion of a newly defined transposable element. *Proc. Natl. Acad. Sci. U.S.A.* **85**, 3938–3942.

Geyer, P. K., Green, M. M., and Corces, V. G. (1988b). Mutant gene phenotypes mediated by a *Drosophila melanogaster* retrotransposon require sequences homologous to mammalian enhancers. *Proc. Natl. Acad. Sci. U.S.A.* **85**, 8593–8597.

Geyer, P. K., Richardson, K. L., Corces, V. G., and Green, M. M. (1988c). Genetic instability in *Drosophila melanogaster:* P-element mutagenesis by gene conversion. *Proc. Natl. Acad. Sci. U.S.A.* **85**, 6455–6459.

Geyer, P. K., Green, M. M., and Corces, V. G. (1990). Tissue-specific transcriptional enhancers may act in *trans* on the gene located in the homologous chromosome: the molecular basis of transvection in *Drosophila*. *EMBO J.* **9**, 2247–2256.

Geyer, P. K., Chien, A. J., Corces, V. G., and Green, M. M. (1991). Mutations in the *su(s)* gene affect RNA processing in *Drosophile melanogaster*. *Proc. Natl. Acad. Sci. U.S.A.* **88**, 7116–7120.

Goldberg, M. J., Paro, R., and Gehring, W. J. (1982). Molecular cloning of the *white* locus of *Drosophila melanogaster* using a large transposable element. *EMBO J.* **1**, 93–98.

Green, M. M. (1967). The genetics of a mutable gene at the *white* locus of *Drosophila melanogaster*. *Genetics* **56**, 467–482.

Green, M. M. (1977). Genetic instability in *Drosophila melanogaster:* de novo induction of putative insertion mutations. *Proc. Natl. Acad. Sci. U.S.A.* **74**, 3490–3493.

Gubb, D., Roote, J., Harrington, G., McGill, S., Durrant, B., Shelton, M., and Ashburner, M. (1985). A preliminary analysis of TE146, a very large transposing element of *Drosophila melanogaster*. *Chromosoma* **92**, 116–123.

Hansen, L. J., Chalker, D. L., and Sandmeyer, S. B. (1988). Ty3, a yeast tRNA-gene associated retrotransposon, has homology to animal retroviruses. *Mol. Cell. Biol.* **8**, 5245–5256.

Harden, N., and Ashburner, M. (1990). Characterization of the FB–NOF transposable element of *Drosophila melanogaster*. *Genetics* **126**, 387–400.

Hartl, D. L. (1989). Transposable element mariner in *Drosophila* species. *In* "Mobile DNA" (D. E. Berg and M. M. Howe, eds.), pp. 531–536. Am. Soc. Microbiol., Washington, D.C.

Hatzopoulos, P., Monastirioti, M., Yannopoulos, G., and Louis, C. (1987). The instability of the TE-like mutation Dp(2;2)GYL of *Drosophila melanogaster* is intimately associated with the hobo element. *EMBO J.* **6**, 3091–3096.

Haymer, D. S., and Marsh, J. L. (1986). Germ line and somatic instability of a *white* mutation in *Drosophila mauritiana* due to a transposable element. *Dev. Genet.* **6**, 281–291.

Hinton, C. W. (1984). Morphogenetically specific mutability in *Drosophila ananassae*. *Genetics* **106**, 631–653.

Hinton, C. W. (1988). Formal relations between *Om* mutants and their suppressors in *Drosophila ananassae*. *Genetics* **120**, 1035–1042.

Hope, I. A., Mahadevan, S., and Struhl, K. (1988). Structural and functional characterization of the short acidic transcriptional activation region of yeast GCN4 protein. *Nature (London)* **333**, 635–640.

Howes, G., O'Connor, M., and Chia, W. (1988). On the specificity and effects on transcription of P-element insertions at the *yellow* locus of *Drosophila melanogaster*. *Nucleic Acids Res.* **16**, 3039–3052.

Huijser, P., Kirchhoff, C., Lankenau, D.-H., and Hennig, W. (1988). Retrotransposon-like sequences are expressed in Y chromosomal lampbrush loops of *Drosophila hydei*. *J. Mol. Biol.* **203**, 689–697.

Inouye, S., Yuki, S., and Saigo, K. (1984). Sequence-specific insertion of the *Drosophila* transposable element 17.6. *Nature (London)* **310**, 332–333.

Inouye, S., Yuki, S., and Saigo, K. (1986). Complete nucleotide sequence and genome organization of a *Drosophila* transposable genetic element, 297. *Eur. J. Biochem.* **154**, 417–425.

Ising, G., and Block, K. (1981). Derivation-dependent distribution of insertion sites for a *Drosophila* transposon. *Cold Spring Harbor Symp. Quant. Biol.* **45**, 527–549.

Ising, G., and Ramel, C. (1976). The behavior of a transposable element in *Drosophila melanogaster*. *In* "The Genetics and Biology of Drosophila" (M. Ashburner and E. Novitski, eds.), Vol. 1B, pp. 947–954. Academic Press, New York.

Jacobson, J. W., and Hartl, D. L. (1985). Coupled instability of two X-linked genes in *Drosophila mauritiana:* germinal and somatic instability. *Genetics* **111**, 57–65.

Jacobson, J. W., Medhora, M. M., and Hartl, D. L. (1986). Molecular structure of a somatically unstable transposable element in *Drosophila*. *Proc. Natl. Acad. Sci. U.S.A.* **83**, 8684–8688.

Jarrell, K. A., and Meselson, M. M. (1991). *Drosophila* retrotransposon promoter includes an essential sequence at the initiation site and requires a downstream sequence for full activity. *Proc. Natl. Acad. Sci. U.S.A.* **88**, 102–104.

Jenkins, N. A., Copeland, N. G., Taylor, B. A., and Lee, B. K. (1981). Dilute (*d*) coat color mutation of DBA/2J mice is associated with the site of integration of an ecotropic MuLV genome. *Nature (London)* **293**, 370–374.

Johnson, M. S., McClure, M. A., Feng, D.-F., Gray, J., and Doolittle, R. F. (1986). Computer analysis of retroviral *pol* genes: assignment of enzymatic functions to specific sequences and homologies with nonviral enzymes. *Proc. Natl. Acad. Sci. U.S.A.* **83**, 7648–7652.

Johnson-Schlitz, D., and Lim, J. K. (1987). Cytogenetics of *Notch* mutations arising in the unstable X chromosome Uc of *Drosophila melanogaster*. *Genetics* **115**, 701–709.

Karess, R. E., and Rubin, G. M. (1982). A small tandem duplication is responsible for the unstable *white-ivory* mutation in *Drosophila*. *Cell* **30**, 63–69.

Karess, R. E., and Rubin, G. M. (1984). Analysis of P transposable element functions in *Drosophila*. *Cell* **38**, 135–146.

Karlik, C. C., and Fyrberg, E. A. (1985). An insertion within a variably spliced *Drosophila* tropomyosin gene blocks accumulation of only one encoded isoform. *Cell* **41**, 57–66.

Kaufman, P. K., Doll, R. F., and Rio, D. C. (1989). *Drosophila* P element transposase recognizes internal P element DNA sequences. *Cell* **59**, 359–371.

Kazazian, H. H., Jr., Wong, C., Youssoufian, H., Scott, A. F., Phillips, D. G., and Antonarakis, S. E. (1988). Haemophilia A resulting from de novo insertion of L1 sequences represents a novel mechanism for mutation in man. *Nature (London)* **332**, 164–166.

Kelley, M. R., Kidd, S., Berg, R. L., and Young, M. W. (1987). Restriction of P element insertions at the *Notch* locus of *Drosophila melanogaster*. *Mol. Cell. Biol.* **7**, 1545–1548.

Kidd, S., and Young, M. W. (1986). Transposon-dependent mutant phenotypes at the *Notch* locus of *Drosophila*. *Nature (London)* **323**, 89–91.

Kidwell, M. G. (1981). Hybrid dysgenesis in *Drosophila melanogaster:* the genetics of cytotype determination in a neutral strain. *Genetics* **98**, 275–290.

Kidwell, M. G. (1983). Evolution of hybrid dysgenesis determinants in *Drosophila melanogaster*. *Proc. Natl. Acad. Sci. U.S.A.* **80**, 1655–1659.

Kidwell, M. G. (1985). Hybrid dysgenesis in *Drosophila melanogaster:* nature and inheritance of P element regulation. *Genetics* **111**, 337–350.

Kidwell, M. G., Kidwell, J. F., and Sved, J. A. (1977). Hybrid dysgenesis in *Drosophila melanogaster:* a syndrome of aberrant traits including mutation, sterility and male recombination. *Genetics* **86**, 813–833.

Kidwell, M. G., Novy, J. B., and Feeley, S. M. (1981). Rapid unidirectional change of hybrid dysgenesis potential in *Drosophila*. *J. Hered.* **72**, 32–38.

Kim, A. I., Belyaeva, E. S., and Aslanian, M. M. (1990). Autonomous transposition of gypsy mobile elements and genetic instability in *Drosophila melanogaster*. *Mol. Gen. Genet.* **224**, 303–308.

Klug, A., and Rhodes, D. (1987). "Zinc fingers": a novel protein motif for nucleic acid recognition. *Trends Biochem. Sci.* **12**, 464–469.

Landschulz, W. H., Johnston, P. F., and McKnight, S. L. (1988). The leucine zipper: a hypothetical structure common to a new class of DNA binding proteins. *Science* **240**, 1759–1764.

Laski, F. A., and Rubin, G. M. (1989). Analysis of *cis*-acting requirements for germ-line-specific splicing of the P element ORF2–ORF3 intron. *Genes Dev.* **3**, 720–728.

Laski, F. A., Rio, D. C., and Rubin, G. M. (1986). Tissue specificity of *Drosophila* P element transposition is regulated at the level of mRNA splicing. *Cell* **44**, 7–19.

Laverty, T. R., and Lim, J. K. (1982). Site-specific instability in *Drosophila melanogaster:* evidence for transposition of destabilizing element. *Genetics* **101**, 461–476.

Leigh Brown, A. J., Ross, A. J., Alphey, L. S., Flavell, A. J., and Gerasimova, T. I. (1989). Instability in the ct^{mr2} strain of *Drosophila melanogaster:* role of P element functions and structure of revertants. *Mol. Gen. Genet.* **218**, 208–213.

Levis, R., and Rubin, G. M. (1982). The unstable w^{DZL} mutation of *Drosophila* is caused by a 13 kb insertion that is imprecisely excised in revertants. *Cell* **30**, 543–550.

Levis, R., Collins, M., and Rubin, G. M. (1982). FB elements are the common basis for the instability of the w^{DZL} and w^c *Drosophila* mutations. *Cell* **30**, 551–565.

Levis, R., O'Hare, K., and Rubin, G. M. (1984). Effects of transposable element insertions on RNA encoded by the *white* gene of *Drosophila*. *Cell* **38**, 471–481.

Lewis, A. P., and Brookfield, J. F. Y. (1987). Movement of *Drosophila melanogaster* transposable elements other than P elements in a P–M dysgenic cross. *Mol. Gen. Genet.* **208**, 506–410.

Lewis, E. B. (1954). The theory and application of a new method of detecting chromosomal rearrangements in *Drosophila melanogaster*. *Am. Nat.* **88**, 225–239.

Lim, J. K. (1979). Site-specific instability in *Drosophila melanogaster:* the origin of the mutation and cytogenetic evidence for transposable elements. *Genetics* **93**, 681–701.

Lim, J. K. (1981). Site-specific instability in *Drosophila melanogaster:* cytogenetic evidence for transposable elements. *Cold Spring Harbor Symp. Quant. Biol.* **45**, 553–560.

Lim, J. K. (1988). Intrachromosomal rearrangements mediated by hobo transposons in *Drosophila melanogaster*. *Proc. Natl. Acad. Sci. U.S.A.* **85**, 9153–9157.

Lim, J. K., Simmons, M. J., Raymond, J. D., Cox, N. M., Doll, R. F., and Culbert, T. P. (1983). Homologue destabilization by a putative transposable element in *Drosophila melanogaster Proc. Natl. Acad. Sci. U.S.A.* **80**, 6624–6627.

Markopoulou, K., Welshons, W. J., and Artavanis-Tsakonas, S. (1989). Phenotypic and molecular analysis of the *facets,* a group of intronic mutations at the *Notch* locus of *Drosophila melanogaster* which affect postembryonic development. *Genetics* **122**, 417–428.

Marlor, R. L., Parkhurst, S. M., and Corces, V. G. (1986). The *Drosophila melanogaster* gypsy transposable element encodes putative gene products homologous to retroviral proteins. *Mol. Cell. Biol.* **6**, 1129–1134.

Mattox, W. W., and Davidson, N. (1984). Isolation and characterization of the *Beadex* locus of *Drosophila melanogaster:* a putative *cis*-acting negative regulatory element for the *heldup-a* gene. *Mol. Cell. Biol.* **4**, 1343–1353.

Mazo, A. M., Mizrokhi, L. J., Karavanov, A. A., Sedkov, Y. A., Krichevskaya, A. A., and Ilyin, Y. V. (1989). Suppression in *Drosophila:* su(Hw) and su(f) gene products interact with a region of mdg4 (gypsy) regulating its transcriptional activity. *EMBO J.* **8**, 903–911.

McGinnis, W., Shermoen, A. W., and Beckendorf, S. K. (1983). A transposable element inserted just 5′ to a *Drosophila* glue protein gene alters gene expression and chromatin structure. *Cell* **34**, 75–84.

Medhora, M. M., MacPeek, A. H., and Hartl, D. L. (1988). Excision of the *Drosophila* transposable element mariner: identification and characterization of the *Mos* factor. *EMBO J.* **7**, 2185–2189.

Mével-Ninio, M., Mariol, M.-C., and Gans, M. (1989). Mobilization of the gypsy and copia retrotransposons in *Drosophila melanogaster* induces reversion of the ovo^D dominant female-sterile mutations: molecular analysis of revertant alleles. *EMBO J.* **8**, 1549–1558.

Miller, K., Rosenbaum, J., Zbrzezna, V., and Pogo, A. O. (1989). The nucleotide sequence of *Drosophila melanogaster* copia-specific 2.1 kb mRNA. *Nucleic Acids Res.* **11**, 2134.

Misra, S., and Rio, D. C. (1990). Cytotype control of P element transposition: the 66 kd protein is a repressor of transposase activity. *Cell* **62**, 269–284.

Mizrokhi, L. J., and Mazo, A. M. (1990). Evidence for horizontal transmission of the mobile element jockey between distant *Drosophila* species. *Proc. Natl. Acad. Sci. U.S.A.* **87**, 9216–9220.

Mizrokhi, L. J., Obolenkova, L. A., Priimagi, A. F., Ilyin, Y. V., Gerasimova, T. I., and Georgiev, G. P. (1985). The nature of unstable insertion mutations and reversion in the locus *cut* of *Drosophila melanogaster:* molecular mechanisms of transposition memory. *EMBO J.* **4**, 3781–3787.

Mizrokhi, L. J., Georgieva, S. G., and Ilyin, Y. V. (1988). Jockey, a mobile *Drosophila* element similar to mammalian LINEs, is transcribed from the internal promoter by RNA polymerase II. *Cell* **54**, 685–691.

Modolell, J., Bender, W., and Meselson, M. (1983). *D. melanogaster* mutations suppressible by the *suppressor of Hairy-wing* are insertions of a 7.3 kb mobile element. *Proc. Natl. Acad. Sci. U.S.A.* **80,** 1678–1682.

Morse, B., Rotherg, P. G., South, V. J., Spandorfer, J. M., and Astrin, S. M. (1988). Insertional mutagenesis of the myc locus by a LINE-1 sequence in a human breast carcinoma. *Nature (London)* **333,** 87–90.

Mount, S. M., and Rubin, G. M. (1985). Complete nucleotide sequence of the *Drosophila* transposable element copia: homology between copia and retroviral proteins. *Mol. Cell. Biol.* **5,** 1630–1638.

Mount, S. M., Green, M. M., and Rubin, G. M. (1988). Partial revertants of the transposable element-associated suppressible allele *white-apricot* in *Drosophila melanogaster:* structures and responsiveness to genetic modifiers. *Genetics* **118,** 221–234.

Müller, H.-P., Sogo, J. M., and Schaffner, W. (1989). An enhancer stimulates transcription in *trans* when attached to the promoter via a protein bridge. *Cell* **58,** 767–777.

Mullins, M. C., Rio, D. C., and Rubin, G. M. (1989). *Cis*-acting DNA sequence requirements for P-element transposition. *Genes Dev.* **3,** 729–738.

Nitasaka, E., Mukai, T., and Yamazaki, T. (1987). Repressor of P elements in *Drosophila melanogaster:* cytotype determination by a defective P element with only open reading frames 0 through 2. *Proc. Natl. Acad. Sci. U.S.A.* **84,** 7605–7608.

O'Hare, K., and Rubin, G. M. (1983). Structures of P transposable elements and their sites of insertion and excision in the *Drosophila melanogaster* genome. *Cell* **34,** 25–35.

O'Hare, K., Murphy, C., Levis, R., and Rubin, G. M. (1984). DNA sequence of the *white* locus in *Drosophila melanogaster. J. Mol. Biol.* **180,** 437–455.

Parkhurst, S. M., and Corces, V. G. (1985). *forked,* gypsys, and suppressors in *Drosophila. Cell* **41,** 429–437.

Parkhurst, S. M., and Corces, V. G. (1986a). Interactions among the gypsy transposable element and the *yellow* and the *suppressor of Hairy wing* loci in *Drosophila melanogaster. Mol. Cell. Biol.* **6,** 47–53.

Parkhurst, S. M., and Corces, V. G. (1986b). Retroviral elements and suppressor genes in *Drosophila. BioEssays* **5,** 52–57.

Parkhurst, S. M., and Corces, V. G. (1987). Developmental expression of *Drosophila melanogaster* retrovirus-like transposable elements. *EMBO J.* **6,** 419–424.

Parkhurst, S. M., Harrison, D. A., Remington, M. P., Spana, C., Kelley, R. L., Coyne, R. S., and Corces, V. G. (1988). The *Drosophila su(Hw)* gene, which controls the phenotypic effect of the gypsy transposable element, encodes a putative DNA binding protein. *Genes Dev.* **2,** 1205–1215.

Paro, R., Goldberg, M. L., and Gehring, W. J. (1983). Molecular analysis of large transposable elements carrying the *white* locus of *Drosophila melanogaster. EMBO J.* **2,** 853–860.

Peifer, M., and Bender, W. (1986). The *anterobithorax* mutations of the *bithorax* complex. *EMBO J.* **5,** 2293–2303.

Peifer, M., and Bender, W. (1988). Sequences of the gypsy transposon of *Drosophila* necessary for its effects on adjacent genes. *Proc. Natl. Acad. Sci. U.S.A.* **85,** 9650–9654.

Pélisson, A., Finnegan, D. J., and Bucheton, A. (1991). Evidence for retrotransposition of the I factor, a LINE element of *Drosophila melanogaster. Proc. Natl. Acad. Sci. U.S.A.* **88,** 4907–4910.

Peng, X., and Mount, S. M. (1990). Characterization of teh *Enhancer-of-white apricot* in *Drosophila melanogaster. Genetics* **126,** 1061–1069.

Posakony, J. W., Fischer, J. A., and Maniatis, T. (1985). Identification of DNA sequences required for the regulation of *Drosophila alcohol dehydrogenase* gene expression. *Cold Spring Harbor Symp. Quant. Biol.* 50, 515–520.

Potter, S. S. (1982a). DNA sequence of a foldback transposable element in *Drosophila*. *Nature (London)* 297, 201–204.

Potter, S. S. (1982b). DNA sequence analysis of a *Drosophila* foldback transposable element rearrangement. *Mol. Gen. Genet.* 188, 107–110.

Potter, S. S., Truett, M., Philips, M., and Maher, A. (1980). Eucaryotic transposable elements with inverted terminal repeats. *Cell* 20, 639–647.

Rabinow, L., and Birchler, J. A. (1989). A dosage-sensitive modifier of retrotransposon-induced alleles of the *Drosophila white* locus. *EMBO J.* 8, 879–889.

Rasmusson, K. E., Simmons, M. J., Raymond, J. D., and McLarnon, C. F. (1990). Quantitative effects of P elements on hybrid dysgenesis in *Drosophila melanogaster*. *Genetics* 124, 647–662.

Rio, D. C., and Rubin, G. M. (1988). Identification and purification of a *Drosophila* protein that binds to the terminal 31-base-pair inverted repeats of the P transposable element. *Proc. Natl. Acad. Sci. U.S.A.* 85, 8929–8933.

Rio, D. C., Laski, F. A., and Rubin, G. M. (1986). Identification and immunochemical analysis of biologically active *Drosophila* P element transposase. *Cell* 44, 21–32.

Robertson, H. M., and Engels, W. R. (1989). Modified P elements that mimic the P cytotype in *Drosophila melanogaster*. *Genetics* 123, 815–824.

Robertson, H. M., Preston, C. R., Phillis, R. W., Johnson-Schlitz, D., Benz, W. K., and Engels, W. R. (1988). A stable genomic source of P element transposase in *Drosophila melanogaster*. *Genetics* 118, 461–470.

Roiha, H., Rubin, G. M., and O'Hare, K. (1988). P element insertions and rearrangements at the *singed* locus of *Drosophila melanogaster*. *Genetics* 119, 75–83.

Rosales, R., Vigneron, M., Macchi, M., Davidson, I., Xiao, J. H., and Chambon, P. (1987). *In vitro* binding of cell-specific and ubiquitous nuclear proteins to the octamer motif of the SV40 enhancer and related motifs present in other promoters and enhancers. *EMBO J.* 6, 3015–3025.

Rubin, G. M., and Spradling, A. C. (1982). Genetic transformation of *Drosophila* with transposable element vectors. *Science* 218, 348–353.

Rubin, G. M., Kidwell, M. G., and Bingham, P. M. (1982). The molecular basis of P–M hybrid dysgenesis: the nature of induced mutations. *Cell* 29, 987–994.

Rutledge, B. J., Mortin, M. A., Schwarz, E., Thierry-Mieg, D., and Meselson, M. (1988). Genetic interactions of modifier genes and modifiable alleles in *Drosophila melanogaster*. *Genetics* 119, 391–397.

Saigo, K., Kugimiya, W., Matsuo, Y., Inouye, S., Yoshioka, K., and Yuki, S. (1984). Identification of the coding sequence for a reverse transcriptase-like enzyme in a transposable genetic element in *Drosophila melanogaster*. *Nature (London)* 312, 659–661.

Salz, H. K., Cline, T. W., and Schedl, P. (1987). Functional changes associated with structural alterations induced by mobilization of a P element inserted in the *Sex-lethal* gene of *Drosophila*. *Genetics* 117, 221–231.

Savakis, C., and Ashburner, M. (1985). A simple gene with a complex pattern of transcription: the *alcohol dehydrogenase* gene in *Drosophila melanogaster*. *Cold Spring Harbor Symp. Quant. Biol.* 50, 505–514.

Scheinker, V. S., Lozovskaya, E. R., Bishop, J. G., Corces, V. G., and Evgen'ev, M. B. (1990). A long terminal repeat-containing retrotransposon is mobilized during hybrid dysgenesis in *Drosophila virilis*. *Proc. Natl. Acad. Sci. U.S.A.* 87, 9615–9619.

Schwartz, H. E., Lockett, T. J., and Young, M. W. (1982). Analysis of transcripts from two families of nomadic DNA. *J. Mol. Biol.* **157**, 49–68.

Scott, M. P., Weiner, A. J., Hazelrigg, T. F., Polisky, B. A., Pirrotta, V., Scalenghe, F., and Kaufman, T. C. (1983). The molecular organization of *Antennapedia* locus of *Drosophila*. *Cell* **35**, 763–776.

Searles, L. L., and Voelker, R. A. (1986). Molecular characterization of the *Drosophila* *vermilion* locus and its suppressible alleles. *Proc. Natl. Acad. Sci. U.S.A.* **83**, 404–408.

Searles, L. L., Greenleaf, A., Kemp, W. E., and Voelker, R. A. (1986). Sites of P element insertion and structures of P element deletions in the 5′ region of *Drosophila melanogaster RpII215*. *Mol. Cell. Biol.* **6**, 3312–3319.

Searles, L. L., Ruth, R. S., Pret, A.-M., Fridell, R., and Ali, A. J. (1990). Structure and transcription of the *Drosophila melanogaster vermillion* gene and several mutant alleles. *Mol. Cell. Biol.* **10**, 1423–1431.

Shiba, T., and Saigo, K. (1983). Retrovirus-like particles containing RNA homologous to the transposable element copia in *Drosophila melanogaster*. *Nature (London)* **302**, 119–124.

Shrimpton, A. E., Montgomery, E. A., and Langley, C. H. (1986). *Om* mutations in *Drosophila ananassae* are linked to insertions of a transposable element. *Genetics* **114**, 125–135.

Siebel, C. W., and Rio, D. C. (1990). Regulated splicing of the *Drosophila* P transposable element third intron *in vitro:* somatic repression. *Science* **248**, 1200–1208.

Silber, J., Bazin, C., Lemeunier, F., Aulard, S., and Volovitch, M. (1989). Distribution and conservation of the foldback transposable element in *Drosophila melanogaster*. *J. Mol. Evol.* **28**, 220–224.

Simmons, M. J., and Bucholz, L. M. (1985). Transposase titration in *Drosophila melanogaster:* a model of cytotype in the P–M system of hybrid dysgenesis. *Proc. Natl. Acad. Sci. U.S.A.* **82**, 8119–8123.

Simmons, M. J., Raymond, J. D., Culbert, T., and Laverty, T. (1984). Analysis of dysgenesis-induced lethal mutations on the X chromosome of a Q strain of *Drosophila melanogaster*. *Genetics* **107**, 49–63.

Simmons, M. J., Raymond, J. D., Rasmusson, K. E., Miller, L. M., McLarnon, C. F., and Zunt, J. R. (1990). Repression of P element-mediated hybrid dysgenesis in *Drosophila melanogaster*. *Genetics* **124**, 663–676.

Simonelig, M. C., Bazin, C., Péllisson, A., and Bucheton, A. (1988). Transposable and non-transposable elements homologous to the I factor involved in I–R hybrid dysgenesis in *Drosophila melanogaster* coexist in various *Drosophila* species. *Proc. Natl. Acad. Sci. U.S.A.* **85**, 1141–1145.

Snyder, M. P., Kimbrell, D., Hunkapiller, M., Hill, R., Fristrom, J. and Davidson, N. (1982). A transposable element that splits the promoter region inactivates a *Drosophila* cuticle protein gene. *Proc. Natl. Acad. Sci. U.S.A.* **79**, 7430–7434.

Spana, C., and Corces, V. G. (1990). DNA bending is a determinant of binding specificity for a *Drosophila* zinc finger protein. *Genes Dev.* **4**, 1505–1515.

Spana, C., Harrison, D. A., and Corces, V. G. (1988). The *Drosophila melanogaster suppressor of Hairy-wing* protein binds to specific sequences of the gypsy retrotransposon. *Genes Dev.* **2**, 1414–1423.

Spradling, A. C. (1986). P element-mediated transformation. *In Drosophila:* A Practical Approach" (D. B. Roberts, ed.), pp. 175–197. IRL Press, Oxford.

Spradling, A. C., and Rubin, G. M. (1982). Transposition of cloned P elements into *Drosophila* germ line chromosomes. *Science* **218**, 341–347.

Stoye, J. P., Fenner, S., Greenoak, G. E., Moran, C., and Coffin, J. M. (1988). Role of endogenous retroviruses as mutagens: the *hairless* mutation of mice. *Cell* **54**, 383–391.

Strand, D. J., and McDonald, J. F. (1989). Insertion of a copia element 5′ to the *Drosophila melanogaster* alcohol dehydrogenase gene (*adh*) is associated with altered developmental and tissue-specific patterns of expression. *Genetics* **121**, 787–794.

Streck, R. D., MacGaffey, J. E., and Beckendorf, S. K. (1986). The structure of hobo transposable elements and their insertion sites. *EMBO J.* **5**, 3615–3623.

Sved, J. A. (1987). Hybrid dysgenesis in *Drosophila melanogaster:* evidence from sterility and Southern hybridization that P cytotype is not maintained in the absence of chromosomal P factors. *Genetics* **115**, 121–127.

Swaroop, A., Paco-Larson, M. E., and Garen, A. (1985). Molecular genetics of a transposon-induced dominant mutation in the *Drosophila glued* locus. *Proc. Natl. Acad. Sci. U.S.A.* **82**, 1751–1755.

Tanda, S., and Corces, V. G. (1991). Retrotransposon-induced overexpression of a homeobox gene causes defects in eye morphogenesis in *Drosophila. EMBO J.* **10**, 407–417.

Tanda, S., Shrimpton, A. E., Ling-Ling, C., Itayama, H., Matsubayashi, H., Saigo, K., Tobari, Y. N., and Langley, C. H. (1988). Retrovirus-like features and site specific insertions of a transposable element, tom, in *Drosophila ananassae. Mol. Gen. Genet.* **214**, 405–411.

Tanda, S., Shrimpton, A. E., Hinton, C. W., and Langley, C. H. (1989). Analysis of the *Om(1D)* locus in *Drosophila ananassae. Genetics* **123**, 495–502.

Templeton, N. S., and Potter, S. S. (1989). Complete foldback elements encode a novel protein found in *Drosophila melanogaster. EMBO J.* **8**, 1887–1894.

Truett, M. A., Jones, R. S., and Potter, S. S. (1981). Unusual structure of the FB family of transposable elements in *Drosophila. Cell* **24**, 753–763.

Tsubota, S., and Schedl, P. (1986). Hybrid dysgenesis-induced revertants of insertions at the 5′ end of the *rudimentary* gene in *Drosophila melanogaster:* transposon-induced control mutations. *Genetics* **114**, 165–182.

Tsubota, S., Ashburner, M., and Schedl, P. (1985). P element induced control mutations at the *r* gene of *Drosophila melanogaster. Mol. Cell. Biol.* **5**, 2567–2574.

Voelker, R. A., Greenleaf, A. L., Gyurkovics, H., Wisely, G. B., Huang, S.-M., and Searles, L. L. (1984). Frequent imprecise excision among reversions of a P element-caused lethal mutation in *Drosophila. Genetics* **107**, 279–294.

Voelker, R. A., Graves, J., Gibson, W., and Eisenberg, M. (1990). Mobile element insertions causing mutations in the *Drosophila suppressor of sable* locus occur in DNase I hypersensitive subregions of 5′-transcribed nontranslated sequences. *Genetics* **126**, 1071–1082.

Voelker, R. A., Gibson, Graves, J. P., Sterling, J. F., and Eisenberg, M. T. (1991). The *Drosophila suppressor of sable* gene encodes a polypeptide with regions similar to those of RNA-binding proteins. *Mol. Cell. Biol.* **11**, 894–905.

Weiner, A. M., Deininger, P. L., and Efstratiadis, A. (1986). Nonviral retroposons: genes, pseudogenes, and transposable elements generated by the reverse flow of genetic information. *Annu. Rev. Biochem.* **55**, 631–661.

Williams, J. A., Pappu, S. S., and Bell, J. B. (1988a). Molecular analysis of hybrid dysgenesis-induced derivatives of a P element allele at the *vg* locus. *Mol. Cell. Biol.* **8**, 1489–1497.

Williams, J. A., Pappu, S. S., and Bell, J. B. (1988b). Suppressible P element alleles of the *vestigial* locus in *Drosophila melanogaster. Mol. Gen. Genet.* **212**, 370–374.

Woodruff, R. C., Blount, J. L., and Thompson, J. N., Jr. (1987). Hybrid dysgenesis in *D. melanogaster* is not a general release mechanism for DNA transposition. *Science* **237**, 1206–1207.

Yannopoulos, G., Zacharopoulou, A., and Stamatis, N. (1982). Unstable chromosome rearrangements associated with male recombination in *Drosophila melanogaster*. *Mutat. Res.* **96**, 41–51.

Yannopoulos, G., Stamatis, N., Zacharopoulou, A., and Pelecanos, M. (1983a). Differences in the induction of specific deletions and duplications by two male recombination factors isolated from the same *Drosophila* natural population. *Mutat. Res.* **83**, 383–393.

Yannopoulos, G., Stamatis, N., Zacharopoulou, A., and Pelecanos, M. (1983b). Site specific breaks induced by the male recombination factor 23.5MRF in *Drosophila melanogaster*. *Mutat. Res.* **108**, 185–202.

Yannopoulos, G., Stamatis, N., Monastirioti, M., Hatzopoulos, P., and Louis, C. (1987). hobo is responsible for the induction of hybrid dysgenesis by strains of *Drosophila melanogaster* bearing the male recombination factor 23.5MRF. *Cell* **49**, 487–495.

Yoshioka, K., Honma, H., Zishi, M., Kondo, S., Togashi, S., Miyake, T., and Shiba, T. (1990). Virus-like particle formation of *Drosophila* copia through autocatalytic processing. *EMBO J.* **9**, 535–541.

Yuki, S., Inouye, S., Ishimaru, S., and Saigo, K. (1986). Nucleotide sequence characterization of a *Drosophila* retrotransposon 412 element. *Eur. J. Biochem.* **158**, 4033–410.

Zachar, Z., and Bingham, P. M. (1982). Regulation of *white* locus expression: the structure of mutant alleles at the *white* locus of *Drosophila melanogaster*. *Cell* **30**, 529–541.

Zachar, Z., Davison, D., Garza, D., and Bingham, P. M. (1985a). A detailed developmental and structural study of the transcriptional effects of insertion of the copia transposon into the *white* locus of *Drosophila melanogaster*. *Genetics* **111**, 495–515.

Zachar, Z., Chapman, C. H., and Bingham, P. M. (1985b). On the molecular basis of transvection effects and the regulation of transcription. *Cold Spring Harbor Symp. Quant. Biol.* **50**, 337–346.

Zachar, Z., Chou, T.-B., and Bingham, P. M. (1987). Evidence that a regulatory gene autoregulates splicing of its transcript. *EMBO J.* **6**, 4105–4111.

THE GENETICS AND MOLECULAR BIOLOGY OF zeste IN Drosophila melanogaster

Vincenzo Pirrotta

Department of Cell Biology, Baylor College of Medicine, Texas Medical Center, Houston, Texas 77030

ADVANCES IN GENETICS, Vol. 29

I. Introduction

The reductionist approach of molecular biology frequently leads us to consider genes as isolated entities and to overlook the fact that they are embedded in a much larger DNA molecule complexly organized in a chromosome that may interact with other parts of the genome, with other nuclear structures, and with a large variety of proteins. The phenomena discussed in this review indicate that the behavior of a gene can depend on its arrangement with respect to other chromosomes or chromosome regions within the nucleus. Molecular analysis has shown that a given transcriptional unit may overlap with other transcriptional units and may contain or be contained within other units transcribed in the same or in the opposite direction and expressed at different times or in different tissues. The information required for transcriptional control resides in regulatory sequences that may be located in the 5' flanking sequences, sometimes at considerable distances upstream, but may also be found within the transcribed region or even downstream from it. The regulatory regions of many developmentally important genes in *Drosophila* can be exceedingly complex and may extend for many tens of kilobases beyond the transcriptional unit. We know little or nothing about the mechanisms that allow factors bound at such distant regulatory sequences to affect RNA polymerase bound at the promoter site. Even less is understood about the converse: how neighboring or even overlapping genes obey their own regulatory elements with little apparent interference from their neighbors. The study of the *zeste* gene and of the processes in which it takes part has given a glimpse of what some of these mechanisms might be. In this review I have not attempted to discuss all aspects of transvection, chromatin domains, matrix attachment, etc., all topics that would require lengthy reviews of their own. I have concentrated instead on those features that have a bearing on the genetic and molecular interactions of *zeste*.

II. The Discovery of *zeste*

The *zeste* gene came to light as a result of two very different and independent lines of research: E. B. Lewis' discovery of the phenomenon that he called transvection while studying the genetics of the bithorax complex (BX-C) and the finding by M. Gans of a mutation affecting eye color, which she called *zeste*. These discoveries were taking place at the same time although they were separated by an ocean and a continent.

A. EFFECTS AT THE *bithorax* LOCUS

While analyzing rearrangements in the BX-C, Lewis (1954) found that the mutant phenotypes of certain *bithorax* alleles were strongly enhanced when heterozygous for chromosomal rearrangements affecting the complex, especially many of those with a break between the centromere and the BX-C locus, on the right arm of the third chromosome. He interpreted this effect, which he called transvection, as implying that the two homologous copies of the BX-C were expressed differently if they were able to pair physically than if the pairing was inhibited by the chromosomal rearrangement. The physical pairing of homologous chromosomes in somatic cells of *Drosophila* and other dipteran insects had been known from the early days of cytological analysis. Lewis' observation suggested that this pairing might have a functional significance and he proposed that it might affect gene expression by allowing the transport of some gene product from one copy of the BX-C to the other copy. Lewis found the transvection phenomenon useful because the enhancement of the phenotype was a selective indicator for detecting breakpoints of rearrangements that he needed to analyze the structure of the BX-C. In the course of this analysis he found that one rearrangement that gave the phenotypic enhancement was exceptional in that it affected not the third but the X chromosome and was due to a small inversion with breakpoints at 4F and 3A. This suggested the existence of a gene function that was required for the higher activity of paired copies of the BX-C and whose lack had the same effect as the rearrangements that prevented pairing. Lewis named this mutation *enhancer of bithorax, e(bx)*. A point mutation that had the same effect, $e(bx)^2$, was later shown by Lewis to map near the proximal breakpoint of the *e(bx)* inversion, at position 3A on the X chromosome.

B. EFFECTS AT THE *white* GENE

An apparently unrelated line of experiments by Gans (1953) characterized a mutation mapping at 3A3 on the X chromosome, which caused a great reduction in eye pigmentation, resulting in a lemon-yellow eye instead of the wild-type red. The mutation, called *zeste* (or lemon peel), affected eye pigmentation only in females. In a series of elegant experiments, Gans showed that this sex specificity was not caused by hormonal factors or by the presence of a complementing locus on the Y chromosome but was dependent on the number of *white* genes. Because the *white* gene, which had been shown to be required for the normal bright red pigmentation of the eye, resides on the X chromosome, females carry two copies and males have only one copy. Gans demonstrated that the sexual dimorphism of the *zeste* mutation depended on the presence of two copies of *white* in females versus one in males. The *zeste* females heterozygous for a deletion of the *white* gene did not give the *zeste* eye color whereas *zeste* males with a duplication of the *white* gene had a yellow eye (see Table 1). This analysis was complicated by the fact that both *zeste* and *white* are on the X chromosome and that

TABLE 1[a]

Eye-Color Phenotypes of the Principal *zeste* Mutants

Mutant	Phenotype
$z^1 w^+/z^1 w^+$	Yellow
$z^1 w^+/Y$	Red
$z^1 w^+/z^+ w^+$	Red
$z^1 w^+/z^1 Df(w)$	Red
$z^1 w^+/z^1 w^{sp}$	Red
$z^1 Dp(w)/z^1 w^+$	Orange/mottled
$z^1 Dp(w)/z^1 Dp(w)$	Yellow
$z^a w^+/z^a w^+$	Red
$z^1 w^+/z^a w^+$	Yellow
$ln(1)e(bx) w^+/ln(1)e(bx) w^+$	Red
$z^1 w^+/ln(1)e(bx) w^+$	Yellow–orange
$z^{op6} w^+/Y$	Yellow
$z^{op6} w^+/z^{op6} w^+$	Yellow
$z^{op6} w^+/z^+ w^+$	Yellow–orange
$z^{op6} w^+/z^+ Df(w)$	Red
$z^{11G3} w^+/z^{11G3} w^+$	Red
$z^1 w^+/z^{11G3} w^+$	Red–brown variegated
$z^{v77h} w^+/z^{v77h} w^+$	Light brown variegated
$z^{v77h} w^+/Y$	Light brown variegated
$z^{v77h} w^+/z^1 w^+$	Yellow
$z^{v77h} w^+/z^+ w^+$	Red
$z^{v77h} w^+/z^{v77h} w^+$; P[$z^+$]	Red
$z^{v77h} w^+/ln(1)e(bx) w^+$	Red

[a] This table was compiled from results first obtained by Gans (1953), Green (1959, 1984), Kaufman *et al.* (1973), Jack and Judd (1979), Lifschytz and Green (1984), and V. Pirrotta (unpublished data). *Df(w)* indicates a deficiency of the *white* locus or its proximal part; *Dp(w)* is a tandem duplication of the *white* gene; P[z^+] indicates a P transposon carrying a functional z^+ gene.

they map relatively close to one another. It was possible to show, however, that neither of these facts is relevant to the phenomenon and that in some way the *zeste* mutation has an effect in trans on the phenotypic expression of the *white* gene. The curious and paradoxical aspect of this interaction is that it requires two copies of the target gene, *white*, and that a single copy is not visibly affected. Gans found that the *zeste* mutation initially isolated was an unusual allele with a neomorphic character because deletions of the *zeste* locus did not give the *zeste*-encoded phenotype, although they failed to complement the *zeste* mutation. Other alleles, such as z^a, failed to complement *zeste* but had no phenotype by themselves and were considered to be hypomorphic.

The identity of Lewis' *e(bx)* gene and Gans' *zeste* was only discovered many years later as a result of the saturation mapping of the chromosomal interval between *zeste* and *white* by Judd *et al.* (1972). Kaufman *et al.* (1973) found that the two were allelic and that the *e(bx)* mutation failed to complement the *zeste* mutation. Furthermore, loss-of-function alleles of *zeste* (alleles of the z^a type) had the same phenotype with respect to transvection as the *e(bx)* mutations of Lewis. The relationship between the two *zeste*-dependent phenomena, *zeste–white* interaction and transvection at the BX-C, was further strengthened by the discovery that both required the pairing of the target loci. Jack and Judd (1979) demonstrated that the two copies of the *white* gene necessary for *zeste* to reduce the phenotypic expression of *white* must be homologously paired or in close proximity due to tandem duplication. If the two copies cannot pair because of chromosomal rearrangements, the eye color remains bright red. In conclusion, both transvection and the *zeste–white* effect involve the interaction of two paired copies of the target gene; in the first case, however, the wild-type *zeste* gene is required and in the second case the effect is specific for the mutant *zeste* allele, which I will henceforth refer to as z^1.

III. Transvection

Effects resembling transvection have been detected in a number of different loci. At *Ultrabithorax* (*Ubx*) (Lewis, 1954), *decapentaplegic* (*dpp*) (Gelbart, 1982; Gelbart and Wu, 1982), *white* (*w*) (Babu and Bhat, 1980; Gelbart and Wu, 1982) and *yellow* (*y*) (Geyer *et al.*, 1990), these effects have been shown to require the function of the *zeste* gene whereas transvection-like effects at *brown* (*bw*) do not (Henikoff and Dreesen, 1989). Interactions that are suggestive of transvection have been reported at the *cubitus interruptus* (*ci*) locus (Stern and

Heidenthal, 1944) and at *Notch* (Sirén and Portin, 1988), but whether they are *zeste* dependent is not known. In addition, two puff sites in salivary gland chromosomes, the *Sgs-4* locus at 3C12 (Korge, 1981; Kornher and Brutlag, 1986) and a site at 64C (Ashburner, 1970), puff in some strains but not in others, but when a puffing allele is paired with a nonpuffing allele, both appear to puff. This effect of one gene copy on another, paired copy, is typical of transvection effects but it is not known whether it is dependent on *zeste* in either of these cases. There remain significant differences among these examples. In some cases pairing enhances gene activation while in others it decreases it. Some of these phenomena are in some way dependent on the *zeste* gene or one of its mutants while in other cases the *zeste* gene does not appear to be involved. Tartof and Henikoff (1991) have attempted to differentiate this broad class of phenomena on these bases. They propose the term "trans-sensing" for the general class of phenomena implying the influence of one copy of a gene on the expression of a second paired copy and reserve the term "transvection" for the specific cases of pairing-dependent interallelic complementation. While "trans-sensing" is an excellent and descriptive term, it is not clear how fundamental the distinctions really are. Since this review is more concerned with *zeste* and with the insights that the work on *zeste* may contribute to understanding the general phenomena, I will continue to use "transvection" in the discussion that follows.

Many instances of transvection are manifested as a form of pairing-dependent interallelic complementation. In other words, two alleles of a gene can partly complement, provided the two genes are brought in close physical proximity by chromosome pairing (Fig. 1). Some cases of transvection are particularly instructive because they do not cause complementation between two alleles but rather result in mutant regulation of a wild-type gene by a dominant regulatory mutation on the other copy of the gene. This is the case of the effect observed in flies with genotype *Cbx Ubx/ + +* , where *Ubx* is a mutation in the coding region of the *Ubx* locus and *Cbx* is a regulatory mutation of *Ubx* that results in its inappropriate expression (White and Akam, 1985). When the doubly mutant chromosome is paired with the fully normal chromosome, transvection causes the inappropriate expression of the wild-type copy of the *Ubx* gene under the influence of the *Cbx* mutation on the other chromosome (Lewis, 1955; Gelbart and Wu, 1982). Such effects strongly imply that, unlike the familiar type of interallelic complementation that is frequently observed in genes whose products have multiple functions or form oligomeric structures, the complementation displayed in transvection involves gene regulation. It depends on chromo-

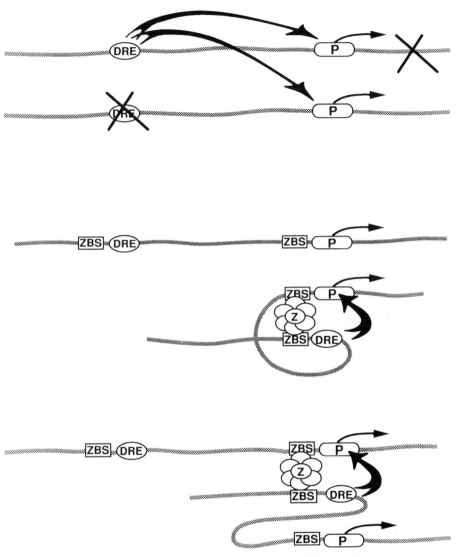

FIG. 1. Transvection and long-distance gene regulation. The top illustration represents a typical transvection effect in which the distant regulatory element (DRE) of a gene carrying a mutation in the coding region is able to activate the promoter (P) of another copy of the gene whose own DRE is inactivated by mutation. The middle illustration represents a *zeste*-mediated looping model. A *zeste*-encoded protein complex (Z) binding to its target sites (ZBS) near the promoter and near the DRE brings the two together and allows the DRE to activate the promoter. The bottom illustration applies the same looping model to account for transvection. Here the *zeste*-encoded protein complex brings the DRE of a second copy of the gene in contact with the promoter of the first.

some configuration, hence it must occur in the nucleus and act at the level of the DNA or of transcription or immediately thereafter.

A. Transvection Mechanisms

A variety of possible mechanisms has been proposed to account for transvection effects: (1) template switching of RNA polymerase from one copy of the gene to another (Babu and Bhat, 1980); (2) trans splicing of transcription products (Judd, 1979); (3) somatic recombination between the two genes; (4) the assembly of chromatin structures that propagate from one gene copy to the other (Ashburner, 1977; Babu et al., 1987; Henikoff and Dreesen, 1989); (5) the binding of genes to specific locations on the nuclear envelope or matrix, required for transcription (Zachar et al., 1985); (6) DNA looping, enabling enhancer-bound transcriptional activators on one gene copy to act on the promoter of the second gene (Pirrotta et al., 1985; Biggin et al., 1988; Benson and Pirrotta, 1988; Mansukhani et al., 1988b); and (7) the effect on the promoter of one gene, by regulatory molecules with limited diffusion, produced by the other gene copy (Lewis, 1954; Jack and Judd, 1979; Micol and Garcia-Bellido, 1988).

All these mechanisms could account for the effect of one copy of the gene on the transcriptional activity of another copy closely apposed to it by homologous pairing. We may begin by eliminating two possible mechanisms that involve a sequence rearrangement: somatic recombination between two mutations or *trans* splicing between nascent RNA molecules. Both of these mechanisms are ruled out by the fact that *Ubx* alleles known to map at the two ends of the transcription unit fail to give transvection effects (Lewis, 1985). If recombination occurred anywhere between them, either at the DNA or at the RNA level, they should complement. The same argument rules out transcriptional template switching. This is not to say that mechanisms of this sort could not occur elsewhere and produce transvection-like effects. In fact, trans-splicing is a well-documented activity in *C. elegans* (Krause and Hirsh, 1986; Bloomenthal and Thomas, 1988) and trypanosome (Sutton and Boothroyd, 1986; Laird, 1989) gene expression. However, since such models cannot explain many typical cases of transvection we must consider the existence of other types of mechanism. The remaining four models have a certain similarity. They all imply the involvement of regulatory sequences that control transcriptional activity and are consistent with the fact that all known transvection effects involve pairs of alleles, of which at least one is a transcriptional regulatory mutation. The assembly of higher order chromatin structures is very likely involved in the transvection effects at the *brown* locus, where rearrangements that cause the partial inactivation of the *brown* gene also inactivate a wild-type copy that is homologously paired with it (Henikoff and Dreesen, 1989). Because the inactivating rearrangements place the gene in the vicinity of the chromocenter, it is not unlikely that chromatin condensation is involved and that the assembly of heterochromatin, a process thought to be highly cooperative (Locke *et al.*, 1988), may induce a similar process on a paired copy of the gene. Interestingly, this is a case of transvection that has been shown not to be affected by known *zeste* mutations and points out the likelihood that the molecular basis of transvection might differ in detail at different loci. The possibility that gene activation (or inactivation such as that occurring at *bw* or at *w*) is dependent on localization to some particular nuclear compartment or attachment to a nuclear structure has not been excluded. This class of explanation might apply to general mechanisms for enhancer action. It could account for some transvection effects if two paired copies of a gene tend to behave as a unit, allowing a gene lacking an active regulatory element to be passively brought into the right nuclear location by association with another copy bearing a functional regulatory element (Zachar *et al.*, 1985; Bingham and Zachar, 1985; Davison *et al.*, 1985). However, this kind of mechanism has remained hypothetical and, despite suggestive evidence for nuclear matrix or chromosome scaffold attachment sites on the chromatin (Gasser and Laemmli, 1986, 1987; Cockerill and Garrard, 1986), no direct evidence for their involvement in gene expression is available.

More evidence is available for the notion that enhancer action involves a looping of the DNA to allow the physical juxtaposition of enhancer-bound factors and the transcription complex at the promoter (Ptashne, 1988). This model would be easily extended to account for transvection effects if the enhancer complex from one chromosome is allowed to loop and interact with the promoter of the other copy of the gene on the homologously paired chromosome (Biggin *et al.*, 1988; Benson and Pirrotta, 1988). The role of *zeste* in this model would be to facilitate the looping between the two chromosomes (Fig. 1). Finally, the short-range diffusion of direct products of one gene was the concept underlying Lewis' term, "transvection." A version of this concept, specifically involving the transcription product of the *white* gene, was advanced by Jack and Judd (1979). A more recent form of this model invokes the existence of regulatory RNA species that, in the case of the *Ubx* gene, are the products of transcription from the regulatory elements governing the gene, can diffuse over short nuclear distances, and are required for regulating transcription (Micol and Garcia-Bellido,

1988; Micol *et al.*, 1990). Support for the existence of regulatory RNA molecules has come recently from the finding that a transcription factor required by RNA polymerase III appears to be composed of RNA (Young *et al.*, 1991). In the case of *Ubx*, there is no evidence for such regulatory transcripts but their existence is hard to disprove, because, by definition, they might be very short lived to account for their short range of activity within the nucleus. It is probably fair to say that, at present, the best account of *zeste*-mediated transvection effects is given by the enhancer-looping model, although it is far from being proved and it does not exclude the possibility that different mechanisms can apply to different cases of transvection.

B. THE *zeste–white* INTERACTION AS A TRANSVECTION-LIKE PHENOMENON

The interaction of *zeste* with *white* is a phenomenon clearly related to transvection: it exhibits a striking dependence on the pairing of two target gene copies, it implies the ability of one copy to communicate with the other and it involves the *zeste* gene. It is distinct, however, from transvection because it requires a mutant form of the *zeste* gene and operates on wild-type copies of the target gene, *white*. Transvection in the form of interallelic complementation does occur at the *white* gene, for example, when a mutation in the regulatory region (w^{sp1}) is paired with a hypomorphic mutation in the coding region (e.g., w^a). In the presence of the wild-type *zeste* function, this combination results in a darker eye color than that of either mutant alone (Babu and Bhat, 1980). Like most other transvection effects, this complementation is abolished by z^a-type mutations.

The interaction of *white* with the z^1 mutation is specific for the expression of *white* in the adult eye. No effect of z^1 is observed on the *white*-dependent pigmentation of the Malpighian tubules, of the testes, or even of the ocelli. In consequence, the transcriptional basis for the effect was difficult to establish in whole-body RNA (Pirrotta and Bröckl, 1984; O'Hare *et al.*, 1983), but was demonstrated by Bingham and Zachar (1985) using RNA from the heads of carefully staged animals. Transcription of *white* in other tissues is not affected. The tissue specificity favors a mechanism involving the regulatory region responsible for eye-specific expression. Other evidence pointing to the regulatory region comes from genetic experiments showing that the requirement for two paired copies of *white* is satisfied if one of the copies is represented just by the proximal or regulatory region of the gene

(Judd, 1961). Furthermore, partial deletions and mutations affecting this region of the gene, such as the w^{sp} series, w^e and w^h, are not recognized by *zeste*, fail to give the *zeste* effect when homozygous, and suppress the effect when heterozygous with a normal copy of *white* (Green, 1959; Kaufman *et al.*, 1973) (see Table 1). More detailed analysis of the target sites in the *white* gene has been possible by the use of *white* transposon constructs. These have shown that the *zeste* interaction requires a part of the regulatory region of *white* located more than 1 kb upstream of the promoter and approximately corresponding to the region affected by the w^{sp} mutations (Pirrotta *et al.*, 1985; Levis *et al.*, 1985). However, the interaction is very sensitive to position effects: transposons inserted in some chromosomal sites may respond to *zeste* but fail to respond when inserted at other sites. Occasional sites behave as if they already contained a *zeste* response element and give the *zeste* interaction even when the flies are heterozygous for the transposon inserted there (Hazelrigg *et al.*, 1984).

C. The z^1 Mutation and the Pairing Requirement

The z^1 mutation is clearly neomorphic: it does not correspond to lack of function or reduced function. Mutations of the *zeste* gene to z^1-like alleles are very rare. Most frequently the gene gives rise to z^a-like mutations that behave like loss-of-function alleles in being unable to support transvection effects or to complement z^1. A few alleles that resemble z^1 have been isolated but generally have much weaker effects on the expression of *white* (Gelbart, 1971; Jack, 1979). Normally z^1 appears to be recessive to z^+. In fact, it is semidominant, as is revealed by the behavior of tandem duplications of the *white* gene. These duplications allow the increase in the number of copies that can be made to pair and the construction of flies that have two, three, four, or more copies of the *white* gene in close proximity. In these strains, the z^1/z^+ heterozygotes give red, orange, and yellow eyes, respectively, indicating the increasing dominance of the z^1 allele over z^+ in the presence of increasing numbers of *white* gene copies (Jack and Judd, 1979) (see Table 1). In contrast to genetically produced duplications, transposons containing two or more tandem copies of the *white* regulatory region do not give the *zeste* effect in single copy (C. Zucker, personal communication; S. Qian and V. Pirrotta, unpublished data). When homozygous, however, they tend to produce stronger *zeste* effects. A major difference between the genetic and the engineered duplications is in the length of the duplicated region and the distance between the two copies.

In the genetic duplications, the distance between the tandem copies of *white* is of the order of 30 kb, whereas in the duplications constructed *in vitro*, the tandem repeats are immediately adjacent. It is possible that additional upstream sequences are required or that the distance between the repeats has to be such that the tandem repeats can actually loop back and pair with one another, mimicking the pairing of two chromosomes.

D. THE z^{op} MUTATIONS

In 1976, Lifschytz and Green mutagenized the original z^1 mutant of Gans and isolated a remarkable series of *zeste* mutations that gave reduced or yellow eye color even with a single copy of *white* (Lifschytz and Green, 1984). These mutations, called z^{op} (for overproducer), demonstrated that pairing of two *white* genes is not a requisite for the *zeste–white* interactions, hence distinguishing the phenomenon conceptually from classical transvection (defined as a pairing-dependent effect on gene expression), but that pairing enhanced the ability of the mutated *zeste* product to interfere with the expression of the *white* gene (see Table 1). The strongest of Lifschytz' alleles, z^{op6}, was analyzed molecularly (see below) and shown to be not an overproducer of z^1 but the result of an additional point mutation in the gene making the z^{op6} product simply more effective. Using *white* transposons as targets of z^{op6}, single copies give the effect, as expected (Pirrotta *et al.*, 1985). In some lines, however, no effect is obtained unless the transposons are paired, showing again that genomic flanking sequences influence the response but that even with the z^{op6} product, pairing has a potentiating effect.

Although the z^1 and z^{op6} mutations have a powerful inhibitory effect on the expression of *white*, they still retain at least part of the normal *zeste* function. Both are still able to support transvection effects at the *Ubx* locus (Kaufman *et al*, 1973; V. Pirrotta, unpublished data). Unlike z^a mutations, z^1 and z^{op6} act in this respect as entirely wild type. The discovery of transvection at the *decapentaplegic* gene (Gelbart, 1982) revealed, however, that the effects of *zeste* are strongly dependent on the target gene. At this locus, both z^a and z^1 mutations disrupt transvection effects (Gelbart and Wu, 1982). It appears then that the z^1 product has different effects at different loci: it is repressive for *white* expression in the eye, wild type for transvection at *Ubx*, but inactive for transvection at *dpp*. It is likely that these differences depend on the detailed configuration of the regulatory region with which *zeste* interacts.

IV. Molecular Biology of *zeste*

A. THE SEQUENCE OF THE *zeste* GENE

The *zeste* gene was cloned by two different approaches. One made use of the microcloning technique to dissect a fragment from the 3A1–3A4 region of the polytene chromosomes (Mariani *et al.*, 1985). An independent approach made use of chromosome walking using a deletion that allowed jumping from the vicinity of the previously cloned *white* gene to the vicinity of *zeste* (Gunaratne *et al.*, 1986). The *zeste* locus was identified using P element insertions that cause a z^a mutant phenotype, by the breakpoint of the *e(bx)* inversion, which splits the gene in two, and, most decisively, by P-mediated germ-line transformation using a 4-kb wild-type genomic fragment that complemented the z^1 mutant phenotype as well as by a z^1 fragment that conferred the yellow eye phenotype.

The *zeste* gene appears to be a simple transcriptional unit containing two small introns spliced out to produce a 2.4-kb transcript. The sequence of the gene and of cDNA clones was determined by Pirrotta *et al.* (1987) and by Mansukhani *et al.* (1988a). When correction is made for a supernumerary nucleotide (Bickel and Pirrotta, 1990), the two sequences are in essential agreement except for a duplication of codon 325 (Gly 325), which appears to be a genuine polymorphism. The sequence predicts a slightly acidic 61,981-Da protein (p*I* 6.1) of 575 amino acids with a number of striking peculiarities. The N-terminal sequence is extremely rich in glycine residues (19 of 43), suggesting a highly flexible and structurally loose N-terminal arm. The protein contains three regions with runs of Gln, Ala, or alternating Gln-Ala, motifs related to the *OPA* repeat (Wharton *et al.*, 1985) found in a large number of *Drosophila* regulatory proteins as well as in vertebrate transcription factors, for example, the rat glucocorticoid receptor (Miesfeld *et al.*, 1986). Its significance, function, or secondary structure is unknown.

B. COMPARISON WITH THE *Drosophila virilis zeste* GENE

The homologous *zeste* gene from *Drosophila* virilis, a species believed to have diverged from the branch that evolved into *D. melanogaster* some 45 million years ago (Beverley and Wilson, 1984), has been sequenced (Chen *et al.*, 1991) and displays extensive homology (Fig. 2). The structure of the gene is very highly conserved, with presumptive introns occurring at exactly the same positions as in *D. melanogaster*.

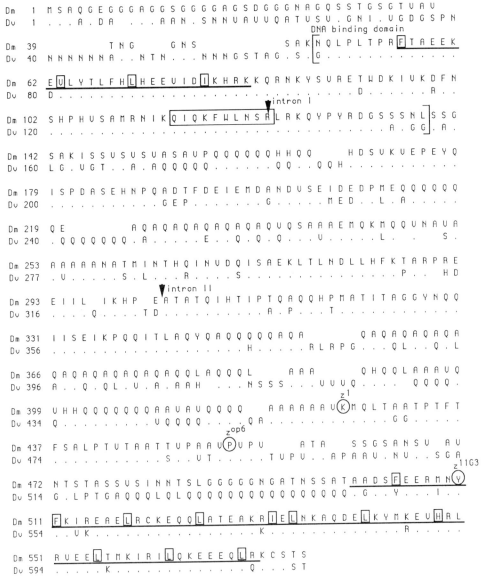

FIG. 2. Amino acid sequence of the *D. melanogaster* (Dm) zeste-encoded protein, compared with that of *D. virilis* (Dv). The two sequences are aligned, with gaps introduced to maximize the homology. The dots in the *D. virilis* sequence indicate identity with the *D. melanogaster* sequence. The DNA-binding domain defined by Mansukhani *et al.* (1988b) is shown in brackets from residue 48 to 138 of *D. melanogaster*. The heavy underlines indicate regions predicted to form extensive helical domains and the boxed positions point out the heptad repeats of hydrophobic residues. The sequence shown boxed resembles the highly conserved recognition helix of homeodomain proteins (Scott *et al.*, 1989). The sites of the z^1 (Lys to Met), z^{op6} (Pro to Leu), and z^{11G3} (deletion of Tyr) mutations are circled.

The predicted *D. virilis zeste* is larger by 43 amino acids but its amino acid sequence shows a high degree of conservation (62%), with large blocks of sequence nearly identical to that of the *D. melanogaster* gene. There are a few interesting differences: the N-terminal sequence is the most divergent part and is rich in Asn rather than Gly, and the Gln and Ala repeats are well conserved but tend to be longer than the corresponding runs in *D. melanogaster* and lack the distinct Gln-Ala alternation. *Drosophila virilis* has one additional Gln tract that is absent in the *D. melanogaster* sequence. The *D. virilis zeste* gene, introduced into *D. melanogaster*, is fully functional and can substitute for the *D. melanogaster* gene in complementing the z^1 mutation. Figure 2 shows the two sequences aligned and points out the sites of the several mutations and other important features that will be discussed below.

C. Expression of *zeste* during Development

Northern hybridization shows that the gene is generally expressed at a low rate, but a developmental profile reveals that the greatest concentration of *zeste* RNA is found in unfertilized eggs (Pirrotta *et al.*, 1988). The abundance decreases during embryonic development, dropping to a minimum in first and second instar larvae, but rises again at the end of the third instar to a peak occurring during pupal development. Adult flies return to an intermediate level. The Northern blots show that the *zeste* locus gives rise also to 4.1-kb RNA, transcribed from the opposite strand and hybridizing to the region preceding the 5' end of *zeste* as well as the region beyond the 3' end (Mariani *et al.*, 1985; Gunaratne *et al.*, 1986; Royden *et al.*, 1987). This transcript follows approximately the same developmental profile but its significance or function is unknown. That it is not related to *zeste* function is shown by the fact that *zeste* transposons that contain neither the beginning nor the end of this transcriptional unit give all the known *zeste* functions.

The developmental pattern of *zeste* expression was also determined using transposons in which the *zeste* upstream region and the first 49 codons were fused to the *lacZ* gene (Pirrotta *et al.*, 1988). This construct shows intense and ubiquitous expression in the late embryo but not before germ band extension. Despite the stability of β-galactosidase, expression gradually disappears after hatching and, in third instar larvae, it is detectable only in the brain and gonads, returning again in late third instar larvae and pupae in all imaginal tissues and in the salivary glands. The cloning and sequencing of the *zeste* gene made possible the isolation of antibodies against *zeste* and the direct localization of the *zeste* product in tissues, cells, and nuclei. Taking care to avoid the repetitive Gln and Ala regions of the polypeptide, Benson and Pirrotta (1987) and later Pirrotta *et al.* (1988) raised antibodies against the C-terminal region of *zeste*. These were used to detect the *zeste* product in extracts from staged embryos. The inconsistency between the abundance of the transcript in maternal RNA and the lack of expression of the *zeste–lacZ* construct in the early embryo was confirmed by immunoassay of the *zeste*-encoded protein in Western blots (S. Bickel and V. Pirrotta, unpublished observations). Appreciable *zeste*-encoded protein becomes detectable only in 4- to 6-hour embryos, implying that maternal *zeste* mRNA is translationally blocked. It may be relevant to point out that all transvection effects known so far are detected in the adult. While this may be due to chance and the difficulty of detecting subtle phenotypic changes it is possible that transvection does not occur in the embryo.

V. *zeste* Product on Polytene Chromosomes

Not surprisingly, the *zeste*-encoded protein is found in the nuclear fraction. It is not highly abundant and its detection in Western blots of crude nuclear extracts requires special precautions. The first attempts to detect *zeste* product *in situ* in embryos or tissue culture cells were unsuccessful even when affinity-purified antibody preparations were used (S. Bickel and V. Pirrotta, unpublished data). *In situ* detection was first achieved using flies that overproduced *zeste* product from a transposon carrying the *zeste* gene driven by the *hsp70* promoter. Salivary gland preparations from such flies after heat induction revealed high levels of *zeste* product-specific immunofluorescence confined to the nuclei (Pirrotta *et al.*, 1988) (Fig. 3). Chromosome squashes from salivary glands of normal flies showed that the endogenous *zeste* product, though much less abundant, could also be detected in a series of sharply defined bands at specific chromosomal sites. Approximately 60 strong bands of immunofluorescence were counted in the chromosomes of late third instar larvae. Although the sites were highly reproducible in larvae of comparable developmental stages, some changes were apparent in third instar larvae and prepupae. It is interesting to note that no *zeste* product immunofluorescence was detected at the *white* locus, at position 3C1-2, although *white* is clearly a prime target for *zeste* product action. Because the *white* gene is not expressed in salivary glands, this suggests that the binding of *zeste* product at a given target gene is dependent on some other event, presumably associated with gene activation. Control chromosome preparations using *In(1)e(bx)* larvae gave no

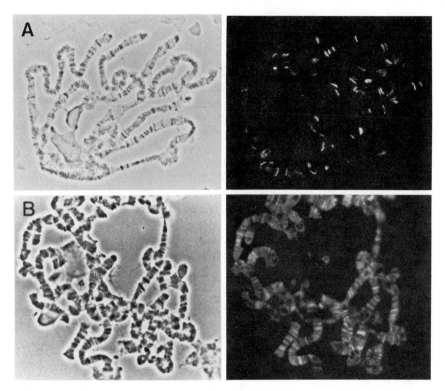

FIG. 3. Indirect immunofluorescence of *zeste* product on polytene chromosomes. (A) Photographs showing phase contrast and immunofluorescence views of endogenous *zeste*-encoded protein on salivary gland chromosomes. (B) Photographs showing the immunofluorescence of *zeste* product produced from a transposon containing a *hsp70–zeste* gene, after heat shock.

detectable immunofluorescence. In this mutant, the *zeste* gene is truncated by the breakpoint of the *e(bx)* inversion and therefore lacks the region encoding the C terminus of *zeste* product, against which the antibody had been raised. In z^1 and z^{op6} mutants, the bands are present and are indistinguishable from the wild type. They are absent in most but not all mutants of the z^a type (V. Pirrotta, unpublished data). Increased levels of *zeste* product, obtained from the *hsp70–zeste* construct, caused stronger immunofluorescence and a progressive increase in the number of bands until, after a 37°C shock, thousands of bands were detected. No staining was observed in the chromocenter, in the nucleolus, or in puff regions and, even after heat shock, only a few bands were found on the largely heterochromatic fourth chromosome.

The lack of staining in puffs could be explained as due to the spreading out of the signal over a decondensed chromosome region. In the case of the chromocenter, the absence of immunofluorescence might be attributed to the underreplication of these genomic sequences. In any case, the results show that *zeste* is not generally associated with satellite sequences and suggest that *zeste* product-binding sites are preferentially found in euchromatic chromosome regions. The discrete distribution of *zeste* product bands indicates that the protein cannot be regarded as a general chromosome glue, holding together two homologous chromosomes, but that it appears to bind to a large number of specific chromosomal locations, much larger than suggested by the three or four well-characterized cases of transvection. Whether any or all of the chromosomal sites at which the *zeste*-encoded protein is found represent functional targets of the protein's action is a very different question that cannot be answered at present. No evidence was found for the association of *zeste*-encoded protein with other nuclear structures such as the matrix, the lamina, or nuclear envelope, or in unsquashed salivary gland nuclei (Pirrotta *et al.*, 1988) or in mitotic embryonic cells (J. Wilcox, S. Bickel, and V. Pirrotta, unpublished data). It is possible, however, that such associations are overshadowed by the chromatin in polytene nuclei whereas higher resolution and greater sensitivity might be necessary for mitotic nuclei.

VI. DNA Binding and Looping

A. THE *zeste* PRODUCT-BINDING CONSENSUS SEQUENCE

Bacterial expression clones provided *zeste*-encoded protein for molecular experiments. Using an immunoprecipitation assay, Benson and Pirrotta (1987) showed that the protein made in bacteria binds specifically to DNA from known target genes such as *white* and *Ubx*. Mansukhani *et al.* (1988b) obtained similar results using a *zeste* product–β-galactosidase fusion protein. Furthermore, the proteins encoded by the mutants z^1 and z^{op6} bind to DNA as well as the wild-type protein, insofar as could be determined by the immunoprecipitation assay (Bickel and Pirrotta, 1990). Footprint analysis of a number of binding sites in different genes (Biggin *et al.*, 1988; Benson and Pirrotta, 1988) showed that each footprint contained a core consensus sequence Pyr-GAG-Pyr-G or its complement. However, additional sequence features are probably required for binding because not all such consensus sequences are sites of *zeste* product binding *in vitro*. There is a decided preference for T over C in the pyrimidine positions and for an additional T to precede the consensus. The most common feature of the binding sites detected by the immunoprecipitation assay is that they always contain two or more consensus sequences in either direct or inverse orientation and spaced at distances varying from 16 to 55 nucleotides. The footprinting analysis strongly suggested that the binding at such neighboring sites showed considerable cooperativity such that the protection of a given site was affected by the presence of the other site(s) on the same fragment (Biggin *et al.*, 1988; Benson and Pirrotta, 1988). Using a synthetic oligonucleotide containing the consensus sequence, binding by immunoprecipitation was not detectable with a single cloned copy of the sequence but became detectable and increasingly stronger with two, three, four, or five tandem copies. Cooperative effects apparently extend over longer distances. Binding to two neighboring consensus sequences was enhanced some fivefold by the presence of two other consensus sequences 400 bp distant (Benson and Pirrotta, 1988). The interaction is probably significantly dependent also on the presence of near-consensus sequences. The examination of a number of strong binding sites shows that such imperfect consensus sequences are almost invariably found in the immediate vicinity of the true consensus. Such considerations are probably responsible for the fact that although the consensus sequence is short and contains two twofold degeneracies, the incidence of binding sites detectable by the immunoprecipitation assay is much lower than statistically expected.

The apparent cooperativity of the binding, the highly variable distance between cooperating sites, and the fact that they are orientation independent suggest that the molecular species of *zeste* product that binds is most likely an oligomer with remarkable features. It is clearly a species that can bind simultaneously to two or more DNA sites. This was shown by the fact that a preformed complex between *zeste* product and a labeled DNA fragment containing consensus sequences can still be retained on an affinity column containing immobilized multimeric oligonucleotides with the consensus sequence (Benson and Pirrotta, 1988). This ability has implications for transvection because it shows that the *zeste* product could, in principle, interact simultaneously with DNA sequences on two different chromosomes.

B. *zeste* PRODUCT-BINDING SITES IN TARGET GENES

The fact that the *zeste* product is a specific DNA-binding protein helps to restrict the variety of possible models for transvection, making less likely those that invoke an RNA intermediate. This conclusion is further strengthened by the presence and distribution of *zeste* product-binding sites at target genes. Using the immunoprecipitation assay, binding sites were in fact found at the three best known targets of *zeste*-dependent transvection effects, *white, Ubx,* and *dpp* (Benson and Pirrotta, 1988; Mansukhani *et al.,* 1988b). All three of these genes contain *zeste* product-binding sites in the immediate vicinity of the promoter, as well as more distant binding sites in the general vicinity of known regulatory mutations (Fig. 4). In the *white* gene, binding sites are found approximately 1.2 kb upstream of the promoter, in the region of the w^{sp} mutations, which are implicated in the *zeste–white* interac-

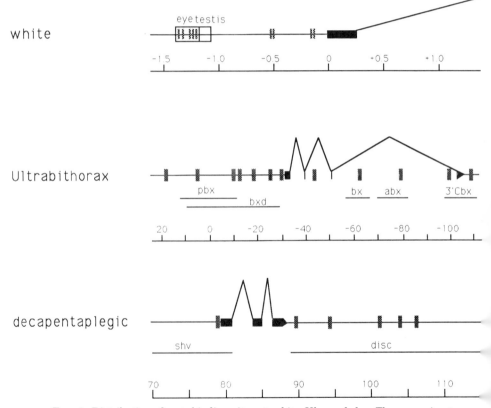

FIG. 4. Distribution of *zeste* binding sites at *white, Ubx,* and *dpp*. The approximate position of the binding sites is indicated by gray vertical bars. Exon sequences are shown by black bars but only the first exon of the *white* gene is given. Regulatory regions of the three genes are indicated. The binding data are derived from immunoprecipitation experiments (Benson and Pirrotta, 1988).

tion and within an element that has eye enhancer activity (Qian and Pirrotta, submitted). In the *Ubx* gene, binding sites occur in the upstream *bxd* regulatory region as well as downstream of the promoter, including the regions of the *bx* and *abx* mutations. Binding sites at the *dpp* region are found scattered in the 3' disk regulatory region whose mutations give transvection effects. In addition, binding sites were found at the *Antennapedia* and *engrailed* loci as well as near the promoter of the *zeste* gene (Benson and Pirrotta, 1988). However, *zeste* product binding is not ubiquitous and was not observed with a number of other genomic clones.

C. Promoter Effects

The footprinting analysis of *zeste*-encoded protein-binding sites at the *Ubx* and *dpp* promoters showed that they are not only immediately upstream of the transcription start site but that they consist of an impressive array of footprinting sites (Biggin *et al.*, 1988; Benson and Pirrotta, 1988). At the *Ubx* promoter, five *zeste* product-binding and footprinting sites are clustered between 40 and 140 nucleotides upstream of the transcription start site. At *dpp*, four *zeste* product-binding and footprinting sites are clustered in an interval within 130 bp from the start of the 4.2-kb transcript. At the *white* promoter, two *zeste* product footprinting sites are found between 110 and 140 nucleotides preceding the transcription start. The binding of other *Drosophila* proteins to the *Ubx* promoter was studied by Biggin and Tjian (1988), who found that the *zeste* product footprinting sites are interspersed and partly overlapping with the binding sites of at least two other proteins. One of these is the GAGA factor, so called because its footprints contain GAGAG or related sequences. Thummel (1989) found two *zeste* product footprinting sites between position -46 and -117 from the transcription start site of the *E74* gene, an ecdysone-induced gene corresponding to a major early puff site but not other wise known to interact with *zeste*. As in the *Ubx* promoter, these *zeste* sites overlap with a set of GAGA factor-binding sites. Both the GAGA factor and *zeste* product stimulate transcription from the *Ubx* promoter in an *in vitro* transcription assay (Biggin and Tjian, 1988; Biggin *et al.*, 1988). The effect of *zeste* product is specific for a *Ubx* promoter containing the *zeste* product-binding sites and is lost if those sites are deleted. Although Jackson and Tjian (1988) found that the *Drosophila zeste* product is O glycosylated, bacterially produced *zeste*-encoded protein and *zeste*-encoded protein purified from *Drosophila* embryos are equally effective in stimulating transcription, indicating that such posttranscriptional modification is not essential for this function.

The effect of *zeste* product on transcription *in vitro* indicates that, whatever other functions it may have, when it binds in the vicinity of the *Ubx* promoter, it behaves like a typical promoter-proximal transcription factor. Similar stimulatory effects have been also observed in tissue culture cells cotransfected with a target promoter linked to the bacterial *CAT* gene and a *zeste*-expressing construct (Miller and Pirrotta, 1991; M. Krasnow, B. Williams, A. Crickmore, and M. L. Goldberg, unpublished data, cited in Wu and Goldberg, 1989). The results of these experiments show that, as in the *in vitro* experiments, *zeste* product stimulates transcription from the *Ubx* promoter but also from the *E74* promoter (M. Krasnow and M. L. Goldberg, unpublished experiments, cited in Thummel, 1989). In addition, transcription from a *hsp70* promoter deleted down to the TATA box (hs-43) is also stimulated if synthetic *zeste* product-binding sites are ligated upstream of the promoter (Miller and Pirrotta, 1991). In contrast, *zeste*-encoded protein appears to lower transcription from the *Antennapedia* promoter (M. Krasnow, B. Williams, A. Crickmore, and M. L. Goldberg, unpublished data, cited in Wu and Goldberg, 1989). Miller and Pirrotta also found that the products encoded by z^1 and z^{op6} are as active as the wild-type *zeste* product in these experiments, whereas a truncated gene, containing the N-terminal half of the *zeste* coding region [corresponding to the *e(bx)* mutation], still stimulates transcription, though only about half as efficiently as the wild type.

The significance of these promoter-proximal stimulatory effects is not clear. A direct effect of *zeste* on the promoter complex is not inconsistent with the genetic results on transvection or the *zeste–white* interaction, but it is certainly not required by them. Furthermore, mutations of *zeste* that are inactive in promoting transvection do not seem to cause defects in *Ubx*, *E74*, or *Antp* expression. It is possible that these direct transcriptional effects represent a distinct activity of the *zeste* product, separable from the transvection-mediating activity.

D. The Looping Model

The association of *zeste* product-binding sites with promoters on the one hand and on the other hand with regions that contain genetically known distant regulatory elements in the *white, Ubx,* and *dpp* genes is most consistent with a looping model for both transvection and gene regulation by distant elements (Fig. 1). This model proposes that genes whose regulatory elements may lie tens of kilobases from the promoter they control require special mechanisms to link together these physically remote regions. Proteins such as *zeste* would take on this role, facilitating and stabilizing the loop between factors bound at the control element and the transcription machinery at the promoter. The *zeste* protein may not be unique in this respect and many transcription factors may play a similar role to a greater or lesser extent. Several reports illustrate the fact that enhancer elements can control a promoter even if located on a different DNA molecule, provided that enhancer and promoter are held in physical proximity by some device such as a protein bridge (Müller-Storm *et al.,* 1989) or the topological concatenation of plasmids (Dunaway *et al.,* 1989; Wedel *et al.,* 1990).

We have no evidence at present concerning which, if any, of the *zeste* product-binding sites at *Ubx* or *dpp* are in fact important for transvection effects or whether *zeste* product-binding at both distal and proximal sites is essential. Alternative models in which *zeste* product may interact with other proteins bound at the promoter or at distant sites have been considered by Wu and Goldberg (1989). According to the model proposed by Benson and Pirrotta (1988), the *zeste* product bound to the immediate vicinity of the promoter would interact with *zeste* product bound near distant regulatory sites and cause the DNA looping that juxtaposes these sites to the promoter. This looping mechanism might help to account for the action of regulatory elements that may be 30–50 kb distant from the promoter, as is the case in the *Ubx* and *dpp* loci. If *zeste* product is involved in mediating such intragenic looping, it could, by the same mechanism, mediate a similar looping between the regulatory elements of one gene and the promoter of another copy of the gene paired alongside. This is an attractive and economical concept but one very difficult to prove. The model has a few important requirements that could, in principle, be tested: (1) *zeste* product-binding sites are in fact associated with regulatory elements, (2) *zeste* product can bind simultaneously to two DNA sites or, alternatively, it can bring together two distant DNA regions, (3) distant *zeste* product-binding sites, as well as promoter-proximal sites, are important for long-distance regulation or for transvection effects, and (4) *zeste* product is required or is at least involved in gene regulation by distant control elements. The ability of *zeste* product to bind simultaneously to two DNA molecules has been discussed above. The question of how well the rest of these requirements are met is examined in the following sections.

E. Distant *zeste* Product-Binding Sites at *white*

The ability of *zeste* product to bind specifically to two DNA molecules supports a looping model for transvection and perhaps for intragenic regulatory functions. One end of the loop is clearly in the immediate vicinity of the promoter, at least in several cases studied, but what is at the other end? The looping model predicts that distant regulatory elements should be found in the vicinity of distant *zeste* product-binding sites. In the *white* gene, the upstream binding sites are located about 1.2 kb from the promoter, in the region that had been shown to be required for the *zeste–white* interaction as well as for expression in the testes (Pirrotta *et al.*, 1985; Levis *et al.*, 1985). The w^{sp} mutations that affect this region have a twofold effect of decreasing eye pigmentation and abolishing the *zeste–white* interaction. Benson and Pirrotta (1988) found five *zeste* footprinting sites in this region, approximately -1175 to -1375 nucleotides from the transcription start. Three of these are deleted in the w^{sp2} mutation, a small deletion of 111 bp, whereas the w^{sp1} mutation, an insertion of an 8.7-kb B104 transposon, separates two of the sites from the other three.

A functional analysis of this region shows that it contains multiple eye-specific enhancer elements and that the 80 nucleotides immediately more proximal contain a testis-specific enhancer element (Qian *et al.*, 1991b). This distribution is consistent with the fact that eye expression is affected by the *zeste–white* interaction but testis expression is not. However, when the *zeste* product-binding sites are altered by *in vitro* mutagenesis so that they are no longer recognized by the *zeste* product, the eye enhancer activity is not strongly affected, at least when the enhancer is placed immediately in front of a heterologous promoter driving the bacterial *lacZ* reporter gene. The *zeste* product-binding sites are therefore not an essential element of the eye enhancer. More surprising is the fact that the wild-type eye enhancer, placed in front of a TATA box minimal promoter, is not sensitive to the z^1 mutation. This suggests that additional response elements are necessary to reconstruct the behavior of the *white* gene. Such elements might be the promoter-proximal *zeste* product-binding sites. When the eye enhancer is placed in front of the *white* gene deleted up to position -110 (and therefore lacking the promoter-proximal *zeste* product-binding sites) or even to position -17, the resulting eye expression is still strong and sensitive to the z^1 mutation in at least some of the lines. These results do not exclude the possibility that the *zeste–white* effect requires the binding of some other factor near the *white* promoter, but, if so, it is probably not in the upstream region. With respect to the looping model, these experiments also showed that the proximal *zeste* product-binding sites are not necessary to mediate the effect of the eye enhancer on the promoter 1 kb away. Although this is a very modest distance compared to the 30- to 50-kb distances involved in the *Ubx* or *dpp* genes, it suggests that the looping model as outlined in Fig. 1 is oversimplified or incorrect or that some other protein binding near the promoter can substitute for *zeste* product or that special aids to looping are not required over the short distances involved at the *white* gene. These results raise the question of what exactly is the function of the quintuple *zeste* product-binding site in the eye enhancer.

F. Distant *zeste* Product-Binding Sites at *Ubx*

The region surrounding one of the distant *zeste* product-binding sites in the *Ubx* gene has been also studied in detail. This binding site falls in an interval of approximately 10 kb, within which have been mapped the *bx* regulatory mutations. When a 8.8-kb fragment of this region is placed in a transposon construct in front of the *Ubx* promoter and *lacZ* reporter gene, it activates transcription in the embryo, from blastoderm on, in a pattern related to that of the normal *Ubx* embryonic expression pattern (Qian *et al.*, 1991a). Further dissection showed that this control element was entirely contained in a 500-bp fragment that lies about 1 kb from the *zeste* product-binding site and could be functionally separated from it. If, as is likely, this element corresponds to the genetically identified *bx* element, its proximity to a *zeste* product-binding site provides a rationale for the *zeste*-dependent transvection effects in which the *bx* element participates. However, no evidence at present demonstrates that the *zeste* product-binding site is necessary for or involved in *bx* transvection or whether the *zeste* product-binding sites near the *Ubx* promoter are also required. The fact that a *zeste* product-binding site is found near a distant regulatory element may be entirely fortuitous. Of the other binding sites in the *Ubx* gene, one has been broadly mapped and falls in the vicinity of the *abx* element; several other sites are in the upstream region, which is considerably more complex and is only beginning to be analyzed in more detail. Should these *zeste* product-binding sites also be found to fall within a short distance of a functional control element, the case for their significance would be greatly strengthened. Progress toward elucidation of the mechanism, however, will require the reconstruction of a transvection system by the use of transposons. At present, this is a very difficult enterprise because it involves introducing mutations in one copy of a transposon but not in a second copy that can be paired with the first.

G. *zeste* and Transvection at the *yellow* Locus

A case of transvection that may help to assess the role of *zeste* in mediating the action of distant enhancers is that discovered at the *yellow* locus. The *yellow* gene is responsible for the pigmentation of a variety of structures. Regulatory elements required for expression in the larval mouth parts and denticles are found within the transcription unit. Pigmentation of the adult bristles is controlled by an element just upstream of the promoter whereas pigmentation of the wings and of the body cuticle depends on two elements located further upstream (Geyer and Corces, 1987; Martin *et al.*, 1989). In the y^2 mutant, the insertion of a gypsy transposable element between these last two enhancer elements and the promoter prevents the expression of the gene in the wings and body cuticle but does not alter the activity of the other enhancers. This apparent block in the communication between upstream enhancers and promoter is caused by the binding of a protein, the product of the *su(Hw)* gene, to a target within the gypsy transposon (Geyer and Corces, 1987). Wing and body enhancer action can be provided in *trans* by a transvection mechanism (Geyer *et al.*, 1990). Pairing with another allele, e.g., y^{59b}, in which a part of gypsy that includes the binding site of the *su(Hw)*-encoded protein and part of the *yellow* gene itself have been deleted, allows expression of *yellow* in the wings and body cuticle. This transvection effect is dependent on *zeste* because it is blocked in flies carrying the z^{v77h} mutation (see Section VII). Geyer *et al.* (1990) found that, to be able to provide enhancer function in *trans*, the paired *yellow* locus must have its own promoter deleted, suggesting that the enhancer prefers the *cis* promoter over the *trans* promoter. The *zeste*-encoded protein in this case may act simply as a cross-linking device to bring the two copies of the gene together. However, the sites with which this protein must interact to mediate this transvection effect are not yet established, although a set of excellent *zeste* consensus sequences are found in the part of the gypsy transposon that remains in the y^{59b} allele. It is also not entirely clear how the *su(Hw)*-encoded protein blocks the interaction of enhancer with promoter and therefore in what way the paired copy of the enhancer could bypass this block. The great ease with which the *yellow* gene can be experimentally manipulated should make it possible to analyze the molecular details of this transvection effect and to determine the role of *zeste*.

VII. *zeste*-Null Flies and the Function of *zeste*

A. DELETIONS OF *zeste*

The looping model suggested the possibility that *zeste* might play a more general role in the expression of its target genes. The widespread distribution of *zeste* product-binding sites on the polytene chromosomes suggested that there may be many more target genes in the *Drosophila* genome than those known from transvection effects. If *zeste* product were a necessary mediator of the activity of distant regulatory elements in genes such as *Ubx* or *dpp,* a complete loss-of-function mutation would be expected to be lethal or to show severe phenotypes. The genetic evidence, however, does not support such conjectures. A variety of mutations of the z^a class have been isolated over the years: they fail to complement z^1 and cannot support transvection effects but they are in general viable, fertile, and apparently normal in other respects. However, some of these mutations are demonstrably not completely null (Pirrotta *et al.,* 1987) and the possibility remained that some essential *zeste* function might have been retained. To generate true *zeste*-null flies, deletions completely removing the *zeste* gene were sought. Such deletions were obtained by Goldberg *et al.* (1989) and by Pirrotta, unpublished data with identical results. The *zeste*-null flies were constructed using overlapping deficiencies that complemented one another except for the *zeste* gene. Females completely lacking the *zeste* gene could be obtained in the appropriate crosses and, for the most part, appeared to be normal and fertile and did not exhibit homeotic transformations or developmental abnormalities. However, these flies had a characteristic brown eye color instead of the normal brilliant red, indicating that the expression of the *white* gene was not fully normal. In addition, the *zeste*-deleted flies appeared at a frequency much below that expected. This could be attributed to two effects. One is the low viability of the *zeste*-null flies: some died as pharate adults and could be recovered from the pupal cases, others emerged with wing or leg malformations and died in the fly food shortly afterward. Although normal *zeste*-null flies can be obtained, developmental difficulties evidently arise at high frequency. It is not clear whether these defects are attributable to the lack of *zeste* product or to other lesions incurred in the mutagenesis. The second abnormality revealed in these experiments by both Goldberg *et al.* and Pirrotta *et al.* is that the *zeste*-deleted flies exhibit high frequencies of abnormal chromosome segregation. Not only *zeste*-null flies but also flies heterozygous for *zeste* deletions showed a tendency for the maternal X chromosomes to segregate together, consequently acquiring an XXY constitution in a high proportion of the individuals. This effect interferes considerably with the genetic analysis of *zeste*-null flies but it is most likely not attributable to the lack of *zeste* function but rather to some other locus in the vicinity of *zeste* whose activity is required in two copies for normal chromosome segregation.

B. OTHER NULL ALLELES

The reasons for this conclusion depend on results indicating that certain other *zeste* alleles are also functionally null. The most conclusive of these is the z^{v77h} allele isolated by Green (1984). It was generated by crosses with a P element-containing male and most probably was caused by the insertion of a P transposon near the *zeste* promoter (the preferred P insertion site at *zeste*), followed by excision of the transposon and some flanking sequences. The result is a small deletion of 300 bp within the transcribed region (Pirrotta *et al.*, 1987; Mansukhani *et al.*, 1988a). A similar mutation, z^{π}, was isolated by Mariani *et al.* (1985) and contains a P element inserted very near the transcription start site, accompanied by a flanking deletion of 300 bp almost, but not exactly, identical to that found in z^{v77h}. The two mutants have very different properties: z^{π} behaves like a hypomorph that produces protein encoded by *zeste* but in insufficient amounts to complement z^1 or to support transvection. The z^{v77h} mutant phenotype is unusual because it alters the eye color in both male and female flies to a light brown with a somewhat uneven pigment distribution (variegated). It fails to complement z^1 (see Table 1) or to support transvection. The unusual genetic interactions reported by Green (1984) are attributable to the fact that the mutant eye color is strongly dependent on the genetic background and, in some cases, can appear virtually wild type (Pirrotta *et al.*, 1991). That the z^{v77h} mutant is in fact *zeste* null is shown by the molecular analysis of the mutant gene. The sequence shows that, unlike the deletion in the z^{π} mutant, the 300-bp deletion in z^{v77h} removes the AUG translational start codon (Pirrotta *et al.*, 1991). No other in-frame AUG codons occur in the mRNA sequence until well within the coding region. Translational restarts at these AUGs would produce a protein lacking the DNA-binding region (see below). In fact, no *zeste*-encoded polypeptide can be detected in extracts from these flies. If the mutant gene is overexpressed using the *hsp70* promoter, some lower molecular weight products become detectable. These products have no functional activity, however. Overexpression of the z^{v77h} gene or of a hybrid z^{v77h}–z^{op6} gene, whose C-terminal half comes from the z^{op6} gene, fails to give any detectable change in phenotype. The eye color of z^{v77h} flies resembles the brown color of the *zeste*-null flies produced by overlapping deletions. The z^{v77h} flies are also sickly, though not to the same degree as the *zeste*-deleted flies, but show no anomalies in chromosome segregation. Similar properties were also found in a derivative of the z^{π} mutant, generated by mobilizing the P element inserted near the transcription start. In this mutant, called $z^{\pi L}$, the P element has excised and the 5' leader region of the *zeste* gene is deleted together with 3 kb of the upstream sequence. This mutant also has light brownish eyes in the female, slightly darker in the male, and produces no detectable *zeste*-encoded protein.

In conclusion, the major visible phenotype of complete loss of *zeste* function is the decreased activity of the *white* gene in the eye. It is not unlikely that other genes may be similarly affected, possibly accounting for the lack of robustness of the flies, but not enough to produce visible phenotypes. The *zeste* product may or may not play a role in the normal interaction between distant regulatory elements and the promoter. However, if it does, it functions as an adjuvant and not as an essential participant. It may be important for higher efficiency and for survival advantage, as suggested by its conservation in *D. virilis,* but other gene products must be able to play a similar role.

C. *zeste*-LIKE GENES IN OTHER ORGANISMS

The fact that the *zeste* gene function is not essential for normal growth, development, and fertility of *Drosophila* has raised the possibility that other genes with similar function may exist. Such genes might be able to replace some essential *zeste* functions but not, of course, substitute for it in transvection effects. It is not unlikely that many other DNA-binding proteins, transcription factors, or chromatin proteins share some of the properties of *zeste* product and may produce similar effects. However, the *zeste* gene seems to have no close relatives in the *Drosophila* genome. Hybridization to Southern blots of *Drosophila* genomic DNA reveals no obvious cognate sequences even at very reduced stringency, provided the probe used avoids the region of repetitive *Opa*-like sequence (V. Pirrotta, unpublished). The fact that a *zeste* gene with the same function and the same specificity was found in *D. virilis* argues that it is conserved because it confers a selective advantage. Mutations reminiscent of the *Drosophila* z^1 mutation have been found in two other insects, both dipterans and not too distantly related to *Drosophila*. In *Calliphora erythrocephala,* a sex-linked mutation reduces eye color, but, like *zeste,* only in females (Tate, 1947; also cited in Gans, 1953). Just as in the *Drosophila zeste* mutant, the eye-color effect is temperature dependent and the Malpighian tubules are not affected. A *white* eye mutation in *Muscina stabulans* (Paterson, 1958) is also sex linked and sex limited like *zeste,* so only the female displays the mutant eye color. The original interpretation given by the discoverers in both cases was that a wild-type allele is present on the Y chromosome, but the similarity to the *Drosophila zeste* mutation and the relative phylogenetic proximity of the species strongly suggest that these flies have a *zeste* function similar to that found in *Drosophila*.

In an attempt to determine if nucleotide sequences related to those of the *Drosophila zeste* gene exist in more phylogenetically distant organisms, probes derived from the nonrepetitious 5' or 3' end of the gene were hybridized at low stringency to genomic DNA from a variety of other organisms (Pirrotta *et al.*, 1987). The results were not conclusive. Bands of hybridization were seen in the DNA of *Caenorhabditis elegans, Calliphora,* sea urchin, chicken, and mouse, although in many cases the number of bands is too high to argue for a single conserved gene. The possibility that a function related to that of *zeste* in *Drosophila* is conserved in these organisms must be considered still open.

VIII. Structural Properties of *zeste*-Encoded Protein

A. THE DNA-BINDING DOMAIN

The N-terminal half of the polypeptide encoded by *zeste* is fully able to bind specifically to DNA. Sequences essential for DNA binding were mapped to amino acids 48–138 by Mansukhani *et al.* (1988b) by making fusions to the bacterial β-galactosidase gene and testing the fusion protein for ability to bind selectively to target DNA. This corresponds to the first block of extensive conservation between the *D. melanogaster* and *D. virilis zeste* gene (see Fig. 2), in agreement with the fact that the *D. virilis* protein can substitute for the *D. melanogaster* protein. Because DNA binding of the *zeste* product is highly cooperative, the fusion protein must have at least some residual ability to form the correct *zeste–zeste* product interactions. Chen *et al.* (1991) found three features in this interval that suggested possible involvement in interactions with DNA. The interval 55–81, which is predicted to constitute an extensive helical domain, contains heptad repeats of hydrophobic residues that would constitute an adhesive ridge, potentially used as a dimerization motif (Fig. 2). A cluster of basic residues from 78 to 86 are reminiscent of the DNA-contacting domains in most types of DNA-binding proteins. As noted also by Wingender (1990), amino acids 114–126 bear a significant resemblance to the sequence of the DNA recognition helix of many homeobox proteins, characterized by the core sequence Lys-Ile-Trp-Phe (Scott *et al.*, 1989) (Fig. 5). Mutations that disrupt the hydrophobic ridge of the helical region or reduce the extent of the basic region or change the conserved tryptophan in the homeobox homology all abolish or greatly reduce the ability of the *zeste*-encoded protein to bind to target sequences *in vitro* (Chen *et al.*, 1991). These results suggest that this protein binds to DNA as an oligomer and probably uses a motif similar to that of homeobox proteins to recognize the target nucleotide sequence. This is consistent with the observation

```
zeste    NIKQIQ-KFWLNSRLRKQYPYR
          .  I I.I.. I  I
Antp     CLTERQIKIWFQNRRMKWKKEN
          . I I I.I.. I  I   .
DII      GLTQTQUKIWFQNRRSKYKKMM
          . II I I.  I II
MATa2    SLSRIQIKNWUSNRRRKEKTIT
          .  I I.I.  I I.
bcd      ALGTAQUKIWFKNRRRRHKIQS
   .      .I   ..I.    II
unc86    DLKKNUURUWFCNQRQKQKRDF
         I.     I.I.. I  I    I
eve      NLPESTIKUWFQNRRMKDKRQR
         I.    I I.I.. I  I   .
ems      NLSETQUKUWFQNRRTKHKRMQ
         ━━━━━━━━━━━━━━━━━━━━
```

helix 3

FIG. 5. Homology in the *zeste* product-binding domain with the homeobox helix-3 sequence. The amino acid sequences of the DNA recogniton helix, helix-3, are shown for seven representative homeobox-containing proteins and are compared to a sequence in the DNA-binding domain of *zeste* product. A vertical line under a residue indicates identity with the *zeste* product sequence; a dot indicates a homologous replacement. The homeobox sequences were taken from a compilation by Scott *et al.* (1989) except for the *Distal-less* sequence (Cohen *et al.*, 1989) and the *empty spiracles* sequence (Dalton *et al.*, 1989).

that many *zeste* product-binding sites contain not only one copy of the consensus sequence but also near-consensus sequences in the immediate vicinity.

The helical domain near the N terminal of the *zeste* product is part of the DNA-binding domain identified by Mansukhani *et al.* (1988b). It is in close proximity to the proposed DNA-binding motif described above and is probably required for high-affinity binding. We have shown that the *zeste* product binds poorly or not at all to DNA containing only one *zeste* product recognition sequence (Benson and Pirrotta, 1988). Strong binding requires the presence of two or more recognition sequences but is not very sensitive to the precise distance between them. We suppose that the interaction between two N-terminal helical regions is responsible for holding together the DNA-binding domains of two *zeste* product molecules in a flexible arrangement able to accommodate a range of distances between binding sites on the DNA. That the N-terminal half of the *zeste* product (truncated at position 325) can still form small aggregates was shown by gel filtration (Bickel and Pirrotta, 1990). The DNA-binding domain is separated by a stretch of Gln and Ala repeats from a region (residues 174–212) of very high negative charge: 15 of 38 residues are acidic and none is basic. Such high concentrations of negative charges are a frequent feature of transcriptional activating domains. Because *zeste* product can act as a transcriptional activator by binding to the *Ubx* promoter *in vitro* (Biggin et al., 1988) and both the intact *zeste*-encoded protein and the N-terminal half (truncated at position 325) can activate transcription in tissue culture cells (Miller and Pirrotta, 1991), this region is likely to be the activation domain of the *zeste* product. It is interesting to note that the *e(bx)* allele of *zeste*, although truncated at position 310 in the amino acid sequence (Bickel and Pirrotta, 1990), seems to have residual function. It is unable to complement z^1 or to support transvection effects but it imparts a bright red eye color, it complements the brown eye color of z^{v77h} (see Table 1), and it interferes partially with the action of some of the *zeste* overproducer transposons (V. Pirrotta, unpublished data). Its behavior suggests that its product can bind to DNA *in vivo* and can still stimulate the promoter of the *white* gene. These results confirm the presence of a transcription activation domain and suggest that, at least at the *white* gene, the normal *zeste* product has a stimulatory effect on the promoter *in vivo*.

B. Aggregation Properties

Insights that may help to explain the mechanism of transvection phenomena were gained by examining the properties of the *zeste*-encoded protein. Whether expressed in bacteria or in the fly, this protein appears to be very difficult to extract in the native form. Although some active protein can be recovered by extraction of nuclear preparations at high ionic strength (Biggin *et al.*, 1988), the majority of the protein present remains with the insoluble fraction and requires treatment with urea or other solubilizing agents (Bickel and Pirrotta, 1990). This difficulty can be attributed to the fact that the protein, whether bacterially produced or extracted from flies, in crude extracts or after purification to near homogeneity, tends to form large, fast-sedimenting aggregates. Most of the experimental work has therefore been done with material solubilized in 4 M urea and then dialyzed to remove the urea. In these preparations, the removal of urea results in the reaggregation of the protein to a degree dependent on the concentration during the renaturation step. The product is active *in vitro* in DNA-binding reactions or in stimulating transcription, even though it is present in aggregates of several hundred monomers. The size of the aggregates and the resulting sedimentation rate allow a simple measure of the degree of aggregation: a sample is centrifuged for a few minutes in a microfuge tube and the supernatant and pellet fractions are assayed by gel electrophoresis and Western blotting. This assay showed that the bacterial protein does not differ from the *Drosophila* protein and both behave in a similar way from the moment the cells or nuclei are lysed. The aggregation is resistant to 2 M NaCl and nonionic detergents and is only partly alleviated by certain zwitterionic detergents of intermediate chain length.

C. AGGREGATION AND TRANSVECTION EFFECTS

The determinants of aggregation are found predominantly in the C-terminal half of the protein, although some more limited oligomerization was observed also with N-terminal half. The z^1 and z^{op6} mutant proteins aggregate to the same degree as the wild-type protein, but the z^{11G3} mutant protein, a pseudorevertant of the z^1 mutant protein, showed a significantly lower tendency to aggregate. *In vitro*, this protein binds to DNA as well as the z^1 or z^{op6} mutant proteins. *In vivo*, the z^{11G3} mutation complements z^1 but, by itself, it does not give the *zeste–white* effect, it does not support transvection (Kaufman *et al.*, 1973), and behaves otherwise like a z^a or lack-of-function allele (see Table 1). This could be explained if the z^{11G3} mutant protein were not only defective in forming large aggregates but also were able to interfere with the ability of the z^1 mutant protein to aggregate. Because the aggregation *in vitro* could be driven by increasing the concentration of the protein, this hypothesis could be tested by overexpressing the z^{11G3} mutant protein *in vivo*. Bickel and Pirrotta (1990) constructed an overproducing transposon in which the z^{11G3} gene is expressed from the *hsp70* promoter. Flies overproducing z^{11G3} mutant protein reverted to the phenotype of z^1 and regained not only the *zeste–white* effect but also the ability to support transvection at *Ubx*. This result implied that the formation of large oligomers is necessary for the ability of the *zeste* gene to produce its known *in vivo* phenotypes. It also suggests that the pairing dependence of the *zeste–white* interaction might be simply a device to produce larger local aggregates by coalescing the aggregates formed at the two copies of *white*. In fact, if the z^1 product is overexpressed, the expression of the *white* gene is strongly depressed in the male (with a single copy of *white*). The eye color never quite reaches the yellow seen in the female, probably because excessive expression of the *zeste*-encoded protein in the early pupa is lethal.

These surprising results have several implications. The first, that aggregates of *zeste* product are required for transvection effects, is consistent with the looping model and provides the kind of sticky properties that *zeste* product would require to bring together two chromosomal regions, whether on the same or on paired chromosomes. This does not prove that the size of the aggregates that is functional *in vivo* is of the same order as that which is observed *in vitro,* but it does imply that *zeste–zeste* product interactions are involved. The second implication is that mere binding of z^1 mutant protein to the *white* eye enhancer is not in itself inhibitory but that only very large aggregates interfere with *white* expression. A factor of two in the size of the total aggregate makes the difference between normal expression, as in the male, and 90% inhibition, as in the female. The z^{op6} mutant protein, which gives the *zeste* effect with a single copy of *white,* is, as far as could be determined, not superaggregating. Its effects, therefore, must be caused by a heightened ability of the z^{op6} product to interfere with transcription even when present as a smaller aggregate. Finally, the same large size of aggregate is necessary to support transvection effects.

An additional observation resulting from these experiments was that overexpression of the *zeste* product has lethal effects but only if it occurs in the late larval or early pupal stage. Death can occur throughout pupal development without specifically attributable defects. It is not surprising that overproduction of a protein with potentially widespread binding sites (see Fig. 3) and with the ability to tie up the chromatin as suggested by the *in vitro* experiments would be lethal. The unexpected is that it only does so at this particular stage, suggesting that perhaps the lethal aspect of its overproduction is not a general knotting of the chromatin but interference with a smaller set of genes that are important only in the early stages of metamorphosis.

D. Aggregation Domains

The ability to form large aggregates *in vitro* is one of the most striking features of the *zeste*-encoded protein and is apparently necessary for its activity *in vivo*. Bickel and Pirrotta (1990) showed that the the C-terminal half of the protein contains most of the determinants for self-association, although the N-terminal half can also form lower oligomers. The C-terminal region of the protein, residues 500–571, contains an extensive region predicted to assume a helical conformation with two sets of heptad repeats characterized by hydrophobic amino acids every eighth residue (Fig. 2). These produce two extensive hydrophobic ridges on nearly opposite sides of the helix. As shown in Fig. 6, one involves five heptad repeats in the first half of the helical domain, aligning FFLLI, and another one involves six heptads at the C

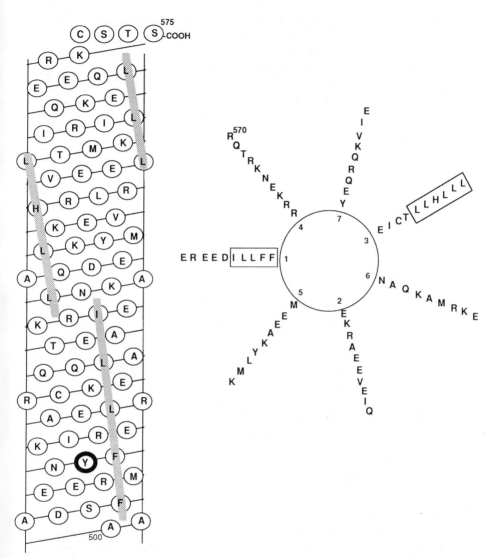

FIG. 6. Diagrammatic views of the C-terminal helical domain of *zeste* product. In the diagram on the left, the helix is opened and flattened out. The amino acid residues are indicated from Ala 500 at the bottom to the C-terminal Ser 575 at the top. Note that residues that are split in half in this display are represented both at the right edge and at the left edge. The gray stripes represent the two hydrophobic ridges. The Tyr 510 circled in bold, is deleted in the z^{11G3} mutant, causing a misalignment and shortening of the first hydrophobic ridge. The helical wheel diagram on the right represents the amino acid sequence from Phe 504, at the innermost position 1, to Arg 570, in the outermost circle. The hydrophobic ridges, indicated by boxes, are on opposite sides, as well as opposite ends, of the helix.

terminal of the helix, aligning LLHLLL. This latter feature has been noticed by Wu and Goldberg (1989), who referred to it as a leucine zipper. (Chen et al., 1991) proposed that, because these surfaces are on opposite sides and at the opposite ends of the helical region, they are favorably arranged to allow hydrophobic interactions with similar surfaces on other molecules of zeste product and showed that mutations that disrupt the hydrophobic ridges (one of these is the z^{11G3} mutation) cause a reduction in the tendency to aggregate in vitro. The arrangement of the hydrophobic ridges resembles that found in proteins that form typical coiled-coil structures and would, in principle, permit the formation of long chains of zeste product monomers. Furthermore, these chains could be cross-linked by the action of the shorter helical domain in the DNA-binding region, resulting in the formation of extensive networks. However, even a short peptide representing the C-terminal helical domain is, by itself, able to form the fast-sedimenting aggregates (Chen et al., 1991).

E. GLUTAMINE REPEATS

We know very little about the significance of the runs of glutamines and alanines other than that such runs have been found in a large number of Drosophila regulatory proteins, some of them nonnuclear, as well as some vertebrate transcription factors (Miesfeld et al., 1986). They might serve as contact surfaces for homotypic interactions, they may be introduced by a stuttering process in DNA replication and have no functional significance, they might act as spacers between functional domains, or they might be involved in the activation of transcription. Courey and Tjian (1988) found that glutamine-rich stretches in the vertebrate SP1 transcription factor have a transcription-activating function. However, in SP1 these stretches contain scattered glutamine residues, very different from the runs encountered in the Drosophila proteins, and may not have the same structural or functional significance. In the zeste-encoded polypeptide, these runs tend to occur at transitions between structural or functional domains. They are found between the DNA-binding domain and the acidic region; they precede the region containing the z^1 and z^{op6} mutations, and, at least in D. virilis, they mark the transition to the long helical domain in the C-terminal region.

F. THE z^1 REGION

The region that contains the sites of the z^1 and z^{op6} mutations is of particular interest because mutations affecting it have profound effects on the interaction of *zeste* with the *white* gene, implying that it has an important though unknown function. This region (424–457) is well conserved in *D. virilis* and might be involved in contacts with other proteins through which the z^1 mutant protein mediates its effect on the promoter of the *white* gene. Lys 425, which is changed to Met in the z^1 mutant, is strategically situated. It is the only charged residue in the central part of the protein (from residue 336 to 505) and is converted to a hydrophobic residue by the mutation (see Fig. 2). Why such a change should convert *zeste* product to a transcription inhibitor (but only at the *white* gene, and only for expression in the eye and only when very large aggregates of *zeste* product are formed) is at present beyond my ken. It would be interesting to study what other amino acid replacements at or near this position produce similar effects. A glimpse may be offered by the z^{op6} mutation, which, in addition to the z^1 change, converts Pro 454 into Leu with the effect of producing the inhibitory form of *zeste* product even with smaller aggregates. When separated from the z^1 mutation by *in vitro* recombination, this mutation has no detectable phenotypic effect and behaves like wild-type *zeste* (V. Pirrotta, unpublished data). Both changes are toward increased hydrophobicity. The Lys 425 is in a stretch with strong helical potential whereas the Pro 454 is in a β-sheet region. It is perhaps possible to speculate that these two regions, which normally might tend to fold back on one another, in the mutants form a tight hydrophobic core that may be difficult to unfold.

IX. *zeste* and Chromatin Packaging

A. *zeste* AND THE NUCLEAR MATRIX

In recent years, much evidence has pointed to the fact that the nucleus has considerable internal structure, that the chromosomes are not randomly entangled but assume particular arrangements and dispositions (Mathog *et al.*, 1984; Hochstrasser and Sedat, 1987a,b), and that a kind of framework exists both around and within the nuclear plasm: the nuclear envelope (Gerace and Burke, 1988) and the nuclear matrix (Nelson *et al.*, 1986). Matrixlike structures within the nucleus have been identified by procedures that strip the nuclear membrane, remove most chromatin-bound proteins, and digest the exposed DNA. The residual insoluble material has been variously named *nuclear matrix* or *nuclear scaffold*, sometimes without a clear conceptual definition of what structural role it might play in the nucleus. Without prejudice to other models, we may distinguish between, on one hand, an extrachromosomal matrix, perhaps associated with the nuclear envelope and in which chromosomes are embedded, and, on the other hand, a chromosome scaffold, a framework to which the chromatin constituting the chromosome is anchored. In either case, some such nuclear structure has frequently been thought to participate in the formation of chromatin loops, organizing DNA replication domains, in mediating transcriptional regulation and RNA processing.

So far, these nuclear structures have been operationally defined as the fast-sedimenting material that remains after nuclear preparations have been extracted with high salt or lithium iodosalicylate and with endonucleases. Such preparations contain residual DNA fragments of specific chromosomal origin that remain associated with a rapidly sedimenting structure. These have been called matrix or scaffold attachment regions (MARs or SARs) and have been found in the vicinity of many genes, both in the 5' regulatory regions and in the 3' regions, forming loops that may reflect a functional organization (Cockerill and Garrard, 1986; Gasser and Laemmli, 1986). Might *zeste* product be one of the proteins that mediate such attachments? In fact, Bickel and Pirrotta (1990) found that typical nuclear matrix preparations from *Drosophila* nuclei contain the majority of the total *zeste*-encoded protein found in the cell. This does not necessarily mean that *zeste* product is associated with the nuclear matrix or other specific structure, because the properties of *zeste* product, whether produced in bacteria or in *Drosophila,* whether purified or immediately upon lysis of the nucleus, would cause it to be rapidly sedimenting and therefore to cosediment with matrix preparations. More serious is the consideration that DNA fragments bound to *zeste* product or to any other DNA-binding protein with similar properties would make it appear that matrix preparations have intrinsic DNA-binding properties. This does not necessarily mean that matrix attachment sites on the DNA do not exist but it suggests that some of the sites that appear to be matrix bound are in fact binding to other fast-sedimenting proteins. Of the *Drosophila* genes in which SARs have been mapped (Gasser and Laemmli, 1986), the *fushi tarazu* gene has also been examined for *zeste* product-binding sites (Benson and Pirrotta, 1988). In this case, no *zeste* product-binding sites were detected but other proteins or protein complexes might be involved.

The possibility that *zeste*-encoded protein or other similar proteins might anchor chromatin domains to other nuclear structures cannot be ruled out. The C-terminal helical domain of *zeste* product could, for example, present an adhesive surface for other protein–protein contacts. In particular, its structure would consent interactions with other coiled-coil domains such as those found in the nuclear lamins and other nuclear factors (McKeon *et al.,* 1986; Fisher *et al.,* 1986; Diffley and

Stillman, 1989). A *zeste* product aggregate bound to the regulatory region of a gene such as *white* might therefore be able to append this chromatin region to the nuclear lamina. However, no connection between *zeste* product-binding sites detected *in situ* and any other nuclear structure has yet been detected: with the resolution available at present, *zeste* product immunofluorescence in polytene or in mitotic nuclei is not detected in any part of the nucleus that does not also stain for DNA (J. Wilcox, S. Bickel, and V. Pirrotta, unpublished data).

B. MODIFIERS OF *zeste*

Whatever might be the detailed mechanism of transvection-like effects, it is clear that they require more than the *zeste*-encoded protein. There may be many other functions that participate to make transvection possible and the full requirements may differ from one target locus to another. Green (1967), looking for revertants of the *zeste* eye-color phenotype, isolated the first mutation that suppressed the *zeste–white* interaction but affected neither gene. Additional mutations of this kind were found by Gelbart (1971), Kalisch and Rasmuson (1974), Persson (1976), and Wu (1984). At least five loci are now known that can mutate to dominant, gain-of-function alleles that interfere with the *zeste–white* interaction. These are *Su(z)2, Su(z)3, Psc, Su(z)301* [also known as *E(z)* or *pco*], and *Su(z)302* (also called *Scm*). *Su(z)2, Su(z)3,* and *Psc* form a tightly linked cluster on the right arm of chromosome 2 that may also show genetic interactions (Wu *et al.*, 1989; Brunk *et al.*, 1991; C.-T. Wu, personal communication). The *Su(z)301/E(z)/pco* locus was discovered independently for the different phenotypes its mutations can produce (Kalisch and Rasmuson, 1974; Wu *et al.*, 1989; Phillips and Shearn, 1990). Similarly, the *Psc* and *Scm* loci were identified for the homeotic effects of their alleles (Jürgens, 1985). Different alleles of the same locus can in fact produce different phenotypes and some can either enhance or suppress the *zeste* eye-color effects. The phenotypic effects of the modifier mutations are additive and enhancer mutations can counteract suppressor mutations (Kalisch and Rasmuson, 1974; Persson, 1976). These mutations do not act by regulating the expression of the *zeste* gene nor, probably, by regulating the translation of the *zeste* mRNA. The *Su(z)2* and *Su(z)3* mutations can suppress the effects of *zeste* transcribed from a heterologous promoter. They suppress equally well the z^1 and z^{op6} mutations and continue to suppress if the *zeste* product is overproduced by more than 10-fold, indicating that the suppressor products are not titratable by *zeste* product and do not compete with it (V. Pirrotta, unpublished data). An attractive but untested hypothesis is that the products of these loci interact directly or indirectly with the domain of the *zeste*-encoded protein in which the z^1 and z^{op6} changes are found. It is unlikely, however, that all these gene products contact *zeste* product. Their number and properties suggest rather that they may be involved in a larger scale structural phenomenon, perhaps affecting chromatin structure. The fact that suppressor mutations also affect the interaction of z^{op6} with a single copy of the *white* gene indicates that they are not simply involved in chromosome pairing. Whether they also suppress *zeste*-mediated transvection effects at *Ubx* or *dpp* remains unclear. Three of the modifier loci, *Su(z)2, Psc*, and *E(z)/pco*, have been cloned recently (Brunk and Adler, 1990; Phillips and Shearn, 1990; Jones and Gelbart, 1991) and sequence information on their products is available (Brunk and Adler, 1991, and personal communication; R. Jones, personal communication). All three are predicted to encode large proteins with little obvious homology to other known proteins. All three predicted proteins contain cysteine-rich regions that may perhaps constitute CC-type zinc fingers such as are implicated in DNA interactions in many transcription factors. However, the distribution of the cysteine residues is different from that found in typical zinc fingers and no information is available yet on the molecular interactions of these proteins with DNA or with the *zeste* product.

C. RELATIONSHIP BETWEEN MODIFIERS OF *zeste* AND *Polycomb* GROUP GENES

At least three of the modifiers of *zeste* loci are associated with homeotic transformations (Wu *et al.*, 1989; Jones and Gelbart, 1991; Phillips and Shearn, 1990). In most cases these can be interpreted as due to derepressed or inappropriate expression of the *Antennapedia* and *bithorax* complexes and result in partial homeotic transformations of the posterior legs to prothoracic legs, as indicated by the designations of the mutations: *Psc* (*Posterior sex combs*) and *Scm* (*Sex comb on midleg*) (Jürgens, 1985). Loss-of-function mutations at the *Su(z)301/E(z)/pco* and of *Su(z)302/Scm* loci are homozygous lethal and cause homeotic phenotypes (Jones and Gelbart, 1991; Phillips and Shearn, 1990). All three loci are in fact members of the *Polycomb* group (*Pc* group) of genes. *Su(z)2* and *Su(z)3* mutations have not shown any homeotic effects so far. However, misexpression of *Su(z)2* can have homeotic effects, as shown by the phenotype of *Aristapedioid* (Adler, 1984; Adler *et al.*, 1989; Brunk and Adler, 1990). This is associated with a small inversion that alters the expression of *Su(z)2* and results in the partial transformation of distal antenna to distal leg. Other rearrangements that cause abnormal or excessive expression of *Su(z)2* result in loss of chaetae or abnormal development of bristle sense organs (Brunk *et al.,* 1991). Although *Su(z)2* is not a typical member of the *Pc* group, certain alleles of *Su(z)2* interact with mutations in some members of the group, failing to complement them [e.g., *Su(z)2* and *Psc*] or either enhancing or suppressing one another's phenotypes (Wu, 1984; Adler *et al.,* 1989).

The *Pc* group includes more than 30 different genes whose mutations cause related phenotypes and whose interactions imply that they are synergistically involved in a common process (for a recent review see Paro, 1991). Mutations in one member of the group are often enhanced by mutations in another member whereas duplications of one gene may alleviate the effects of mutations in another member of the group (Jürgens, 1985). Their homeotic effects are due to inappropriate expression of the two major homeotic gene complexes, which appear to be expressed outside their normal domains (Lewis, 1978; Duncan and Lewis, 1982). In mutant embryos, expression of the homeotic genes initiates normally and is correctly regulated by the action of the segmentation genes, but the normal pattern fails to be maintained at later stages. The function of *Pc* group genes seems to be to keep the homeotic genes repressed in those parts of the embryo in which they were not originally active while allowing continued expression in the appropriate domains. Individual members of the group may have additional functions. For example, total loss of *Psc* function may induce embryonic dorsoventral transformation in addition to the anteroposterior homeotic transformations (Adler *et al.,* 1989). The *Su(z)301/E(z)/pco* gene function is also required for cell proliferation and chromosome integrity (Phillips and Shearn, 1990; Gatti and Baker, 1989).

Some idea of the mode of action of the *Pc* group genes is suggested by their collective features. The large number of genes that the group includes, the fact that they may fail to complement one another, that they may be haplo insufficient, and that they can mutate to give antimorphic products all suggest that they are involved in the assembly of extensive structures composed of many interacting gene products. The hypothesis that they organize or package chromatin in a number of genomic regions is suggested by parallels between their interactions and those of the suppressor of variegation genes [*Su(var)* genes], which are believed to be involved in the packaging of heterochromatin (see recent reviews in Tartof *et al.,* 1989; Eissenberg, 1989; Henikoff, 1990). The similarity between the action of *Pc* genes in maintaining the state of expression of homeotic genes through subsequent development and that of the *Su(var)* genes in maintaining the pattern of inactivation of heterochromatinized genes (position-effect variegation) has been noted and discussed (Reuter *et al.*, 1990; Pirrotta, 1990; Paro, 1990).

D. Position-Effect Variegation and the *zeste* Effect

In position-effect variegation, genes that are placed near heterochromatin by chromosomal rearrangements become subject to inactivation by the chromatin condensation that spreads from the heterochromatic region (for an older but comprehensive review see Spofford, 1976). It is not unlikely that this spreading effect also induces condensation in a synaptically paired chromosome region. This would provide a possible explanation for the transvection-like inactivation that occurs at the brown locus when a wild-type allele is paired with the brown-variegated allele (Henikoff and Dreesen, 1989). The spread of chromatin condensation varies from cell to cell but, like the maintenance of a state of expression by the *Pc* genes, the degree of inactivation is inherited by progeny cells, giving rise to variegated expression. The degree of inactivation is highly dependent on the total availability of heterochromatin products produced by the *Su(var)* genes, hence on the ratio between heterochromatin and euchromatin. It can be alleviated by mutations in the *Su(var)* genes or by the presence of supernumerary Y chromosomes, which are essentially heterochromatic. It is also very sensitive to temperature, as might be expected for a process that involves multimolecular assembly (Locke *et al.*, 1988). Low temperature enhances inactivation, presumably by favoring the assembly of heterochromatin. A remarkable similarity between position-effect variegation and the effect of *zeste* on the expression of *white* was noted from the earliest days of the study of *zeste* (Chen, 1948; Gans, 1953). In fact, the yellow color produced by the *zeste* effect is often uneven and can display a darkening and mottling similar to the effects of position-effect variegation. These effects are visible in conditions of partial complementation of z^1 such as in z^1/z^{11G3} flies (Gans, 1953), in newly eclosed flies, when development is slowed down by *minute* mutations (Persson, 1976) or by the quality of the food, or after development at low temperature (Gans, 1953). However, this mottling of the *zeste* eye color does not involve the *Su(var)* heterochromatin proteins, is not influenced by the presence of a Y chromosome, and has the opposite temperature dependence: z^1 flies raised at 17°C have darker eyes with strongly pigmented ommatidia interspersed among less pigmented ones. It is possible that this effect may be attributable to temperature-dependent differences in chromosome pairing (Goldschmidt, 1952). More interesting is the hypothesis that it might be caused by a heterochromatic modification, first advanced with remarkable intuition by Gans (1953). The discoveries in more recent years lead us again to the conclusion that the *zeste* effect involves a packaging of chromatin similar to the condensation of heterochromatin but involving proteins such as the *Su(z)* and *Pc* group products rather than the *Su(var)* products. The *zeste*-dependent packaging of *white* gene chromatin takes place not, like the condensation of heterochromatin, before cell division has terminated, but at the time when the *white* gene is activated in the pigment cells of the eye (Chen, 1948), and must be interpreted as part of the process through which the expression of the *white* gene is regulated.

E. CONCLUSION

These comparisons, similarities, and relationships between *zeste*, the suppressors of *zeste*, the *Pc* group genes, and the *Su(var)* genes suggest that the *zeste–white* effect, long-distance gene regulation, transvection, and the maintenance of a determined state might be related phenomena that involve the folding and packaging of chromatin domains and their disposition in the nucleus. The assembly of *zeste* product into large DNA-binding aggregates might be a prototype and an intimation of vastly more complex assemblages. At this stage, we know little more about the mechanisms that underlie these structures and these effects. We know, however, that they involve many components and we know many of the genes encoding them. Greater enlightenment cannot be far behind.

ACKNOWLEDGMENTS

I am grateful to many people who have contributed comments, suggestions, and information. In particular, I acknowledge Ting Wu, whose doctoral dissertation is a veritable mine of interesting observations and reflections, and Paul Adler, who has been generous with preprints, unpublished results, and clones. My work is supported by a grant from the NIH.

REFERENCES

Adler, P. N. (1984). A new dominant homeotic mutation associated with a P element mediated inversion in *Drosophila melanogaster. Genetics* **107**, s1.
Adler, P. N., Charlton, J., and Brunk, B. P. (1989). Genetic interactions of the *Suppressor 2 of zeste* region genes. *Dev. Genet.* **10**, 249–260.
Ashburner, M. (1970). A prodromus to the genetic analysis of puffing in *Drosophila. Cold Spring Harbor Symp. Quant. Biol.* **35**, 533–538.
Ashburner, M. (1977). Happy birthday puffs! *Chromosomes Today* **6**, 213–222.
Babu, P., and Bhat, S.G. (1980). Effects of *zeste* on *white* complementation. *In* " Develop-

ment and Neurobiology of *Drosophila*." O. Siddiqi, P. Babu, L. M. Hall, and J. C. Hall, eds.), pp. 35–38. Plenum, New York.

Babu, P., Selvakumar, K. S., and Bhosekar, S. (1987). Studies on transvection at the bithorax complex in *Drosophila melanogaster*. *Mol. Gen. Genet.* **210**, 557–563.

Benson, M., and Pirrotta, V. (1987). The product of the *Drosophila zeste* gene binds to specific DNA sequences in *white* and *Ubx. EMBO J.* **6**, 1387–1392.

Benson, M., and Pirrotta, V. (1988). The *Drosophila zeste* protein binds cooperatively to sites in many gene regulatory regions: implications for transvection and gene regulation. *EMBO J.* **12**, 3907–3915.

Beverley, S. M., and Wilson, A.C. (1984). Molecular evolution in *Drosophila* and the higher Diptera. II. A time scale for fly evolution. *J. Mol. Biol.* **21**, 1–13.

Bickel, S., and Pirrotta, V. (1990). Self-association of the *Drosophila zeste* protein is responsible for transvection effects. *EMBO J.* **9**, 2959–2967.

Biggin, M. D., and Tjian, R. (1988). Transcription factors that activate the *Ultrabithorax* promoter in developmentally staged extracts. *Cell* **53**, 699–711.

Biggin, M. D., Bickel, S., Benson, M., Pirrotta, V., and Tjian, R. (1988). *Zeste* encodes a sequence-specific transcription factor that activates the *Ultrabithorax* promoter *in vitro. Cell* **53**, 713–722.

Bingham, P. M., and Zachar, Z. (1985). Evidence that two mutations, w^{DZL} and z^1, affecting synapsis-dependent genetic behavior of *white* are transcriptional regulatory mutations. *Cell* **40**, 819–825.

Bloomenthal, T., and Thomas, J. (1988). cis and trans mRNA splicing in *C. elegans. Trends Genet.* **4**, 305–308.

Brunk, B. P., and Adler, P. N. (1990). *Aristapedioid*: a gain of function, homeotic mutation in *Drosophila melanogaster. Genetics* **124**, 145–156.

Brunk, B. P., and Adler, P. N. (1991). The sequence of the *Drosophila* regulatory gene *suppressor two of zeste. Nucleic Acids Res.* **19**, 3149.

Brunk, B. P., Martin, E. C., and Adler, P.N. (1991). Molecular genetics of the *Posterior Sex Combs/Supressor 2 of zeste* region of *Drosophila*: aberrant expression of the *Supressor 2 of zeste* gene results in abnormal bristle development. *Genetics* **128**, 119–132.

Chen, J. D., Chan, C. S., and Pirrotta, V. (1991). Submitted.

Chen, S. Y. (1948). Action de la température sur trois mutants à panachures de *Drosophila melanogaster*, $w^2$58-18, w^{m5} et *z. Bull. Biol. Fr. Belg.* **82**,(2/3), 114–129.

Cockerill, P. N., and Garrard, W.T. (1986). Chromosomal loop anchorage of the *kappa* immunoglobulin gene occurs next to the enhancer in a region containing topoisomerase II sites. *Cell* **44**, 273–282.

Cohen, S. M., Brönner, G., Küttner, F., Jürgens, G., and Jäckle, H. (1989). *Distal-less* encodes a homeodomain protein required for limb development in *Drosophila. Nature (London)* **338**, 432–434.

Courey, A. J., and Tjian, R. (1988). Analysis of Sp1 *in vivo* reveals multiple transcriptional domains including a novel glutamine-rich activation motif. *Cell* **55**, 887–898.

Dalton, D., Chadwick, R., and McGinnis, W. (1989). Expression and embryonic function of *empty spiracles*: a *Drosophila* homeobox gene with two patterning functions on the anterior–posterior axis of the embryo. *Genes Dev.* **3**, 1940–1956.

Davison, D., Chapman, C., Wedeen, C., and Bingham, P. (1985). Genetic and physical studies of a portion of the *white* locus participating in transcriptional regulation and in synapsis-dependent interactions in *Drosophila* adult tissue. *Genetics* **102**, 179–189.

Diffley, J. F. X., and Stillman, B. (1989). Transcriptional silencing and lamins. *Nature (London)* **342**, 24.

Duncan, I., and Lewis, E. B. (1982). Genetic control of body segment differentiation in

Drosophila. In "Developmental Order: Its Origin and Regulation" S. Subtelny, and P. B. Green, (eds.), pp. 533–544. Alan R. Liss, New York.

Eissenberg, J. C. (1989). Position effect variegation in *Drosophila*: towards a genetics of chromatin assembly. *BioEssays* **11**, 14–17.

Fisher, D. Z., Chaudhary, N., and Blobel, G. (1986). cDNA sequencing of nuclear lamins A and C reveals primary and secondary structural homology to intermediate filaments. *Proc. Natl. Acad. Sci. U.S.A.* **83**, 6450–6454.

Gans, M. (1953). Étude génétique et physiologique du mutant *z* de *Drosophila melanogaster. Bull. Biol. Fr. Belg., Suppl.* **38**, 1–90.

Gasser, S. M., and Laemmli, U. K. (1986). Cohabitation of scaffold binding regions with upstream/enhancer elements of three developmentally regulated genes of *D. melanogaster. Cell* **46**, 521–530.

Gasser, S. M., and Laemmli, U. K. (1987). A glimpse at chromosomal order. *Trends Genet.* **3**, 16–22.

Gatti, M., and Baker, B. S. (1989). Genes controlling essential cell-cycle functions in *Drosophila melanogaster. Genes Dev.* **3**, 438–453.

Gelbart, W. M. (1971). Cytogenetics of *zeste* expression in *Drosophila melanogaster*. Ph.D. Thesis, Univ. of Wisconsin, Madison.

Gelbart, W. M. (1982). Synapsis-dependent allelic complementation at the *decapentaplegic* gene complex in *Drosophila melanogaster. Proc. Natl. Acad. Sci. U.S.A.* **79**, 2636–2640.

Gelbart, W. M., and Wu, C.-T. (1982). Interactions of *zeste* mutations with loci exhibiting transvection effects in *Drosophila melanogaster. Genetics* **102**, 179–189.

Gerace, L., and Burke, B. (1988). Functional organization of the nuclear envelope. Review. *Annu. Rev. Cell Biol.* **4**, 335–374.

Geyer, P. K., and Corces, V. G. (1987). Separate regulatory elements are responsible for the complex pattern of tissue-specific and developmental transcription of the *yellow* locus in *Drosophila melanogaster. Genes Dev.* **1**, 996–1004.

Geyer, P. K., Green, M. M., and Corces, V.G. (1990). Tissue-specific enhancers may act in *trans* on the gene located in the homologous chromosome: the molecular basis of transvection in *Drosophila. EMBO J.* **9**, 2247–2256.

Goldberg, M. L., Colvin, R. A., and Mellin, A.F. (1989). The *Drosophila zeste* locus is nonessential. *Genetics* **123**, 145–155.

Goldschmidt, E. (1952). The influence of temperature on synapsis in hybrid salivary glands. *Biol. Bull. (Woods Hole, Mass.)* **103**, 67–73.

Green, M. M. (1959). Spatial and functional properties of pseudoalleles at the *white* locus in *Drosophila melanogaster. Heredity* **13**, 303–315.

Green, M. M. (1967). Variegation of the eye color mutant *zeste* as a function of rearrangements at the *white* locus in *Drosophila melanogaster. Biol. Zentralbl.* **86**, Suppl., 211–220.

Green, M. M. (1984). Genetic instability in *Drosophila melanogaster*: transpositions of the *white* gene and their role in the phenotypic expression of the *zeste* gene. *Mol. Gen. Genet.* **194**, 275–278.

Gunaratne, R. H., Mansukhani, A., Lipari, S. E., Liou, H., Martindale, D. W., and Goldberg, M. L. (1986). Molecular cloning, germ line transformation, and transcriptional analysis of the *zeste* locus of *Drosophila melanogaster. Proc. Natl. Acad. Sci. U.S.A.* **83**, 701–705.

Hazelrigg, T., Levis, R., and Rubin, G.M. (1984). Transformation of *white* locus DNA in *Drosophila*: dosage compensation, *zeste* interaction, and position effects. *Cell* **36**, 469–481.

Henikoff, S. (1990). Position-effect variegation after 60 years. *Trends Genet.* **6**, 422–426.

Henikoff, S., and Dreesen, T. D. (1989). *Trans*-inactivation of the *Drosophila brown* gene: evidence for transcriptional repression and somatic pairing dependence. *Proc. Natl. Acad. Sci. U.S.A.* **86,** 6704–6708.

Hochstrasser, M., and Sedat, J.,W. (1987a). Three-dimensional organization of *Drosophila melanogaster* interphase nuclei. I. Tissue-specific aspects of polytene nuclear architecture. *J. Cell Biol.* **104,** 1455–1470.

Hochstrasser, M., and Sedat, J. W. (1987b). Three-dimensional organization of *Drosophila melanogaster* interphase nuclei. II. Chromosome spatial organization and gene regulation. *J. Cell Biol.* **104,** 1471–1483.

Jack, J. W. (1979). The *zeste* and *white* loci: a model for gene regulation in *Drosophila melanogaster*. Ph.D. Thesis, Univ. of Texas, Austin.

Jack, J. W., and Judd, B. H. (1979). Allelic pairing and gene regulation: a model for the *zeste-white* interaction in *Drosophila melanogaster*. *Proc. Natl. Acad. Sci. U.S.A.* **76,** 1368–1372.

Jackson, S. P., and Tjian, R. (1988). O-glycosylation of eukaryotic transcription factors: implications for mechanisms of transcriptional activation. *Cell* **55,** 125–133.

Jones, R. S., and Gelbart, W. M. (1990). Genetic analysis of the *Enhancer of zeste* locus and its role in gene regulation in *Drosophila melanogaster*. *Genetics* **126,** 186–199.

Judd, B. H. (1961). Formation of duplication-deficiency products by asymmetrical exchange within a complex locus. *Proc. Natl. Acad. Sci. U.S.A.* **47,** 545–550.

Judd, B. H. (1979). Allelic complementation and transvection in *Drosophila melanogaster*. *ICN–UCLA Symp. Mol. Cell Biol.* **15,** 107–115.

Judd, B. H., Shen, M. W., and Kaufman, T.C. (1972). The anatomy and function of segment of the X chromosome of *Drosophila melanogaster*. *Genetics* **71,** 139–156.

Jürgens, G. (1985). A group of genes controlling the spatial expression of the *Bithorax Complex* in *Drosophila*. *Nature (London)* **316,** 153–155.

Kalisch, W.-E., and Rasmuson, B. (1974). Changes of *zeste* phenotype induced by autosomal mutations in *Drosophila melanogaster*. *Hereditas* **78,** 97–103

Kaufman, T. C., Tasaka, S. E., and Suzuki, D.T. (1973). The interaction of two complex loci, *zeste* and *bithorax* in *Drosophila melanogaster*. *Genetics* **75,** 299–321.

Korge, G. (1981). Genetic analysis of the larval secretion gene *sgs-4* and its regulatory chromosome sites in *Drosophila melanogster*. *Chromosoma* **84,** 373–390.

Kornher, J. S., and Brutlag, D. (1986). Proximity-dependent enhancement of *Sgs-4* gene expression in *D. melanogaster*. *Cell* **44,** 879–883.

Krause, M., and Hirsh, D. (1987). A trans spliced leader sequence on actin mRNA in *C. elegans*. *Cell* **49,** 753–761.

Laird, P. W. (1989). Trans-splicing in trypanosomes. Archaism or adaptation? *Trends Genet.* **5,** 204–208.

Levis, R., Hazelrigg, T., and Rubin, G. M. (1985). Separable cis-acting control elements for expression of the *white* gene of *Drosophila*. *EMBO J.* **4,** 3489–3499.

Lewis, E. B. (1954). The theory and application of a new method of detecting chromosomal rearrangements in *Drosophila melanogaster*. *Am. Nat.* **88,** 225–239.

Lewis, E. B. (1955). Some aspects of position pseudoallelism. *Am. Nat.* **89,** 73–89.

Lewis, E. B. (1978). A gene complex controlling segmentation in *Drosophila*. *Nature (London)* **276,** 565–570.

Lewis, E. B. (1985). Regulation of the genes of the *bithorax* complex in *Drosophila*. *Cold Spring Harbor Symp. Quant. Biol.* **50,** 155–164.

Lifschytz, E., and Green, M. M. (1984). The *zeste-white* interaction: induction and genetic analysis of a novel class of *zeste* alleles. *EMBO J.* **3,** 999–1002.

Locke, J., Kotarski, M. A., and Tartof, K. D. (1988). Dosage-dependent modifiers of position effect variegation in *Drosophila* and a mass action model that explains their effect. *Genetics* **120,** 181–198.

Mansukhani, A., Gunaratne, P. H., Sherwood, P. W., Sneath, B. J., and Goldberg, M. L. (1988a). Nucleotide sequence and structural analysis of the *zeste* locus of *Drosophila melanogaster*. *Mol. Gen. Genet.* **211**, 121–128.

Mansukhani, A., Crickmore, A., Sherwood, P. W., and Goldberg, M. L. (1988b). DNA-binding properties of the *Drosophila melanogaster zeste* gene product. *Mol. Cell. Biol.* **8**, 615–623.

Mariani, C., Pirrotta, V., and Manet, E. (1985). Isolation and characterization of the *zeste* locus of *Drosophila*. *EMBO J.* **4**, 2045–2052.

Martin, M., Meng, Y. B., and Chia, W. (1989). Regulatory elements involved in the tissue-specific expression of the *yellow* gene of *Drosophila*. *Mol. Gen. Genet.* **218**, 118–126.

Mathog, D. M., Hochstrasser, M., Gruenbaum, Y., Saumweber, H., and Sedat, J. (1984). Characteristic folding pattern of polytene chromosomes in *Drosophila* salivary gland nuclei. *Nature (London)* **308**, 428–433.

McKeon, F. D., Kirschner, M. W., and Caput, D. (1986). Primary and secondary structural homology between the major nuclear envelope and cytoplasmic intermediate filament proteins. *Nature (London)* **319**, 463–468.

Micol, J.-L., and Garcia-Bellido, A. (1988). Genetic analysis of "transvection' effects involving Contrabithorax mutations in *Drosophila melanogaster*. *Proc. Natl. Acad. Sci. U.S.A.* **85**, 1146–1150.

Micol, J.-L., Castelli-Gair, J. E., and Garcia-Bellido, A. (1990). Genetic analysis of transvection effects involving cis-regulatory elements of the *Drosophila Ultrabithorax* gene. *Genetics* **126**, 365–373.

Miesfeld, R., Rusconi, S., Godowski, P. J., Maler, B. A., Okret, S., Wikstrom, A. C., Gustafsson, J.-A., and Yamamoto, K. R. (1986). Genetic complementation of a glucocorticoid receptor deficiency by expression of cloned receptor cDNA. *Cell* **46**, 389–399.

Miller, P., and Pirrotta, V. (1991). In preparation.

Nelson, W. G., Pienta, K. J., Barrack, E. R., and Coffey, D. S. (1986). The role of the nuclear matrix in the organization and function of DNA. *Annu. Rev. Biophys. Biophys. Chem.* **15**, 457–475.

O'Hare, K., Levis, R., and Rubin, G. M. (1983). Transcription of the *white* locus in *Drosophila melanogaster*. *Proc. Natl. Acad. Sci. U.S.A.* **80**, 6917–6921.

Paro, R. (1990). Imprinting a determined state into the chromatin of *Drosophila*. *Trends Genet.* **6**, 416–421.

Paterson, H. E. (1958). Sex-linked and sex-limited mutation of the fly *Muscina stabulans* (Fall.) (Muscidae). *Nature (London)* **181**, 932–933.

Persson, K. (1976). Modification of the eye colour mutant *zeste* by *Suppressor, Enhancer* and *Minute* genes in *Drosophila melanogaster*. *Hereditas* **82**, 111–120.

Phillips, M. D., and Shearn, A. (1990). Mutations in *polycombeotic*, a *Drosophila polycomb*-group gene, cause a wide range of maternal and zygotic phenotypes. *Genetics* **125**, 91–101.

Pirrotta, V. (1990). Transvection and long distance gene regulation. *BioEssays* **12**, 409–414.

Pirrotta, V., and Bröckl, C. (1984). Transcription of the *Drosophila white* locus and some of its mutants. *EMBO J.* **3**, 563–568.

Pirrotta, V., Steller, H., and Bozzetti, M.P. (1985). Multiple upstream regulatory elements control the expression of the *Drosophila white* gene. *EMBO J.* **4**, 3501–3508.

Pirrotta, V., Manet, E., Hardon, E., Bickel, S.E., and Benson, M. (1987). Structure and sequence of the *Drosophila zeste* gene. *EMBO J.* **6**, 791–799.

Pirrotta, V., Bickel, S., and Mariani, C. (1988). Developmental expression of the *Drosoph-*

ila zeste gene and localization of zeste protein on polytene chromosomes. Genes Dev. **2,** 1839–1850.

Ptashne, M. (1988). How eukaryotic transcriptional activators work. Nature (London) **335,** 683–689.

Qian, S., Capovilla, M., and Pirrotta, V. (1991a). The bx region enhancer, a distant cis-control element of the Drosophila Ubx gene and its regulation by hunchback and other segmentation genes. EMBO J. **10,** 1415–1425.

Qian, S., Varjavand, B., and Pirrotta, V. (1991b). The eye enhancer of the Drosophila white gene and its interaction with the zeste gene and with promoter-proximal sequences. Submitted.

Reuter, G., Giarre, M., Farah, J., Gausz, J., Spierer, A., and Spierer, P. (1990). Dependence of position-effect variegation in Drosophila on dose of a gene encoding an unususal zinc-finger protein. Nature (London) **344,** 219–223.

Royden, C. S., Pirrotta, V., and Jan, L. Y. (1987). The tko locus, site of a behavioral mutation in Drosophila melanogaster, codes for a protein homologous to prokaryotic ribosomal protein S12. Cell **51,** 165–173.

Scott, M. P., Tamkun, J. W., and Hartzell, G. W., III (1989). The structure and function of the homeodomain. Biochim. Biophys. Acta **989,** 25–48

Sirén, M., and Portin, P. (1988). Effect of transvection on the expression of the Notch locus in Drosophila melanogaster. Heredity **61,** 107–110.

Spofford, J. B. (1976). Position-effect variegation in Drosophila. In "The Genetics and Biology of Drosophila." M. Ashburner, and E. Novitski, (eds.), Vol. 1C, pp. 955–1018, Academic Press, New York.

Stern, C., and Heidenthal, G. (1944). Materials for the study of position effect of normal and mutant genes. Genetics **30,** 197–205.

Sutton, R. E., and Boothroyd, J. C. (1986). Evidence for trans splicing in trypanosomes. Cell **47,** 527–535.

Tartof, K. D., and Henikoff, S. (1991). Trans-sensing effects from Drosophila to humans. Cell **65,** 201–203.

Tartof, K. D., Bishop, C., Jones, M., Hobbs, C., and Locke, J. (1989). Towards an understanding of position effect variegation. Dev. Genet. **10,** 162–176.

Tate, P. (1947). A sex-linked and sex-limited white-eyed mutation of the blow-fly (Calliphora erythrocephala). Nature (London) **160,** 361–362

Thummel, C. S., (1989). The Drosophila E74 promoter contains essential sequences downstream from the start site of transcription. Genes Dev. **3,** 782–792.

Wharton, K. A., Yedvobnick, B., Finnerty, V. G., and Artavanis-Tsakonas, S. (1985). opa: A novel family of transcribed repeats shared by the Notch locus and other developmentally regulated loci in D. melanogaster. Cell **40,** 55–62.

White, R. A. H., and Akam, M. A. (1985). Contrabithorax mutations cause inappropriate expression of Ultrabithorax products in Drosophila. Nature (London) **318,** 567–569.

Wingender, E. (1990). Transcription regulating proteins and their recognition sequences. Crit. Rev. Eukaryotic Gene Exp. **1,** 11–48.

Wu, C.-t. (1984). A genetic analysis of transvection in Drosophila melanogaster. Ph.D. Thesis, Harvard Univ., Cambridge, Massachusetts.

Wu, C.-t., and Goldberg, M. L. (1989). The Drosophila zeste gene and transvection. Trends Genet. **5,** 189–194.

Wu, C.-t., Jones, R. S., Lasko, P. F., and Gelbart, W. M. (1989). Homeosis and the interaction of zeste and white in Drosophila. Mol. Gen. Genet. **218,** 559–564.

Zachar, Z., Chapman, C. H., and Bingham, P. M. (1985). On the molecular basis of transvection effects and the regulation of transcription. Cold Spring Harbor Symp. Quant. Biol. **50,** 337–346.

INDEX

A

ABF1, yeast ribosomes and, 77
Abf1p, yeast ribosomes and, 77–70, 84, 103
Acetylcholine receptor, evolutionary genetics of fish and, 178
achaete gene, *Drosophila* transposable elements and, 245–246
ACTH, evolutionary genetics of fish and, 197–198
Adaptation, evolutionary genetics of fish and, 158–161, 163–164, 202
Adh gene, *Drosophila* transposable elements and, 249–250, 254
Aggregation, *zeste* in *Drosophila melanogaster* and, 332–336, 339
Albula, evolutionary genetics of fish and, 124
Alleles
  Drosophila transposable elements and, 230
    foldback elements, 286–288
    hobo, 274
    mariner, 278–280
    P elements, 260, 262–264, 268–269, 271–273
    retrotransposons, 241–258, 260
  evolutionary genetics of fish and
    detection of variation, 123–126, 128
    development, 174–175
    environmental change, 164–166, 171
    immune system, 188
    nomenclature, 131, 134
  Neurospora crassa and, 2, 19, 41, 43
    gene transfer, 6–7, 9
  yeast ribosomes and, 98, 104
    nucleolus, 89, 91
    ribosomal protein genes, 72, 74
    ribosomal proteins, 70–71
  zeste in *Drosophila melanogaster* and
    chromatin packaging, 339, 342

discovery, 303, 305
function, 326–329
transvection, 306, 311–312
Amia calva, evolutionary genetics of fish and, 127
Amino acids
  Drosophila transposable elements and, 244–245, 269, 278
  evolutionary genetics of fish and, 200
  detection of variation, 123, 126, 131
  endocrine system, 195–199
  environmental change, 168–169, 172
  immune system, 181–182, 187, 189
  multigene families, 151, 154
  nervous system, 178
  Neurospora crassa and, 15, 36, 38–41, 43, 49
  yeast ribosomes and, 89, 98
  ribosomal protein genes, 72–73
  ribosomal proteins, 65, 68, 71
  synthesis changes, 84–85
  zeste in *Drosophila melanogaster* and, 313, 315, 330, 332, 337
Anquilla, evolutionary genetics of fish and, 127
Antennapedia, zeste in *Drosophila melanogaster* and, 321–322, 340
Anterior pituitary, evolutionary genetics of fish and, 190–196
Antibiotics, yeast ribosomes and, 65, 70, 73–74, 99–100
Antibodies
  Drosophila transposable elements and, 266, 285
  evolutionary genetics of fish and, 167–168, 181, 183–184, 200
  Neurospora crassa and, 24
  yeast ribosomes and, 72, 89–90
  zeste in *Drosophila melanogaster* and, 316
Antifreeze genes, evolutionary genetics of fish and, 162–163

349

proteins, 87–90
small nucleolar RNAs, 90–91
Nucleoplasmin, yeast ribosomes and, 88
Nucleotides
  Drosophila transposable elements and,
    235, 262, 265, 278, 281–282
  evolutionary genetics of fish and, 142,
    185
    detection of variation, 127, 130
    endocrine system, 199–200
    nervous system, 177–178
  Neurospora crassa and, 2, 5, 7, 23, 43
    genetic material, 13, 15, 17–18
    mitochondria, 26–27, 29–30, 34–35
  yeast ribosomes and, 65, 72–73, 75, 94
  zeste in *Drosophila melanogaster* and,
    313, 319, 321, 324, 329–330
  nuc mutants, *Neurospora crassa* and,
    9–10, 23, 40

O

Oligonucleotides
  evolutionary genetics of fish and, 129
  Neurospora crassa and, 17, 32
  yeast ribosomes and, 90, 99
  zeste in *Drosophila melanogaster* and,
    318–319
Om, Drosophila transposable elements
  and, 248–249
Oncogenes, evolutionary genetics of fish
  and, 144, 170–173
Open reading frames (ORFs)
  Drosophila transposable elements and,
    275, 278, 285
    P elements, 260, 264–269, 273
    retrotransposons, 231–232, 235,
      237–238
  Neurospora crassa and, 34–35, 43, 46
Orthologous gene loci, evolutionary
  genetics of fish and, 133
Osmoregulation, evolutionary genetics of
  fish and, 190–196, 198
Oxatocin, evolutionary genetics of fish
  and, 197
Oxidation, *Neurospora crassa* and, 25–28
Oxygen, evolutionary genetics of fish
  and, 148–151, 158, 166, 174
Oxytocin, evolutionary genetics of fish
  and, 196–197, 200

P

PAB1, yeast ribosomes and, 102
Paleogenome, evolutionary genetics of
  fish and, 142–143
Palindromes, *Neurospora crassa* and, 27
Pancreas, evolutionary genetics of fish
  and, 198
Pathogens, evolutionary genetics of fish
  and, 188–189
P elements
  Drosophila transposable elements and
    chromosomes, 276–277
    foldback elements, 284, 286
    gene expression, 269–274
    mariner, 279
    mechanism, 262–269
    retrotransposons, 238–239, 252
    structure, 260–262
  zeste in *Drosophila melanogaster* and,
    328
Peptides
  Drosophila transposable elements and,
    285
  evolutionary genetics of fish and, 178,
    196–200
  zeste in *Drosophila melanogaster* and,
    336
per genes, *Neurospora crassa* and, 46
Phenotype
  Drosophila transposable elements and,
    230–231
    cis-acting effects of retrotransposons,
      241, 243–249, 251–257
    foldback elements, 287–288
    hobo, 278
    mariner, 279–280
    P elements, 262–263, 268–274
    retrotransposons, 235–236
    trans-acting effects of
      retrotransposons, 257–258, 260
  Neurospora crassa and, 9, 19,
    31–32, 45
  yeast ribosomes and
    assembly, 98
    genetic analysis, 98, 100–101
    nucleolus, 89–90
    ribosomal protein genes, 72, 74
    ribosomal proteins, 70–71
  zeste in *Drosophila melanogaster* and
    chromatin packaging, 339–341